Y0-BCS-238

CONCORDIA UNIVERSITY CHICAGO

3 4211 00186 9059

WITHDRAWN

ANNUAL REVIEW OF PHYSIOLOGY

EDITORIAL COMMITTEE (1975)

W. R. DAWSON
I. S. EDELMAN
E. KNOBIL
S. M. McCANN
S. G. SCHULTZ
R. R. SONNENSCHEIN
K. L. ZIERLER

Responsible for the organization of Volume 37
(Editorial Committee, 1972)

J. R. BROBECK (Guest)
J. M. BROOKHART (Guest)
J. H. COMROE, JR.
I. S. EDELMAN
G. GIEBISCH
E. KNOBIL
A. W. MARTIN
E. R. PERL
R. R. SONNENSCHEIN
K. L. ZIERLER

Assistant Editor KATHLEEN A. GARDNER
Indexer MARY A. GLASS
Subject Indexers VICTOR E. HALL
FRANCIS M. HALL

ANNUAL REVIEW OF PHYSIOLOGY

JULIUS H. COMROE, Jr., *Editor*
University of California Medical Center, San Francisco

RALPH R. SONNENSCHEIN, *Associate Editor*
University of California, Los Angeles

I. S. EDELMAN, *Associate Editor*
University of California School of Medicine, San Francisco

VOLUME 37

1975

KLINCK MEMORIAL LIBRARY
Concordia Teachers College
River Forest, Illinois 60305

ANNUAL REVIEWS INC. 4139 EL CAMINO WAY PALO ALTO, CALIFORNIA 94306

ANNUAL REVIEWS INC.
Palo Alto, California, USA

COPYRIGHT © 1975 BY ANNUAL REVIEWS INC.
ALL RIGHTS RESERVED

International Standard Book Number: 0-8243-0337-7
Library of Congress Catalog Card Number: 39-15404

Annual Reviews Inc. and the Editors of its publications assume no responsibility for the statements expressed by the contributors to this *Review.*

REPRINTS

The conspicuous number aligned in the margin with the title of each article in this volume is a key for use in ordering reprints. Available reprints are priced at the uniform rate of $1 each, postpaid. The minimum acceptable reprint order is 10 reprints and/or $10.00, prepaid. A quantity discount is available.

PRINTED AND BOUND IN THE UNITED STATES OF AMERICA

107155

PREFACE

The appearance of Volume 37 marks the end of Julius Comroe's tenure as the third Editor of the *Annual Review of Physiology*. This volume itself pays tribute to the capable leadership of Dr. Comroe and of his two predecessors, Dr. Victor E. Hall and Dr. J. Murray Luck. In collaboration with their dedicated Associate Editors, Editorial Committee members, and literally hundreds of authors, they have brought the *Annual Review of Physiology* to its present maturity and renown.

In the Preface to the first volume of this series in 1939, the Editorial Committee wrote:

> We offer no apologies for launching the *Annual Review of Physiology*. We are confident that it will fill a distinctive and useful rôle in providing the reader with a comprehensive survey of the year's research in physiology . . .
>
> The number of investigators in Physiology is great, and the volume of work published is of such dimensions that the reviewer who would do justice to all papers published in his field in the period under review is baffled at every turn. Confronted by this problem, we have chosen to advise the authors of the reviews to attempt, rather, a critical appraisal of the contemporary field—an analysis and interpretation of the most significant contributions.
>
> It is our hope that this new Review will supplement the invaluable service which has been rendered for many years by *Physiological Reviews* and the *Ergebnisse der Physiologie*. We have not thought of publishing exhaustive treatments of selected topics such as may be found in these journals. The *Annual Review of Physiology* will have a somewhat different function and will be of value to the reader, not because of its depth of penetration into stated subjects, but because of its breadth, through year by year resumés of the significant work in the entire field of physiology . . .

The acceptance and widespread influence of the *Annual Review of Physiology* for more than three decades has amply justified the confidence and hope expressed in 1939. And, in truth, the need for the kind of selective critical distillations of fundamental research that have been the hallmark of the Annual Reviews is even greater today because of the flourishing of many new areas within the discipline of physiology. Although it is no longer possible to do full justice to the entire field of physiology year by year, remarkably complete coverage is still achieved over intervals of several years in this as well as in other Annual Reviews series.

We are pleased to announce that Dr. Ernst Knobil, the Richard Beatty Mellon Professor of Physiology of The University of Pittsburgh School of Medicine, has accepted our invitation to become the next Editor of the *Annual Review of Physiology*, to which he has already made many contributions both as an author and as a member of the Editorial Committee. Our debt of gratitude to all who have supported the *Annual Review of Physiology* over the years is immense, as is our confidence in its destiny as its future course is charted through the challenging years ahead.

ANNUAL REVIEWS INC.

CONTENTS

ANNUAL REVIEWS INC. is a nonprofit corporation established to promote the advancement of the sciences. Beginning in 1932 with the *Annual Review of Biochemistry*, the Company has pursued as its principal function the publication of high quality, reasonably priced Annual Review volumes. The volumes are organized by Editors and Editorial Committees who invite qualified authors to contribute critical articles reviewing significant developments within each major discipline.

Annual Reviews Inc. is administered by a Board of Directors whose members serve without compensation.

BOARD OF DIRECTORS
1975

Dr. J. Murray Luck
Founder Emeritus, Annual Reviews Inc.
Department of Chemistry
Stanford University

Dr. Esmond E. Snell
President, Annual Reviews Inc.
Department of Biochemistry
University of California, Berkeley

Dr. Joshua Lederberg
Vice President, Annual Reviews Inc.
Department of Genetics
Stanford University Medical School

Dr. William O. Baker
President
Bell Telephone Laboratories

Dr. Ivan L. Bennett, Jr.
Provost and Dean
New York University Medical Center

Dr. James E. Howell
Graduate School of Business
Stanford University

Dr. Wolfgang K. H. Panofsky
Director
Stanford Linear Accelerator Center

Dr. John Pappenheimer
Department of Physiology
Harvard Medical School

Dr. Colin S. Pittendrigh
Department of Biological Sciences
Stanford University

Dr. Richard N. Thomas
Institut d'Astrophysique
Paris, France

Dr. Alvin M. Weinberg
Director, Energy Research and Development Office
Federal Energy Bureau

Dr. Harriet Zuckerman
Department of Sociology
Columbia University

Annual Reviews are published in the following sciences: Anthropology, Astronomy and Astrophysics, Biochemistry, Biophysics and Bioengineering, Earth and Planetary Sciences, Ecology and Systematics, Entomology, Fluid Mechanics, Genetics, Materials Science, Medicine, Microbiology, Nuclear Science, Pharmacology, Physical Chemistry, Physiology, Phytopathology, Plant Physiology, Psychology, and Sociology (to begin publication in 1975). In addition, two special volumes have been published by Annual Reviews Inc.: *History of Entomology* (1973) and *The Excitement and Fascination of Science* (1965).

Alan C. Burton

Copyright 1975. All rights reserved

VARIETY—THE SPICE OF SCIENCE AS WELL AS OF LIFE

The Disadvantages of Specialization

Professor Alan C. Burton
Department of Biophysics, University of Western Ontario, London, Ontario, Canada

> *Even the dogs may eat the crumbs which fall from the rich man's table; and in these days, when the rich in knowledge eat such specialized food at such separate tables, only the dogs have a chance of a balanced diet.*
>
> Sir Geoffrey Vickers[1]

I have been one of the fortunate dogs and I am sorry for the young physiologists of today, most of whom must sit at the separate tables, whether these are rich in knowledge or not. They must learn "more and more about less and less."

By the accident of being born into Edwardian middle class England, the vicissitudes of the economic state of my parents (my father was a dental surgeon, whose practice fluctuated with changes in suburban London), and the profound social changes of two World Wars, I have experienced the greatest variety of life styles; I have known family affluence (when I was eight my parents and six children had as many as five servants and lived in a 20-room house), as well as the insecurity of poverty and how a family must work together for survival, the New World as well as the Old, the prosperous twenties, and the Great Depression. I was educated under the extremes of education, from the stupidity of ultraclassical "private schools" (in the English sense) to modern grammar schools. My continuing education has been at London University and the Universities of Toronto, Rochester, New York, Pennsylvania, and my present University of Western Ontario. This variety has taught me that there is something to be learned from all kinds of people, that all types of education have some merits, and that there are many different ways of tackling problems in science.

I think this great variety contributed to my development. Perhaps it influenced my decision to pursue such a variety of disciplines in scholarship and research. My first research was an attempt to match the absorption bands of the major planets (Jupiter, Uranus, Neptune) in the laboratory; my latest has been an adventure in

[1]Preface to *The Art of Judgment.* Chapman & Hall, 1965.

theoretical biology in the control of cellular division. In between I have written papers in physics on atomic nuclear structure, the superconductivity of metals at liquid helium temperatures, the heating of electrolytes in high-frequency fields, and odd subjects like the floating of mercury droplets on water. My introduction to the field of biological research was more or less accidental, in that I was trying to discover why workmen making "shortwave" (then down to 5 m) machines developed fever. Shortwaves were then used as a tool for producing artificial fever, so I went to conferences on this to tell physiologists and physicans why the tissues became hotter.

A detailed list of the variety of my research problems in the more than 40 years that followed would be boring. They went from the study of animal heat exchanges, the mechanisms of temperature regulation, the control of peripheral blood flow, and the development of hemodynamic principles to the biophysics of the equilibrium of the wall of blood vessels and of the red blood cell, and to the biophysics of cellular membranes. The Second World War gave me the opportunity to learn of the fascination of applied physiology, of devising ways of obtaining objective and valid subjective data in the field, from design of life jackets and the flashing lights on them, to the best colors of life rafts for air-sea rescue. I enjoyed a chance to develop a "science of protective clothing" (which did not really exist before the war). I suppose there was a theme linking all this diversity; the desire to "put things in order" and my love of simple physical and mathematical analysis (what is this but the "shorthand of logic") to create "model systems" of living behavior, which is often so much more ingenious and much more successful than the devices of engineers.

Ever since a colleague introduced me to it, I have treasured the description written by Francis Bacon of the mind of the scientist. It is engraved on the wall of our Health Sciences building.

The Scientific Mind

> A Mind, Nimble and Versatile enough to catch the Resemblances of things, which is the chief point, and at the same time Steady enough to Fix and Discern their Subtle Differences; endowed by Nature with the Desire to Seek, Patience to Doubt, Fondness to Meditate, Slowness to Assert, Readiness to Reconsider, Carefulness to Set in Order, and neither Affecting what is New nor Admiring what is Old, and Hating every kind of Imposture.
>
> Francis Bacon[2]

It has been my aspiration to live up to Bacon's description, which explains, perhaps, how anyone could so spread his efforts on such a variety of topics in science (resemblances of things).

In the first published history of the Royal Society (the first 62 years of it) Thomas Sprat[3] praised variety in science and academic goals in a delightfully quaint way

[2]Francis Bacon. 1955. *Selected writings on the interpretation of Nature,* p. 151. New York: Random House.

[3]Sprat's book is not so much a history of the Society as an apology explaining the need for existence of the Society. (Sprat, T. 1722. *The History of the Royal Society of London,* p. 245. London: Roy. Soc. 3rd. ed.)

(this quotation hangs in the hall outside the office of our Biophysics Department). It makes a plea for variety in experiments and in scholarly activity. I paid an art student to illuminate the words printed here in capitals in the manner of the medieval monks.

> "It is stranger that we are not able to inculcate into the minds of many men, the necessity of that DISTINCTION of my Lord BACON'S, that there ought to be EXPERIMENTS of LIGHT, as well as of FRUIT. It is their usual word, WHAT SOLID GOOD WILL COME FROM THENCE? They are indeed to be commended for being so severe EXACTORS of GOODNESS. And it were to be wish'd, that they would not only exercise this vigour, about EXPERIMENTS, but on their own LIVES, and ACTIONS: that they would still question with themselves, in all that they do; WHAT SOLID GOOD WILL COME FROM THENCE? But they are to know, that in so large, and so various an ART as this of EXPERIMENTS, there are many degrees of usefulness: some may serve for real, and plain BENEFIT, without much DELIGHT: some for TEACHING without apparent PROFIT: some for LIGHT now, and for USE hereafter; some only for ORNAMENT, and CURIOSITY. If they will persist in contemning all EXPERIMENTS, except those which bring with them immediate GAIN, and a present HARVEST: they may as well cavil at the Providence of God, that He has not made all the seasons of the year, to be times of MOWING, REAPING, and VINTAGE."

I am well aware of my susceptibility to the charge that I have been a "Jack-of-all trades, master of none." In my defense I would borrow from Edna St. Vincent Millay (forgive the alteration).

But Oh! my Friends, and Ah! my Foes
It's been a lot of Fun.

I suppose that I have been unusually fortunate that it was possible for me to work on all these problems, and yet find the generous support that enabled me to do so. I wonder if today any young scientists will be given such opportunities to be so general, rather than specialized, in their interest and researches. Most of them are doomed to stay in some restricted field of study. It is my contention that this is a great pity, that creativity in science (as in physiology) is likely to be discouraged, and that today's excessive specialization is likely to lead to impoverishment of ideas.

THE TREND TO ULTRASPECIALIZATION

Perhaps ultraspecialization, for example in physiological research, is an inevitable consequence in modern laboratories of the increasing complexity of technical methods and of analysis by computer. As someone has wisely said, if one uses relatively simple apparatus to answer a question, the answer is likely to be a very complicated one. To obtain a simple set of answers, very complicated methods usually have to be employed. With the very impressive technical methods at our disposal, we drift into spending a great deal of time and money on accumulating mountains of data, even where any underlying idea worth pursuing may have been lacking. I spent many years serving on committees of grant-giving bodies and on Study Sections of the National Institutes of Health of the US. Applicants almost always requested

12-channel recorders to report, simultaneously, 12 different physiological variables. I usually recommended that we give them instead a recorder with only, say, four channels, not because it cost less, but because the research would be likely to reach worthwhile new concepts much better with fewer channels. True, the 12-channeler might publish a more impressive article (to some readers). Probably the piles of data would be relegated to "data-storage" journal facilities, just as the data would be relegated to unused files in his own laboratory. But will any useful new idea emerge that would not better be supported by designing crucial experiments based on a preconceived idea, and settling the point by using only one or two channels? My views were not popular.

I have never forgotten a general lecture I heard many years ago on cancer research by the great Peyton Rous (of "Rous sarcoma" fame). He pointed out that while research required painstaking collation of reliable data, that was not enough to justify the effort to collect it. He illustrated this with the tale of a graduate student who was told by his supervising professor to decide for himself the problem in research that he (the graduate student) wished. After many months, and after taking up a great deal of the professor's time, the student had not made a decision. Finally the professor said, "All right, I will assign you a research problem. Cut off the tails of a thousand rats and analyze each of them for cholesterol." There is very little value in the most extensive and well-documented research, unless there is some idea behind it. With technical specialization this is apt to be forgotten.

A VIRTUE OF IGNORANCE

The temptation for the technical specialist is to continue to accumulate data with the apparatus and techniques he has developed long after they have served their purpose in opening new fields and prompting new basic questions. New ideas in research come from asking ourselves simple, often quite naive questions. The more "expert" we become in a narrow field of knowledge, the less likely we are to be willing to ask such questions, not only in other fields, but particularly in our specialized field. The diffidence of the "professional" is natural, since asking a "stupid question" might suggest that, with all his detailed knowledge, he lacks a grasp of fundamental principles.

A few years ago I was asked to address the Royal College of Physicians and Surgeons of Canada and the United Kingdom at their annual meeting in Toronto, on the role of biophysics in medicine. I chose the title "A Virtue of Ignorance," with the subheading "A Biophysicist Asks Simple Questions About Medicine and Medical Research," and gave several examples. One of these was that every medical student is taught the location of the auscultory areas on the chest where the stethoscope should be placed to best hear the various heart sounds originating in the four valves of the heart (aortic, pulmonary, mitral, and tricuspid) at the time of their closure in the cardiac cycle. Yet, if a transparency showing the anatomical position of these four valves is superimposed over the textbook picture of the position of these auscultory areas, it appears that they are nowhere near the points closest to the origin of the sounds, if it is assumed that these travel in straight lines through the tissues. My point is that if Dr. J. Faber, who was a graduate student with us at the time, and I had been "experts" in cardiology, it is very unlikely that we would have asked the question, "How do the heart sounds travel from their point of origin to the stethoscope of the physician?" The "experts" were sure they knew the answer. Dr. Faber provided the unexpected answer very conclusively by his research. After the heart sounds reach the stethoscope head they are travelling as sounds, but in most of the circuitous pathway from the heart valves these are not sounds at all! Instead they are transverse vibrations, travelling, with much less velocity than would sounds, over the surfaces of blood vessels or ventricular walls, to emerge where these walls are in contact with the thorax. From the auscultory areas the vibrations travel over the chest like ripples on a pond. Surely this fundamental knowledge should be the basis of understanding how the best places to hear specific heart sounds or murmurs (e.g. the murmur of patent ductus) in diseased states are often in unexpected locations. Variety in training and interest in physiology and biophysics can pay dividends in leading one to ask such simple questions.

SPECIALIZATION IN PHYSIOLOGY

I suppose it is because the majority of departments of physiology on this continent are in faculties of medicine, and draw their financial support from such faculties, that there has been undue emphasis on mammalian physiology in teaching and research. Physiologists should never forget that the normal behavior of cells and organisms, and its mechanisms, in the whole field of living things, is their province. While the application to the advance of medical science might justify a special interest in mammals, so much of the understanding we need may come from study of lower forms. *What does he know of mammals, who only mammals knows?*

It is not difficult to find departments of physiology in which nearly every member of the faculty is expected to join in a concerted research on some rather narrow branch of physiology, even though the teaching of the curriculum to medical students requires that many of them have to teach other topics in physiology. Not only is this likely to lead to poor teaching (in my opinion enthusiasm for the topic is about the most important ingredient in good teaching), but also to an eventual decline in the quality and originality of research in such departments, even in their own specialty.

"CENTERS OF EXCELLENCE?" THE RISE OF ULTRASPECIALIZED RESEARCH INSTITUTES

Neglect of the virtues of variety is seen in its most extreme form in the proliferation in recent years of specialized research institutes, devoted to intensive pursuit of narrow goals. Even within a narrow field (e.g. cancer research) one finds restriction in the various institutes to pursuit of research exclusively based on one particular concept (e.g. virology, or disturbed biochemistry, or genetics). Some years ago in an attempt to place one of the PhD's of our department in a cancer institute, I tried to persuade the director, a friend of mine, that he should have someone in his institute that knew other ways than molecular biochemistry to attack the problem of cancer. I well remember his response: "Alan, I may be wrong, but I decided to put all my eggs in one basket." I did not think at the time of the apt reply, which would be to quote what I hope may become known as "Burton's Law." This is: *"However many hens sit on however many eggs for however long, nothing creative will result unless the eggs are fertilized."* Fertilization only occurs when there is interaction between different kinds of fowl.

We all resort to "defense mechanisms," as the psychologists put it. C. P. Snow, in his famous *Two Cultures,* pointed out one difference in attitudes between scientists and their colleagues in the humanities. Most scientists are a little ashamed that they do not know more history, philosophy, or sociology. In contrast, some humanists are actually proud that they know little about science. Ultraspecialization and compartmentalization of science, including physiology, has generated subcultures, and the same defense mechanisms are seen in some of the ultraspecialists. For example, I heard a public lecture from a very eminent molecular biologist (very eminent indeed; perhaps one should call him a biophysicist). At the end of the lecture he was asked what seemed to most of us a very relevant question. He replied with apparent pride: "I am interested only in proteins." I regret that this was not greeted with derisive laughter as it should have been, but with a reverent silence. Incidentally, his "ploy" was not as good "one-up-manship" as that of a very well-known physiologist, a specialist in nutrition, whose reply to a specific question at the end of his lecture was only to declare, "That is in my published work!" Why should he waste time on stupid people who had not studied his work?

ULTRASPECIALIZATION IN JOURNALS OF PHYSIOLOGY

Everyone knows of the explosive proliferation of journals in science, particularly in biology. Every month we receive announcements of new ones in one particular field. While, I am glad to see, a few of the new media of publication declare that they will coordinate and synthesize wide areas of knowledge and scientific enquiry, and some are new "interdisciplinary" journals, I think the majority of the new publications represent narrower and narrower subdivisions of science. I suppose that somewhere there must be provided a place for publication of the frightening mass of little "bits" of specialized information that leave the general reader saying "so what?" This is a problem we must solve somehow, like the Malthusian problem of excessive growth of human population; yet I have not heard of any proposed solution. My point is that the papers in such narrowly restricted journals tend to be written in more and more technical jargon, quite unintelligible to a generalist reader (even as well educated in a variety of science as I am!). Cross-fertilization of ideas is hardly served by this successive splitting of publication into narrow topics. The problem is timely, since members of the American Physiological Society are being polled (at the time of writing this) as to whether or not the *American Journal of Physiology* should be subdivided into several compartmentalized journals.

I have reason to be very grateful that a few journals still exist that have a declared editorial policy of providing a place for new ideas that synthesize concepts cutting across disciplines, and may be written by nonexperts with little expertise in topics on which they touch, i.e. those outside the "Establishment" of specialized knowledge. Three or four years ago I was excited by the discoveries of W. R. Loewenstein (physiologist and biophysicist) and his students of the existence and importance of intercellular communication in tissues where contiguous cells have "tight junctions," and of the possible role of this in controlling proliferation by "contact inhibition." After six months of reading the literature in control of growth in tissue culture and the many different theories of how it was mediated, I produced a general, highly speculative and simplistic, theory of "intercellular communication, cell clocks, and cancer." I think I would have found it difficult to have this accepted by most journals, even interdisciplinary ones, except the journal *Perspectives in Biology and Medicine* (I happened to know the editor). The result of publication of this set of "wild" ideas has been quite extraordinary, since I received over 1400 requests for reprints from all sorts of biologists all over the world (extraordinary in this day of xerography). Yet, after three years, I know of practically no references to this theory in the established "respectable" literature on growth and cancer. Indeed, in reading recent annual assessments by well-known experts of "where we stand in cancer research," I am struck with the complete absence of any reference to intercellular communication as a factor (the evidence of its importance in control of growth is most impressive).

My bold venture, uninhibited by my incompetence in the specialized fields on which it touched, certainly accomplished fertilization of ideas, even if to many the fertilizer used may smell excessively! I have succeeded since then in publishing a more detailed mathematic theory in another journal that is willing to explore new ideas, i.e. *The Journal of Theoretical Biology.* It is interesting that I am now having the greatest difficulty in publishing a paper that directly resulted from the theory. I spent a year studying the cancer statistics from different regions that were available to me, from the point of view that there might be a correlation with altitude. This was based on the idea that acid-base relations in the cell might be the key factor in my theory, and the knowledge that acclimatization to altitude involves chronic changes in acid-base relations. I discovered that there were quite remarkable correlations. The paper has been already rejected by two different general-interest journals. Rejection was on the advice of referees, who, judging from their criticisms, must have been ultraspecialized experts in a narrow subfield of cancer research. They were, apparently, not familiar with either the physiology of acclimatization to altitude, nor with statistical evaluation (I am of course highly prejudiced in the matter, and may be mistaken).

Somehow, while providing some way of storing all the detailed bits of unconnected scientific information that pour out of the laboratories, we must preserve the opportunities for publication of integrative concepts and generalizations, even if advanced by nonexperts.

GRADUATE STUDENTS; DON'T FENCE THEM IN

The graduate student of today is given little opportunity to pursue any kind of research suggested by something that may have turned up in the course of his specific research project, which might well be of much more importance than what he was told to investigate. The restriction extends beyond his acquisition of the PhD, for it seems to be expected of him that his postdoctoral research, perhaps for the rest of his life, will be devoted to further investigation in depth of the narrow problem on which he was started. If his thesis was on, say, the physiology of some cells of the central nervous system, he is apt to think he must continue in this field. The impression of what is expected of him will be confirmed if he should be bold enough to seek postdoctoral experience in another field. He will find it difficult to find the support he needs or to be accepted into the specialized research laboratories or institutes that are eminent in the new field he may choose.

I had personal experience of this some years ago. One of my best PhD's, whose thesis was about the biophysics of capillary flow, sought postdoctoral experience in X-ray scattering work in molecular biology. Since he was very well trained in physics and had a flair for applied mathematics, I wrote to several eminent directors of research institutes where such work was done, highly recommending him for a place in their laboratories. I received the reply from one such that he never accepted anyone in his laboratory who was not already fully trained in X-ray scattering technique. The "rat race" of narrow specialization can easily lead to such deplorable parasitism on the body of science. Fortunately the reply from the United Kingdom was very different. The head of a laboratory was very willing to have my man, but had no place immediately because the laboratory was moving to new quarters. Then I received a letter, quite unsolicited, from another famous British scientist saying that he had heard of my student's desire. "Send him to me and I will look after him until there is a place in that laboratory for him." The contrast in attitudes was striking. The PhD in question is now back on this continent as a professor of biology, making significant contributions in the general field of relation of geometry of cells and tissues to their physiological function.

At the time of my retirement as head of our department a few years ago, my colleagues arranged with the editors of the *Canadian Journal of Physiology and Pharmacology* to consider, with the usual rules of criteria of acceptability, original papers by any of my former students, to be published in a single number of that journal.[4] (A delightful gesture with no grounds for the valid objections that might be raised to a special complimentary issue of a journal.) Ten papers were acceptable, i.e. this number of the former students happened to have acceptable contributions at the right time. It was remarkable how divergent were the topics of these papers from the particular topic of the PhD theses of the authors. At least I can say that I did not inhibit the curiosity and creativity of these students, and I think they have contributed more to science than if I had "fenced them in." Actually, one of the faculty of our present department obtained his PhD under my supervision some

[4]1970. *Can. J. Physiol. Pharmacol.* 48(6).

years ago. Though through the years he has made many fine contributions in research, he has yet to tackle the particular problem that I originally suggested as the topic for his thesis.

Our good students are "endowed by Nature with the desire to seek," as Bacon put it, and we must be careful to nurture that desire, not to frustrate it. Training to the level of the PhD should be regarded as preparing the student to tackle any problem in his general field (such as physiology or biophysics). It is training in scientific methods of how to reduce careful observations to quantitative data that can be used to test ideas about the models that may underlie biological behavior. Of course, to reach the level of the PhD the candidate must make some original contribution to new knowledge, adequately supported with evidence; but why should this be expected to remain his special interest for the rest of his career?

THE DEDICATED SPECIALIST

What I have said against ultraspecialization is not directed against a dedicated persistence in research in a narrow field by any individual. Some of the most important contributions to physiology have been made by those who refused to give up until every detail of the problem was elucidated, and this is likely to take a lifetime of research. There are admirable examples among the Nobel prize winners. What I am deploring is the segregation of some "perfectionists" in research into ultraspecialized departments or institutes (often they become directors of such institutes), where they are cut off from new ideas in other fields or disciplines. The most successful dedicated specialists that I have known did their work in environments where they were exposed to all sorts of ideas arising from the quite different research interests of their colleagues.

VARIETIES OF LOGIC

Just as the tools of experimental research have become more and more complicated and specialized, so have the tools of thinking (problem solving). We must not be trapped into forgetting that there are usually several quite different logical ways of solving a given problem. (I think someone has written a book about this, describing "horizontal" vs "vertical" thinking.) An intriguing simple example is the problem facing anyone arranging, say, a singles tennis tournament with 41 persons entered. The question asked is "How many matches are required to arrive at the champion?" To anyone trained in logic (simple mathematics), the problem is tackled in a routine manner; simple but a little tedious. A number, x, of entrants must be given a "bye" in the first round. The number can be proved to be $x = 2^n - N$ where 2^n is the power of 2 that is both greater than the total number of entrants N and closest to N. (2^n is 64 if N 41.) There will have to be 23 byes, and the remaining 18 will play a preliminary round. The 9 survivors will join the 23 byes, so the second round will consist of 32 players, 16 matches; the next round will have 8 matches, the next 4, the next 2, and then the final. The total number of matches turns out, in this numerical example, to be 40. Of course, one can, by knowing how to sum a geometric series, deduce algebraically that the total number of matches must be $(N - 1)$, but this is by no means very easily accomplished nor is the result obvious. However, if we want the answer only to the question of how many matches are needed in all, this can be given in a simple logical step, which perhaps would occur only to a nonmathematically trained person. This step is that every player, except the ultimate winner, may play in any number of matches, but eventually plays in only one match which he loses. Thus each match is uniquely associated with the loser of that match. Therefore, there must be $(N - 1)$ matches! We must, by constant communication with those who use other ways of thinking than ours, remain open to radical new methods of tackling specialized problems.

AN OCEAN OF UNDISCOVERED TRUTH

The young physiologist of today is apt to think that there remain very few questions of physiological function that could be investigated by the classic methods of physiology, such as denervation, blocking, or stimulation of nerves with observation of altered function in the relatively intact animal. Instead he may think the only type of research worth doing is with complicated techniques on isolated bits and pieces of animals. This point of view is quite unjustified. There remain, even in mammalian physiology (meaning of course dogs, cats, rabbits, rats, or, if there is enough money, monkeys), enormous areas of ignorance. Physiologists need to ask more simple questions. For example, Ulf Von Euler in his book on adrenergic innervation of various tissues, pointed out that the liver is very richly supplied with sympathetic nerves. Some of these, of course, may control the circulation of the liver, though vasomotor control in this region is not very great compared to others. What else are all these nerves controlling? Did any physiologists ever cut the nerves and see whether the many biochemical functions of the liver were affected; or stimulate these nerves to see what happens? Another naive question! In acclimatization to cold (certainly in the rat) the metabolism even of liver slices studied by the Warburg technique increases several times, yet the temperature of the liver was presumably never reduced in the chronic exposure to cold that elicited the changes seen. What triggered these changes in the liver cells?

To give an example in the biophysical field, the very devoted group of "sliding-modelists" (muscle contraction) find it very difficult to explain how muscles could shorten to less than half their resting length, yet nature abounds with muscles that contract to much smaller fractions than this. We do not even have to go outside the higher mammals to find them. The dilator pupillae (radial muscles of the iris) appear to shorten to ⅛ of their length! I know of no studies of the biochemical composition, tension development, ultrastructure, or anything else on these muscles. This is all the more astonishing since here is a thin sheet of muscle cells easily accessible and isolated. Is the apparent lack of curiosity in reality because these muscles are in a radial arrangement, not parallel fibers? or is it because in this specialized subculture of muscle physiologists, one does not ask embarrassingly simple questions, for which the experts have no answer? Instead they learn more and more about frog sartorius muscle, or in a few cases, insect flight muscles, and seem to think all contractile mechanisms must be basically related to what they find.

There seems to be an obligation on famous scientists, like other famous men, to utter memorable last words on their deathbed. Those of Sir Isaac Newton, certainly one of the greatest scientists of all time, are variously reported, so I have taken the liberty to paraphrase and to attempt to put them lyrically.

Sir Isaac Newton said it, just before he died:

> I know not what the world will say, or history teach,
> Of all my labors, less or more.
> To me, we have been children, playing on the shore.
> Picking up pretty pebbles from the beach.
> At times I've found one prettier than the rest
> And polished it, and boast with childish pride,
> While there beside us lay an Ocean, wide
> With undiscovered Truth.

That extraordinary combination of the self-serving, unscrupulous politican and mathematical genius, Louis LeCompt de Laplace, 50 years later felt he had to compete in such deathbed pronouncements; and said the same thing without poetic imagery.

"What we know is very little, what we do not know is immense." This is still true, particularly in physiology, in spite of the explosion of scientific knowledge.

Physiology is a lady of whom it can be said, "Age does not dim nor custom stale her infinite variety." Let us not spoil our appreciation of this by over-emphasis on narrow specialization. In doing so we risk stifling curiosity (as Bacon put it, our endowment with the desire to seek). The addiction of the creative scientist still is the thrill he finds in "adventures of the mind." Minor poets (very minor in my case) have so little opportunity to present their attempts, that I must be excused for trying verse to describe how solving a problem in physiology or biophysics seems to me.

DISCOVERY

> Little rivulets of thought
> Erode the broad surface of the problem posed,
> Idle, wandering and aimless rills
> Like garden freshets after heavy rain.
>
> And now the streams have quickened, coalesced,
> To eddy round the hillock of a doubt,
> Find well-worn channels, ditches study-dug,
> And flow with purpose in a common trend.
>
> Ideas break surface with salmon splash,
> While from the deep,
> Wise intuition adds its hidden flow,
> A rhythmic pulse is growing, surge on surge,
> Insistent logic in bolero time.

At last the turgid waters will not stay—
Glide swiftly through the gorges of analogy,
Go leaping down the rapids of hypothesis, and break
Into a quiet flood of certainty.

If there remain any readers who have read this chapter to this point, and they have been influenced to read, in this Annual Review, not only the chapter reviewing their own specialized field of physiology, but also at least some of the other chapters, my purpose in this prefatory chapter will have been served.

Copyright 1975. All rights reserved

THE SODIUM PUMP ❖1122

I. M. Glynn and S. J. D. Karlish[1]
Physiological Laboratory, University of Cambridge, England

INTRODUCTION

The recent startling growth of the literature on the sodium pump may make a review timely, but it does not make the task of writing it easy. If the great mass of work that has been done had led to the general acceptance, even provisionally and even in outline, of a hypothesis accounting for the working of the pump, we could have described that hypothesis and then considered the evidence for it. Unfortunately, no such hypothesis exists and we must adopt a more piecemeal approach. In the first six sections of this review we discuss, in turn, various ways in which the investigation of the pump has been attempted. In the final seventh section we consider a number of mechanisms that have been suggested to account for the working of the pump in the light of conclusions reached in the earlier sections.

The limited space available means that if we wish to be critical we cannot also be comprehensive. For this reason, we do not discuss recent work on the role of lipids, and we consider only briefly problems connected with the "low K" "high K" dimorphism of certain red cells. We also exclude any consideration of Na transport by systems other than the widespread cardiac-glycoside-sensitive (Na + K)-ATPase.

References 6, 47, 84, 88, 168, 211–213, 241 are to earlier reviews that discuss the Na pump. Another invaluable source of references is the report of the Symposium on (Na + K)-ATPase arranged by the New York Academy of Sciences (222).

STUDIES ON ION MOVEMENTS

It is now clear that by suitable manipulation of the conditions it is possible to make the sodium pump operate in five different modes, namely: 1. Na-K exchange—the normal mode, 2. a reversed mode, 3. Na–Na exchange, 4. K–K exchange, and 5. Na efflux not accompanied by the uptake of Na or K (88). Modes 2 and 4 have been seen only in red cells, but they would be difficult to demonstrate in other cells; there is no reason to think that they cannot occur generally. The belief that all five kinds of behavior are brought about by the same system depends on their sensitivity to

[1]EMBO Fellow. Present address: Weizmann Institute, Rehovoth, Israel.

cardiac glycosides, on similarities in their responses to various physiological ligands, and on the fact that, with the exception of the reversed mode, which has not been tested, all are inhibited by an antiserum to a partially purified preparation of pig kidney (Na + K)-ATPase (89).

Na–K Exchange

Under physiological conditions, internal Na is exchanged for external K at the expense of energy derived from the hydrolysis of ATP at the inner surface of the cell membrane. Evidence for the coupling of the Na and K movements, for the location, external or internal, of the sites at which the ions activate the ATPase, and for the identity of pump and ATPase may be found in earlier reviews (6, 47, 84, 88, 168, 211–213, 241). In human red cells the hydrolysis of each molecule of ATP is accompanied by the outward movement of about three Na ions and the inward movement of about two K ions (76, 198, 240), and there is evidence for a similar ratio of Na ions pumped to ATP molecules hydrolyzed in nerve, muscle, and a variety of other tissues (18, 36, 55). In red cells, at any rate, the number of Na ions expelled for each molecule of ATP hydrolyzed is much the same whether pumping is downhill, on the level, or uphill (76, 198, 240).

The inequality in the active movements of Na and K in the human red cell, and a similar inequality in the squid axon (19), suggests that the pump may be "electrogenic"; that is to say, its action leads directly to a net movement of charge across the membrane. That this is indeed so is shown by the ouabain-sensitive hyperpolarization seen in a number of excitable tissues when the internal Na concentration is raised by repeated stimulation (tetanus), by injection of Na, or by storage in K-free solutions rich in Na (1, 45, 51, 122, 125, 150, 164, 224, 225). It might be suggested that the hyperpolarization comes about merely because the increased activity of the Na pump lowers the K concentration immediately adjacent to the cell membrane, but that possibility has been excluded in two ways: 1. In experiments on unmyelinated nerves, post-tetanic hyperpolarization was greatly reduced in K-free media, but promptly increased when K was added to the medium shortly after a tetanus. Addition of K could not lower the concentration at the cell surface (164). 2. In the crayfish stretch receptor, a single impulse is followed by a short after-potential caused by the persistence, for something of the order of 100 msec, of a high K permeability that displaces the membrane potential in the direction of the K equilibrium potential. If post-tetanic hyperpolarization were the result of K depletion in the region just outside the cell membrane, a single stimulus given during the period of post-tetanic hyperpolarization should cause an action potential with a greatly increased after-potential. This has not been found (150).

In voltage-clamped snail ganglion neurones, Thomas (224) has shown that the outward current generated by Na pumping after iontophoresis of Na into the cell is equivalent to ¼–⅓ of the total charge on the Na ions expelled. This is roughly what would be expected if three Na ions were exchanged for two K ions. On the basis of similar experiments, Kostyuk et al (125) recently claimed that the current generated by the pump may vary with the membrane potential, being very small when the membrane is hyperpolarized. A variable coupling ratio between Na and

K is also suggested by work on frog muscle (1, 45) and on perfused squid axon. In the axon, Mullins & Brinley (37, 147) found that the Na efflux and K influx varied in quite different ways as the internal Na concentration was changed, the Na/K ratio dropping from 3:1 to 1:1 as the internal Na concentration was decreased.

Reversal

By arranging the concentration gradients for Na and K to be steeper than normal, and the ratio [ATP]/([ADP]•[P_i]) lower than normal, it is possible to make the red cell sodium pump run backwards and synthesize ATP at the expense of downhill movements of the cations (77, 90, 131, 132, 135). The rate of synthesis is roughly proportional to the external Na concentration (90), and synthesis is inhibited by external K with a $K_{0.5}$ of about 1.3 mM ($[\mathrm{Na}]_o$ = 150 mM). This is similar to the $K_{0.5}$ for stimulation of ouabain-sensitive K efflux by external K under similar conditions (91), and it is also similar to the $K_{0.5}$ for activation of the forward running of the pump by external K when normal cells are incubated in media containing 150 mM Na (81, 189). It is difficult to obtain accurate figures for the stoichiometry of the pump when it is running backwards, but the synthesis of each molecule of ATP seems to be associated with the loss of something like two or three K ions. The ratio of ATP molecules synthesized to Na ions entering is much lower, but this is almost certainly because most of the ouabain-sensitive Na entry is associated with Na–Na exchange (see below) rather than with reversal of the pump.

Because the free energy of hydrolysis of ATP is so high, one would not expect to observe reversal of the pump in situations in which energy was not available from ion gradients, and in fact the incorporation of P_i into ATP is never seen when fragmented membranes are incubated in solutions of fixed composition. Recently Post et al (163) showed that ^{32}P-ATP was synthesized when ADP + Na was added to membrane particles that had been incubated with $^{32}P_i$ in a (Na + K)-free medium. Here, of course, the energy is provided by the act of changing the concentration in the medium.

Na–Na Exchange

When red cells are incubated in K-free, high-Na media, they show a ouabain-sensitive exchange of internal and external Na ions (32, 73, 75, 184). A similar exchange has been seen in partially poisoned giant axons (19, 41, but cf 146) and probably also in frog muscle (104, 123, 209). Na–Na exchange, in red cells at any rate, is roughly one-for-one, but it shows a very marked asymmetry in the affinity for Na on the two sides of the membrane (69, 75, 184). Internally it is nearly saturated at 10–15 mM Na, but externally the Na activation curve is slightly S-shaped and flattens off only at levels well above 150 mM Na (69). K in the external solution inhibits Na–Na exchange and makes possible Na–K exchange; since the $K_{0.5}$ for the two effects is identical—about 1 mM—it seems likely that the same binding sites are involved (75, 184). Much more surprisingly, internal K has a facilitatory effect on Na–Na exchange (69). The explanation for this is unknown, but the effect is important because it explains the apparent inhibition of Na–Na exchange at high internal Na concentration (75) (the effect is really caused by lack of K) and because it points to a role for K at the inner face of the pump. Stimulation of Na–K exchange by internal K has also been described recently (69, 124, 188). The intracellular K does not act merely by maintaining the level of ATP through its activating effect on pyruvate kinase (124).

Na–Na exchange is associated with the hydrolysis of little or no ATP (76), but it is not observed in resealed ghosts prepared with no ATP (75). Experiments on resealed ghosts containing a regenerating system to control the ATP and ADP levels have shown that the exchange varies linearly with ADP concentration up to 300 μM, the highest concentration tested, but is independent of ATP concentration over the range 300–1500 μM (86). Unfortunately, the presence of adenylate kinase makes it impossible to obtain ghosts containing sufficient ADP with low ATP levels, so an ATP requirement cannot be proved. In squid axon, too, a dependence of Na–Na exchange on ADP has been demonstrated (50); this probably accounts for the absence of the exchange in fresh axons and its appearance in axons that are partly poisoned.

The fact that ADP is not required for the normal working of the pump, but is required for Na–Na exchange, suggests that the entry of Na is associated directly or indirectly with the rephosphorylation of ADP by the phosphorylated pump protein. That would account, too, for the absence of ATP hydrolysis. The movement of Na must, however, also involve something beyond the transfer of phosphate, since oligomycin inhibits Na–Na exchange (76) but does not inhibit, and may stimulate, the Na-dependent ATP–ADP exchange that presumably reflects the transfer of phosphate to and from the enzyme (33, 34).

K–K Exchange

K–K exchange occurs in human red cells under physiological conditions, about one entering K ion in five being exchanged for an internal K rather than an internal Na (91). It does not depend on the simultaneous occurrence of Na–K exchange, however, and is best studied in resealed ghosts containing little Na (208). Like Na–Na exchange, it is roughly one-for-one, and is not associated with the hydrolysis of ATP (208). The apparent affinities for K on the two sides of the membrane are strikingly asymmetric, and the asymmetry is in the reverse direction to the asymmetry of the affinities for Na in Na–Na exchange (91, 208), suggesting perhaps that the same sites are involved. With 0.7 mM Na inside, the $K_{0.5}$ for K internally is about 10 mM (208), and with no Na outside the $K_{0.5}$ for K externally is about 0.25 mM (91), i.e. the same as for Na–K exchange in a Na-free medium. K–K exchange does not occur unless inorganic phosphate is present inside the cells (91), but ADP is not required (208). If a reversible transfer of phosphate is involved, it is therefore likely to be a transfer between the enzyme and water rather than between the enzyme and ADP. In this connection it is interesting that Dahms & Boyer (48) have shown that (Na + K)-ATPase preparations can catalyze an exchange of ^{18}O between water and P_i, which is presumably the result of the alternate formation and hydrolysis of a phosphorylated intermediate. This exchange is stimulated by K ions.

An interesting feature of the K–K exchange is that it does not occur in the absence of nucleotide (87, 208), though T. J. B. Simons (personal communication) has recently been able to show that the β,γ-imido or methylene analogs of ATP are satisfactory substitutes for ATP. This implies that the role of ATP is not to phosphorylate, though what it is remains obscure. ATP might be necessary to accelerate the release of K (see later, and reference 157).

Uncoupled Na Efflux

A ouabain-sensitive efflux of Na, not associated with the entry of Na or K, may be detected when red cells or resealed ghosts are incubated in choline or Mg media (32, 73, 74, 120, 136). It is not the result of an exchange of Na either for K ions leaking from the cell interior or for ammonium ions contaminating the solution; an exchange with Mg or choline has not been excluded, but is unlikely. A ouabain-sensitive efflux of Na into solutions lacking both Na and K has also been described in crab nerve (17) and frog muscle (31), but in these experiments the observed efflux may have been in exchange for K ions leaking from the cells.

Like Na–K exchange and Na–Na exchange, the uncoupled efflux in red cells appears to involve the combination of intracellular Na with sites of high affinity, the flux being saturated at 2 mM, which is the lowest concentration that has been tested (120, but cf 56) ($[K]_i$ was 1 mM). Uncoupled efflux is associated with the hydrolysis of ATP, about three Na ions leaving for each molecule of ATP hydrolyzed (unpublished experiments by Karlish & Glynn); this suggests that the flux may be related to the ATPase activity detected in broken cell preparations at low ATP concentrations when Na is present without K (33, 46, 117, 152, 157). Comparison of the uncoupled Na efflux from ghosts containing different nucleoside triphosphates shows that the ratio (Na–K exchange)/(uncoupled Na efflux) decreases with decreasing order of nucleotide-binding affinity (120), just like the ratio (Na + K)-ATPase/Na-ATPase (204, 220); with low enough levels of poorly bound nucleotides, K inhibits both efflux and hydrolysis. There are, however, two puzzling differences between the uncoupled Na efflux and the Na-ATPase activity: 1. The concentration of ATP required for half-maximal efflux is about 70 μM (120), much higher than the concentrations of ATP at which Na-ATPase activity is generally observed. This suggests that both high- and low-affinity ATP binding sites may be involved in the Na efflux and the Na-ATPase activity (see also 118, 142). 2. The uncoupled efflux is inhibited more or less completely by external Na at concentrations as low as 5 mM, yet Na-ATPase is observed with broken membrane preparations when the Na concentration must be high at both faces.

The Association of Ion Movements and Biochemical Events

The general picture that emerges from the study of different fluxes and the accompanying biochemical changes is that the outward and inward movements of Na are associated with the transfer of phosphate from ATP to the enzyme and from the phosphoenzyme to ADP, and that the inward and outward movements of K are associated with the transfer of phosphate from the phosphoenzyme to water and from P_i to the phosphoenzyme. Whether the phosphoenzyme transfers its phosphate to ADP or to water depends on the composition of the external medium. If K is present the phosphoenzyme transfers its phosphate to water and K enters. If Na is present without K, the phosphoenzyme transfers its phosphate to ADP and Na enters. If neither is present in the external medium, the phosphate is transferred slowly to water, and the slow hydrolysis of ATP is accompanied by an "uncoupled" efflux of Na.

Ouabain-Insensitive Fluxes

It is generally assumed that fluxes observed in the presence of sufficient concentrations of ouabain are not connected with the sodium pump. For the efflux of Na and K, at least from the human red cell, this is probably true, since the antiserum to pig kidney ATPase inhibits the ouabain-sensitive fluxes completely and does not affect the ouabain-insensitive fluxes (89). The argument is not quite watertight, however, because the antiserum does not inhibit all ouabain-sensitive partial reactions of the (Na + K)-ATPase (11, 14, 89).

For influxes the antiserum test is not available, as influx measurements into resealed ghosts are difficult, and with intact cells the antibody cannot reach the inner surface of the cell membrane where it acts (114). When human red cells are incubated in high-Na media containing saturating concentrations of ouabain, the addition of K to the medium causes a small increase in the Na influx (75, 185); the $K_{0.5}$ for this effect is the same as the $K_{0.5}$ for inhibition of Na–Na exchange by external K. There is also a small saturable component of K influx even in the presence of ouabain (82), and a connection between this flux and the K-induced Na entry is likely since the saturable component of K influx is not seen in Na-free media (91). A very puzzling effect of cardiac glycoside has been described by Mullins (146), who found that the addition of strophanthidin to a squid axon perfused with a solution containing almost no ATP caused a tenfold increase in the (uphill) efflux of Na with no change in the Na influx. He suggests that some of the inward Na movement is carrier-mediated and can become coupled to Na efflux in the presence of strophanthidin.

ENZYME AND TRANSPORT KINETICS

A knowledge of the kinetic parameters describing the transport and enzymic functions of the Na pump is useful in restricting the number and type of conceivable reaction mechanisms. In considering ATPase activity, the pump can be regarded as an enzyme, with ATP as substrate and the various cations as cofactors. In transport experiments with intact cells the alkali-metal ions must be regarded as substrates or products—depending upon which side of the membrane they are on—and the movement across the membrane is formally equivalent to the conversion of substrate to product. Na and K activation with fragmented ATPase preparations is complicated by the fact that Na and K, having access to both faces of the membrane, compete at both internal Na- and external K-activation sites (211) and perhaps have other, unknown, effects. Although this "product inhibition" may be minimized by working over particular ranges of Na and K, it can be eliminated only by the use of intact cells in which the composition of the internal and external media can be controlled.

Cation Activation of Transport and ATPase Activity

Information about the number of Na or K binding sites at each surface, their apparent affinities, and their possible interactions, is obtained from curves showing the activation of fluxes (or of ATPase activity) by Na or K at constant concentrations of the other species. When nerves (19), muscles (209, 210), or red cells (69, 189) are incubated in Na-rich media the curves showing activation of Na–K exchange by external K, or Na–Na exchange by external Na, are both sigmoid. In red cells, two sites of equal apparent affinity for K ($K_K = 0.4$–0.5 mM) are involved in Na–K exchange (189) and three sites of equal apparent affinity for Na ($K_{Na} = 31$ mM) are involved in Na–Na exchange (69). In nerve, however, three sites with different Na affinites seem to be necessary to account for Na activation of Na–Na exchange (19).

At low or zero external Na, the apparent affinity for K activation of Na–K exchange is greatly raised, and the curves are much less sigmoid (19, 74, 209). Although it has sometimes been supposed that Na affects the K affinity only by competition with K, several observations suggest that Na bound to a relatively high-affinity external site has a regulatory effect on the K affinity of the K activation sites. (*a*) In the absence of external Na, the activation of Na–K exchange is best fitted by a two-site model with *unequal* K affinities ($K_K = 5$ and 100 μM) (136). (*b*) Garrahan & Glynn (74) observed that low concentrations of external Na had a large effect on the K affinity of Na–K exchange, but much higher concentrations of Na were necessary to activate Na–Na exchange. (*c*) Independent evidence for the existence of an external high-affinity Na site is provided by the inhibition of the uncoupled Na efflux by low concentrations of external Na (see the section "Studies on Ion Movements"); it is tempting to assume that this is the site at which external Na acts to change the K affinity. Sachs (190) has shown that inhibition of Na–K exchange by external Na requires the binding of only a single Na ion.

The activation of Na–K and Na–Na exchange in red cells by *internal* Na involves multiple binding (69, 184), most probably at three sites of equal apparent affinity ($K_{Na} = 0.19$ mM). Internal K competes with Na (69, 124), probably with a binding affinity that is the same at all three sites ($K_K = 9$ mM). The stimulatory effect of K_i on the V_{max} of Na–K or Na–Na exchange (69, 124, 188, the section "Studies on Ion Movements") indicates the existence of an internal site for K separate from the Na activation sites. Mullins & Brinley (37, 147) made the puzzling observation that when giant axons in K-containing media are perfused with solutions of different Na concentrations, ATP-dependent Na efflux varies linearly with $[Na]_i$ up to 200 mM, whereas ATP-dependent K influx saturates when $[Na]_i$ is about 50 mM. There is much independent evidence from cation activation studies of fragmented membrane ATPase indicating that multiple Na and K binding sites are involved (139, 173, 211).

Although cation activation curves provide useful information, they do not in themselves indicate or exclude any particular kinetic mechanism. A more critical approach, suggested originally by Baker & Stone (20), is to see how the apparent affinities for the cation activation of each flux depend on the cation concentrations at the opposite surface of the membrane. In an important series of experiments, Hoffman & Tosteson (101) and Garay & Garrahan (69, 72) demonstrated that the apparent cation affinities for activation of fluxes from each surface of the membrane are independent of the nature and concentration of the alkali-metal ions at the opposite surface. The relation between the flux and the cation concentrations may, therefore, be described by the product of a constant and two factors that express the saturation of the cation activation sites at the interior and exterior surfaces. The simplest interpretation of these findings is to suppose (*a*) that the apparent affinities for the activating ions at the two surfaces of the membrane are simply related to their true binding affinities, and equal to them if competing ions are absent, and (*b*) that Na and K may bind rapidly, randomly, and independently, at internal and external sites, and that transport occurs only when the pump has bound both Na and K. This conclusion shows that the Na pump is not like the circulating carrier models discussed by Shaw (202) and Caldwell (40), in which Na and K binding sites are formed consecutively and do not exist at the same time. In such models the apparent affinities for ions at each surface of the membrane are complicated functions of the rate constants of the various reactions in the cycle. They are not, except by chance, equal to the true binding constants, and each depends strongly on the ion concentrations at the opposite surface. They would also be expected to vary with the mode of operation of the pump. The finding of Glynn & Lew (90) that in high-Na media K has the same $K_{0.5}$ in activating Na–K exchange and K–K exchange and in inhibiting pump reversal and Na–Na exchange, is also difficult to reconcile with such models.

LK and HK Cells

Before leaving the topic of cation activation, it seems pertinent to mention the curious features of the cation activation of fluxes, or of ATPase activity, in red cells from species showing low red cell K (LK) and high red cell K (HK) dimorphism. There is now evidence that the low rate of active transport in LK cells is the result of competitive inhibition of internal Na sites by K (85, 133, 188). It seems that the internal Na-activation sites in goat LK cells have an affinity for K at least 3 times higher than for Na, which compares with an affinity for K about 50 times lower than for Na in human red cells. It seems also that LK sheep cells have fewer pumps than HK cells, as judged by ouabain binding, although previous estimates (54) have recently been revised (110) and the low K content of LK cells is now attributed more to inhibition of pumping by internal K than to lack of pumps. The specific anti-L antibody, which dramatically increases the rate of pumping in LK cells (60), acts by increasing the relative affinity for Na over K at the internal sites (85, 133, 188), even though it is itself bound externally. Previous claims that the antibody increases the maximal number of ouabain binding sites in LK cells have not been substantiated, although there is an effect on the rate of ouabain binding (110, 187).

Nature of the Nucleotide Substrate of the ATPase. Nucleotide Binding

Although both ATP and Mg are necessary for ATPase activity, it is, perhaps surprisingly, still uncertain which of the species Mg-ATP, free-ATP, and free-Mg combine with the enzyme under physiological conditions. The likely assumption that Mg-ATP is the true substrate was supported by a kinetic test showing that the $K_{0.5}$ for free Mg at a particular total ATP concentration was equal to the $K_{0.5}$ for free ATP at the same total Mg concentration (98, 182). Excess free ATP appeared to inhibit by competing with Mg-ATP, while excess Mg inhibited, uncompetitively in one study (98) and noncompetitively in the other (182) (see ref. 43 for definition of terms). That Mg-ATP is the only substrate has been questioned by Hegyvary & Post (97), who demonstrated that ATP may bind to the enzyme in the total absence of Mg, and once bound may phosphorylate the protein upon subsequent addition of Mg and Na (160, see also 215).

Measurements of equilibrium binding of ATP to microsomal (Na + K)-ATPase preparations have shown that in the absence of Mg and alkali metal ions, ATP binds to a site of very high affinity [$K_d = 0.29$ μM (97) or 0.12 μM (109, 154)] with a hint of binding to a second site of lower affinity (97). In the presence of K, the binding affinity was lowered ($K_d = 30$ μM) but the (calculated) number of molecules bound at infinite ATP concentration was doubled (97). K congeners also antagonized ATP binding with an order of effectiveness: K = Rb > Tl > NH_4 > Cs. Li had no effect; Na slightly enhanced binding when added alone, and counteracted the effect of K with a high affinity ($K_{Na} = 0.9$ mM) (97).

ATP binding was also reduced by competition from other nucleotides, and the following order of affinities was deduced: ATP > ADP > 2'deoxy ATP > β,γ-methylene ATP > CTP > ITP > UTP (97, 109). ATP did not combine with preparations pretreated with ouabain.

The dissociation constant of the high-affinity ATP binding site (0. 12–0.29 μM) is only a little lower than the concentration of ATP that is half maximal for phosphorylation of the enzyme (0.31–3.6 μM) (118, 162) or for Na-dependent ATPase activity (0.1–2 μM) (117, 152). That it is lower is probably due to the absence of Mg in the binding experiments, since the binding of ADP has recently been shown to be reduced by Mg (119). (The effect of Mg on ATP binding cannot be tested because some hydrolysis inevitably occurs if Mg is present.)

An important question to which a clear answer cannot yet be given is whether the K antagonism to ATP binding occurs from an external or an internal site. The relatively high K affinity for the effect [$K_K = 0.2$ mM (97)] suggests that an external K-binding site is involved, and a reduction in nucleotide binding caused by K at the outer surface of the membrane would explain the inhibition by external K of Na efflux from energy-depleted cells (75) and from ghosts containing UTP or low concentrations of CTP (120). It could also account for the effect of K on the substrate affinity of the (Na + K)-ATPase of microsomal preparations (170). On the other hand, Skou (215) has shown that in a medium containing a total (Na + K) concentration of 150 mM, the ratio of Na/K at which ATPase activity was half maximal fell as the total ATP level was raised. This indicates that ATP regulates cation binding to the Na activation sites, increasing the affinity for Na relative to the affinity for K (see page 36). Surprisingly, the effect of ATP on the selectivity of the Na activation sites, was related to the total ATP concentration irrespective of the proportion that was bound to Mg. The order of effectiveness of K and its congeners in inhibiting ATP binding (see above) is different from their order of effectiveness in stimulating dephosphorylation of the phosphoenzyme (Tl > Rb > K > Cs > NH_4 > Li) (97), and this too may indicate the involvement of a site other than, or in addition to, the external K-activation site.

Order of Addition of Substrates and Release of Products

The cation transport kinetics and ATP binding data indicate that ATP, Na_i, and K_o do not have to combine with the enzyme in any fixed order. Several kinetic studies of the ATPase have been reported (98, 155, 170), but interpretation of the initial velocity and product inhibition patterns (cf 43, 66) is not always clear, partly because of the complexity of the enzyme and partly because of conflicting results.

A Lineweaver-Burk plot of the activation of ATPase by ATP at different K concentrations shows a parallel pattern (98, 170), indicating that K raises the V_{max} and K_m for ATP equally. In view of the clear effect of K on ATP binding, it now seems reasonable to accept Robinson's suggestion that the effect of K on V_{max} and K_m is allosteric (170). The surprising suggestion of Peter & Wolf (155) that K must bind before ATP implies that at infinite ATP levels maximal activity could be obtained with vanishingly small concentrations of K. Their view is also difficult to reconcile with the ATP binding experiments discussed above.

Lineweaver-Burk plots with both parallel and intersecting patterns have been reported for the activation of ATPase by ATP at different Na concentrations (98, 155). A random order of ATP and Na binding is certainly possible, since Na increases the initial rate of phosphorylation of enzyme by ATP without affecting the apparent affinity for ATP (235).

The product inhibition patterns of ADP (competitive) and phosphate (noncompetitive) were interpreted by Hexum et al (98) to mean that ADP is released from the enzyme after P_i, although this contradicts the evidence from studies of (*a*) the phosphorylated intermediate (see "Phosphorylated Intermediates"), (*b*) ADP-ATP exchange (see 25, 26, and "Phosphorylated Intermediates"), and (*c*) the metabolic requirements for the various transport modes (see "Studies on Ion Movements"). The pattern with ADP may be explained by supposing that under the conditions of the investigation, the ADP-sensitive form of the enzyme (E_1P) is not an intermediate, for reasons that we will discuss in connection with "half-of-the-sites-reactivity" (see page 45). If this suggestion is correct, ADP could not act as a product inhibitor, but would merely compete with ADP at the substrate site.

Noncompetitive inhibition by phosphate could be explained if the conversion of the form of the enzyme that combines with P_i (presumably E_2K—see "Phosphorylated Intermediates") to the form that combines with ATP (? E_1 or E_1Na) were not readily reversible under the conditions of the experiment. This interpretation is, however, difficult to reconcile with the view that in the presence of K, ATP reacts with E_2K, releasing K from an occluded form (157).

PHOSPHORYLATED INTERMEDIATES

It has always seemed likely that hydrolysis of ATP by the Na pump involves the transfer of phosphate to a group or groups in the enzyme before its ultimate transfer to water. An obvious way to investigate the existence of possible phosphorylated intermediates was to expose membrane fragments to γ^{32}P-ATP and then to look for incorporation of radioactivity into the membrane. It soon became apparent that in the presence of Na + Mg, ^{32}P was incorporated into the membrane lipoprotein and could be released as inorganic phosphate by K ions. For this release neither Na nor Mg was necessary. (See earlier reviews for references.)

The properties of the bound phosphate were those of an acyl phosphate, and there is now good evidence that it is a β-aspartyl phosphate with a serine or threonine on one side of it and a lysine on the other (49, 102, 158, 161). Since acyl phosphates have a high free energy of hydrolysis, it was reasonable to expect the phosphorylation of the protein by ATP to be reversible, but Fahn et al (63, 64) found that they could detect a Na-dependent ATP–ADP exchange only if they either used very low Mg concentrations (but cf 217) or pretreated their preparation with *N*-ethylmaleimide (NEM). It later turned out that a number of other conditions also promote Na-dependent ATP–ADP exchange, or a decrease in membrane bound ^{32}P on the addition of ADP. These include (*a*) substitution of Ca for Mg (226 , 227), (*b*) the presence of oligomycin (34, 64), and (*c*) the presence in equimolar amounts of 2,3-dimercaptopropanol and arsenite (BAL-arsenite) (203). To explain the need for low Mg or NEM etc, Albers and his colleagues (63, 64, 203) suggested that the phosphorylated compound first formed, which they called E_1P, was converted to a lower energy form, E_2P, by a reaction that needed Mg ions and that was blocked by the inhibitors.

The overall hydrolysis of ATP would therefore be represented by

$$E_1 \xrightarrow[\text{(Mg,Na)}]{\text{(ATP)}} E_1P \xrightarrow[\text{(blocked by NEM)}]{\text{(Mg)}} E_2P \xrightarrow{\text{(K)}} E_2 \rightarrow E_1$$

The original justification for assuming the existence of two stable forms of the unphosphorylated enzyme (E_1 and E_2) was that BAL-arsenite caused a big drop in the $K_{0.5}$ for Na activation of the phosphorylation step (203). This implied an action on the unphosphorylated enzyme, and the economical assumption was that BAL-arsenite stabilized a form of the enzyme E_1 with a higher affinity for Na. The existence of more than one form of the dephosphoenzyme is also suggested by observations on the binding of ouabain and of other ligands (see "Inhibitor Studies").

Just as Na in low concentrations appears to shift the equilibrium $E_1 \rightleftharpoons E_2$ to the left, so in high concentrations it appears to shift the equilibrium $E_1P \rightleftharpoons E_2P$ to the left. Tobin et al (226) have recently shown that, in rat brain preparations, phosphorylation in the absence of inhibitors and with 1 mM Mg yields a product of which a fraction is sensitive to ADP; the size of this fraction is increased by high concentrations of Na (see also 159, 163).

Although E_1P and E_2P have different qualities—E_1P being sensitive to ADP but not to K, and E_2P being sensitive to K but not to ADP—treatment with proteolytic enzymes yields peptides with similar electrophoretic behavior (160, 206), suggesting that the difference is a matter of configuration rather than of basic chemical structure. The free energy of hydrolysis of E_1P has been estimated from measurements of the fraction of enzyme phosphorylated after incubation with different ATP/ADP mixtures in the presence of oligomycin (159). It is about 1 kcal/mole less than the free energy of hydrolysis of ATP under the conditions of the experiment.

Since the overall (Na + K)-ATPase reaction is reversible, phosphorylated intermediates should also be formed from inorganic phosphate under appropriate conditions, and it seems that they are. Incorporation of P_i was first detected in experiments in which membrane fragments that had been exposed to ouabain were incubated with P_i + Mg (9) or P_i + Mg + K (137). Na was inhibitory. The properties of the phosphoenzyme obtained in this way, including the results of electrophoresis of proteolytic fragments, suggested that, chemically, the phosphoenzyme was similar to that formed from ATP + Mg in the presence of Na (160, 206). Since acyl phosphates do not normally exchange their phosphate groups with inorganic phosphate, it is likely that energy provided by the combination of the protein with ouabain stabilizes the acyl phosphate. The acyl phosphate must also be able to exist in a fairly low-energy form (? E_2P) without ouabain, however, since some phosphorylation is found even in the absence of ouabain (159, 163).

There are interesting differences in the yields and properties of the phosphoenzyme formed by the incorporation of P_i under different conditions, although all seem to be chemically similar (163). The highest yield was obtained with ouabain and was equal to the maximum yield obtained by incubation with ATP + Na + Mg (9). Incorporation of P_i in the presence of K or its congeners (excluding Na) gave small yields, and the product was sensitive to K but not to ADP, i.e. it was not distinguishable from the phosphoenzyme (E_2P) formed in the presence of ATP + Na + Mg (159, 163). When no alkali metal ions were present, yields were larger and the product was insensitive both to K and to ADP. The addition of Na in high concentration, together with the Mg chelator (1,2-cyclohexylenedinitrilo) tetraacetic acid (CDTA) to prevent further incorporation of P_i, now had the remarkable effect of making the phosphoenzyme sensitive to both K and ADP, as though the Na were converting the "insensitive" form into a mixture of E_2P and E_1P (159, 163). The effect occurred slowly over many seconds, and very high concentrations of Na were required, reminiscent of those required extracellularly for Na–Na exchange or pump reversal in intact red cells. The membrane fragments used in these experiments were vesicular, but it is not known whether the existence of a Na concentration gradient across the membrane played any part.

Phosphoenzyme similar to that formed from ATP can also be formed from other nucleoside triphosphates and from *p*-nitrophenylphosphate (*p*NPP) and acetyl phosphate (24, 35, 52, 106, 107, 175, 195, 204, 205, 220). Mg is always essential. Na is essential for phosphorylation by nucleoside triphosphates, and was found to increase phosphorylation by acetyl phosphate unless K was also present (35). Phosphorylation by *p*NPP and by acetyl phosphate will be discussed further in "Phosphatase Activity of the Sodium Pump."

The Role of Phosphorylated Intermediates in the Normal Working of the Pump

Since, in the presence of ATP, Na causes phosphorylation of a membrane protein and K causes the transfer of the phosphate group from the protein to water, it is tempting to suppose that the occurrence of these events, in sequence, accounts for the hydrolysis of ATP, and that the chemical changes catalyzed by each kind of ion somehow result in the transfer of ions of that kind across the membrane. A long time ago, however, Skou (211, 220) pointed out that the formation of phosphoenzyme might be a side reaction that occurred only in the absence of K, and that under certain conditions (low temperature, use of ITP) K decreased the level of phosphoenzyme at the same time as it decreased, or had no effect on, the overall rate of hydrolysis. K ions have been shown to inhibit the ouabain-sensitive Na-dependent hydrolysis of UTP and CTP (24, 204, 205), and there have now been several reports that with low enough concentrations of ATP the ouabain-sensitive Na-dependent ATPase activity is inhibited by K ions at concentrations that would be stimulatory at normal levels of substrate (34, 46, 117, 152, 157). These observations imply that if the phosphorylated form of the enzyme is indeed an intermediate in the normal working of the pump, K ions must interfere with its formation as well as its breakdown. Competition with Na ions at the Na-loading sites would be negligible at the low concentration of K ions used in these experiments, and some other inhibitory action must be sought.

What this action may be is suggested by a series of ingenious experiments by Post et al (157). They first exposed membrane preparations to Mg + γ^{32}P-ATP + Na at 0°, and by trial and error found concentrations of Li and Rb, which, when added with CDTA to stop further phosphorylation, gave equal rates of breakdown of the phosphoenzyme. They then showed that at these concentrations in the absence of CDTA, the two ions gave quite different rates of hydrolysis and quite different steady state levels of phosphoenzyme. With Rb, the more strongly bound ion, hydrolysis was slower and the steady state of level of phosphoenzyme was lower. This experiment showed that Rb inhibited synthesis more than Li, but did not show at which step in the sequence the inhibition occurred. A further experiment showed that if Rb and Na were present in the medium initially, and phosphorylation was started by the addition of Mg + γ^{32}P-ATP, the level of phosphoenzyme rose sharply and then fell to a steady level; at all times the level was the same as that observed at equal times after the addition of Rb to enzyme fully phosphorylated by Mg + γ^{32}P-ATP + Na already in the medium. This shows that Rb did not inhibit phosphorylation until after the enzyme had been phosphorylated the first time, which is what would be expected if dissociation of Rb from recently dephosphorylated enzyme were rate-limiting.

Further evidence that the release of cation from dephosphoenzyme is slow came from experiments in which the rate of rephosphorylation was studied. In the presence of 200 mM Na (which competes effectively with the low concentrations of Rb or Li used in these experiments) and oligomycin (which blocks the conversion of E_1P to E_2P) any available *free* dehosphoenzyme should be promptly rephosphorylated and trapped as E_1P. The rate of increase in phosphoenzyme when 200 mM Na + oligomycin was added to a preparation of enzyme exposed to Mg + γ^{32}P-ATP + Na in the presence of Li or Rb, gave a measure of the rate of release of Rb or Li from the newly dephosphorylated enzyme. Rb was released more slowly than Li. Furthermore, the difference in rates was unchanged even if the addition of Na was combined with an addition of Li to the Rb samples, or Rb to the Li samples, so that during the rephosphorylation the composition of the solutions was identical. This provides clear evidence that the dephosphoenzyme can "remember" which ion promoted dephosphorylation; much the simplest way to explain the "memory" is to suppose that the ion is still bound to the enzyme. Extra Mg + γ^{32}P-ATP, added with the Na, was found to accelerate rephosphorylation, presumably by accelerating the release of the bound ion; it is lack of this accelerating effect that is thought to account for the inhibitory effect of K on ATPase activity at very low concentrations of ATP.

A quite separate argument for the existence of a rate-limiting step subsequent to dephosphorylation can be based on the findings of Mårdh & Zetterqvist (140), who used a rapid-mixing technique to study rates of phosphorylation. At 21° and with 5 μM ATP, 3 mM Mg, and 120 mM Na, they found that in the absence of K the rate of phosphorylation was about nine times the rate of overall hydrolysis. If 20 mM K was also present in the medium the rate of hydrolysis was unchanged and the steady state level of phosphoenzyme was reduced by a factor of about 5. Yet the initial rate of phosphorylation, when ATP was first added, was at least a quarter of the rate in the absence of K and could not have been rate-limiting. By exclusion, the rate-limiting step must have been subsequent to dephosphorylation. (See references 141 and 159 for further evidence supporting this interpretation of Mårdh & Zetterqvist's results.)

Positive evidence that the phosphoenzyme is an intermediate in the normal working of the pump comes from (*a*) experiments looking at rates of hydrolysis and levels of phosphorylation in the steady state, under various conditions, and (*b*) experiments using rapid-mixing techniques to measure rates of phosphorylation and dephosphorylation.

STEADY STATE EXPERIMENTS At temperatures and ATP levels not too far from physiological, steady state experiments (117, 153) show that under conditions in which phosphorylation should be rate-limiting—Na and K high and fixed, ATP variable or ATP and K high and fixed, Na variable—the rate of hydrolysis is, as might be expected, proportional to the level of phosphoenzyme. Under conditions in which dephosphorylation should be rate-limiting—ATP and Na high and fixed, K variable—the rate of hydrolysis is proportional to the level of dephosphoenzyme. This too is to be expected, though less obviously. In the steady state, the level of phosphoenzyme will be that at which its rate of formation is equal to its rate of breakdown, and both rates will be equal to the overall rate of hydrolysis. But, with

ATP and Na levels both high, the rate of formation will be proportional to the level of dephosphoenzyme, and so the rate of hydrolysis will be also. (Release of K from the dephosphoenzyme will not be rate-limiting because of the high ATP concentration.)

RAPID-MIXING TECHNIQUES Experiments with rapid-mixing techniques have been reported by Tonomura and his colleagues (68, 118, 235) and by Mårdh & Zetterqvist (140–143), and it is convenient to consider the work by the two groups in turn.

One of the most striking pieces of evidence demonstrating that hydrolysis proceeds via the phosphoenzyme is provided by an experiment in which Kanazawa et al (118) measured the time course of EP formation and P_i liberation for one second immediately after the mixing of enzyme with 1 μM ATP in a medium containing 3 mM Mg, 140 mM Na, and 0.6 mM K. The concentration of EP increased without any lag, and approached a steady value within 1 sec. The rate of P_i liberation showed a pronounced lag and did not reach a steady value until the concentration of EP had stopped rising. At any instant, the observed rate of liberation of P_i was close to that calculated from the momentary level of EP, assuming a turnover calculated from the ratio v/EP found during the steady state.

Experiments by Kanazawa et al (118) and by Fukushima & Tonomura (68) have also given information about the steps leading to the formation and breakdown of the phosphoenzyme: 1. The rate constant for the breakdown of phosphoenzyme can be estimated either from the ratio v/EP in the steady state or by measuring the rate constant (k_D) describing the fall of E^{32}P when rephosphorylation by γ^{32}P-ATP is stopped by the addition of EDTA or an excess of unlabelled ATP. In the absence of K the two methods agree well, but with K present v/Ep exceeds k_D and is about double k_D when K is 0.6 mM. 2. In the absence of K, the rate of loss of E^{32}P when resynthesis is stopped is roughly equal to the rate of liberation of $^{32}P_i$. In the presence of K, the liberation of $^{32}P_i$ is faster than the loss of E^{32}P, and with 0.6 mM K the amount of $^{32}P_i$ formed is about double the amount of the E^{32}P lost. 3. When K + EDTA was added to enzyme phosphorylated by γ^{32}P-ATP + Mg + Na, there was an initial rapid fall in EP followed by a slower exponential loss. The rapid fall in EP was accompanied by the formation of an equivalent amount of ATP. 4. With NEM-treated enzymes, the effects of adding ADP at different times after phosphorylation had been started with γ^{32}P-ATP showed that the newly formed phosphoenzyme would not lose ^{32}P to ADP, but the greater part of the phosphoenzyme became sensitive to ADP within a second or two.

The authors suggest that newly formed phosphoenzyme is resistant to added ADP because ADP is still bound to it. The results described in points 1–3 can be explained by supposing (*a*) that there is an equilibrium between a form of the enzyme with tightly bound ATP (E_2S) and the form of the phosphoenzyme with bound ADP (EP•ADP), (*b*) that this equilibrium is normally heavily in favor of EP•ADP, but is displaced toward E_2S by K, 0.6 mM K giving an equilibrium constant near unity, (*c*) that the interconversion of E_2S and EP•ADP does not require Mg, (*d*) that the formation of E_2S from E_1S,[1] the first enzyme–substrate complex to be formed, is not readily reversible and is blocked by EDTA, and (*e*) that the tightly bound ATP is released from the enzyme during extraction with trichloracetic acid.

If these assumptions are correct, it is clear that when phosphorylation by γ^{32}P-ATP is stopped, either by EDTA or by an excess of unlabelled ATP, the formation of *E*P•ADP from E_2S will slow the disappearance of bound ^{32}P, therefore reducing k_D, and the breakdown of that *E*P•ADP will contribute the extra P_i. By increasing the quantity of E_2S, K ions will increase these effects. Some support for this role for K comes from the stimulation of Na-dependent ATP–ADP exchange under certain conditions (26).

Because the hypothetical *E*P•ADP would presumably not react with added ADP, Tonomura and his colleagues identified it with the classical E_2P; and since the experiments of Fukushima & Tonomura (68) showed that the newly formed phosphoenzyme is insensitive to ADP and becomes sensitive with time, they have to assume that E_2P is the precursor of the ADP-sensitive form (E_1P). This hypothesis is difficult to reconcile with an experiment of Post et al (160). When membrane fragments were incubated with Mg and γ^{32}P-ATP in the absence of Na, the γ^{32}P-ATP became bound to the enzyme sites but no phosphorylation occurred. When a "chasing" solution containing Na, Mg, and unlabelled ATP was then added, there was a rapid rise in membrane-bound ^{32}P followed by a slow fall as the phosphoenzyme broke down. The crucial point was that when ADP was present in the chasing solution, the initial rise in membrane-bound ^{32}P was slower, but the rate of fall was the same. This strongly suggests that the ADP-sensitive form of phosphoenzyme (E_1P) precedes the ADP-insensitve form. [It is just possible that ADP acted not by combining with E_1P but by displacing bound ATP by an allosteric effect from another site. Since ADP was more effective than unlabelled ATP this is unlikely (160).]

To accommodate the findings of Post et al (160) together with those of Kanazawa et al (118) and of Fukushima & Tonomura (68) it seems to be necessary to suppose (*a*) that the phosphoenzyme first formed is resistant to ADP because it has ADP still bound to it, (*b*) that the ADP is then lost, giving an ADP-sensitive form, E_1 P, and (*c*) that this is transformed to an ADP-sensitive, K-sensitive form, E_2P.

Quite a different explanation for the results of Kanazawa et al (118) has been suggested by Skou (217). He supposed that when both internal and external sites of the pump carry Na, hydrolysis of ATP is via a phosphorylated intermediate, *E*P, but that when the internal site carries Na and the external site carries K, hydrolysis occurs by a parallel pathway without any phosphorylated intermediate. If ATP bound to the enzyme can continue to be hydrolyzed after the addition of EDTA, it is possible to explain the discrepancy between the liberation of P_i and the disappearance of *E*P, and also the discrepancy between v/EP and k_D.

[1]In describing the results of Tonomura et al (68, 118) we have used their nomenclature, but the forms of the enzyme-substrate complex E_1S and E_2S are not related to the E_1 and E_2 forms of the enzyme first postulated by Siegel & Albers (203).

107155

Mårdh & Zetterqvist (140, 142, 143) used a more elaborate rapid-mixing technique, which allowed them to reduce the total reaction time (including time for stopping the reaction with TCA) to less than 3 msec. They were therefore able to follow phosphorylation with much higher levels of ATP and at 21°.

With 100 μM γ^{32}-ATP, Na-dependent phosphorylation was apparently first order, with a rate constant of 11,000 min^{-1}. Addition of KC1 to a final concentration of 10 mM caused dephosphorylation with a first-order rate constant of at least 14,000 min^{-1} (independent of ATP concentration in the range 5–100 μM). Both rates were, therefore, far more than adequate to account for the overall rate of hydrolysis in the steady state. The rapid disappearance of phosphoenzyme on the addition of K was accompanied by an equally rapid liberation of P_i. Knowing the amount of phosphoenzyme present in the steady state, they calculated the expected hydrolysis rate if all of the phosphoenzyme broke down with a rate constant of 14,000 min $^{-1}$. The answer turned out to be ten times the observed rate of hydrolysis; this discrepancy suggests that in the steady state 90% of the phosphoenzyme must be in a more stable form.

When 10 mM KC1 and excess unlabelled ATP were added simultaneously to enzyme previously phosphorylated by 100 μM γ^{32}P-ATP + Na + Mg, there were two phases of dephosphorylation: an immediate fast phase with a rate constant of at least 14,000 min^{-1}, and a much slower phase. If the fast phase represented the breakdown of E^2P and the slow phase the breakdown of E_1P, then there must have been about three times as much E_2P as E_1P. If KC1 was present before the addition of γ^{32}P-ATP, only the slow phase was seen, suggesting that under steady state conditions with 10 mM K and 120 mM Na nearly all the phosphoenzyme is E_1P. The rate constant for the slow phase in this experiment was about 4600 min^{-1}, and the product of this and the amount of phosphoenzyme present agreed reasonably well with the rate of overall (Na + K)-stimulated hydrolysis at saturating levels of ATP.

The addition of 10 mM KC1 + CDTA to phosphoenzyme also led to two phases of dephosphorylation, but the slow phase was slower than that seen after the addition of KC1 with unlabelled ATP. The difference suggests that Mg is required for the conversion of E_1P to E_2P.

Mårdh & Zetterqvist (142) also drew attention to the existence of bound ATP in their acid-washed precipitates. Acid-resistant ATP binding was first described by Shamoo & Brodsky (38, 201), who believed that the binding involved the (Na + K)-ATPase since it was reduced by ouabain, provided that both Na and K were present. Because, in the absence of ouabain, Na and K did not alter the level of acid resistant binding, any such binding should not affect measurements of Na-dependent ^{32}P incorporation.

Taken together, the results discussed in this section provide strong evidence for an intermediary role of phosphoenzyme in the normal working of the pump, and, more specifically, for the classical Albers scheme. So far, nearly all forms of the phosphoenzyme that have been studied seem to be similar chemically, though Robinson (176) reported that phosphorylation by ^{32}P-pNPP at pH 5 led to K-dependent incorporation of ^{32}P into a serine phosphate. In any event, the possibility that chemically different forms, perhaps with acid-labile phosphate groups, also exist and play a part in the pump cycle cannot be excluded (39, 180).

PHOSPHATASE ACTIVITY OF THE SODIUM PUMP

Identity of (Na + K)-ATPase and K-Dependent Phosphatase

The suggestion of Judah et al (2, 116) that (Na + K)-ATPase is responsible for the K-dependent ouabain-sensitive hydrolysis of *p*NPP is now generally accepted. The ATPase and *p*NPPase activities are similarly distributed (2, 15, 67, 238, 244); both activities increase in parallel when membrane fractions are purified (115, 148), and both decrease in parallel when membrane preparations are subjected to heat or to treatment with trypsin or a wide variety of inhibitors (16, 67, 106, 148, 243). Resemblances in the responses of the two activities to various ligands (see below), and the "sidedness" of the action of these ligands, provide further evidence of identity (78, 80, 166).

The results of radiation inactivation show that the target area for inhibition of *p*NPPase activity is only about half that for inhibition of ATPase activity, suggesting that only a part of the (Na + K)-ATPase system is involved in the hydrolysis of "phosphatase substrates" (121). That makes it easier to understand how dimethyl sulfoxide (DMSO) and phlorizin can inhibit (Na + K)-ATPase activity at the same time as they stimulate *p*NPPase activity (7, 145, 177, 180; see also 44, 67, 172, 239), and may also help to account for the different effects of "anti-Na pump" antisera on the two activities (11, 14, 89).

Substrate Specificity

Although loosely called phosphatase activity, the K-dependent hydrolytic activity of (Na + K)-ATPase preparations is in fact limited to substrates with phosphate groups with a moderate or high free energy of hydrolysis. Acetyl phosphate (AcP), carbamyl phosphate, *p*NPP, and umbelliferone phosphate are hydrolyzed, whereas phenyl phosphate, glucose phosphate, α and β glycerophosphates, and phosphoryl serine are not (67, 156, 243). Nucleoside triphosphates are hydrolyzed only if Na ions are present.

Effects of Physiological Ligands on K-Dependent Phosphatase Activity

The interaction of different ligands is extremely complicated, and, because this was not always appreciated, some of the early work can mislead by suggesting effects on V_{max} that are really effects on the $K_{0.5}$ for some other ligand present in less than saturating concentrations. A second source of confusion is the inhibitory effect of high ionic strength (44). A third, in work on red cells, is that there is evidence that the K-independent hydrolysis of *p*NPP in red cell membranes may not be the action of a separate enzyme, so that estimates of K-dependent activity can be misleading (78). Fortunately, most of the work on tissues other than red cells has been done with preparations in which the K-dependent phosphatase activity accounts for most of the activity.

EFFECTS OF K AND Mg At constant substrate concentrations and Mg concentrations, K activates in sigmoid fashion (but cf 78) with a $K_{0.5}$ of a few millimolar, i.e. much greater than the $K_{0.5}$ for activation of the (Na + K)-ATPase at zero external Na concentrations (8, 78, 216). The activating effect is partly on the V_{max} and partly the result of an increase in the apparent affinity for substrate (8, 78, but cf 216). Even where K ions appear to increase the affinity for *p*NPP, an increase in *p*NPP concentration does not affect the affinity for K ions (78), so at least one of the apparent affinities cannot be an equilibrium binding constant. Inhibition by high K concentrations is probably at least partly an ionic strength effect, since it was not seen in experiments in which choline was used to maintain constant ionic strength (216).

Although the K-dependent dephosphorylation step in (Na + K)-ATPase activity can occur in the absence of Mg, Mg is necessary for phosphatase activity. Ca cannot substitute for Mg (16), and appears to compete with it (148). The optimal level of Mg is not affected by the concentration of substrate (78), but there is a complex relation between the levels of Mg and K required for maximal activity, the optimal level of each being higher at high concentrations of the other (16, 67, 148, 216).

EFFECT OF Na IN THE ABSENCE OF ATP Without K, Na ions promote a minimal phosphatase activity (8, 107, 174) with $K_{0.5}$ for Na of about 3.5 mM (8). At high K concentrations Na inhibits, but only if the Na concentration is also high (67, 148, 216). Of much greater interest is the discovery by Nagai et al (148) that at low K concentrations Na stimulates the hydrolysis of *p*NPP. This has been confirmed by more detailed recent studies (8, 216), which, however, differ from each other in a puzzling way. With K fixed at 2.5 mM, Albers & Koval (8) found that increasing Na gave a large increase in the apparent affinity for substrate, whereas Skou (216) found that the apparent affinity for substrate was little affected. Albers & Koval claimed that with high enough Na concentrations the total enzyme displayed "high" affinity for K, which was not true of Skou's preparation. It is not known if the cause of these discrepancies is related to the use of a DMSO-treated preparation by Albers & Koval.

EFFECT OF ATP There is general agreement that, in the absence of Na, ATP inhibits the hydrolysis of phosphatase substrates (67, 79, 107, 156), but there is disagreement about whether this inhibition is competitive (79, 107) or noncompetitive (67). In any event, as Israel & Titus (107) point out, competitive inhibition does not imply that the ATP and substrate necessarily combine at the same site. ATP might act by keeping the enzyme in a configuration in which it did not combine with *p*NPP. As well as decreasing the apparent affinity for substrate, ATP decreases the apparent affinity for K (79, 148). Nucleoside triphosphates other than ATP are also inhibitory, but only at much higher concentrations (107, 149, 216).

In the presence of Na the effects of nucleoside triphosphates are quite different. Except at high K concentrations, they cause a great increase in the rate of hydrolysis of phosphatase substrates, and the hydrolysis becomes much more like the hydrolysis of ATP in its sensitivity to K and to ouabain (79, 149, 165, 171, 174, 244). The stimulatory effect is prevented by oligomycin (12, 79, 107, 174) and *N*-ethylmaleimide (NEM) (174), although these substances do not inhibit K-dependent phosphatase activity in the absence of both Na and ATP.

Skou (216) recently made a careful study of the effects of 0.1 mM ATP on the rate of *p*NPPase hydrolysis at K concentrations between 0 and 100 mM, using either Na or choline or a mixture of both to keep the ionic strength constant. In the absence of ATP, and with a high Na concentration, the K activation curve showed two steps: a small step that seemed to represent a process with a high affinity for K, and a large step that seemed to represent a process with a low affinity for K. The main effect of 0.1 mM ATP was to cause a very large increase in the height of the first step without altering the apparent affinity for K of the process responsible for that step.

Skou supposed that the activity at low K/Na ratios represents a sluggish activity of the enzyme when the outside (high K-affinity) sites are loaded with K and the inside (low K-affinity) sites are loaded with Na, and that the activity at high K/Na ratios represents a more vigorous activity of the enzyme when both inside and outside sites are loaded with K. The effect of ATP is, he supposed, to increase the activity of the pump in the K_o/Na_i form, so that it becomes comparable to the activity of the K_o/K_i form. A secondary effect of ATP observed by Skou is that in the presence of saturating levels of K the pump was made more sensitive to inhibition by low concentrations of Na. This fits the hypothesis well, since experiments on protection agains NEM inhibition (see "Inhibitor Studies") suggest that ATP increases the preference of the inside sites for Na.

The main weakness of Skou's hypothesis is that it demands a stimulatory effect of internal K and an inhibitory effect of internal Na, yet the evidence from experiments on red cells (166) is that only external K is relevant, and that internal Na is not inhibitory. The hypothesis also gives no clue about the way in which ATP might cause the postulated increase in the activity of the K_o/Na_i form; nor is it clear why, in the presence of ATP, the K_o/Na_i and K_o/K_i forms should give the same V_{max}.

Before we consider alternative hypotheses to explain the stimulatory effect of Na + ATP, we must try to settle a narrower problem, i.e. is phosphorylation of the enzyme an essential step in the stimulation. The following considerations suggest that it is: 1. Acetyl phosphate (AcP), which we know can phosphorylate the enzyme (15, 52, 107), stimulates *p*NPP hydrolysis in the presence of Na (174). 2. Although, in the presence of Na, high concentrations of CTP, ITP, and GTP act like ATP (149, 171, 174, 216, 244), β,γ-methylene ATP, a nonphosphorylating analog, was ineffective (126). Unfortunately, this evidence is weakened by the fact that the α,β-methylene analog, which can be a substrate for (Na + K)-ATPase (unpublished work of J. D. Cavieres and I. M. Glynn), was ineffective. There is conflicting evidence about the effectiveness of ADP (cf 79, 244). 3. Oligomycin and NEM, which are thought to block the conversion of E_1P to E_2P, have no action on phosphatase activity in the absence of Na, but prevent the stimulation of *p*NPPase by Na + nucleotide or Na + AcP (12, 107, 174). The finding that low concentrations of oligomycin can *stimulate* phosphatase activity in the presence of Na but without nucleotide (12) suggests, however, that the action of oligomycin may be more complicated than has been supposed. 4. The parallelism between (*a*) the actions of Na + nucleotide or Na + AcP on *p*NPP hydrolysis and (*b*) the actions of Na + nucleotide or Na + *p*NPP on (Na + K)-ATPase inhibition by Be^{2+} or F^- (178, 179, 181) is so close that a common mechanism seems likely. As shown in the section "Inhibitor Studies," there is now good evidence that phosphorylation is involved in the effects of Na + nucleotide or Na + *p*NPP on inhibition by Be^{2+} or F^-. 5. The fact that Na alone acts to some extent like Na + nucleotide does not prove that phosphorylation is not involved, since we know that phosphatase substrates can phosphorylate the enzyme, yielding a product chemically similar to that formed from ATP (35, 52, 106, 107, 191).

If we accept that Na + ATP acts by phosphorylating the enzyme, we must then ask how phosphorylation brings about the changed behavior; this question cannot be separated from the general question of the nature of the phosphatase activity.

An early idea that substrates like *p*NPP and AcP compete with *E*P for the K-activated dephosphorylating mechanism now seems very unlikely in view of (*a*) the known capacity of these substances to phosphorylate, (*b*) the fact that the formation of *E*P from Na + ATP stimulates phosphatase activity, and (*c*) the fact that AcP interferes with the formation of $E^{32}P$ from $\gamma^{32}P$-ATP, but does not affect the breakdown of $E^{32}P$ present before the addition of AcP (35). We shall therefore assume that the hydrolysis of substances like *p*NPP takes place through the formation and breakdown of phosphoenzyme.

Robinson (174) has suggested that in the absence of Na and ATP, the E_1 form of the enzyme is phosphorylated by the substrate in a reaction that is catalyzed by Mg + K. The need for moderately high concentrations of K reflects, he supposed, the low K affinity of E_1. In the presence of Na, Robinson again supposed that E_1 is phosphorylated by the substrate, but now the phosphorylation may be catalyzed by K or Na, the relative effectiveness of each depending on the substrate. To the extent that catalysis of this step is by Na, K will be required only for the hydrolysis, and the overall reaction will reflect the (presumably) high K affinity of E_2P. In the presence of ATP + Na, Robinson supposed that E_1 is phosphorylated exclusively by ATP, and that the phosphatase substrate phosphorylates E_2P yielding a doubly phosphorylated form of the enzyme. Under these conditions there is no K-activated phosphorylation of E_1 and the low affinity of E_1 for K is therefore not reflected in the K-activation curve of the overall reaction.

An awkwardness of this otherwise attractive theory, as it is stated, is that we have to suppose that phosphorylation of the E_1 configuration of the enzyme can be catalyzed either by Na, presumably acting from the inside surface, or by K, presumably acting from the outside surface in view of the results of Rega et al (166).

Albers & Koval (8) proposed a more general scheme in which sites that must be occupied by K for catalysis to occur are unmasked only if *either* one set of regulatory sites is occupied by K *or* a different set is occupied by Na. If the K catalytic sites have a higher affinity than the K regulatory sites, the kind of stepped K-activation curve that is seen in the presence of Na can be explained. This hypothesis does not explain the effect of ATP or take account of the probable role of phosphorylation.

If Na + ATP acts by phosphorylating the enzyme, and if phosphatase substrates are hydrolyzed via phosphoenzyme, then *either* there must be a doubly phosphorylated enzyme *or* the enzyme must be phosphorylated consecutively by ATP and by the phosphatase substrate. At present, neither possibility can be excluded. There is no evidence for a doubly phosphorylated enzyme, but it might not be easy to isolate and the idea is not unattractive. There is no evidence for consecutive phosphorylation, but a plausible way in which it could account for the observed stimulation of phosphatase activity has been suggested by Post et al (157). They proposed that it is the transient E_2K form of the enzyme that is most readily phosphorylated by substrates like *p*NPP, and that Na + ATP accelerates hydrolysis of such substrates by forming first E_2P and then E_2K. Since *p*NPP itself phosphorylates the enzyme, its own hydrolysis should presumably also lead to the formation of E_2K, but if *p*NPP reacts much more slowly with E_1Na than with E_2K, then ATP should help by "repriming" the system whenever a *p*NPP molecule fails to phosphorylate before E_2K has been converted to E_1 Na. In the presence of Na + ATP, K would be needed only to convert E_2P to E_2K, and the affinity of K should therefore be the same as for (Na + K)-ATPase activity. In the absence of Na and ATP, K in high concentrations is needed to enable *p*NPP to phosphorylate, perhaps because E_2K is formed directly from unphosphorylated enzyme. In the presence of Na without ATP, the K-activation curve for the hydrolysis of a phosphatase substrate would show more or less of the high affinity component, depending on how well the substrate was able to phosphorylate E_1Na.

Is Phosphatase Activity Associated with Ion Transport?

The resemblance between K-dependent phosphatase activity and the dephosphorylation step in the normal pump cycle makes it natural to ask whether the hydrolysis of phosphatase substrates is accompanied by an inward movement of K. Brinley & Mullins (147) were unable to detect any transport in squid axons perfused with AcP. Garrahan & Rega (80) showed that *p*NPP did not support a ouabain-sensitive Rb influx or Na efflux in red cells depleted of ATP by starvation, though it did reduce both fluxes in cells containing ATP, particularly at subnormal concentrations. Na–K exchange and Na–Na exchange were equally sensitive to inhibition by *p*NPP; this is interesting because it implies that even if *p*NPP phosphorylates the E_2K form of the enzyme most readily, it can block reactions with ATP equally well in the absence of K.

Why no ion movements accompany the hydrolysis of *p*NPP is uncertain. An explanation suggested by the need for ATP or its nonphosphorylating analogs in K–K exchange (see "Studies on Ion Movements") is that nucleotide is required in a nonphosphorylating role. This might be the release of K from an occluded form of the enzyme, as postulated by Post et al (157). We may suppose that *p*NPP and P_i phosphorylate the same form of the enzyme (? E_2 or E_2K). In the absence of nucleotide, K may bring about dephosphorylation, and hence *p*NPP hydrolysis or $P_i/H_2{}^{18}O$ exchange (48), but may remain in an occluded form. The puzzling findings of Askari & Rao (13) suggesting a role for nucleotides at the outer surface of the cell remain unexplained.

INHIBITOR STUDIES

In this section we discuss two groups of inhibitors which have provided useful information on the working of the pump: 1. irreversible inhibitors, and 2. cardiac glycosides. The effects of oligomycin have been mentioned in the sections "Studies on Ion Movements" and "Phosphorylated Intermediates."

Use of Irreversible Inhibitors to Measure the Affinities of the (Na + K)-ATPase for Physiological Ligands

If the initial rate of inhibition by an irreversible inhibitor is affected by the concentration of a ligand, then measurement of the rate of inactivation at different ligand concentrations gives a measure of the affinity of the ligand for the site at which it exerts its effect on the inhibition. Binding affinities can be measured under conditions in which ATP is not being hydrolyzed, and the method is particularly useful for ligands where low affinity or lack of specificity makes methods like equilibrium dialysis inapplicable (181). For the results to be interesting it is, of course, necessary to provide evidence that the site at which the ligands act to slow or hasten inhibition is the same as that at which they exert their physiological effects.

A number of inhibitors have been employed in this way, chiefly to measure the affinities of the (Na + K)-ATPase for Na and K.

N-ETHYLMALEIMIDE (NEM) The effects of NEM on (Na + K)-ATPase include: (*a*) inhibition of the hydrolysis of ATP (27, 63, 214, 219); (*b*) alteration of the enzyme so that the phosphoenzyme formed in the presence of Mg + Na + ATP reacts with ADP (160) but its hydrolysis is no longer stimulated by K (27, 63, 65, 160) (on the "Albers scheme" this is thought to be the result of inhibiting the conversion of E_1P to E_2P); (*c*) prevention of the effect of Na + ATP on the K affinity of *p*NPPase (174) (this too, is probably because NEM blocks the conversion of E_1P to E_2P); (*d*) stimulation and, at higher concentrations or after longer exposure, inhibition of Na-dependent ATP–ADP exchange (28, 63, 65); (*e*) prevention of K-stimulation of Na-dependent ATP–ADP exchange (25, 26); (*f*) inhibition of phosphorylation of the enzyme by ATP under certain conditions (27, 28, 64); (*g*) inhibition of the incorporation of inorganic phosphate into the ouabain-treated enzyme (206).

Measurements of (Na + K)-ATPase activity under standard conditions, following exposure to NEM in the absence of Mg and in the presence of different concentrations of ATP, Na, and K, have shown (*a*) that ATP protects against inhibition by NEM, (*b*) that K or ouabain abolishes this protection, and (*c*) that Na reduces it (219). In the presence of ATP and K, the addition of Na restores the protection; in the presence of ATP and high concentrations of Na, the addition of small amounts of K restores full protection (219). CTP, GTP, UTP, and ITP have effects similar to those of ATP but much smaller (27, 214), probably in line with the much lower affinities of the enzyme for these nucleotides (97, 154). ADP has effects similar to those of ATP, but roughly double the concentration is required, and, with ADP, Na does not reduce the protection though it does reverse the "antiprotective" action of K. Skou has made a careful comparison of the effects of various levels of ATP, Na, and K on inactivation by NEM on the one hand, and on ATPase activity of the same preparation untreated with NEM on the other (214). The parallelism between the effects of Na and K on the susceptibility to NEM inhibition and on ATPase activity, at different ATP concentrations, suggested that binding of ATP by the enzyme raised the affinity of the internal Na-activation sites for Na relative to their affinity for K. The ratio (Na affinity)/(K affinity) increased from 0.4:1 to 3:1. (See also "Enzyme and Transport Kinetics.") This effect of nucleotide on the selectivity of the Na activation sites appears not to involve phosphorylation since ADP had an effect similar to that of ATP.

Skou also examined the concentration of K necessary to overcome the antagonistic effect of Na on protection by ATP. The effective range of K concentration was the same as that for activation of ATP hydrolysis in the presence of high concentrations of Na. Since the enzyme was preincubated with NEM and ligands in the presence of EDTA, the results appear to suggest that external K-activation sites with a high affinity for K exist even before the enzyme is phosphorylated. This conclusion is probably not justified. There are reasons to suspect that even in the presence of EDTA some phosphorylation occurred when ATP + Na was present. In the first place, Skou found that extremely low levels of free Mg (3 mM EDTA + 1 mM Mg) were sufficient to make the enzyme susceptible to NEM. Secondly, Na alone did not reduce the protective effect of ADP, suggesting that the effect of Na with ATP depends on phosphorylation.

The presence of physiological ligands can affect not only the speed of inhibition by NEM but also the nature of that inhibition. Banerjee (27, 28) and his colleagues showed that under many conditions exposure to NEM led to inhibition of dephosphorylation of the phosphoenzyme, a parallel fall in overall ATPase activity, and a stimulation of ATP–ADP exchange. Unless very high concentrations of NEM were used, phosphorylation was not affected. When the enzyme was preincubated with NEM in the presence of Mg, Mg + P_i, or Mg + ATP + Na, the main effect was inhibition of phosphorylation. Since the conditions leading to NEM inhibition of phosphorylation are also those that promote ouabain binding (see below), Banerjee et al suggested that phosphorylation is inhibited if NEM alkylates an E_2 form of the enzyme, and that dephosphorylation is prevented if NEM alkylates an E_1 form of the enzyme.

To account for the different results of NEM inhibition, Banerjee et al (27, 28) supposed that in different states of the enzyme different groups were alkylated by NEM. This view is supported by measurements of NEM binding by Hart & Titus (95, 96), who used ^{14}C- and ^{3}H-labelled NEM to compare the binding in the presence and absence of different ligands. All effects of the ligands were confined to the binding of NEM to the 98,000 Dalton peptide, separated by acrylamide gel electrophoresis (see "Purification of the Sodium Pump"). In the presence of ATP + Na, about 2 molecules of NEM were bound per molecule of peptide. With Mg + ATP + Na (? E_2P) about 4 molecules were bound, and with Mg + ATP + Na + oligomycin (? E_1P) about 6 molecules were bound. The effects of selectively blocking inward facing or outward facing sulfhydryl groups (100) also show that the blocking of different groups has different effects.

BERYLLIUM (Na + K)-ATPase activity is inhibited by Be ions, provided that both Mg and K are present (178, 234). The onset of inhibition is first order, the dependence of the rate constant on the concentration of K, at a fixed concentration of Mg and Be, is independent of the Mg and Be concentrations and gives a measure of the affinity for K ions at the sites controlling Be inhibition (178). Robinson found that the dissociation constant for K was 1.4 mM in the absence of Na, and was increased by Na (acting either by direct competition or indirectly from its own site) with a K_I of 7 mM. CTP alone caused a slight decrease in the affinity for K, but CTP and Na together caused a 20-fold increase in K affinity, strongly reminiscent of their combined effect on *p*NPPase activity (178). Inhibition of umbelliferone phosphatase activity by Be showed a similar dependence on the concentration of K and Na (178). The presence of umbelliferone phosphate during the exposure to Be had no effect if Na was absent, but greatly increased the affinity for K if Na was present. Be inactivation and *p*NPPase activity showed a similar dependence on K concentration, both in the presence and absence of Na, suggesting that the same K binding sites are involved in both processes.

That the increase in K affinity caused by Na + nucleotide, or Na + phosphatase substrate, depends on phosphorylation of the enzyme is shown by further experiments in which Robinson (179) compared the effects on K affinity, measured by the Be inhibition technique, of Na + *p*NPP and of Na + a nonphosphorylating analog, *p*-nitrobenzyl phosphonate. Na + *p*NPP increased the K affinity, but Na added with the nonphosphorylating analog appeared merely to compete with K. The analog was shown to be a powerful competitive inhibitor of *p*NPPase activity and must therefore have been able to reach the substrate sites.

The effects of phlorizin and of dimethyl sulfoxide (DMSO) provide further evidence that K binds at the same external sites in promoting Be inhibition and ATPase and phosphatase activity. There is a parallelism—closer for phlorizin than for DMSO—between the effects of these substances on the sensitivity to K and Na of (*a*) the rate of inhibition by Be, (*b*) the rate of hydrolysis of ATP, and (*c*) the rate of hydrolysis of *p*NPP (145, 172, 177–181). The relative effectiveness of T1, K, and ammonium ions in the three processes is also similar (178).

If the identity of the K binding sites involved in these three processes is accepted, the lack of effect of Na + *p*-nitrobenzyl phosphonate on K affinity measured by the Be inhibition technique leads to the extremely important conclusion that phosphorylation is necessary for the appearance of the external high-affinity K-binding sites (181). (See also experiments with fluoride described below.)

FLUORIDE Because nucleotides bind Be ions, their effects on the rate of onset of Be inhibition may be complicated by binding. Fortunately, fluoride ions resemble Be in causing an irreversible inhibition provided that Mg and K ions are present.

Robinson (181) has investigated the effects of nucleotides, and of nucleotides + Na, on the K dependence of the rate of onset of inhibition by LiF. Na and ATP together caused a 12-fold increase in K affinity, and Na + CTP had an even greater effect. On the other hand, Na with EDTA, or with the nonphosphorylating β,γ-methylene analog of ATP, seemed merely to compete with K. Again the implication is that phosphorylation is necessary for the appearance of high-affinity K-binding sites. Remarkably, oligomycin did not prevent the effect of Na + CTP, suggesting that the formation of E_1P is sufficient to give the effect on K affinity. The fact that oligomycin does prevent the (Na + CTP)-stimulation of K-dependent *p*NPPase activity (12, 174) is understandable if stimulation of phosphatase activity requires not merely phosphorylation but also the subsequent formation of E_2K.

DICYCLOHEXYLCARBODIIMIDE (DCCD) Robinson (183) has taken advantage of the protective action of Na against inactivation of (Na + K)-ATPase by DCCD (194) to measure the Na affinity of the enzyme. The site at which Na exerts its protective action is thought to be the internal Na-activation site because the $K_{0.5}$ for protection in the absence of other ligands was similar to the $K_{0.5}$ for Na activation of ATPase at low K concentrations, and because the $K_{0.5}$ for both effects was similarly increased by phlorizin. The apparent affinity for Na, measured by its protective action, was roughly halved by Mg alone, perhaps because Mg stabilizes the E_2 form of the enzyme. ATP in the absence of Mg roughly doubled the affinity, and Mg and ATP together had little effect on the affinity. This is an important finding because, as Robinson points out, it implies that phosphorylation, which, as we saw above, causes a 12- to 20-fold increase in the affinity of the external K-activation sites, has little effect on the affinity of the internal Na-activation sites.

Interaction of Cardiac Glycosides with the (Na + K)-ATPase

Since the discovery by Schatzmann (192) of the inhibitory effect of cardiac glycosides on the Na pump, a voluminous literature on the subject has appeared. Early work establishing the molecular features necessary for inhibition, the external site of action, the parallel inhibition of transport and ATPase activity, and the protective effect of external K, is described in reference 83 and the reviews mentioned in the Introduction. It is now generally agreed that the glycosides act by inhibiting dephosphorylation of the phosphoenzyme or phosphorylation of the dephosphoenzyme (199).

The introduction of tritiated glycosides has facilitated measurements of glycoside uptake, made either for the purpose of counting sites (22, 59, 70, 99) or in experiments using glycoside binding as a tool for investigating the pump mechanism (9, 10, 59, 99, 144, 197, 233). It has become clear that the enzyme–ouabain interaction is described by a single reversible equilibrium: $E + \mathrm{Ou} \rightleftharpoons E \cdot \mathrm{Ou}$ (21, 92, 233). The association rate has been demonstrated to be first order with respect to both enzyme and ouabain concentration (29, 61, 138), the dissociation follows exponential kinetics (61, 231, 232), and the measured equilibrium constant is not significantly different from the quotient of dissociation and association rate constants (61,

231). The different binding constants of ouabain to ATPase preparations vary, reflecting mainly differences in the rates of dissociation of the enzyme–ouabain complex (231, 232).

The rate of glycoside binding was observed to depend on the presence of various physiological ligands, and the rate of onset of inhibition always varied in parallel with the rate of glycoside binding (9, 10, 29, 82, 94, 99, 105, 144, 197, 207, 218). The picture that has emerged is that ligands, or combinations of ligands, that stabilize the E_2 or E_2P conformation of the enzyme—Mg, Mg + P_i, Mg + Na + nucleoside triphosphates, Mg + Na + phosphorylating ATP analogs, Mg + Na + phosphatase substrates—all increase the rate of binding and lower the dissociation constant, whereas ligands or combinations of ligands that stabilize E_1 or E_1P—Na, nonphosphorylating ATP analogs, Na + nonphosphorylating ATP analogs—decrease the rate of binding and raise the dissociation constant (62, 229). Previous reports, claiming that stimulation of binding by CTP, UTP, ITP, and ADP implies that the nucleotide action does not involve phosphorylation, are now regarded as mistaken since these nucleotides do phosphorylate (204, 220, 230). With ADP, the phosphorylation is probably due to traces of ATP produced by adenylate kinase present in some membrane preparations. In the presence of added ATP, ADP inhibits binding (93). Nonphosphorylating ATP analogs reduce the effect of ATP on binding and cause a release of glycoside previously bound in the presence of Mg + P_i (62, 228, 229).

Although physiological ligands alter the rate of binding and the dissociation constant, they do not affect the amount of binding at infinite glycoside concentrations, which presumably gives a measure of the number of enzyme sites present (94, 102).

A great deal of attention has been given to the effects of K and its congeners (excluding Na) on glycoside inhibition of transport (22, 82) and ATP hydrolysis (53, 193). At low glycoside concentrations inhibition can be completely prevented, but at high concentrations there seem to be mixed competitive and noncompetitive interactions between glycoside and K (53, 82, 128, 193, 242).

K reduces inhibition by cardiac glycosides by affecting their binding, and not by conferring activity on the enzyme–glycoside complex. There is clear evidence from experiments with ATPase preparations that the rate of ouabain binding in the presence of Mg, Mg + P_i, or Mg + Na + ATP is reduced by K (3, 4, 9, 21, 138, 144, 231–233, 237). Surprisingly perhaps, under some conditions K has also been observed to lower the rate of dissociation of ouabain from the enzyme–ouabain complex (4, 5), but under all conditions K decreases the binding affinity (62, 94, 233). The binding capacity is not affected.

In red cells and HeLa cells it is clear that it is external K that counteracts the effects of low concentrations of ouabain (21, 82). If choline is taken as a standard, K and Rb decrease, and Na, and to a lesser extent Cs and Li, increase the binding affinity (70, 71). Part of this increase may be the result of competition with K ions leaking from the cells, but the effect is too big to be accounted for entirely in this way, and there is other evidence in red cells (30) and squid nerve (23) suggesting a genuine Na–ouabain interaction (see also 138).

Although the K congeners seem to affect ouabain binding with the same order of affinity in both whole cells and microsomal preparations (i.e. Rb > K > NH_4 > Cs > Li) (21, 22, 62, 70, 71, 196), certain anomalies suggest that the cation effects in the microsomal preparations may not be restricted to the external face of the membrane. The effects of K on the dissociation constant in Erdman & Schoner's brain preparation were not saturated by up to 10 mM K (62), although in other preparations (94, 138) the K concentrations for half-maximal effects were 0.2–0.3 mM, as expected for an effect at the external sites. Cs and Li appear to increase the binding affinity in red cells (71), but decrease it in brain (Na + K)-ATPase (62, 196). Recent measurements of the initial rates of ouabain binding to brain ATPase (105, 138) indicate that K and Na compete for an external site (K_K 0.2 mM; K_{Na} 13.7 mM) from which K inhibits and Na stimulates the rate, and that in addition Na stimulates the rate of binding at a high affinity site (K_{Na} 0.63 mM) on the inner surface.

The kinetics of the K–ouabain interaction in whole cells (21), and in microsomal ATPase preparations (138), suggest that only one cation binding site interacts with each glycoside binding site, although at least two cation sites are involved in activation of transport and ATPase activity (see "Enzyme and Transport Kinetics").

Scatchard plots of equilibrium binding data suggest that at low glycoside concentrations there is only a single type of binding site in red cells and in most (Na + K)-ATPase preparations (61, 70), but in brain preparations a number of investigators have reported complex binding (61, 231). Taniguchi & Iida (223), using a medium containing Mg, ATP, Na, and K, observed equal numbers of sites of low affinity ($K_{0.5} = 20$ μM) and high affinity ($K_{0.5} = 0.18$ μM); these results suggest that there may be negative cooperativity between two ouabain binding sites. Reports (99, 187) that Cs or K reduce the amount of ouabain bound to the Na pump in red cells in addition to that required to inhibit transport suggest that there are at least two binding sites per pump, and that binding of ouabain to only one of them is sufficient to inhibit. The view that one glycoside molecule per pump is sufficient to inhibit activity is supported by experiments relating rates of ATP hydrolysis (128, 242) or rates of transport (186) to glycoside concentration. The idea that the pump contains two ouabain binding sites, only one of which needs to be occupied to block transport or ATPase activity, fits in well with a recent observation by J. C. Ellory & S. R. Levinson (personal communication). In experiments on llama red cell ghosts, they found that the "molecular weight" of the ouabain binding unit determined by radiation inactivation was about 140,000, whereas the "molecular weight" of the ATPase was about 250,000. (See also "Purification of the Sodium Pump.")

PURIFICATION OF THE SODIUM PUMP

Since P. L. Jorgensen is preparing a detailed review of work on the purification of the (Na + K)-ATPase, we give only a very brief survey.

All attempts at purification have started with membrane preparations from tissues rich in (Na + K)-ATPase activity—brain (151, 236), outer medulla of kidney

(111–113, 127, 129, 130), *Electrophorus* electric organ, or dogfish rectal gland (102, 103)—and have then employed two alternative strategies. One is to extract irrelevant material from the membrane by treatment with NaI or detergents, leaving the (Na + K)-ATPase in situ. The other is to solubilize a large fraction of the membrane, including the (Na + K)-ATPase, by more vigorous treatment with detergents, and then to fractionate the mixture by selective precipitation or by gel or ion-exchange chromatography. Each method of attack may be used alone (102, 103, 112) or the first may be followed by the second (102, 127, 129, 130, 151). ATP may be used to protect the enzyme during treatment with detergents (112).

The purification may be followed by measuring the hydrolytic activity of the preparation, but since the various treatments alter the turnover rate, it is desirable also to measure the ability of the preparation to incorporate ^{32}P from ATP or to bind ATP or ouabain. Finally, the purified preparation may be solubilized with sodium dodecyl sulfate (SDS) and subjected to electrophoresis on polyacrylamide gels to determine the molecular weight of the component polypeptides.

Preparations with purities approaching 100% have now been obtained from several sources (102, 112, 113, 127, 129, 130, 151). Most investigators find that SDS treatment yields two polypeptides, a large one of 89,000–135,000 Daltons containing the phosphorylation site, and a smaller glycopeptide (35,000–57,000 Daltons). There is no direct evidence that the glycopeptide is connected with the pump, but the fact that both peptides are generally found together, that their yields increase in parallel on purification (236), and that they can be cross-linked in a 1:1 fashion by treatment of the native enzyme with dimethyl suberimidate (129), makes the connection extremely likely.

Partly because of uncertainties in the molecular weight measurements (129), there is disagreement about the ratio of large to small peptides; estimates of 2:1 (102, 103), 1:1 (113, 127, 130), and 1:2 (129) have all been obtained. Radiation inactivation (121) gives a figure of about 250,000 Daltons for the molecular weight, so that if the ratio of large to small peptides is 1:1 the enzyme would be a dimer of which each half consists of one large and one small peptide.

There is also disagreement about the ratio of ATP binding sites, or ouabain binding sites, to sites capable of being phosphorylated. Jorgensen found the maximum molecular weight was 137,000 per phosphorylation site, 250,000 per ATP binding site, and 278,000 per ouabain binding site. This supports the idea that the enzyme contains two large peptides, and suggests that under the conditions of Jorgensen's experiments (113) both can be phosphorylated but only one at a time can bind ouabain or ATP. Lane et al (130) also found 1 mole of ouabain bound per 250,000–330,000 g of protein. Using radiation inactivation J. C. Ellory and S. R. Levinson (personal communication) showed that the molecular weight of the ouabain binding unit was 140,000, presumably because inactivation of half of the dimer does not prevent binding to the other half. A ratio of phosphorylation sites to ouabain binding sites of 2:1 was also found by Albers et al (9) in electric organ ATPase, though in a preparation from cat brain they found a ratio of 1:1. Kyte (128) found 0.8–1.2 glycoside binding sites per large polypeptide chain, but at maximum phosphorylation only about 0.36 moles of ^{32}P were bound to the protein per mole of glycoside binding site. The cause of these discrepancies is not clear, but they are of the kind that might be expected if the enzyme consisted of two identical subunits, and if the behavior of each affected the other in a way that depended critically on the conditions. Less interesting explanations cannot be excluded however.

THE MECHANISM OF THE PUMP

Any satisfactory model for the working of the pump must be based on the pump's structure, as well as on its behavior under different conditions. Knowledge of structure is still too limited to give any detailed understanding of the mechanism, but the strong suggestion that the pump may be a dimer—each monomer containing a large and a small peptide—has important implications. The dimeric structure is supported by the existence of two phosphorylation sites (9, 113) and, under appropriate conditions, two ATP binding sites (97) and two ouabain binding sites (223). The fact that under other conditions it is possible to see only one ATP binding site or one ouabain binding site (and in other preparations only one phosphorylation site) suggests that the two halves of the dimer interact in such a way that binding of ATP or ouabain to one half reduces the affinity of the other half.

The phosphorylation site on the large polypeptide must make contact with the inside surface of the membrane, at least at some stage in the cycle. Whether other parts of the peptide make contact with the outside surface is not clear, though with a molecular weight of 100,000 the peptide would certainly be big enough to bridge the membrane. The glycopeptides are generally thought to make contact with the outer surface of the membrane on the grounds that it is the outer surfaces of cell membranes that are rich in glycoproteins. The argument is not altogether convincing, but if this view is correct it ought to be possible to get immunological evidence for the accessibility of these peptides from the outside of the cell.

We do not know which peptide, if either, carries the ion binding sites, and, apart from their selectivity, we know little about the nature of these sites. The relative effectiveness of Rb, Cs, Li, Tl, and NH_4 as K substitutes can probably be explained in terms of relative affinities of the binding sites (see Eisenman 57, 58), but Na is irreplaceable in a way that is not paralleled by the behavior of inanimate systems. It is clear that the pump makes use of differences in reactivity of pump–ion complexes, as well as of differences in affinity (85). The recent extraction from membranes of ionophoric material able to distinguish between Na and K is obviously extremely interesting (200).

The kinds of mechanism that have been suggested, from time to time, to explain the movement of ions from one side of the membrane to the other, can be classified loosely as (*a*) carriers, (*b*) gated channels, and (*c*) internal transfer mechanisms. By "carriers" we mean any system in which a group binds an ion at one side of the membrane, moves through the membrane carrying the bound ion with it, and discharges the ion at the opposite side of the membrane. The carrier may be a mobile binding site on a large molecule or it may be a small molecule. "Gated channels" are self-explanatory. By "internal transfer mechanism" we mean a mechanism in which ions originating from each surface exchange binding groups in an occluded region within the membrane and then pass on to the opposite surface.

This classification cuts across that of Skou (212, 213), who divides models into "one-site" models, in which the groups responsible for moving Na and K are interconvertible and only one form exists at any time, and "two-site" models, in which separate groups are responsible for moving Na and K. The two-site models may involve carriers that move right across the membrane, or there may be an interchange in an occluded region within the membrane. Skou's classification is obviously closely related to the division of mechanisms into "sequential" and "simultaneous" (20, 69, 72, 101), depending on whether the inward movement of K follows or accompanies the outward movement of Na. It is unfortunate that in enzyme kinetics a "sequential mechanism" is generally understood to mean a mechanism in which all reactants combine with the enzyme before any products are released (43). This behavior is specifically excluded in the "sequential" model for the pump, and to avoid confusion we suggest that the term "consecutive" be used instead.

Until recently, the transport of ions by the pump was generally explained by some kind of circulating carrier model (40, 202), in which a carrier responsible for moving Na outwards was converted at the outer face of the membrane into a carrier that moved K inwards. Energy was supposed to be fed into the sytem by driving the conversion of one form of the carrier into the other at one face of the membrane, the reversion at the other face being thermodynamically downhill. This one-site, consecutive, carrier system provided a ready explanation of the coupling between Na and K movements, and it was able to account for the various fluxes observed under unphysiological conditions and most of the biochemical changes accompanying them. It has had to be abandoned, however, because it is not compatible with the observations on the constancy of ion affinities discussed in the section "Enzyme and Transport Kinetics," nor with the evidence from inhibitor studies (see "Inhibitor Studies") showing that external sites with a moderately high affinity for K and internal sites with a moderately high affinity for Na exist before the enzyme is phosphorylated. It is important, however to remember that, although external K-binding sites with a moderately high affinity for K may exist before phosphorylation, their affinity is much increased following phosphorylation (see "Inhibitor Studies").

Rejecting the circulating carrier model still leaves open the question of the kind of transfer mechanism involved. A simple way to account for the finding that the rate of exchange is proportional to the product of the probabilities of finding the binding sites at each surface appropriately filled is to suppose (*a*) that there is a molecule bridging the membrane with binding sites at each end, (*b*) that if the binding sites are filled by the proper ions, this molecule is actively rotated, and (*c*) that this rotation is accompanied by a change in affinity of the binding sites so that the outward facing sites always prefer K and the inward facing sites always prefer Na. This model would account for the coexistence of Na and K sites, and would accommodate the observed independence of the affinities; but it is not likely on structural grounds.

It is more plausible, in view of the probable dimeric structure of the enzyme, to imagine two carriers (in the sense defined above) coupled together so that their movements are always 180° out of phase. Repke & Schön's (167, 169) model is basically of this type, though the main interest of that model is in the interactions of the two transporting units.

It is not necessary, however, that the cation binding sites move all the way across the membrane, and models with internal transfer have been proposed on the basis of structural and kinetic evidence (72, 213, 221). Internal transfer models are attractive because their occluded form can provide an obvious explanation of the very slow dissociation of K from E_2K (157), and they can also account for the inhibition of the uncoupled Na efflux by low concentrations of external Na (221). Both features could, however, have alternative explanations. Garrahan & Garay (72) have shown that internal transfer models are compatible with their observations on the independence of ion affinities of conditions at the opposite surface only if the lifetime of the occluded state is short compared with the time during which exchange with the medium is allowed. Hints that the independence of affinities does not hold in Na-free media (42, 186) perhaps suggest that in these conditions the lifetime of occluded states is prolonged.

Gated channel systems are plausible since we know that selective gated channels exist in excitable membranes. But in order to accommodate the various features of the pump—coupling between Na and K movements, coupling between ion movements and ATP hydrolysis, constancy of affinities—the channel would need to be so sophisticated that, in the absence of any specific information, it is not profitable to speculate further. The simple system proposed by Jardetsky (108), in which a channel is opened alternately to the inner and outer surfaces of the membrane, and the affinity of sites within the channel is determined by which end is open, does not give affinities independent of conditions on the opposite side.

In considering the ways in which cations move across the membrane during the pump cycle it is important to remember that not all the effects of cations are associated with a movement of the ions across the membrane. Examples of effects thought not to be associated with cation movements are (*a*) the K-dependent hydrolysis of phosphatase substrates, (*b*) the Na-stimulated ATP–ADP exchange seen in the presence of oligomycin, and (*c*) the K-stimulated exchange of ^{18}O between water and P_i when this exchange occurs in the absence of ATP.

Where Na or K ions are cofactors in biochemical events but do not themselves cross the membrane, we must suppose either that the ions exert their effects while bound at the surface of the membrane, or, if the ions leave the surface, that they never pass beyond an occluded region of the membrane to reach the opposite face. Even if the movement of K is blocked by lack of ATP, or the movement of Na is blocked by oligomycin, it is likely that the nature of the cations "on" or "in" the enzyme determine the fate of the phosphoenzyme. K favors the transfer of phosphate to water, and Na favors the transfer to ADP.

Half-of-the-Sites-Reactivity

An interesting suggestion made by Stein et al (221) is that the Na pump may show *half-of-the-sites-reactivity,* as defined by Lazdunski and his colleagues (134) in connection with the behavior of the alkaline phosphatase of *E. coli.* The *E. coli* enzyme is dimeric, and the characteristic feature of its behavior is that, because of conformational changes associated with phosphorylation or with binding of substrate, only one of the subunits can bind phosphate covalently, or ATP noncovalently, at any time. The phosphorylation of one subunit by ATP is accompanied by dephosphorylation of the other, so that the two subunits go through the reaction cycle 180° out of phase. If the Na pump behaves analogously, its cycle must include the forms E_1ATP:E_2P and E_2P:E_1ATP, though at any instant these forms can account for only a fraction of the total enzyme since we know that in the presence of Na + K most of the enzyme is not phosphorylated.

The scheme suggested by Stein et al (221) combines half-of-the-sites-reactivity with internal transfer, and is consistent with the known structure of the enzyme. Half-of-the-sites-reactivity in connection with the Na pump has been discussed more recently by Siegel et al (205) and by Robinson (182). Repke et al (167, 169) have proposed a "flip-flop" scheme that has the surprising feature that during part of the normal cycle both halves of the enzyme exist in a phosphorylated state. A further feature of their scheme is that the steps leading to changes in affinity for the ions are separate from the steps leading to translocation, only the former being associated with the conversion of the "R/T" form of the enzyme to the "T/R" form.

An advantage of models assuming half-of-the-sites-reactivity that has not been commented on is that they provide a simple explanation for the discrepancies between v/EP and k_D, and between loss of phosphoenzyme and appearance of P_i, seen by Kanazawa et al (118). (See "Phosphorylated Intermediates.") These discrepancies can be explained, as they point out, by the existence of γ^{32}P-ATP bound in such a way that it can still form phosphoenzyme after further reaction with γ^{32}P-ATP in the medium has been blocked with EDTA or by an excess of unlabelled ATP. In a half-of-the-sites-reactive enzyme this bound ATP could represent ATP carried by the unphosphorylated half of the enzyme, i.e. ATP in the form E_1ATP:E_2P. In the absence of K, Kanazawa et al found no discrepancies; this could be *either* because the lower rate of dephosphorylation allowed ATP to dissociate from the enzyme before it could phosphorylate, *or* because, in the absence of K, both halves of the enzyme were phosphorylated (9, 113).

Half-of-the-sites-reactivity also provides a ready explanation of the observation that ADP does not behave as a noncompetitive product inhibitor of the ATPase, as might be expected if ADP is released from the enzyme before P_i (see "Enzyme and Transport Kinetics"). If binding of ATP to the form E_2:E_1P • ADP converts it to the form E_1ATP:E_2P + ADP without intervention of the ADP-sensitive form E_2:E_1P, ADP could not act as a product inhibitor. Under conditions in which this conversion cannot occur (NEM, oligomycin) the phosphoenzyme would become ADP-sensitive following the release of ADP from E_2:E_1P • ADP (cf 68).

It is crucial to explanations of this kind that forms of the enzyme binding ATP to one half and $\sim$ P to the other half should exist, and the finding of Tobin et al (229) that nonphosphorylating ATP analogs accelerate the release of ouabain from enzyme phosphorylated by Mg + P_i is therefore important since it suggests that ATP can react with phosphoenzyme.

Literature Cited

1. Adrian, R. H., Slayman, C. L. 1966. Membrane potential and conductance during transport of sodium, potassium and rubidium in frog muscle. *J. Physiol. London* 184:970–1014
2. Ahmed, K., Judah, J. D. 1964. Preparation of lipoproteins containing cation-dependent ATPase. *Biochim. Biophys. Acta* 93:603–13
3. Akera, T. 1971. Quantitative aspects of the interaction between ouabain and $(Na^+ + K^+)$-activated ATPase *in vitro*. *Biochim. Biophys. Acta* 249:53–62
4. Akera, T., Brody, T. M. 1971. Membrane adenosine triphosphatase: the effect of potassium on the formation and dissociation of the ouabain-enzyme complex. *J. Pharmacol. Exp. Ther.* 176:545–57
5. Akera, T., Brody, T. M., So, R. H. M., Tobin, T., Baskin, S. I. 1974. Factors and agents which influence cardiac glycoside-Na^+, K^+-ATPase interaction. *Ann. NY Acad. Sci.* In press
6. Albers, R. W. 1967. Biochemical aspects of active transport. *Ann. Rev. Biochem.* 36:727–56
7. Albers, R. W., Koval, G. J. 1972. Sodium-potassium-activated adenosine triphosphatase. VII. Concurrent inhibition of $Na^+ + K^+$-adenosine triphosphatase and activation of K^+-nitrophenylphosphatase activities. *J. Biol. Chem.* 247:3088–92
8. Albers, R. W., Koval, G. J. 1973. Na-K-activated ATPase of *Electrophorus* electric organ. VIII. Monovalent cation sites regulating phosphatase activity. *J. Biol. Chem.* 248:777–84
9. Albers, R. W., Koval, G. J., Siegel, G. J. 1968. Studies on the interaction of ouabain and other cardio-active steroids with sodium-potassium-activated adenosine triphosphatase. *Mol. Pharmacol.* 4:324–36
10. Allen, J. C., Lindenmayer, G. E., Schwartz, A. 1970. An allosteric explanation for ouabain-induced time-dependent inhibition of sodium, potassium-adenosine triphosphatase. *Arch. Biochem. Biophys.* 141:322–28
11. Askari, A. 1974. The effects of antibodies to Na^+, K^+-ATPase on the reactions catalysed by the enzyme. *Ann. NY Acad. Sci.* In press
12. Askari, A., Koyal, D. 1971. Studies on the partial reactions catalyzed by the $(Na^+ + K^+)$-activated ATPase. II. Effects of oligomycin and other inhibitors of the ATPase on the *p*-nitrophenylphosphatase. *Biochim. Biophys. Acta* 225:20–25
13. Askari, A., Rao, S. N. 1969. Functional organization of the partial reactions of $Na^+ + K^+$-activated ATPase within the red cell membrane. *Biochem. Biophys. Res. Commun.* 36:631–38
14. Askari, A., Rao, S. N. 1972. Na^+, K^+-ATPase complex: effects of anticomplex antibody on the partial reactions catalyzed by the complex. *Biochem. Biophys. Res. Commun.* 49:1323–28
15. Bader, H., Post, R. L., Bond, G. H. 1968. Comparison of sources of a phosphorylated intermediate in transport ATPase. *Biochim. Biophys. Acta* 150: 41–46
16. Bader, H., Sen, A. K. 1966. (K^+)-dependent acyl phosphatase as part of the $(Na^+ + K^+)$-dependent ATPase of cell membranes. *Biochim. Biophys. Acta* 118:116–23
17. Baker, P. F. 1964. An efflux of ninhydrin positive material associated with the operation of the Na^+ pump in intact crab nerve immersed in Na^+-free solutions. *Biochim. Biophys. Acta* 88: 458–60
18. Baker, P. F. 1965. Phosphorus metabolism of intact crab nerve and its relation to the active transport of ions. *J. Physiol. London* 180:383–423
19. Baker, P. F. et al 1969. The ouabain-sensitive fluxes of sodium and potassium in squid giant axons. *J. Physiol. London* 200:459–96
20. Baker, P. F., Stone, A. J. 1966. A kinetic method for investigating hypothetical models of the sodium pump. *Biochim. Biophys. Acta* 126:321–29
21. Baker, P. F., Willis, J. S. 1970. Potassium ions and the binding of cardiac glycosides to mammalian cells. *Nature* 226:521–23
22. Baker, P. F. Willis, J. S. 1972. Binding of the cardiac glycoside ouabain to intact cells. *J. Physiol. London* 224: 441–62
23. Baker, P. F., Willis, J. S. 1972. Inhibition of the sodium pump in squid giant axons by cardiac glycosides: dependence on extracellular ions and metabolism. *J. Physiol. London* 224:463–75
24. Banerjee, S. P. 1974. Participation of cytidine triphosphate in sodium ion-dependent phosphorylation, transphosphorylation, and hydrolysis: Evidence for two hydrolytic sites in sodium ion

plus potassium ion dependent adenosine triphosphatase. *Ann. NY Acad. Sci.* In press

25. Banerjee, S. P., Wong, S. M. E. 1972. Potassium ion stimulated and sodium ion-dependent adenosine diphosphate-adenosine triphosphate exchange activity in a kidney microsomal fraction. *Biochem. J.* 129:775–79
26. Banerjee, S. P., Wong, S. M. E. 1972. Effect of potassium on sodium-dependent adenosine diphosphate-adenosine triphosphate exchange activity in kidney microsomes. *J. Biol. Chem.* 247:5409–13
27. Banerjee, S. P., Wong, S. M. E., Khanna, V. K., Sen, A. K. 1972. Inhibition of Na- and K-dependent adenosine triphosphatase by *N*-ethylmaleimide. I. Effects on Na-sensitive phosphorylation and K-sensitive dephosphorylation. *Mol. Pharmacol.* 8:8–17
28. Banerjee, S. P., Wong, S. M. E., Sen, A. K. 1972. Inhibition of Na- and K-dependent ATPase by *N*-ethylmaleimide. II. Effects on Na-activated transphosphorylation. *Mol. Pharmacol.* 8:18–29
29. Barnett, R. E. 1970. Effect of monovalent cations on the ouabain inhibition of the sodium and potassium ion activated adenosine triphosphatase. *Biochemistry* 9:4644–48
30. Beaugé, L. A., Andragna, N. 1971. The kinetics of ouabain inhibition and the partition of rubidium influx in human red blood cells. *J. Gen. Physiol.* 57:576–92
31. Beaugé, L. A., Ortiz, O. 1972. Further evidence for a potassium-like action of lithium ions on sodium efflux in frog skeletal muscle. *J. Physiol. London* 226:675–97
32. Beaugé, L. A., Ortiz, O. 1973. Na fluxes in rat red blood cells in K-free solutions. *J. Membrane Biol.* 13:165–84
33. Blostein, R. 1968. Relationships between erythrocyte membrane phosphorylation and adenosine triphosphate hydrolysis. *J. Biol. Chem.* 243:1957–65
34. Blostein, R. 1970. Sodium activated adenosine triphosphatase activity of the erythrocyte membrane. *J. Biol. Chem.* 245:270–75
35. Bond, G. H., Bader, H., Post, R. L. 1971. Acetyl phosphate as a substitute for ATP in $(Na^+ + K^+)$-dependent ATPase. *Biochim. Biophys. Acta* 241:57–67
36. Bonting, S. L., Caravaggio, L. L. 1963. Studies on Na:K activated ATPase. V. Correlation of enzyme activity with cation flux in six tissues. *Arch. Biochem. Biophys.* 101:37–46
37. Brinley, F. J., Mullins, L. J. 1974. Effect of membrane potential on Na + K fluxes in squid axons. *Ann. NY Acad. Sci.* In press
38. Brodsky, W. A., Shamoo, A. E. 1973. Binding of ATP to and release from microsomal $(Na^+ + K^+)$-ATPase. *Biochim. Biophys. Acta* 291:208–28
39. Brodsky, W. A., Sohn, R. J. 1974. Acid-stable and heat-stable phosphoenzyme complexes of (Na + K)-ATPase in the eel electric organ; and the related concept of active Na transport. *Ann. NY Acad. Sci.* In press
40. Caldwell, P. C. 1969. Energy relationships and the active transport of ions. *Curr. Top. Bioenerg.* 3:251–78
41. Caldwell, P. C., Hodgkin, A. L., Keynes, R. D., Shaw, T. I. 1960. The effects of injecting 'energy-rich' phosphate compounds on the active transport of ions in the giant axons of *Loligo*. *J. Physiol. London* 152:561–90
42. Chipperfield, A. R., Whittam, R. 1974. Evidence that ATP is hydrolysed in a one-step reaction of the sodium pump. *Proc. Roy. Soc. B.* In press
43. Cleland, W. W. 1970. Steady state kinetics. In *The Enzymes,* ed. P. D. Boyer, Vol. 2, 1–65. New York: Academic
44. Cotterrell, D., Whittam, R. 1972. The uptake and hydrolysis of *p*-nitrophenyl phosphate by red cells in relation to ATP hydrolysis by the sodium pump. *J. Physiol. London* 223:773–802
45. Cross, S. B., Keynes, R. D., Rybová, R. 1965. The coupling of Na influx and K efflux in frog muscle. *J. Physiol. London* 181:865–80
46. Czerwinski, A., Gitelman, H. J., Welt, L. G. 1967. A new member of the ATPase family. *Am. J. Physiol.* 213: 786–92
47. Dahl, J. L., Hokin, L. E. 1974. The sodium-potassium adenosinetriphosphatase. *Ann. Rev. Biochem.* 43:327–56
48. Dahms, A. S., Boyer, P. D. 1973. Occurrence and characteristics of ^{18}O exchange reactions catalysed by Na and K dependent ATPase. *J. Biol. Chem.* 248:3155–62
49. Degani, C., Boyer, P. D. 1974. *Ann. NY Acad. Sci.* In press
50. De Weer, P. 1970. Effects of intracellular 5'ADP and P_i on the sensitivity of Na efflux from squid axon to external Na and K. *J. Gen. Physiol.* 56:583–620

51. De Weer, P., Geduldig, D. 1973. Electrogenic Na pump in squid giant axon. *Science* 179:1326–28
52. Dudding, W. F., Winter, C. G. 1971. On the reaction sequence of the K^+-dependent acetyl phosphatase activity of the Na^+ pump. *Biochim. Biophys. Acta* 241:650–60
53. Dunham, E. T., Glynn, I. M. 1961. Adenosine triphosphatase activity and the active movements of alkali metal ions. *J. Physiol. London* 156:274–93
54. Dunham, P. B., Hoffman, J. F. 1971. Active cation transport and ouabain binding in high potassium and low potassium red blood cells of sheep. *J. Gen. Physiol.* 58:94–116
55. Dydynska, M., Harris, E. J. 1966. Consumption of high-energy phosphates during active Na and K interchange in frog muscle. *J. Physiol. London* 182: 92–109
56. Eilam, Y., Stein, W. D. 1973. The efflux of sodium from human red blood cells. *Biochim. Biophys. Acta* 323:606–18
57. Eisenman, G. 1961. On the elementary atomic origin of equilibrium ionic specificity. In *Membrane Transport and Metabolism,* ed. A. Kleinzeller, A. Kotyk, 163–79. New York: Academic
58. Eisenman, G., Krasne, S. J. 1974. The ion selectivity of carrier molecules, membranes and enzymes. In *M.T.P. International Review of Science, Biochemistry Series,* ed. C. F. Fox, Vol. 2. London: Butterworth
59. Ellory, J. C., Keynes, R. D. 1969. Binding of tritiated digoxin to human red cell ghosts. *Nature* 221:776
60. Ellory, J. C., Tucker, E. M. 1969. Stimulation of the potassium transport system in low potassium type sheep red cells by a specific antigen antibody reaction. *Nature* 222:477–78
61. Erdmann, E., Schoner, W. 1973. Ouabain-receptor interactions in (Na^+ + K^+)-ATPase preparations from different tissues and species. Determination of kinetic constants and dissociation constants. *Biochim. Biophys. Acta* 307:386–98
62. Erdmann, E., Schoner, W. 1973. Ouabain-receptor interactions in (Na^+ + K^+)-ATPase preparations. II. Effect of cations and nucleotides on rate constants and dissociation constants. *Biochim. Biophys. Acta* 330:302–15
63. Fahn, S., Hurley, M. R., Koval, G. J., Albers, R. W. 1966. Sodium-potassium-activated adenosine triphosphatase of *Electrophorus* electric organ. II. Effects of *N*-ethylmaleimide and other sulfhydryl reagents. *J. Biol. Chem.* 241: 1890–95
64. Fahn, S., Koval, G. J., Albers, R. W. 1966. Sodium-potassium-activated adenosine triphosphatase of *Electrophorus* electric organ. I. An associated sodium-activated transphosphorylation. *J. Biol. Chem.* 241:1882–89
65. Fahn, S., Koval, G. J., Albers, R. W. 1968. Sodium-potassium-activated adenosine triphosphatase of *Electrophorus* electric organ. V. Phosphorylation by adenosine triphosphate-^{32}P. *J. Biol. Chem.* 243:1993–2002
66. Frieden, C. 1964. Treatment of enzyme kinetic data. I. The effect of modifiers on the kinetic parameters of single substrate enzymes. *J. Biol. Chem.* 239: 3522–31
67. Fujita, M., Nakao, T., Tashima, Y., Mizuno, N., Nagano, K., Nakao, M. 1966. Potassium-ion stimulated *p*-nitrophenylphosphatase activity occurring in a highly specific adenosine triphosphatase preparation from rabbit brain. *Biochim. Biophys. Acta* 117: 42–53
68. Fukushima, Y., Tonomura, Y. 1973. Two kinds of high energy phosphorylated intermediate, with and without bound ADP, in the reaction of Na^+-K^+-dependent ATPase. *J. Biochem.* 74:135–42
69. Garay, R. P., Garrahan, P. J. 1973. The interaction of sodium and potassium with the sodium pump in red cells. *J. Physiol. London* 231:297–325
70. Gardner, J. D., Conlon, T. P. 1972. The effects of sodium and potassium on ouabain binding by human erythrocytes. *J. Gen. Physiol.* 60:609–29
71. Gardner, J. D., Frantz, C. 1974. Effects of cations on ouabain binding by intact human erythrocytes. *J. Membrane Biol.* 16:43–64
72. Garrahan, P. J., Garay, R. P. 1974. A kinetic study of the Na pump in red cells. Its relevance to the mechanism of active transport. *Ann. NY Acad. Sci.* In press
73. Garrahan, P. J., Glynn, I. M. 1967. The behavior of the sodium pump in red cells in the absence of external potassium. *J. Physiol. London* 192:159–74
74. Garrahan, P. J., Glynn, I. M. 1967. The sensitivity of the sodium pump to *external* sodium. *J. Physiol. London* 192: 175–88
75. Garrahan, P. J., Glynn, I. M. 1967. Factors affecting the relative magni-

tudes of the sodium:potassium and sodium:sodium exchanges catalysed by the sodium pump. *J. Physiol. London* 192:189–216
76. Garrahan, P. J., Glynn, I. M. 1967. The stoichiometry of the sodium pump. *J. Physiol. London* 192:217–35
77. Garrahan, P. J., Glynn, I. M. 1967. The incorporation of inorganic phosphate into adenosine triphosphate by reversal of the sodium pump. *J. Physiol. London* 192:237–56
78. Garrahan, P. J. Pouchan, M. I., Rega, A. F. 1969. Potassium activated phosphatase from human red blood cells. The mechanism of potassium activation. *J. Physiol. London* 202:305–27
79. Garrahan, P. J., Pouchan, M. I., Rega, A. F. 1970. Potassium-activated phosphatase from human red blood cells. The effects of adenosine triphosphate. *J. Membrane Biol.* 3:26–42
80. Garrahan, P. J., Rega, A. F. 1972. Potassium activated phosphatase from human red blood cells. The effects of *p*-nitrophenylphosphate on cation fluxes. *J. Physiol. London* 223:595–617
81. Glynn, I. M. 1956. Sodium and potassium movements in human red cells. *J. Physiol. London* 134:278–310
82. Glynn, I. M. 1957. The action of cardiac glycosides on sodium and potassium movements in human red cells. *J. Physiol. London* 136:148–73
83. Glynn, I. M. 1964. The action of cardiac glycosides on ion movements. *Pharmacol. Rev.* 16:381–407
84. Glynn, I. M. 1968. Membrane adenosine triphosphatase and cation transport. *Brit. Med. Bull.* 24:165–69
85. Glynn, I. M., Ellory, J. C. 1972. Stimulation of a sodium pump by an antibody that increases the apparent affinity for sodium ions of the sodium-loading sites. In *Role of Membranes in Secretory Processes,* ed. L. Bolis, R. D. Keynes, W. Wilbrandt, 224–37. New York: Elsevier
86. Glynn, I. M., Hoffman, J. F. 1971. Nucleotide requirements for sodium-sodium exchange catalysed by the sodium pump in human red cells. *J. Physiol. London* 218:239–56
87. Glynn, I. M., Hoffman, J. F., Lew, V. L. 1971. Some 'partial reactions' of the sodium pump. *Phil. Trans. Roy. Soc. B* 262:91–102
88. Glynn, I. M., Karlish, S. J. D. 1974. The association of biochemical events and cation movements in (Na:K)-dependent adenosine triphosphatase activity. In *Membrane Adenosine Triphosphatases and Transport Processes,* ed. R. Bronk. London: Biochem. Soc.
89. Glynn, I. M. et al 1974. The effects of an antiserum to Na^+,K^+-ATPase on the ion-transporting and hydrolytic activities of the enzyme. *Ann. NY Acad. Sci.* In press
90. Glynn, I. M., Lew, V. L. 1970. Synthesis of adenosine triphosphate at the expense of downhill cation movements in intact human red cells. *J. Physiol. London* 207:393–402
91. Glynn, I. M., Lew, V. L., Lüthi, U. 1970. Reversal of the potassium entry mechanism in red cells, with and without reversal of the entire pump cycle. *J. Physiol. London* 207:371–91
92. Hansen, O. 1971. The relationship between g-strophanthin-binding capacity and ATPase activity in plasma-membrane fragments from ox brain. *Biochim. Biophys. Acta* 233:122–32
93. Hansen, O., Jensen, J., Norby, J. G. 1971. Mutual exclusion of ATP, ADP and g-strophanthin binding to Na K-ATPase. *Nature New Biol.* 234:122–24
94. Hansen, O., Skou, J. C. 1973. A study on the influence of the concentration of Mg^{2+}, P_i, K^+, Na^+, and Tris on $(Mg^{2+} + P_i)$-supported g-strophanthin binding to $(Na^+ + K^+)$-activated ATPase from ox brain. *Biochim. Biophys. Acta* 311:51–66
95. Hart, W. M., Titus, E. O. 1973. Isolation of a protein component of sodium-potassium transport adenosine triphosphatase containing ligand-protected sulfhydryl groups. *J. Biol. Chem.* 248:1365–71
96. Hart, W. M., Titus, E. O. 1973. Sulfhydryl groups of sodium-potassium transport adenosine triphosphatase. Protection by physiological ligands and exposure by phosphorylation. *J. Biol. Chem.* 248:4674–81
97. Hegyvary, C., Post, R. L. 1971. Binding of adenosine triphosphate to sodium and potassium ion-stimulated adenosine triphosphatase. *J. Biol. Chem.* 246:5235–40
98. Hexum, T., Samson, F. E., Himes, R. H. 1970. Kinetic studies of membrane $(Na^+ + K^+ + Mg^{2+})$-ATPase. *Biochim. Biophys. Acta* 212:322–31
99. Hoffman, J. F. 1969. The interaction between tritiated ouabain and the Na-K pump in red blood cells. *J. Gen. Physiol.* 54:343*s*–50*s*
100. Hoffman, J. F. Sidedness of the red cell Na:K pump. See Ref. 85, 203–14

101. Hoffman P. G., Tosteson, D. C. 1971. Active sodium and potassium transport in high potassium and low potassium sheep red cells. *J. Gen. Physiol.* 58:438–66
102. Hokin, L. E. 1974. Purification and properties of the Na:K activated ATPase and reconstitution of Na transport. *Ann. NY Acad. Sci.* In press
103. Hokin, L. E. et al 1973. Studies on the characterization of the sodium-potassium transport adenosine triphosphatase. X. Purification of the enzyme from the rectal gland of *Squalus acanthias. J. Biol. Chem.* 248:2593–2605
104. Horowicz, P., Taylor, J. W., Waggoner, D. M. 1970. Fractionation of sodium efflux in frog sartorius muscles by strophanthidin and removal of external sodium. *J. Gen. Physiol.* 55:401–25
105. Inagaki, C., Lindenmayer, G. E., Schwartz, A. 1974. Effects of sodium and potassium on binding of ouabain to the transport adenosine triphosphatase. *J. Biol. Chem.* In press
106. Inturrisi, C. E., Titus, E. O. 1970. Ouabain-dependent incorporation of ^{32}P from *p*-nitrophenyl phosphate into a microsomal phosphatase. *Mol. Pharmacol.* 6:99–107
107. Israel, Y., Titus, E. O. 1967. A comparison of microsomal ($Na^+ + K^+$)-ATPase with K^+-acetylphosphatase. *Biochim. Biophys. Acta* 139:450–59
108. Jardetsky, O. 1966. Simple allosteric model for membrane pumps. *Nature* 211:969–70
109. Jensen, J., Nørby, J. G. 1971. On the specificity of the ATP-binding site of ($Na^+ + K^+$)-activated ATPase from brain microsomes. *Biochim. Biophys. Acta* 233:395–403
110. Joiner, C. H., Lauf, P. K. 1974. ^3H-ouabain binding to HK and LK sheep red cells and the effect of anti-L. *Fed. Proc.* 33:265
111. Jorgensen, P. L. 1974. Purification of Na^+,K^+)-ATPase: Active site determination and criteria of purity. *Ann. NY Acad. Sci.* In press
112. Jorgensen, P. L. 1974. Purification and characterization of ($Na^+ + K^+$)-ATPase. III. Purification from the outer medulla of mammalian kidney after selective removal of membrane components by SDS. *Biochem. Biophys. Acta* 356:36–52
113. Jorgensen, P. L. 1974. Purification and characterization of ($Na^+ + K^+$)-ATPase. IV. Estimation of the purity and of the molecular weight and polypeptide content per enzyme unit in preparations from the outer medulla of rabbit kidney. *Biochim. Biophys. Acta* 356:53–67
114. Jorgensen, P. L., Hansen, O., Glynn, I. M., Cavieres, J. D. 1973. Antibodies to pig kidney ($Na^+ + K^+$)-ATPase inhibit the Na^+ pump in human red cells provided they have access to the inner surface of the cell membranes. *Biochim. Biophys. Acta* 291:795–800
115. Jorgensen, P. L., Skou, J. C., Solomonson, L. P. 1971. Purification and characterization of ($Na^+ + K^+$)-ATPase. II. Preparation by zonal centrifugation of highly active ($Na^+ + K^+$)-ATPase from the outer medulla of rabbit kidneys. *Biochim. Biophys. Acta* 233: 381–94
116. Judah, J. D., Ahmed, K., McLean, A. E. M. 1962. Ion transport and phosphoproteins of human red cells. *Biochim. Biophys. Acta* 65:472–80
117. Kanazawa, T., Saito, M., Tonomura, Y. 1967. Properties of a phosphorylated protein as a reaction intermediate of the Na + K sensitive ATPase. *J. Biochem. Tokyo* 61:555–66
118. Kanazawa, T., Saito, M., Tonomura, Y. 1970. Formation and decomposition of a phosphorylated intermediate in the reaction of Na^+-K^+ dependent ATPase. *J. Biochem. Tokyo* 67:693–711
119. Kaniike, K., Erdmann, E., Schoner, W. 1973. ATP binding to ($Na^+ + K^+$)-activated ATPase. *Biochim. Biophys. Acta* 298:901–5
120. Karlish, S. J. D., Glynn, I. M. 1974. An uncoupled efflux of Na from human red cells probably associated with Na-dependent ATPase activity. *Ann. NY Acad. Sci.* In press
121. Kepner, G. R., Macey, R. I. 1968. Membrane enzyme systems. Molecular size determinations by radiation inactivation. *Biochim. Biophys. Acta* 163: 188–203
122. Kernan, R. P. 1962. Membrane potential changes during sodium transport in frog sartorius muscle. *Nature* 193: 986–87
123. Keynes, R. D., Steinhardt, R. A. 1968. The components of the Na efflux in frog muscle. *J. Physiol. London* 198:581–600
124. Knight, A. B., Welt, L. G. 1974. Intracellular K. A determinant of the Na:K pump rate. *J. Gen. Physiol.* 63:351–73
125. Kostyuk, P. G., Krishtal, O. A., Pidoplichko, V. I. 1972. Potential dependent membrane current during the active

transport of ions in snail neurones. *J. Physiol. London* 226:373–92
126. Koyal, D., Rao, S. N., Askari, A. 1971. Studies on the partial reactions catalyzed by the (Na^+ + K^+)-activated ATPase. I. Effects of simple anions and nucleoside triphosphates on the alkali-cation specificity of the *p*-nitrophenylphosphatase. *Biochim. Biophys. Acta* 225:11–19
127. Kyte, J. 1971. Purification of the sodium- and potassium-dependent adenosine triphosphatase from canine renal medulla. *J. Biol. Chem.* 246:4157–65
128. Kyte, J. 1972. The titration of the cardiac glycoside binding site of the (Na^+ + K^+)-adenosine triphosphatase. *J. Biol. Chem.* 247:7634–41
129. Kyte, J. 1972. Properties of the two polypeptides of sodium- and potassium-dependent adenosine triphosphatase. *J. Biol. Chem.* 247:7642–49
130. Lane, L. K., Copenhaver, J. H., Lindenmayer, G. E., Schwartz, A. 1973. Purification and characterization of and [^{3}H] ouabain binding to the transport adenosine triphosphatase from outer medulla of canine kidney. *J. Biol. Chem.* 248:7197–7200
131. Lant, A. F., Priestland, R. N., Whittam, R. 1970. The coupling of downhill ion movements associated with reversal of the Na pump in human red cells. *J. Physiol. London* 207: 291–301
132. Lant, A. F., Whittam, R. 1968. The influence of ions on labelling of ATP in red cell ghosts. *J. Physiol, London* 199:457–84
133. Lauf, P. K. et al 1970. Stimulation of active potassium transport in LK sheep red cells by blood group-L-antiserum. *J. Membrane Biol.* 3:1–13
134. Lazdunski, M. 1972. Flip-flop mechanisms and half-site enzymes. In *Current Topics in Cellular Regulation,* ed. B. I. Horecker, E. R. Stadtman, Vol. 6, 267–310. New York: Academic
135. Lew, V. L., Glynn, I. M., Ellory, J. C. 1970. Net synthesis of ATP by reversal of the sodium pump. *Nature* 225: 865–66
136. Lew, V. L., Hardy, M. A., Ellory, J. C. 1973. The uncoupled extrusion of Na^+ through the Na^+ pump. *Biochim. Biophys. Acta* 323:251–66
137. Lindenmayer, G. E., Laughter, A. H., Schwartz, A. 1968. Incorporation of inorganic phosphate-32 into a Na^+,K^+-ATPase preparation: stimulation by ouabain. *Arch. Biochem. Biophys.* 127:187–92
138. Lindenmayer, G. E., Schwartz, A. 1973. Nature of the transport adenosine triphosphatase digitalis complex. IV. Evidence that sodium-potassium competition modulates the rate of ouabain interaction with (Na^+ + K^+) adenosine triphosphatase during enzyme catalysis. *J. Biol. Chem.* 248:1291–1300
139. Lindenmayer, G. E., Schwartz, A., Thompson, H. K. 1974. A kinetic description for sodium and potassium effects on (Na^+ + K^+)-adenosine triphosphatase: a model for a two-nonequivalent site potassium activation and an analysis of multiequivalent site models for sodium activation. *J. Physiol. London* 236:1–28
140. Mårdh, S., Zetterqvist, Ö. 1972. Phosphorylation of bovine brain Na^+,K^+-stimulated ATP phosphohydrolase by adenosine [^{32}P] triphosphate studied by a rapid-mixing technique. *Biochim. Biophys. Acta* 255:231–38
141. See Ref. 245
142. Mårdh, S., Zetterqvist, Ö. 1974. Phosphorylation and dephosphorylation reactions of bovine brain Na^+,K^+-stimulated ATP phosphohydrolase studied by a rapid-mixing technique. *Biochim. Biophys. Acta.* In press
143. Mårdh, S. 1974. *Studies on Na^+,K^+-stimulated ouabain-sensitive ATPase.* PhD thesis. Univ. Uppsala, Sweden
144. Matsui, H., Schwartz, A. 1968. Mechanism of cardiac glycoside inhibition of the (Na^+ + K^+)-dependent ATPase from cardiac tissue. *Biochim. Biophys. Acta* 151:655–63
145. Mayer, M., Avi-Dor, Y. 1970. Interaction of solvents with membranal and soluble potassium ion-dependent enzymes. *Biochem. J.* 116:49–54
146. Mullins, L. J. 1972. Active transport of Na^+ and K^+ across the squid axon membrane. See Ref. 85, 182–202
147. Mullins, L. J., Brinley, F. J. 1969. Potassium fluxes in dialysed squid axons. *J. Gen. Physiol.* 53:704–40
148. Nagai, K., Izumi, F., Yoshida, H. 1966. Studies on potassium dependent phosphatase: its distribution and properties. *J. Biochem. Tokyo* 59:295–303
149. Nagai, K., Yoshida, H. 1966. Biphasic effects of nucleotides on potassium-dependent phosphatase. *Biochim. Biophys. Acta* 128:410–12
150. Nakajima, S., Takahashi, K. 1966. Post-tetanic hyperpolarization and electrogenic Na pump in stretch receptor

neurone of crayfish. *J. Physiol. London* 187:105–27

151. Nakao, M. et al 1974. Purification and properties of Na,K-ATPase from pig brain. *Ann. NY Acad. Sci.* In press
152. Neufeld, A. H., Levy, H. M. 1969. A second ouabain-sensitive Na dependent ATPase in brain microsomes. *J. Biol. Chem.* 244:6493–97
153. Neufeld, A. H., Levy, H. M. 1970. The steady state level of phosphorylated intermediate in relation to the two sodium-dependent adenosine triphosphatases of calf brain microsomes. *J. Biol. Chem.* 245:4962–67
154. Norby, J. G., Jensen, J. 1971. Binding of ATP to brain microsomal ATPase. Determination of the ATP-binding capacity and the dissociation constant of the enzyme-ATP complex as a function of K^+ concentration. *Biochim. Biophys. Acta* 233:104–16
155. Peter, H. W., Wolf, H. U. 1972. Kinetics of (Na^+,K^+)-ATPase of human erythrocyte membranes. I. Activation by Na^+ and K^+. *Biochim. Biophys. Acta* 290:300–9
156. Pitts, B. J. R., Askari, A. 1971. A fluorimetric assay method for the K^+-phosphatase associated with the (Na^+ + K^+)-activated ATPase. *Biochim. Biophys. Acta* 227:453–59
157. Post, R. L., Hegyvary, C., Kume, S. 1972. Activation by adenosine triphosphate in the phosphorylation kinetics of sodium and potassium ion transport adenosine triphosphatase. *J. Biol. Chem.* 247:6530–40
158. Post, R. L., Kume, S. 1973. Evidence for an aspartyl phosphate residue at the active site of sodium and potassium ion transport adenosine triphosphatase. *J. Biol. Chem.* 248:6993–7000
159. Post, R. L., Kume, S., Rogers, F. N. 1973. Alternating paths of phosphorylation of the sodium and potassium ion pump of plasma membranes. In *Mechanisms in Bioenergetics,* ed. G. F. Azzone, L. Ernster, S. Papa, E. Quagliariello, N. Siliprandi, 203–18. New York: Academic
160. Post, R. L., Kume, S., Tobin, T., Orcutt, B., Sen, A. K. 1969. Flexibility of an active centre in sodium-plus-potassium adenosine triphosphatase. *J. Gen. Physiol.* 54:306*s*–326*s*
161. Post, R. L., Orcutt, B. 1973. Active site of phosphorylation of Na:K ATPase. In *Organization of Energy-Transducing Membranes,* ed. M. Nakao, L. Packer, 35–46. Tokyo: Univ. Tokyo Press
162. Post, R. L., Sen, A. K., Rosenthal, A. S. 1965. A phosphorylated intermediate in adenosine triphosphate-dependent sodium and potassium transport across kidney membranes. *J. Biol. Chem.* 240:1437–45
163. Post, R. L., Taniguchi, K., Toda, G. 1974. Synthesis of adenosine triphosphatase by Na^+, K^+-ATPase. *Ann. NY Acad. Sci.* In press
164. Rang, H. P., Ritchie, J. M. 1968. On the electrogenic Na pump in mammalian non-myelinated nerve fibres and its activation by various external cations. *J. Physiol. London* 196:183–221
165. Rega, A. F., Garrahan, P. J., Pouchan, M. I. 1968. Effects of ATP and Na^+ on a K^+-activated phosphatase from red blood cell membranes. *Biochim. Biophys. Acta* 150:742–44
166. Rega, A. F., Garrahan, P. J., Pouchan, M. I. 1970. Potassium activated phosphatase from human red blood cells. The asymmetrical effects of K^+, Na^+, Mg^{++} and adenosine triphosphate. *J. Membrane Biol.* 3:14–25
167. Repke, K. R. H., Schön, R. 1973. Flip-flop model of (Na, K)-ATPase function. *Acta Biol. Med. Ger.* 31:K19–K30
168. Repke, K. R. H., Schön, R. 1974. *Biochim. Biophys. Acta.* In press
169. Repke, K. R. H. et al 1974. Experimental and theoretic examination of the flip-flop model of (Na+K)-ATPase function. *Ann. NY Acad. Sci.* In press
170. Robinson, J. D. 1967. Kinetic studies on a brain microsomal adenosine triphosphatase. Evidence suggesting conformational changes. *Biochemistry* 6: 3250–58
171. Robinson, J. D. 1969. Kinetic studies on a brain microsomal adenosine triphosphatase. II. Potassium-dependent phosphatase activity. *Biochemistry* 8: 3348–55
172. Robinson, J. D. 1969. Effects of phlorizin on membrane cation-dependent adenosine triphosphatase and *p*-nitrophenyl phosphatase activities. *Mol. Pharmacol.* 5:584–92
173. Robinson, J. D. 1970. Interactions between monovalent cations and the (Na^+ + K^+)-dependent adenosine triphosphatase. *Arch. Biochem. Biophys.* 139:17–27
174. Robinson, J. D. 1970. Phosphatase activity stimulated by Na^+ plus K^+: implications for the (Na^+ plus K^+)-dependent adenosine triphosphatase. *Arch. Biochem. Biophys.* 139:164–71

175. Robinson, J. D. 1971. K^+-stimulated incorporation of ^{32}P from nitrophenyl phosphate into a ($Na^+ + K^+$)-activated ATPase preparation. *Biochem. Biophys. Res. Commun.* 42:880–85
176. Robinson, J. D. 1971. Proposed reaction mechanism for the ($Na^+ + K^+$)-dependent adenosine triphosphatase. *Nature* 233:419–20
177. Robinson, J. D. 1972. Differential modification of the ($Na^+ + K^+$)-dependent ATPase by dimethylsulfoxide. *Biochim. Biophys. Acta* 274:542–50
178. Robinson, J. D. 1973. Variable affinity of the ($Na^+ + K^+$)-dependent adenosine triphosphatase for potassium. Studies using beryllium inactivation. *Arch. Biochem. Biophys.* 156:232–43
179. Robinson, J. D. 1973. Cation sites of the ($Na^+ + K^+$)-dependent ATPase. Mechanisms for the Na^+-induced changes in K^+ affinity of the phosphatase activity. *Biochim. Biophys. Acta* 321:662–70
180. Robinson, J. D. 1974. Specific modifications of the ($Na^+ + K^+$)-dependent ATPase by dimethyl sulfoxide. *Ann. NY Acad. Sci.* (DMSO Conference) In press
181. Robinson, J. D. 1974. Cation interactions with different functional states of the Na^+,K^+-ATPase. *Ann. NY Acad. Sci.* In press
182. Robinson, J. D. 1974. Nucleotide and divalent cation interactions with the ($Na^+ + K^+$)-dependent ATPase. *Biochim. Biophys. Acta.* In press
183. Robinson, J. D. 1974. Affinity of the ($Na^+ + K^+$)-dependent ATPase for Na^+ measured by Na^+-modified enzyme inactivation. *FEBS Lett.* 38:325–28
184. Sachs, J. R. 1970. Sodium movements in the human red blood cell. *J. Gen. Physiol.* 56:322–41
185. Sachs, J. R. 1971. Ouabain-insensitive sodium movements in the human red blood cell. *J. Gen. Physiol.* 57:259–82
186. Sachs, J. R. 1974. Interaction of external K, Na, and cardioactive steriods with the Na-K pump of the human red blood cell. *J. Gen. Physiol.* 63:123–43
187. Sachs, J. R., Dunham, P. B., Kropp, D. L., Ellory, J. C., Hoffman, J. F. 1974. Interaction of HK and LK goat red blood cells with ouabain. *J. Gen. Physiol.* In press
188. Sachs, J. R., Ellory, J. C., Kropp, D. L., Dunham, P. B., Hoffman, J. F. 1974. Antibody-induced alterations in the kinetic characteristics of the Na:K pump in goat red blood cells. *J. Gen. Physiol.* 63:389–414
189. Sachs, J. R., Welt, L. G. 1967. The concentration dependence of active K transport in the human red blood cell. *J. Clin. Invest.* 46:65–76
190. Sachs, J. R. 1967. Competitive effects of some cations on active potassium transport in the human red blood cell. *J. Clin. Invest.* 46:1433–41
191. Sachs, S., Rose, J. D., Hirschowitz, B. I. 1967. Acetyl phosphatase in brain microsomes: a partial reaction of $Na^+ + K^+$ ATPase. *Arch. Biochem. Biophys.* 119:277–81
192. Schatzmann, H. J. 1953. Herzglykoside als Hemmstoffe für den aktiven Kaliumund Natriumtransport durch die Erythrocytenmembran. *Helv. Physiol. Pharmacol. Acta* 11:346–54
193. Schatzmann, H. J. 1965. The role of Na^+ and K^+ in the ouabain-inhibition of the $Na^+ + K^+$-activated membrane adenosine triphosphatase. *Biochim. Biophys. Acta* 94:89–96
194. Schoner, W. 1971. Active transport of Na^+ and K^+ through animal cell membranes. *Angew. Chem. Int. Ed. Engl.* 10:882–89
195. Schoner, W., Beusch, R., Kramer, R. 1968. On the mechanism of Na^+- and K^+-stimulated hydrolysis of ATP. 2. Comparison of nucleotide specificities of Na^+- and K^+-activated ATPase and Na^+-dependent phosphorylation of cell membranes. *Eur. J. Biochem.* 7:102–10
196. Schönfeld, W., Schön, R., Menke, K. H., Repke, K. R. H. 1972. Identification of conformational states of transport ATPase by kinetic analysis of ouabain binding. *Acta Biol. Med. Ger.* 28:935–56
197. Schwartz, A., Matsui, H., Laughter, A. H. 1968. Tritiated digoxin binding to ($Na^+ + K^+$)-activated adenosine triphosphatase: possible allosteric site. *Science* 160:323–25
198. Sen, A. K., Post, R. L. 1964. Stoichiometry and localization of ATP dependent Na and K transport in the erythrocyte. *J. Biol. Chem.* 239:345–52
199. Sen, A. K., Tobin, T., Post, R. L. 1969. A cycle for ouabain inhibition of sodium- and potassium-dependent adenosine triphosphatase. *J. Biol. Chem.* 244:6596–6604
200. Shamoo, A. E., Albers, R. W. 1973. Na^+-selective ionophoric material derived from electric organ and kidney membranes. *Proc. Nat. Acad. Sci. USA* 70:1191–94
201. Shamoo, A. E., Brodsky, W. A. 1971. Identification of intact ATP bound to

($Na^+ + K^+$)ATPase. *Biochim. Biophys. Acta* 241:846–56
202. Shaw, T. I. 1954. *Sodium and potassium movements in red cells.* PhD thesis. Univ. Cambridge, England
203. Siegel, G. J., Albers, R. W. 1967. Sodium-potassium activated adenosine triphosphatase of *Electrophorus* electric organ. IV. Modification of responses to sodium and potassium by arsenite plus 2,3-dimercaptopropanol. *J. Biol. Chem.* 242:4972–79
204. Siegel, G. J., Goodwin, B. 1972. Sodium-potassium-activated adenosine triphosphatase: potassium regulation of enzyme, phosphorylation, Sodium-stimulated, potassium-inhibited uridine triphosphate hydrolysis. *J. Biol. Chem.* 247:3630–37
205. Siegel, G. J., Goodwin, B. B., Hurley, M. J. 1974. Regulatory effects of potassium on sodium-plus-potassium-activated adenosinetriphosphatase. *Ann. NY Acad. Sci.* In press
206. Siegel, G. J., Koval, G. J., Albers, R. W. 1969. Sodium-potassium-activated adenosine triphosphatase. VI. Characterization of the phosphoprotein formed from orthophosphate in the presence of ouabain. *J. Biol. Chem.* 244:3264–69
207. Siegel, G. J., Josephson, L. 1972. Ouabain reaction with microsomal (Na + K)-activated ATPase. Characteristics of substrate and ion dependencies. *Eur. J. Biochem.* 25:323–35
208. Simons, T. J. B. 1974. Potassium:potassium exchange catalysed by the sodium pump in human red cells. *J. Physiol. London* 237:123–55
209. Sjodin, R. A. 1971. The kinetics of Na extrusion in striated muscle as functions of the external sodium and potassium ion concentrations. *J. Gen. Physiol.* 57:164–87
210. Sjodin, R. A., Beaugé, L. A. 1968. Strophanthidin-sensitive components of potassium and sodium movements in skeletal muscle as influenced by the internal sodium concentration. *J. Gen. Physiol.* 52:389–407
211. Skou, J. C. 1965. Enzymatic basis for active transport of Na^+ and K^+ across cell membrane. *Physiol. Rev.* 45:596–617
212. Skou, J. C. 1971. Sequence of steps in the (Na + K)-activated enzyme system in relation to sodium and potassium transport. *Curr. Top. Bioenerg.* 4: 357–98
213. Skou, J. C. 1973. The relationship of the ($Na^+ + K^+$)-activated enzyme system to transport of sodium and potassium across the cell membrane. *J. Bioenerg.* 4:1–30
214. Skou, J. C. 1974. Effect of ATP on the intermediary steps of the reaction of the ($Na^+ + K^+$)-dependent enzyme system. I. Studied by the use of *N*-ethylmaleimide inhibition as a tool. *Biochim. Biophys. Acta* 339:234–45
215. Skou, J. C. 1974. Effect of ATP on the intermediary steps of the reaction of the ($Na^+ + K^+$)-dependent enzyme system. II. Effect of a variation in the ATP/Mg^{2+} ratio. *Biochim. Biophys. Acta* 339:246–57
216. Skou, J. C. 1974. Effect of ATP on the intermediary steps of the reaction of the ($Na^+ + K^+$)-dependent enzyme system. III. Effect on the *p*-nitrophenylphosphatase activity of the system. *Biochim. Biophys. Acta* 339:258–73
217. Skou, J. C. 1974. The ($Na^+ + K^+$)-activated enzyme system. In *Perspectives in Membrane Biology,* ed. S. Estrado-O, C. Gitler. Mexico: Mexico Univ. Press
218. Skou, J. C., Butler, K. W., Hansen, O. 1971. The effect of magnesium, ATP, P_i, and sodium on the inhibition of the ($Na^+ + K^+$)-activated enzyme system by g-strophanthin. *Biochim. Biophys. Acta* 241:443–61
219. Skou, J. C., Hilberg, C. 1965. The effect of sulfhydryl-blocking reagents and of urea on the ($Na^+ + K^+$)-activated enzyme system. *Biochim. Biophys. Acta* 110:359–69
220. Skou, J. C., Hilberg, C. 1969. The effects of cations, g-strophanthin and oligomycin on the labeling from [^{32}P]ATP of the ($Na^+ + K^+$)-activated enzyme system and the effect of cations and g-strophanthin on the labeling from [^{32}P]ITP and $^{32}P_i$. *Biochim. Biophys. Acta* 185:198–219
221. Stein, W. D., Lieb, W. R., Karlish, S. J. D., Eilam, Y. 1973. A model for the active transport of sodium and potassium ions as mediated by a tetrameric enzyme. *Proc. Nat. Acad. Sci. USA* 70:275–78
222. Askari, A., Ed. 1974. *Symposium on Na^+,K^+-ATPase, New York, Nov. 1973. Ann. NY Acad. Sci.* In press
223. Taniguchi, K., Iida, S. 1972. Two apparently different ouabain binding sites of ($Na^+ + K^+$)-ATPase. *Biochim. Biophys. Acta* 288:98–102
224. Thomas, R. C. 1969. Membrane current and intracellular sodium changes in a snail neurone during extrusion of in-

jected sodium. *J. Physiol. London* 201:495–514
225. Thomas, R. C. 1972. Electrogenic sodium pump in nerve and muscle cells. *Physiol. Rev.* 52:563–94
226. Tobin, T., Akera, T., Baskin, S. I., Brody, T. M. 1973. Calcium ion and sodium- and potassium-dependent adenosine triphosphatase: its mechanism of inhibition and identification of the E_1-P intermediate. *Mol. Pharmacol.* 9:336–49
227. Tobin, T., Akera, T., Brody, T. M. 1974. Studies on the two phosphoenzyme conformations of Na^+ + K^+ ATPase. *Ann. NY. Acad. Sci.* In press
228. Tobin, T., Akera, T., Hogg, R. E., Brody, T. M. 1973. Ouabain binding to sodium- and potassium-dependent adenosine triphosphatase: inhibition by the β, γ-methylene analogue of adenosine triphosphate. *Mol. Pharmacol.* 9:278–81
229. Tobin, T., Akera, T., Lee, C. Y., Brody, T. M. 1974. Ouabain binding to (Na^+ + K^+)—ATPase. Effects of nucleotide analogues and ethacrynic acid. *Biochim. Biophys. Acta* 345:102–17
230. Tobin, T., Baskin, S. I., Akera, T., Brody, T. M. 1972. Nucleotide specificity of the Na^+-stimulated phosphorylation and [^{3}H]ouabain-binding reactions of (Na^+ + K^+)-dependent adenosine triphosphatase. *Mol. Pharmacol.* 8: 256–63
231. Tobin, T., Brody, T. M. 1972. Rates of dissociation of enzyme-ouabain complexes and $K_{0.5}$ values in (Na^+ + K^+) adenosine triphosphatase from different species. *Biochem. Pharmacol.* 21: 1553–60
232. Tobin, T., Henderson, R., Sen, A. K. 1972. Species and tissue differences in the rate of dissociation of ouabain from (Na^+ + K^+)-ATPase. *Biochim. Biophys. Acta* 274:551–55
233. Tobin, T., Sen, A. K. 1970. Stability and ligand sensitivity of [^{3}H]ouabain binding to (Na^+ + K^+)-ATPase. *Biochim. Biophys. Acta* 198:120–31
234. Toda, G. 1968. The effects of cations on the inhibition of sodium and potassium activated ATPase by beryllium. *J. Biochem. Tokyo* 64:457–64
235. Tonomura, Y., Fukushima, Y. 1974. Kinetic properties of phosphorylated intermediates in the reaction of Na^+, K^+)-ATPase. *Ann. NY Acad. Sci.* In press
236. Uesugi, S. et al 1971. Studies on the characterization of the sodium-potassium transport adenosine triphosphatase. VI. Large scale partial purification and properties of a lubrol-solubilized bovine brain enzyme. *J. Biol. Chem.* 246:531–43
237. Van Winkle, W. B., Allen, J. C., Schwartz, A. 1972. The nature of the transport ATPase-digitalis complex: III. Rapid binding studies and effects of ligands on the formation and stability of magnesium plus phosphate-induced glycoside-enzyme complex. *Arch. Biochem. Biophys.* 151:85–92
238. Vigliocco, A. M., Rega, A. F., Garrahan, P. J. 1970. Membrane phosphatase and active transport in red cells from different species. *J. Cell Physiol.* 75:293–95
239. Wheeler, K. P., Whittam, R. 1964. Structural and enzymic aspects of the hydrolysis of adenosine triphosphate by membranes of kidney cortex and erythrocytes. *Biochem. J.* 93:349–63
240. Whittam, R., Agar, M. E. 1965. The connexion between active cation transport and metabolism in erythrocytes. *Biochem. J.* 97:214–27
241. Whittam, R., Wheeler, K. P. 1970. Transport across cell membranes. *Ann. Rev. Physiol.* 32:21–60
242. Wolf, H. U., Peter, H. W. 1972. Kinetics of (Na^+,K^+)-ATPase of human erythrocyte membranes. II. Inhibition by ouabain. *Biochim. Biophys. Acta* 290: 310–20
243. Yoshida, H., Izumi, F., Nagai, K. 1966. Carbamylphosphate, a preferential substrate of K^+-dependent phosphatase. *Biochim. Biophys. Act* 120:183–86
244. Yoshida, H., Nagai, K., Ohashi, T., Nakagawa, Y. 1969. K^+-dependent phosphatase activity observed in the presence of both adenosine triphosphatase and Na^+. *Biochim. Biophys. Acta* 171:178–85
245. Zetterqvist, Ö., Mårdh, S. 1973. Partial reactions of (Na^+,K^+)-ATPase. Abstr. *9th International Congress of Biochemistry, Stockholm.* p. 277

Copyright 1975. All rights reserved

COMPARATIVE PHYSIOLOGY OF SUSPENSION FEEDING

◆1123

C. Barker Jørgensen
Zoophysiological Laboratory A, August Krogh Institute, Universitetsparken 13,
DK - 2100 Copenhagen Ø, Denmark

INTRODUCTION

Natural waters are dilute suspensions of particles, organic and inorganic. Suspension feeders must therefore clear large volumes of the surrounding water to obtain food for maintenance, growth, and reproduction. This they do by transporting the medium to structures that retain suspended particles and carry the material retained to the mouth. Basic questions bear on the rate of water transport and the efficiency of particle retention in suspension feeders belonging to different systematic groups and inhabiting different environments. Such quantitative aspects of suspension feeding constitute overlapping interests of ecologists and comparative physiologists. The ecologist wants to know the rates of feeding as a basis for estimating energy flows between trophic levels in aquatic food chains. The comparative physiologist primarily wants to understand the mechanisms that control the rates and efficiencies with which suspension feeders process the surrounding water, and the factors (internal and environmental) that influence the mechanisms. A large literature deals with rates of water transport and efficiencies of particle retention in various suspension feeders (79), but the data have often been of restricted value because of uncertainty as to what extent results obtained in the laboratory represent unimpeded activity in nature.

Suspension feeding has especially been studied in bivalves and zooplankton crustaceans. Bivalves are the principal suspension feeders in many benthic habitats, freshwater as well as marine. They include the economically important oysters (52, 205), mussels (109), scallops, clams, and cockles. Zooplankton crustaceans are the principal grazers of the primary production (66, 108, 134, 135, 151, 161, 170, 174). They are represented by copepods and euphausiids in marine environments, by cladocerans and copepods in freshwater, and by brine shrimps *Artemia* in salt lakes.

RATES OF WATER TRANSPORT AND EFFICIENCY OF PARTICLE RETENTION

The rates at which suspension feeders transport the surrounding water through the particle-retaining structures can be determined directly or indirectly. Direct methods have been applied to bivalves and ascidians in which inhalant and exhalant currents can be separated (28, 38, 44, 51, 94, 127, 189, 197). The indirect methods determine the volumes of water cleared of suspended particles per unit time. In suspension feeders that pass the surrounding water through filters or filter-like structures these clearances equal total amounts of transported water, also termed filtration rates, when the suspended particles are totally retained by the filters. In suspension feeders, such as copepods and euphausiids, which are "mixed" feeders that also capture large food, the rates at which particles, e.g. phytoplankton cells, are cleared from suspension are not necessarily related to volumes of water filtered (see below).

Obviously, the indirect methods have wider applicability than the direct methods. The volumes of water cleared can be calculated from the exponential equation that relates changes in concentration of particles in the surrounding medium with time (37, 45, 68, 75). In early studies the media used were enriched with suspended particles—inorganic, such as colloidal graphite or clay, or organic, such as cultures of phytoplankton algae. Concentrations of particles were determined photometrically or by use of radioactively labelled cultures of algae (25, 81). The introduction of electronic particle counters greatly improved the indirect methods by permitting determinations of the natural concentrations of suspended particles in the water (167). It thus became possible to measure the rates at which undisturbed suspension feeders clear the surrounding water of particles of various sizes under natural conditions.

The efficiencies with which suspension feeders retain suspended particles also can be determined directly or indirectly. The direct methods compare concentrations of particles in the inhalant and exhalant current. In the indirect methods clearances of particles of various sizes are compared. The ratios between clearances of particles that may pass through the feeding structures and the clearance of large, completely retained particles directly express the fractions of the smaller particles retained.

Bivalves

RATE OF WATER TRANSPORT The widely held assumption that suspension-feeding bivalves maintain feeding currents independent of the concentration of food and other particles in the water below certain concentrations of particulate matter (see 79) has recently been confirmed (4). Some long-term experiments (175, 176, 199) showed that *Mytilus edulis, Crassostrea virginica,* and *Mercenaria mercenaria* cleared suspended phytoplankton at rates that did not vary with concentrations up to about 1 mg dry organic matter per liter of sea water, that is, up to concentrations in the upper end of normal ranges in nature. The rates at which several species of bivalves cleared natural sea water of 5–10 μ particles seemed not to vary with particle concentrations that ranged from 2.3 X 10^6 to 25 X 10^6 particles per liter, or ∼1–8 mm^3 per liter (193).

Winter (201–203) obtained apparently contradictory results in *Modiolus, Arctica,* and *Mytilus,* which all cleared suspensions of pure cultures of algae at rates that varied inversely as the concentrations. He concluded that the animals adjusted water transport to feeding at constant rates within the range of food concentrations studied, from 0.5 to 3 mg dry algal matter per liter of sea water. Two species of green algae were used, *Chlamydomonas* and *Dunaliella,* both of poor food value to bivalves (191). *Dunaliella* was, moreover, the only one of four species of algae that oysters cleared at low rates when the concentration was raised from 0.6 to 1 mg dry weight per liter of sea water (176). The concentration of algae used in Winter's experiments may therefore have been above incipient limiting levels.

The rates at which suspension-feeding bivalves transport water depend upon the experimental conditions. This is especially conspicuous in the mussel *Mytilus edulis,* the most thoroughly studied species (Figure 1). Walne (193) found that mussels cleared flowing sea water of naturally suspended particles at rates that varied with the rate at which water passed through the trays accommodating the animals, e.g. from 70 ml g^{-1} min^{-1} at a flow rate of 100–200 ml min^{-1} to 100 ml at a flow rate of 400–500 ml. If we accept that the values obtained by Walne approximate the rates at which undisturbed mussels transport water in nature, it follows that measurements made by most other authors reflect inhibiting effects of the experimental conditions on the water transporting capacity. Generally, the measurements amount to half or less of the values recorded by Walne. However, the rates at which mussels clear organic particles, such as yeast cells, or inorganic particles, such as colloidal graphite, suspended in a small volume of standing water may approach the values obtained in flowing sea water when measurements are made on animals with the valves maximally gaping and the mantle extended (78, 80). Also, in other marine bivalves, the rates of water transport measured from clearances of natural particles in flowing water have mostly been higher than measurements made from clearances of enriched suspensions in small volumes of sea water (Table 1).

Clearances presumably vary with the habitat of the species. Bivalves belonging to the epifauna have been found to clear suspended particles faster than do bivalves belonging to the infauna (Table 1). The values measured on infaunal bivalves may tend to be low because most measurements have been made on animals outside their normal substrate. However, Vahl (186) found that specimens of the cockle *Cardium edule,* even when buried normally in a sand bottom, cleared suspended particles from flowing sea water at rates that amounted to only about one third or less of those measured in epifaunal bivalves. In a closed system Winter (201) obtained values amounting to about one fifth of those found by Vahl (Table 1).

Data on suspension-feeding freshwater bivalves are sparse and inconsistent (70, 86, 112, 117, *Dreissena polymorpha;* 42, *Anodonta cygnea*). Mostly low clearances or rates of water transport have been recorded. It remains to be ascertained to what extent the data available represent natural values.

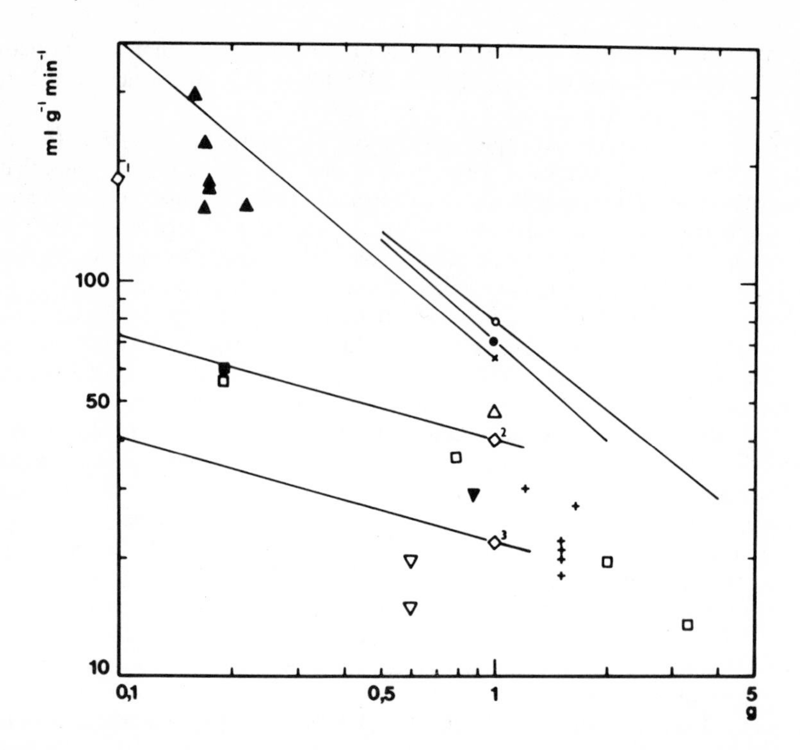

Figure 1 Relationship between body weight and rate of water transport in the mussel *Mytilus edulis*, as measured under various conditions and by different techniques. ● (193) represents clearances of natural particles in flowing water at a flow rate of 200–299 ml min^{-1}; ○, flow rate 300 ml min^{-1}; × (187), flow rate 150 ml min^{-1}; ▼ (201), clearance of *Chlamydomonas* suspension, 1.7 mg dry matter $liter^{-1}$; ◇ (203), clearances of *Dunaliella* suspensions, ◇ [1] 0.53 mg, ◇ [2] 1.07 mg, ◇ [3] 2.13 mg dry matter $liter^{-1}$; + (198, 199), clearances of suspensions of *Tetraselmis* and *Phaeodactylum*, 1.2–1.6 mg dry matter $liter^{-1}$; ▲ (80), clearances of suspensions of yeast cells; □ (179) and ▽ (195), clearances of suspensions of graphite particles; ■ (41) and △ (197), water transport measured directly by methods involving separation of inhalant and exhalant currents. Lines indicate regression of water transport on body weight within the range of body weights studied. Abscissa: dry weight of soft parts in g. Ordinate: clearance or water transport in ml g^{-1} min^{-1}.

POROSITY OF GILL Studies of the efficiency with which supension-feeding bivalves retain particles of different kind and size have led to controversial results. Some workers have found that the bivalve gills retain even large particles with varying efficiency (94, *Crassostrea virginica;* 41, 173, *Mytilus edulis*). Such variable porosity of the oyster and mussel gills has been found in experiments where the animals were equipped with a diaphragm to separate exhalant and inhalant currents. Clearance experiments indicated that mussels cleared 1–2 μ and 200 μ particles at equal rates (78, 81). More recent results support the view that undisturbed bivalves

Table 1 Water transport in suspension-feeding bivalves

Habitat and species	Rates of water transport ml g^{-1} min^{-1}	Liters of water transported for each ml of oxygen consumed	Technique	References
Marine epifauna				
Ostrea edulis	147	14	CNF[a]	47, 48, 193
Crassostrea gigas	112, 173		CNF	193
Crassostrea virginica		2–3	DA[d]	52, 54, 93, 95
Mytilus edulis	see Figure 1	13	CNF	15, 193
		10, 4–9	CEF	15, 16, 49, 180, 187, 198, 199
		3	CES[c]	87, 162, 179
Modiolus demissus	100		CES	88
Modiolus modiolus	15		CES(F)	201, 202
Chlamys opercularis	400	79	CEF[b]	185
	100	13	CES	100
Argopecten irradians	115, 133	16 (10°C) 13 (18°C)	CES	26, 82
Marine infauna				
Cardium edule	33	6	CEF	186
	6		CES(F)	201
Mercenaria mercenaria	76		CNF	193
	43		DC[e]	38
Venerupis decussata	76		CNF	193
Venerupis pullastre	4		CES(F)	201
Mya arenaria, M. truncata	7		CES(F)	201
Arctica islandica	26		CES(F)	201, 202
Freshwater epifauna				
Dreissena polymorpha		0.2, 5	CES	70, 85, 98

[a]CNF, clearance of natural particles in flowing water.
[b]CEF, clearance of enriched suspensions in flowing water.
[c]CES, clearance of enriched suspensions in small volumes of standing water.
[d]DA, direct method, separation of inhalant and exhalant currents.
[e]DC, direct method according to Coughlan & Ansell (38).

tend to maintain a constant low porosity of the gills (12, 17, 69, 80, 184–186). The size limit for retention of particles varies between species. Moreover, the critical size is not well defined, but the efficiency of retention decreases gradually with size of particles, e.g. from 6 to 2 μ in the scallop *Chlamys opercularis* (185) and 3 to <1 μ in *C. virginica* (69) and *M. edulis* (80).

CONTINUOUS OR DISCONTINUOUS FEEDING Yonge's early work (204) on the structure and physiology of the digestive tract in the oyster *Ostrea edulis* and subsequent studies of Yonge and others on a number of bivalves (see 120) led to the widely accepted concept that suspension-feeding bivalves are potentially continuous feeders. The general validity of the concept has been questioned (156, 196). In the intertidal bivalve *Lasaea rubra* the crystalline style and the digestive gland undergo cycles correlated with the tidal rhythm (105, 119). Similar cycles have been described in other bivalves, and not only in species or specimens inhabiting the tidal zone or influenced by the tidal wave (114, *Dreissena polymorpha;* 115, *Cardium edule;* 118, *Ostrea edulis;* 116, *Anodonta cygnea* and *Unio pictorum*). More recent studies in *Cardium, Ostrea,* and other suspension-feeding bivalves not restricted to the tidal zone have, however, not confirmed that digestion is inherently discontinuous and separate in phase from the intake of food (89, 110, 139). Evidence favors the view that digestion is a potentially continuous process in suspension-feeding bivalves, at least in nontidal species.

The question of how much time suspension feeders spend daily in feeding is closely connected with the question of whether the digestive tract, especially the digestive gland, functions continuously or discontinuously, possibly according to endogenous cycles. Most suspension-feeding bivalves have been found to remain open and to transport water during a great part of the day, but data on pattern of movements of valves and lengths of daily periods of water transport and feeding are not consistent. The mean length of the daily active period recorded in various species of suspension-feeding bivalves tends to be shorter in the laboratory than under natural conditions (50, 53, 71, 95, *C. virginica;* 13, 86, 116, 164, *A. cygnea*). Presumably, bivalves are sensitive to changes in their normal environment and react to adverse conditions by closing the valves or reducing the time they remain active. Bivalves maintained in standing water tend to reduce their activity, but species seem to vary greatly in sensitivity (163).

In order to estimate the lengths of active periods in nature we are probably justified in extrapolating from experimental data obtained under conditions closest to natural. Recordings of shell movements of various bivalves (*M. edulis, Mercenaria mercenaria,* and *C. virginica*) under nearly natural conditions showed that the valves remained open for about 90% of the time in *C. virginica* and *M. mercenaria,* and for 97–99% in *M. edulis* (91, 92, 95). Galtsoff (52) described various types of shell movements in *C. virginica* and stated that undisturbed oysters, in flowing sea water, maintain a steady current of water with fairly constant gaping of the valves. Walne (193) found that single individuals of several species of marine bivalves kept in flowing sea water cleared water of natural particles at high rates in the great majority of samples taken on a number of occasions over periods of usually three days. It can be concluded that these species, *O. edulis, Crassostrea gigas, Venerupis decussata, M. mercenaria,* and *M. edulis,* are feeding most of the time when undisturbed.

Data on freshwater bivalves are less conclusive. In *Dreissena polymorpha* kept in the laboratory, Morton (114) described a regular diurnal rhythm of activity and quiescence, the valves being open at night. In *Anodonta cygnea* and *Unio pictorum* kept in flowing water in the laboratory, Morton (116) also observed rhythms of activity and quiescence, with periods of activity being shortest. Salánki & Véró (164) made continuous records, over periods up to 39 days, of shell movements in eight specimens of *A. cygnea* in Lake Balaton. The mussels remained open for about 20–100% of a 24 hr period. The valves were more often closed during the daytime than at night.

Most investigators have recorded shell movements in animals resting on one valve. In the freshwater bivalve *Pleurobema coccineum,* Badman (11) recorded from specimens in the normal upright position to obtain uninhibited activity, and found that the animals' valves remained open nearly 100% of the time.

FUNCTION OF THE BIVALVE GILL Suspension-feeding bivalves transport water and retain suspended particles by means of the gills. Understanding of the mechanisms that control rates of water transport and efficiency of particle retention therefore depends upon knowledge of the function of the gill.

In primitive bivalves, represented by deposit-feeding protobranchs, water transport serves only respiration. Particulate material deposited on the gill is expelled via ciliary tracts on gills and mantle. In suspension-feeding bivalves the water-transporting capacity is greatly increased to serve feeding in addition to respiration, and the cleansing mechanisms of the gills predominantly transport particulate matter toward the mouth.

An extensive literature deals with the mechanisms of feeding in suspension-feeding bivalves (see 79, 80, 138), but much remains controversial, presumably because the function of the gill has been influenced to varying degrees by the experimental conditions.

The gills transport water through the interfilamentar spaces, retain particles suspended in the passing water, and carry the particles along the frontal surface of the filaments toward the free margins or bases of the demibranchs and farther along toward labial palps and mouth. In bivalves with one valve and mantle removed, or on excised pieces of gill or single filaments, it can be observed that the metachronally beating lateral cilia are responsible for the current of water passing between the filaments (3, 61, 62, 168), and the laterofrontal cirri for retention of particles that are transferred to the frontal ciliary tracts of the filaments (see 79, 138).

In preparations of intact gills or excised pieces of gill the lateral cilia usually stop beating, whereas the frontal cilia and the laterofrontal cirri can continue beating until advanced disintegration of the filaments (60, 80). Addition of the nerve transmitter serotonin to the surrounding medium restores normal beating in the lateral cilia. There is good evidence that the serotonergic innervation of the gill filaments is cilio-excitatory (1, 2, 59). The gill filaments in *M. edulis* and other bivalves also receive dopaminergic nerve fibers (143, 145), which may be cilio-inhibitory (144). Presumably, the laterofrontal cirri beat autonomously, independently of the gill innervation. However, the beat can be influenced by serotonin. The laterofrontal cirri beat in a plane vertical to the long axes of the filaments. In the normal beat the recovery phase brings the cirrus into the plane of the gill surface, the angle of beat being ~90°. Addition of serotonin to the surrounding medium reduces the angle of beat. High enough concentrations arrest the cirri in the vertical position. With decreasing angle of beat of the laterofrontal cirri the gill becomes increasingly leaky. When the laterofrontal cirri are oriented perpendicularly to the gill surface most particles smaller than the interfilamentar distances pass through the gill (80).

The concentrations of serotonin needed to reduce the angle of beat are higher than those needed to restore metachronal beating of quiescent lateral cilia. Addition of serotonin in suitable concentrations ($\sim 10^{-7}$ M) to the surrounding water restores water transport in gill preparations without affecting the function of the laterofrontal cirri. The preparations will retain particles, but with efficiencies inferior to those of the intact animal. Efficient retention of particles in feeding, undisturbed mussels seems to depend upon the integrated function of the ciliary systems, whose nature is not finally understood (43, 80, 113).

The finding of both a cilio-excitatory and a cilio-inhibitory innervation in the bivalve gill raises the question about the role played by these nerves in controlling gill function in normal feeding. Jørgensen (80) found that serotonin added to the medium had no effect on the rates at which intact, undisturbed *M. edulis* cleared the water of suspended particles. However, in lesioned mussels that transported water at low rates, serotonin restored water transport to initial levels, but the gills remained leaky. Dopamine given alone or in combination with serotonin did not affect water transport or particle retention in intact mussels. It was concluded that the serotonergic innervation of the bivalve gill maintains the activity of the water-transporting ciliary system, but does not seem to regulate the rate of water transport in undisturbed mussels. The role played by the dopaminergic innervation in the function of the gill remains to be assessed.

Zooplankton Crustaceans

The term suspension feeding is ambiguous when applied to the zooplankton because, strictly speaking, all zooplankton organisms feed on suspended food, whether the food particles are so large that they are sensed and seized singly, or so small that they can only be obtained by some kind of processing of the surrounding water. In zooplankton crustaceans this processing is a filtration by means of specialized limbs bearing plumose setae. In the following we therefore distinguish between filter feeding and other feeding mechanisms in the zooplankton crustaceans.

OBLIGATORY FILTER FEEDERS: CLADOCERANS AND *ARTEMIA* In cladocerans and phyllopods (*Artemia*) the water currents produced by the metachronal activity of the thoracic limbs serve both locomotion and feeding (see 79). The rates at which swimming animals clear the surrounding water of particles have been found to be independent of the concentration of particulate matter, organic or inorganic, below certain concentrations, usually around 1 mg dry weight of suspended matter per liter of water (22, 39, 64, 101, 103, 160, 178, *Daphnia* spp.; 157, *Artemia*). This is within the range of concentrations in nature (19, 22, 39, 64). Below the limiting concentrations various species of *Daphnia* and *Artemia* have been found to clear the surrounding water of suspended particles at rates ranging from 1 to 4 ml per 0.1 mg dry weight per hour at the temperatures of acclimatization, usually about 20°C (21, 22, 39, 64, 101, 103, 160, 178, *Daphnia* spp.; 157, *Artemia*). Clearances of particles in *Daphnia* are independent of particle size from $\sim 1\ \mu$ (the bacterium *Escherichia coli*) to ~30 μ (the ciliate *Tetrahymena pyriformis*), indicating that particles down to 1 μ in diameter are practically completely retained by the filters (103). Above the incipient limiting concentration *Daphnia* regulate collection and ingestion of food by decreasing the frequency of beat of the thoracic limbs and by rejecting excess food from the food groove (19, 101, 102). *Daphnia* may also reject material collected at concentrations below the critical concentrations if this material consists of indigestible particles, such as plastic beads (20).

FACULTATIVE FILTER FEEDERS: COPEPODS AND EUPHAUSIIDS Copepods and euphausiids are primarily macrophagous groups, but many planktonic representatives have adopted filter feeding in addition to raptorial or carnivorous feeding. Filter feeding is especially well developed in ecologically important groups, such as the calanoid copepods (8, 10, 106, 107, 122) and the genus *Euphausia* (111).

Copepods Quantitative studies on feeding in planktonic copepods were long hampered by the difficulty in maintaining the copepods healthy in the laboratory. Recently, however, several species have been successfully cultured: First were coastal species, such as the harpacticoid *Euterpina acutifrons* (126, 132, 172) and the calanoid *Acartia tonsa* (206). More recently typical oceanic copepods, such as *Rhincalanus nasutus* and *Calanus helgolandicus* (*pacificus*), have been brought into continuous cultures (7, 34, 123–125, 140, 141).

Two types of filter feeding have developed within planktonic copepods. In *Calanus, Pseudocalanus, Centropages, Temora,* some other marine genera, and the freshwater *Diaptomus,* the feeding current arises as a pair of eddies produced during swimming, the current flowing around the bases of the maxillipeds to pass through the screen formed by the maxillary setae and their setules (24, 57, 97). The other type is found in *Acartia,* in which the maxillae can be extended to be used as sweeping nets (29). The efficiency with which the filters retain particles depends upon the distances between setae and setules, which may vary between species and with developmental stages. Generally, the filters of copepods are more porous than those of most other groups of filter-feeding invertebrates. In adult filter-feeding copepods, distances between setules mostly vary from about 5 μ to more than 10 μ (57, 107, 183, see also 79). Feeding experiments agree with these measurements in showing decreasing or absent ingestion or clearances of particles smaller than 5–10 μ (66, 104, 153, 200).

The capacity for both microphagous and macrophagous feeding greatly widens the nutritional repertory of planktonic copepods. Adoption of filter feeding or raptorial feeding seems mainly to depend upon the nature, concentration, and size distribution of the particulate material present in the surrounding water. Harvey (68) was the first to experimentally demonstrate selective feeding, using *Calanus finmarchicus* fed mixtures of phytoplankton algae of different size. Studies of this type were later resumed (31, 65, 121–123, 142, 147, 150, 153, 159). Conover observed that *Calanus hyperboreus* that had been filter feeding on small *Thalassiosira* cells for several days ate fewer large *Coscinodiscus* cells when offered a mixture of *Thalassiosira* and *Coscinodiscus* than did animals that had previously been feeding raptorially on the large cells. *Pseudocalanus minutus,* feeding in bottles with coastal sea water obtained off the Fraser River in British Columbia, cleared large diatoms and 8–14 μ flagellates at equal rates when grazing on natural phytoplankton populations at low concentrations (in February), whereas at high concentrations (in May) individuals of the same species cleared only the large diatoms (147). In similar experiments with sea water from the Bedford Basin in Nova Scotia, however, *P. minutus* was found preferentially to clear the water of particles less than 15 μ when the phytoplankton concentration was high, while at low concentrations larger algae were consumed (153).

Also, the nature of the particulate matter is of importance. *C. helgolandicus* cleared fresh phytoplankton cells faster than dead cells. Fecal material was cleared at only low rates and natural detritus obtained from a depth of 100 m was not cleared at all (142). Also *C. hyperboreus* was observed to discard fecal pellets (31). Given the choice between phytoplankton cells and animal food, a number of filter-feeding copepods consumed the animal food as readily as they did phytoplankton (8, 122, 123).

The mechanisms by which planktonic copepods register particles in their surroundings are only poorly understood. Cushing (40) introduced the "encounter" concept in his mathematical model for grazing rates in copepods. Originally the concept implied that the perceptive range of the copepods depends upon sensory function localized in the antennae. Amputation of the antennae, however, did not significantly interfere with feeding in *C. hyperboreus* (30) or *Rhincalanus nasutus* (123). In *C. hyperboreus,* perception of large food particles seemed to be restricted to an area on the ventral surface of the head region (31). In *C. helgolandicus* there was no significant difference between rates of feeding on large phytoplankton cells in light and dark. Visual perception therefore seems to be unimportant in this species (159).

The rates at which filter-feeding copepods transport water through the filter chamber can be determined from the rates at which the copepods clear particles too large to pass through the filters and too small and numerous to be captured individually. It was calculated from the data obtained by Gauld (55) that one *C. finmarchicus* removed on an average one 10 μ *Chlamydomonas* cell per 50 msec. This rate of feeding seems to be incompatible with direct seizing of single cells. In the experiments, *C. finmarchicus* filtered about 4 ml per animal per hour, which may be close to the maximal filtration rates (46, 124). The volumes cleared of large cells that cannot enter the filter chambers with the feeding current (57) can be much higher, up to about 30 ml h^{-1} (36, 141).

High filtration rates also seem to be characteristic of *C. hyperboreus* (121), *R. nasutus* (124), *Pseudocalanus minutus,* and *Acartia* spp. (6), whereas *Metridia lucens* has been found to filter at low rates (65, see also 79).

It has been a matter of discussion whether herbivorous planktonic copepods feed continuously or discontinuously. In nature, Gauld (56) observed that vertically migrating *C. finmarchicus* fed predominantly at night when the animals stayed within the phytoplankton-containing surface layer. However, copepods that remained within the euphotic zone fed at all hours of the day and night, as indicated by the observation that the guts of most animals captured at various times of the day were full of food. Herbivorous copepods can also feed at all hours in laboratory experiments, but feeding is often stated to be discontinuous. Conover (31) observed *C. hyperboreus* to stop feeding on large *Coscinodiscus* cells when the gut was full. Several investigators reported on decreasing rates of feeding during grazing experiments (46, 66, 99, 121). It has been assumed that the initial high rates are characteristic of starved animals and the subsequent low rates are characteristic of fed animals. However, even the initially high clearances recorded in acute grazing experiments have mostly been lower than the mean clearances measured by Paffenhöfer (141) in *C. helgolandicus* maintained in continuous culture. Decrease of clearance with time in experiments with freshly collected *Calanus* may therefore not reflect feeding behavior in nature. Perhaps feeding in herbivorous planktonic copepods is potentially continuous, at least below certain levels of phytoplankton concentrations that are seldom exceeded in nature, in any case not exceeded in oceanic environments.

Grazing studies on natural phytoplankton have indicated that planktonic copepods cease to feed below certain levels of phytoplankton, i.e. below critical concentrations ranging from about 50 μg carbon per liter up to nearly 200 μg (146–148). These concentrations are higher than those needed to maintain *C. helgolandicus* in continuous culture in the laboratory (140, 141). In laboratory experiments, Corner et al (36) found no concentrations below which *Calanus* ceased to feed on the large diatom *Biddulphia.*

In the freshwater calanoid *Diaptomus oregonensis,* Richman (158) measured constant filtration rates of about 0.1 ml h^{-1} per copepod at concentrations up to 2.5×10^4 cells ml^{-1} of the green alga *Chlamydomonas.* As concentrations in the suspensions were increased to $2–5 \times 10^5$ cells ml^{-1}, i.e. concentrations that can be reached during blooms in nature, clearances decreased to 0.05 ml h^{-1} or less. McQueen (104) confirmed that *D. oregonensis* cleared pure or mixed suspensions of phytoplankton algae at concentrations below the incipient limiting levels at rates of about 0.06–0.08 ml h^{-1}. However, the animals filtered natural phytoplankton of cell sizes ranging from 6 to 12 μ at 0.5 ml h^{-1}.

Euphausiids The literature on food and feeding in planktonic euphausiids has been reviewed by Nemoto (131). The variation in feeding types among euphausiids is similar to that of copepods, ranging from pure carnivorous feeding to combinations of raptorial with filter feeding. The relative importance of filter feeding varies, but few definitive quantitative data are available (90, 128–130).

FOOD VALUE OF PHYTOPLANKTON AND OTHER ORGANIC PARTICULATE MATTER

The value of phytoplankton as food for the various groups of suspension feeders has been evaluated in feeding experiments and by determination of the fraction of cleared and ingested algae that is digested and absorbed. The literature dealing with the food value of phytoplankton algae has been reviewed by Jørgensen (79) and Hutner & Provasoli (72). More recently, Walne (191, 192, 194) compared 19 genera of algae, in terms of their food value to several species of bivalves, by measuring the rate of growth or changes in chemical composition of young specimens of bivalves fed on different concentrations of pure cultures of the algae. Most experiments were made on the food value of the flagellate *Isochrysis galbana,* which was therefore used as a reference. In *Ostrea edulis* the food values of the algae varied from 0.3 to 1.4 of that of *Isochrysis galbana,* and in *Mercenaria mercenaria* from 0.14 to 3.3. A mixture of two algal species sometimes produced a synergistic effect on growth.

Our knowledge of the food value of various species of unicellular algae to some herbivorous copepods was greatly increased with the successful culturing of the copepods under laboratory conditions. Thus *C. helgolandicus* could be raised from hatching to adulthood with low mortality when kept at natural concentrations of pure algal cultures of a dinoflagellate (*Gymnodinium*) or one of three species of diatoms (*Chaetoceros, Skeletonema,* and *Lauderia*) (140, 141). Cultures of *Daphnia magna* fed exclusively on *Chlorella pyrenoidosa* remained vigorously growing and reproducing for three years (166).

Bacteria-free, unialgal cultures may be deficient when given alone, but satisfactory when combined. In experiments on *Artemia* and *Tigriopus,* Provasoli et al (155) found that the flagellates *Rhodomonas* and *Isochrysis* given singly were able to support only a restricted number of generations, whereas the two algae fed together maintained normal fertility and survival.

In most comparative studies living phytoplankton algae have been found to be superior to bacteria or detritus as food (137, 166, 171, daphnians; Kirby-Smith, personal communication, scallops). The value of bacteria as food for freshwater daphnians and bivalves has been emphasized by Sorokin and collaborators (112, 169).

Suspension-feeding bivalves and herbivorous zooplankton crustaceans have been found to assimilate about two thirds to four fifths of ingested natural phytoplankton or mixed phytoplankton cultures (23, 67, copepods; 175, 187, bivalves). These results agree with experiments on assimilation of algae in pure cultures. Most algae are assimilated at efficiencies ranging from about 50 to 90% of the amounts ingested, both in bivalves (5, 199, 201, 202) and zooplankton crustaceans (30–32, 35, 65, marine copepods; 171, *Artemia*). In the freshwater *Daphnia longispina* and *Diaptomus gracilis,* Schindler (165) found assimilation efficiencies to vary from 10 to 100%. Usually both species assimilated the algae to roughly the same degree. The greatest deviations were obtained with the flagellate *Tribonema,* which *Daphnia* assimilated to 69% and *Diaptomus* to only 20%, and the green alga *Elakalothrix,* which *Daphnia* assimilated to 100% vs only 31% in *Diaptomus.* Direct observations on gut contents of freshwater zooplankton grazing on natural phytoplankton have confirmed this variation in degree of utilization. Some species of algae were usually found to undergo digestion in the gut, other species remained intact in the gut, and some were capable of reproducing after passage through the gut (152).

RELATIONSHIP BETWEEN CLEARANCES AND OXYGEN CONSUMPTION

In suspension feeders that process the surrounding water at specific rates, that is, rates independent of the concentrations of food and other particles in the medium below certain concentrations, it is of interest to know the relationship between these rates and the energy requirements of the animals. From this relationship it is possible to estimate the concentrations of food that must be present in the water to cover the requirements of the animals.

Tables 1 and 2 correlate data on the amounts of water transported or cleared of particles in relation to minimal energy requirements, as assessed from rates of oxygen consumption, in some bivalves and zooplankton crustaceans. Older data have been reviewed in (79).

In some species of bivalves the relationships between body size, on the one hand, and water transport and oxygen consumption, on the other, have been expressed by the allometric formulas: Water transport $= a_c \times \text{weight}^{b_c}$; and oxygen consumption $= a_o \times \text{weight}^{b_o}$. The values of the exponent b_c tend to be smaller than those of b_o. In *Argopecten irradians* b_c was 0.52 and b_o 0.68 (10°C) and 0.87 (18°C) (82); in *Mytilus edulis* b_c was 0.60 and b_o 0.75 (187); and in *Cardium edule* b_c was 0.58 and b_o 0.77 (186). The ratio of water transport to oxygen consumption therefore

Table 2 Relationship between rates of filtration and oxygen consumption in zooplankton crustaceans

Habitat and species	Liters of water filtered for each ml of oxygen consumed	References
Freshwater		
Daphnia pulex	1.6	178
Daphnia longispina	1.3	178
Diaptomus oregonensis	1	104, 158
	9	104
Saline		
Artemia salina	2.7	58, 157
Marine		
Calanus helgolandicus stage V	22 (10°C) 26 (15°C)	124
– – – ♀	19 (10°C) 13 (15°C)	
Rhincalanus nasutus stage V	30 (10°C) 35 (15°C)	
– – – ♀	21 (10°C) 31 (15°C)	
Pseudocalanus minutus	15–60	6
Acartia clausi	10, 15	6
Acartia tonsa	35, 60	6
Metridia lucens	0.1	65
Euphausia pacifica	0.5	90, 149

tends to decrease with increasing body size. For instance, in 1 g specimens of *M. edulis* the ratio was 11; in 0.007 g specimens, the smallest studied, the ratio was 25. This agrees with the finding that growth efficiency decreases with increasing body size (76). In Table 1 the amounts of water transported for each milliliter of oxygen consumed have been calculated, when possible, for animals with a soft tissue weight of 1 g dry weight. Moreover, values measured at temperatures of acclimatization have been used in calculations of the relationship between water transport and oxygen consumption. The data available are sparse and often the estimated relations are probably not yet definitive. It is indicated that marine epifaunal bivalves, weighing about 1 g, transport about 10–15 liters of water for each milliliter of oxygen consumed. These values agree with previous estimates (79). There is some indication that the ratio may be lower in infaunal and freshwater bivalves [Table 1 and (79)]. All available data are from species inhabiting inshore waters with high concentrations of phytoplankton and detritus. The ratios may be expected to be higher in bivalves inhabiting waters poorer in particulate organic matter.

The costs of transporting water through the gills set lower limits to the concentrations of food particles at which suspension-feeding bivalves can subsist. The amounts of available energy must be higher than the energy needed in transporting the water. The costs of water transport in bivalves are not precisely known. Several investigators who found that oxygen consumption increased with increasing water transport have assumed that the increased oxygen consumption reflects work done in transporting the water (27, *Crassostrea virginica;* 14, *Mytilus perna;* 18, 133, 180, *Mytilus edulis*). The assumption that an increase in oxygen consumption to any great extent results from the work done in transporting water through the gills is untenable, if only because the cells bearing the water-transporting cilia constitute only about one tenth of the gill tissue, which again constitutes only about one tenth of the whole body mass. The oxygen used by the water-transporting ciliated cells can therefore constitute only a small part of the total oxygen consumption, probably of the order of 1% (77). This estimate is in contrast to the suggestion that the greater part (about 90%) of oxygen consumption in active *M. edulis* should be used in work done by ciliary feeding (133). Some of the arguments that use correlation of water transport with oxygen consumption lead to absurd consequences. Thus in *M. mercenaria* an increase in water transport of 1 liter was found to correspond to an increase in oxygen consumption of 0.3 to 1.5 ml (63, 96, 188). It follows that 1 liter of sea water must contain the unrealistic amount of up to 1.5 mg dry weight of available food in order to cover solely the energy required for the transport of this liter of water. The rates of water transport measured seem to be lower than they normally are in nature.

According to the sparse data available on zooplankton crustaceans (Table 2), freshwater species and the brine shrimp *Artemia* filter water at moderate rates in relation to oxygen consumption, and several marine copepods at high rates. These high rates reflect the importance of filter feeding in some species of calanoid copepods, in contrast to other species, e. g. *Metridia lucens,* in which the ratio between filtration and oxygen consumption is low. The values obtained in *Euphausia* have been variable due to irregular filter feeding in the laboratory.

GENERAL DISCUSSION

Studies on feeding, ingestion, and assimilation constitute the basis for drawing up balance sheets for input (food intake) and outputs (catabolism, growth, and reproduction). It is therefore important to make sure that the rates measured in the laboratory also apply in nature. This obvious point has often been neglected, perhaps because suspension feeders may survive in the laboratory for weeks or months, and may continue to feed even under adverse conditions. Quantitative data obtained by different investigators on the same species have often varied greatly, presumably because feeding has been inhibited to varying degrees. Relatively safe extrapolations from laboratory to natural conditions have become possible in suspension feeders that can be maintained in permanent culture in the laboratory, such as daphnians, *Artemia,* and several zooplankton copepods. Extrapolations are more uncertain in bivalves, for instance, which may react to adverse conditions by transporting water discontinuously and at low rates, and by reducing the efficiency of particle retention. Particle retention seems to be most sensitive (26, 80, 82, 94). Rhythms of activity alternating with quiescence, as observed in the laboratory, should therefore be compared with observations made under natural conditions before such rhythms can be regarded as representing behavior in nature. The biological significance of the high sensitivity toward adverse conditions in bivalves remains a matter of speculation. Perhaps reduction or cessation of water transport and closing of the valves can be considered as adaptations to cope with adverse conditions in the surroundings.

Studies on rates of feeding in suspension feeders long centered on measurements of clearances of suspended particles. The finding that clearances may vary with the nature, size, and concentration of the suspended phytoplankton algae discredited clearance determinations in ecological studies as a means of quantitative evaluation of feeding in suspension feeders, especially in zooplankton crustaceans. Measurements of clearances were replaced by direct estimates of food rations according to the formula $R = R_{max} (1-e^{-kp})$, where R is the ration obtained at the food concentration p, R_{max} is the maximum ration, and k is a constant. In 1945 Ivlev (74) introduced this formula to describe the relationship between rate of feeding and food concentration in planktivorous fishes. Later it was adopted for feeding in zooplankton (33, 36, 73, 146, 171). The formula has been found to describe reasonably well the relationship between concentration and uptake of food in herbivorous zooplankton crustaceans, especially in the upper range of natural food concentrations or above this range. Such direct estimates of food rations may be more relevant to the ecologist (33, 177, 193). However, they are less informative to the comparative physiologist who wants to assess the capacities and properties of the feeding structures, as determined by internal and environmental factors.

Conover (33) characterized the life of zooplankton in the ocean and a large lake as a "life in a nutritionally dilute environment." In fact, the low concentration of food may be the clue to understanding the character of suspension feeding. Presumably, energy for functions other than the transport of the surrounding medium through the feeding organs becomes optimal when the water-transporting structures are dimensioned for continuous feeding at low rates, rather than for discontinuous feeding at correspondingly higher rates. If suspension feeding did evolve according to this principle of minimal dimensioning of the water-processing structures, we should expect suspension feeders to be potentially continuous feeders that clear the surrounding water of suspended particles at largely inherent rates, adapted phylogenetically to the level of food particles in the habitat (79, p. 138). Broadly speaking, this characteristic does apply to suspension feeders that live in the sea and in most lakes. It is only in eutrophic waters that food levels seem regularly to reach values above which they begin to control the rates of water transport through the feeding structures.

In environments in which food concentrations normally remain below incipient limiting levels we would expect rates of feeding to vary directly with the concentrations of food particles. As a consequence, growth and reproduction should normally be submaximal and tend to vary with food levels. Studies on the bay scallop *Argopecten irradians* in inshore water at Beaufort, North Carolina did not support the hypothesis that the rate of growth of the scallop was normally controlled by the levels of phytoplankton. During most of the year growth rate seemed to be controlled predominantly by temperature (83, 84). This may be due to the high levels of phytoplankton prevailing in the Beaufort Channel water on which the scallops fed. From other coastal regions there is evidence that food levels, besides temperature, do control growth of various bivalves: *M. mercenaria* (9, 154, 175), *Tellina tenuis* (181, 182), *O. edulis* (190, 192), *C. virginica,* and *M. edulis* (175). Also in herbivorous zooplankton crustaceans, food levels seem to control growth (124, 136, 140, 141, 174, copepods; 128, euphausiids).

Literature Cited

1. Aiello, E. 1960. Factors affecting ciliary activity on the gill of the mussel *Mytilus edulis. Physiol. Zool.* 33:120–35
2. Aiello, E. 1970. Nervous and chemical stimulation of gill cilia in bivalve molluscs. *Physiol. Zool.* 43:60–70
3. Aiello, E., Sleigh, M. A. 1972. The metachronal wave of lateral cilia of *Mytilus edulis. J. Cell Biol.* 54:493–506
4. Ali, R. M. 1970. The influence of suspension density and temperature on the filtration rate of *Hiatella arctica. Mar. Biol.* 6:291–302
5. Allen, J. A. 1962. Preliminary experiments on the feeding and excretion of bivalves using Phaeodactylum labelled with ^{32}P. *J. Mar. Biol. Assoc. U.K.* 42:609–23
6. Anraku, M. 1964. Influence of the Cape Cod Canal on the hydrography and on the copepods in Buzzards Bay and Cape Cod Bay, Massachusetts. II. Respiration and feeding. *Limnol. Oceanogr.* 9:195–206
7. Anraku, M., Hirano, M., Eds. 1973. Plankton symposium: cultivation and mass culture of zooplankton. *Bull. Plankton Soc. Jap.* 20:1–83
8. Anraku, M., Omori, M. 1963. Preliminary survey of the relationship between the feeding habit and the structure of the mouth-parts of marine copepods. *Limnol. Oceanogr.* 8:116–26
9. Ansell, A. D. 1968. The rate of growth of the hard clam *Mercenaria mercenaria* (L.) throughout the geographical range. *J. Cons. Cons. Perma. Int. Explor. Mer* 31:364–409
10. Arashkevich, E. G. 1969. The character of feeding of copepods in the northwestern Pacific. *Okeanologiya* 9:857–73 (In Russian)
11. Badman, D. G. 1974. Changes in activity in a freshwater clam in response to oxygen concentration. *Comp. Biochem. Physiol.* 47A:1265–71
12. Ballentine, D., Morton, J. E. 1956. Filtering, feeding and digestion in the

lamellibranch *Lasaea rubra*. *J. Mar. Biol. Assoc. U.K.* 35:241–74

13. Barnes, G. E. 1955. The behaviour of *Anodonta cygnea* L., and its neurophysiological basis. *J. Exp. Biol.* 32: 158–74
14. Bayne, B. L. 1967. The respiratory response of *Mytilus perna* L. (Mollusca: Lamellibranchia) to reduced environmental oxygen. *Physiol. Zool.* 40: 307–13
15. Bayne, B. L. 1973. Physiological changes in *Mytilus edulis* L. induced by temperature and nutritive stress. *J. Mar. Biol. Assoc. U.K.* 53:39–58
16. Bayne, B. L., Thompson, R. J., Widdows, J. 1973. Some effects of temperature and food on the rate of oxygen consumption by *Mytilus edulis* L. *Effects of Temperature on Ectothermic Organisms,* ed. Wolfgang Wieser, 181–94. Berlin: Springer-Verlag
17. Blake, J. W. 1961. Preliminary measurements of filter-feeding activity of the soft-shelled clam, *Mya arenaria,* by the use of radioactive algae. *Biol. Bull.* 121:383 (Abstr.)
18. Brown, B. E., Newell, R. C. 1972. The effect of copper and zinc on the metabolism of the mussel *Mytilus edulis. Mar. Biol.* 16:108–18
19. Burns, C. W. 1968. Direct observations of mechanisms regulating feeding behaviour of *Daphnia* in lakewater. *Int. Rev. Gesamten Hydrobiol.* 53:83–100
20. Burns, C. W. 1969. Particle size and sedimentation in the feeding behaviour of two species of *Daphnia. Limnol. Oceanogr.* 14:392–402
21. Burns, C. W. 1969. Relation between filtering rate, temperature, and body size in four species of *Daphnia. Limnol. Oceanogr.* 14:693–700
22. Burns, C. W., Rigler, F. H. 1967. Comparison of filtering rates of *Daphnia* in lake water and in suspensions of yeast. *Limnol. Oceanogr.* 12:492–502
23. Butler, E. I., Corner, E. D. S., Marshall, S. M. 1970. On the nutrition and metabolism of zooplankton. VII. Seasonal survey of nitrogen and phosphorus excretion by *Calanus* in the Clyde Sea-Area, *J. Mar. Biol. Assoc. U.K.* 50:525–60
24. Cannon, H. G. 1929. On the feeding mechanism of the copepods, *Calanus finmarchicus* and *Diaptomus gracilis. Brit. J. Exp. Biol.* 6:131–44
25. Chipman, W. A. 1959. The use of radioisotopes in studies of the foods and feeding activities of marine animals. *Pubbl. Sta. Zool. Napoli* 31:Suppl., 154–75
26. Chipman, W. A., Hopkins, J. G. 1954. Water filtration by the bay scallop *Pecten irradians* as observed with the use of radioactive plankton. *Biol. Bull.* 107:80–91
27. Collier, A. 1959. Some observations on the respiration of the American oyster *Crassostrea virginica* (Gmelin). *Inst. Mar. Sci.* 6:92–108
28. Collier, A., Ray, S. M. 1948. An automatic proportioning apparatus for experimental study of the effect of chemical solutions on aquatic animals. *Science* 107:576
29. Conover, R. J. 1956. Oceanography of Long Island Sound, 1952–54. VI. Biology of the copepod genus *Acartia. Bull. Bingham Oceanogr. Coll.* 15:156–233
30. Conover, R. J. 1964. Food relations and nutrition of zooplankton. *Occas. Publ. Grad. Sch. Oceanogr. Univ. Rhode Island* 2:81–91
31. Conover, R. J. 1966. Assimilation of organic matter by zooplankton. *Limnol. Oceanogr.* 11:338–45
32. Conover, R. J. 1966. Factors affecting the assimilation of organic matter by zooplankton and the question of superfluous feeding. *Limnol. Oceanogr.* 11: 346–54
33. Conover, R. J. 1968. Zooplankton—life in a nutritionally dilute environment. *Am. Zool.* 8:107–18
34. Conover, R. J. 1970. Cultivation of plankton populations. *Helgoländer Wiss. Meeresunters.* 21:401–44
35. Corner, E. D. S., Cowey, C. B., Marshall, S. M. 1967. On the nutrition and metabolism of zooplankton. V. Feeding efficiency of *Calanus finmarchicus. J. Mar. Biol. Assoc. U.K.* 47:259–70
36. Corner, E. D. S., Head, R. N., Kilvington, C. C. 1972. On the nutrition and metabolism of zooplankton. VIII. The grazing of *Biddulphia* cells by *Calanus helgolandicus. J. Mar. Biol. Assoc. U.K.* 52:847–61
37. Coughlan, J. 1969. The estimation of filtering rate from the clearance of suspensions. *Mar. Biol.* 2:356–58
38. Coughlan, J., Ansell, A. D. 1964. A direct method for determining the pumping rate of siphonate bivalves. *J. Cons. Cons. Perma. Int. Explor. Mer* 29:205–14
39. Crowley, P. H. 1973. Filtering rate inhibition of *Daphnia pulex* in Wintergreen

Lake water. *Limnol. Oceanogr.* 18:394–402
40. Cushing, D. H. 1968. Grazing by herbivorous copepods in the sea. *J. Cons. Cons. Perma. Int. Explor. Mer* 32:70–82
41. Davids, C. 1964. The influence of suspensions of microorganisms of different concentrations on the pumping and retention of food by the mussel (*Mytilus edulis* L.). *Neth. J. Sea Res.* 2:233–49
42. de Bruin, J. P. C., Davids, C. 1970. Observations on the rate of water pumping of the freshwater mussel *Anodonta cygnea zellensis* (Gmelin). *Neth. J. Zool.* 20:380–91
43. Dral, A. D. G. 1967. The movements of the latero-frontal cilia and the mechanism of particle retention in the mussel (*Mytilus edulis* L.). *Neth. J. Sea Res.* 3:391–422
44. Drinnan, R. E. 1964. An apparatus for recording the water-pumping behaviour of lamellibranchs. *Neth. J. Sea Res.* 2:223–32
45. Fox, D. L., Sverdrup, H. N., Cunningham, J. P. 1937. The rate of water propulsion by the California mussel. *Biol. Bull.* 72:417–38
46. Frost, B. W. 1972. Effects of size and concentration of food particles on the feeding behaviour of the marine planktonic copepod *Calanus pacificus. Limnol. Oceanogr.* 17:805–15
47. Gaarder, T., Alvsaker, E. 1941. Biologie und Chemie der Auster in den norwegischen Pollen. *Bergen Mus. Skr.* 6:1–236
48. Gaarder, T., Eliassen, E. 1954. The energy-metabolism of *Ostrea edulis. Univ. Bergen Skr.* 3:1–6
49. Gabbott, P. A., Bayne, B. L. 1973. Biochemical effects of temperature and nutritive stress on *Mytilus edulis* L. *J. Mar. Biol. Assoc. U.K.* 53:269–86
50. Galtsoff, P. S. 1928. Experimental study of the function of the oyster gills and its bearing on the problems of the oyster culture and sanitary control of the oyster industry. *Bull. U.S. Fish. Bur.* 44:1–39
51. Galtsoff, P. S. 1946. Reaction of oysters to chlorination. *U.S. Fish Wildl. Serv. Res. Rep.* 11:1–28
52. Galtsoff, P. S. 1964. The American oyster *Crassostrea virginica* Gmelin. *Fish. Bull. U.S.* 64:1–480
53. Galtsoff, P. S., Chipman, W. A. Jr., Engle, J. B., Calderwood, H. N. 1947. Ecological and physiological studies of the effect of sulphate pulp mill wastes on oysters in the York River, Virginia. *Fish. Bull. U.S.* 51:58–186
54. Galtsoff, P. S., Whipple, D. V. 1931. Oxygen consumption of normal and green oysters. *Bull. U.S. Fish. Bur.* 46:489–508
55. Gauld, D. T. 1951. The grazing rate of planktonic copepods. *J. Mar. Biol. Assoc. U.K.* 29:695–706
56. Gauld, D. T. 1953. Diurnal variations in the grazing of planktonic copepods. *J. Mar. Biol. Assoc. U.K.* 31:461–74
57. Gauld, D. T. 1966. The swimming and feeding of planktonic copepods. *Some Contemporary Studies in Marine Science,* ed. H. Barnes, 313–34. London: George Allen and Unwin Ltd.
58. Gilchrist, B. M. 1956. The oxygen consumption of *Artemia salina* (L.) in different salinities. *Hydrobiologia* 8: 54–65
59. Gosselin, R. E. 1961. The cilio-excitatory activity of serotonin. *J. Cell. Comp. Physiol.* 58:17–26
60. Gray, J. 1920. The effects of ions upon ciliary movement. *Quart. J. Microsc. Sci.* 64:345–71
61. Gray, J. 1928. *Ciliary Movement.* London: Cambridge Univ. Press
62. Gray, J. 1931. The mechanism of ciliary movement. VI. Photographic and stroboscopic analysis of ciliary movement. *Proc. Roy. Soc. London B* 107:313–32
63. Hamwi, A., Haskin, H. H. 1969. Oxygen consumption and pumping rates in the hard clam *Mercenaria mercenaria:* A direct method. *Science* 163:823–24
64. Haney, J. F. 1973. An *in situ* examination of the grazing activities of natural zooplankton communities. *Arch. Hydrobiol.* 72:87–132
65. Haq, S. M. 1967. Nutritional physiology of *Metridia lucens* and *Metridia longa* from the Gulf of Maine. *Limnol. Oceanogr.* 12:40–51
66. Hargrave, B. T., Geen, G. H. 1970. Effects of copepod grazing on two natural phytoplankton populations. *J. Fish. Res. Bd. Can.* 27:1395–1403
67. Harris, R. P. 1973. Feeding, growth, reproduction and nitrogen utilization by the harpacticoid copepod, *Tigriopus brevicornis. J. Mar. Biol. Assoc. U.K.* 35:785–800
68. Harvey, H. W. 1937. Note on selective feeding by *Calanus. J. Mar. Biol. Assoc. U.K.* 22:97–100
69. Haven, D. S., Morales-Alamo, R. 1970. Filtration of particles from suspension

by the American oyster *Crassostrea virginica. Biol. Bull.* 139:248–64
70. Hinz, W., Scheil, H.-G. 1972. Zur Filtrationsleistung von *Dreissena, Sphaerium* und *Pisidium* (Eulamellibranchiata) *Oecologia* 11:45–54
71. Hopkins, A. E. 1931. Temperature and the shell movement of oysters. *Bull. U.S. Fish. Bur.* 47:1–14
72. Hutner, S. H., Provasoli, L. 1965. Comparative physiology: nutrition. *Ann. Rev. Physiol.* 27:19–50
73. Ivanova, M. B. 1971. Influence of food concentration upon the rate of filtration in cladocera. *Zh. Obshch. Biol.* 31: 721–31 (In Russian)
74. Ivlev, V. S. 1955. *Experimental Ecology of Nutrition of Fishes.* Moscow; 1961. Transl. D. Scott. New Haven: Yale Univ. Press
75. Jørgensen, C. B. 1943. On the water transport through the gills of bivalves. *Acta Physiol. Scand.* 5:297–304
76. Jørgensen, C. B. 1952. Efficiency of growth in *Mytilus edulis* and two gastropod veligers. *Nature London* 170:714
77. Jørgensen, C. B. 1955. Quantitative aspects of filter feeding in invertebrates. *Biol. Rev.* 30:391–454
78. Jørgensen, C. B. 1960. Efficiency of particle retention and rate of water transport in undisturbed lamellibranchs. *J. Cons. Cons. Perma. Int. Explor. Mer* 26:94–116
79. Jørgensen, C. B. 1966. *Biology of Suspension feeding.* Oxford: Pergamon
80. Jørgensen, C. B. 1974. On gill function in the mussel *Mytilus edulis* L. *Ophelia* 13: In press
81. Jørgensen, C. B., Goldberg, E. D. 1953. Particle filtration in some ascidians and lamellibranchs. *Biol. Bull.* 105:477–89
82. Kirby-Smith, W. W. 1970. *Growth of the scallops Argopecten irradians (Say) and Argopecten gibbus (Linné), as influenced by food and temperature.* PhD dissertation. Duke Univ., Durham N.C.
83. Kirby-Smith, W. W. 1972. Growth of the bay scallop: the influence of experimental water currents. *J. Exp. Mar. Biol. Ecol.* 8:7–18
84. Kirby-Smith, W. W., Barber, R. T. 1974. Suspension-feeding aquaculture systems: effects of phytoplankton concentrations and temperature on the growth of the bay scallop. *Aquaculture.* In press
85. Klee, O. 1971. Plädoyer für eine Vielgeschmähte. *Kosmos* 67:363–68
86. Koch, H. J., Hers, M. J. 1943. Influence de facteurs respiratoires sur les interruptions de la ventilation par la siphon exhalant chez *Anodonta cygnea* L. *Ann. Soc. Roy. Zool. Belg.* 74:32–44
87. Krüger, F. 1960. Zur Frage der Grössenabhängigkeit des Sauerstoffverbrauchs von *Mytilus edulis* L. *Helgoländer Wiss. Meeresunters.* 7:125–48
88. Kuenzler, E. J. 1961. Phosphorus budget of a mussel population. *Limnol. Oceanogr.* 6:400–15
89. Langton, R. W., Gabbott, P. A. 1974. The tidal rhythm of extracellular digestion and the response to feeding in *Ostrea edulis. Mar. Biol.* 24:181–87
90. Lasker, R. 1966. Feeding, growth, respiration, and carbon utilization of a euphausiid crustacean. *J. Fish. Res. Bd. Can.* 23:1291–1317
91. Loosanoff, V. L. 1939. Effect of temperature upon shell movements of clams, *Venus mercenaria* (L.). *Biol. Bull.* 76:171–82
92. Loosanoff, V. L. 1942. Shell movements of the edible mussel, *Mytilus edulis* (L.) in relation to temperature. *Ecology* 23:231–34
93. Loosanoff, V. L. 1958. Some aspects of behavior of oysters at different temperatures. *Biol. Bull.* 114:57–70
94. Loosanoff, V. L., Engle, J. B. 1947. Effect of different concentrations of micro-organisms on the feeding of oysters (*O. virginica*). *Fish. Bull. U.S.* 51:31–57
95. Loosanoff, V. L., Nomejko, C. A. 1946. Feeding of oysters in relation to tidal states and to periods of light and darkness. *Biol. Bull* 90:244–64
96. Loveland, R. E., Chu, D. S. K. 1969. Oxygen consumption and water movement in *Mercenaria mercenaria. Comp. Biochem. Physiol.* 29:173–84
97. Lowndes, A. C. 1935. The swimming and feeding of certain calanoid copepods. *Proc. Zool. Soc. London* Pt. 3:687–715
98. Ludwig, W., Kryvienczyk, J. 1950. Körpergrösse, Körperzeiten und Energiebilanz. III. Der Sauerstoffverbrauch von Muscheln in Abhängigkeit von der Körpergrösse. *Z. Vergl. Physiol.* 32: 464–67
99. McAllister, C. D. 1970. Zooplankton rations, phytoplankton mortality and the estimation of marine production. *Marine Food Chains,* ed. J. H. Steele, 419–57. Edinburgh: Oliver & Boyd
100. McLusky, D. S. 1973. The effect of temperature on the oxygen consumption and filtration rate of *Chlamys*

(*Aequipecten*) *opercularis* (L.) (Bivalvia). *Ophelia* 10:141–54
101. McMahon, J. W. 1965. Some physical factors influencing the feeding behavior of *Daphnia magna* Straus. *Can. J. Zool.* 43:603–11
102. McMahon, J. W., Rigler, F. H. 1963. Mechanisms regulating the feeding rate of *Daphnia magna* Straus. *Can. J. Zool.* 41:321–32
103. McMahon, J. W., Rigler, F. H. 1965. Feeding rate of *Daphnia magna* Straus in different food labelled with radioactive phosphorus. *Limnol. Oceanogr.* 10:105–14
104. McQueen, D. J. 1970. Grazing rates and food selection in *Diaptomus oregonensis* (Copepoda) from Marion Lake, British Columbia. *J. Fish. Res. Bd. Can.* 27:13–20
105. McQuiston, R. W. 1969. Cyclic activity in the digestive diverticula of *Lasaea rubra* (Montagu) (Bivalvia: Eulamellibranchia). *Proc. Malacol. Soc. London* 38:483–92
106. Marshall, S. M., Orr, A. P. 1955. *The Biology of a Marine Copepod Calanus finmarchicus* (*Gunnerus*). Edinburgh: Oliver & Boyd
107. Marshall, S. M., Orr, A. P. 1956. On the Biology of *Calanus finmarchicus.* IX. Feeding and digestion in the young stages. *J. Mar. Biol. Assoc. U.K.* 35:587–603
108. Martin, J. H. 1970. Phytoplankton-zooplankton relationships in Narragansett Bay. IV. The seasonal importance of grazing. *Limnol. Oceanogr.* 15:413–18
109. Mason, J. 1972. The cultivation of the European mussel, *Mytilus edulis* Linnaeus. *Oceanogr. Mar. Biol. Ann. Rev.* 10:437–60
110. Mathers, N. F. 1972. The tracing of a natural algal food labelled with a carbon 14 isotope through the digestive tract of *Ostrea edulis. Proc. Malacol. Soc. London* 40:115–24
111. Mauchline, T., Fisher, L. R. 1969. The biology of euphausiids. *Advan. Mar. Biol.* 7:1–454
112. Mikheev, V. P., Sorokin, Yu. I. 1966. Quantitative studies of *Dreissena polymorpha* habits using the radiocarbon method. *Zh. Obshch. Biol.* 27:463–72 (In Russian)
113. Moore, H. J. 1971. The structure of the latero-frontal cirri on the gills of certain lamellibranch molluscs and their role in suspension feeding. *Mar. Biol.* 11:23–27
114. Morton, B. S. 1969. Studies on the biology of *Dreissena polymorpha* Pall. 2. Correlation of the rhythms of adductor activity, feeding, digestion and excretion. *Proc. Malacol. Soc. London* 38:401–14
115. Morton, B. S. 1970. The tidal rhythm and rhythm of feeding and digestion in *Cardium edule. J. Mar. Biol. Assoc. U.K.* 50:499–512
116. Morton, B. S. 1970. The rhythmical behaviour of *Anodonta cygnea* L. and *Unio pictorum* L. and its biological significance. *Forma Functio* 2:110–20
117. Morton, B. 1971. Studies on the biology of *Dreissena polymorpha* Pall. V. Some aspects of filter-feeding and the effect of micro-organisms upon the rate of filtration. *Proc. Malacol. Soc. London* 39:289–301
118. Morton, B. 1971. The diurnal rhythm and tidal rhythm of feeding and digestion in *Ostrea edulis. Biol. J. Linn. Soc.* 3:329–42
119. Morton, J. E. 1956. The tidal rhythm and action of the digestive system of the lamellibranch *Lasaea rubra. J. Mar. Biol. Assoc. U.K.* 35:563–86
120 Morton, J. E. 1960. The functions of the gut in ciliary feeders. *Biol. Rev.* 35:92–140
121. Mullin, M. M. 1963. Some factors affecting the feeding of marine copepods of the genus *Calanus. Limnol. Oceanogr.* 8:239–50
122. Mullin, M. M. 1966. Selective feeding by calanoid copepods from the Indian Ocean. See Ref. 57, 545–554
123. Mullin, M. M., Brooks, E. R. 1967. Laboratory culture, growth rate and feeding behaviour of a planktonic marine copepod. *Limnol. Oceanogr.* 12:657–66
124. Mullin, M. M., Brooks, E. R. 1970. Growth and metabolism of two planktonic marine copepods as influenced by temperature and type of food. See Ref. 99, 74–95
125. Mullin, M. M., Brooks, E. R. 1970. Production of the planktonic copepod *Calanus helgolandicus. Bull. Scripps Inst. Oceanogr.* 17:89–103
126. Nassogne, A. 1970. Influence of food organisms on the development and culture of pelagic copepods. *Helgoländer Wiss. Meeresunters.* 20:333–45
127. Nelson, T. C. 1935. Water filtration by the oyster and a new hormone effect thereon. *Anat. Rec.* 64:Suppl. 1, 68
128. Nemoto, T. 1966. Feeding of baleen whales and krill, and the value of krill as a marine resource in the Antarctic.

Symp. Antarctic. Oceanogr. 1966: 240–53
129. Nemoto, T. 1967. Feeding pattern of euphausiids and differentiations in their body characters. *Inform. Bull. Planktol. Jap.* Commemoration Number of Dr. Y. Matsue, 157–71
130. Nemoto, T. 1968. Chlorophyll pigments in the stomach of euphausiids. *J. Oceanogr. Soc. Jap.* 24:253–60
131. Nemoto, T. 1972. History of research into the food and feeding of Euphausiids. *Proc. Roy. Soc. Edinburgh B* 73:259–65
132. Neunes, H. W., Pongolini, G. F. 1965. Breeding a pelagic copepod *Euterpina acutifrons* (Dana) in the laboratory. *Nature London* 208:571–73
133. Newell, R. C., Pye, V. J. 1970. Seasonal changes in the effect of temperature on the oxygen consumption of the winkle *Littorina littorea* (L.) and the mussel *Mytilus edulis* (L.). *Comp. Biochem. Physiol.* 34:367–83
134. Nielsen, E. S. 1958. The balance between phytoplankton and zooplankton in the sea. *J. Cons. Cons. Perma. Int. Explor. Mer* 23:178–88
135. Nielsen, E. S. 1972. The rate of primary production and the size of the standing stock of zooplankton in the oceans. *Int. Rev. Gesamten Hydrobiol.* 57:513–16
136. Omori, M. 1970. Variations in length, weight, respiratory rate, and chemical composition of *Calanus cristatus* in relation to its food and feeding. See Ref. 99, 113–26
137. Otsuki, A., Hanya, T., Yamagishi, H. 1969. Residue from bacterial decomposition of green algal cells as food for *Daphnia. Nature London* 222:1182
138. Owen, G. 1966. Feeding. *Physiology of Mollusca,* ed. K. M. Wilbur, C. M. Yonge, II: 1–51. New York: Academic
139. Owen, G. 1972. Lysosomes, peroxisomes and bivalves. *Sci. Progr. Oxford* 60:299–318
140. Paffenhöfer, G.-A. 1970. Cultivation of *Calanus helgolandicus* under controlled conditions. *Helgoländer Wiss. Meeresunters.* 20:346–59
141. Paffenhöfer, G.-A. 1971. Grazing and ingestion rates of nauplii, copepodids and adults of the marine planktonic copepod *Calanus helgolandicus. Mar. Biol.* 11:286–98
142. Paffenhöfer, G.-A., Strickland, J. D. 1970. A note on the feeding of *Calanus helgolandicus* on detritus. *Mar. Biol.* 5:97–99
143. Paparo, A. 1972. Innervation of the lateral cilia in the mussel *Mytilus edulis. Biol. Bull.* 143:592–604
144. Paparo, A., Aiello, E. 1970. Cilio-inhibitory effects of branchial nerve stimulation in the mussel, *Mytilus edulis. Comp. Gen. Pharmacol.* 1:241–50
145. Paparo, A., Finch, C. E. 1972. Catecholamine localization, content and metabolism in the gill of two lamellibranch molluscs. *Comp. Gen. Pharmacol.* 3:303–9
146. Parsons, T. R., LeBrasseur, R. J. 1970. The availability of food to different trophic levels in the marine food chain. See Ref. 99, 325–43
147. Parsons, T. R., LeBrasseur, R. J., Fulton, J. D., Kennedy, O. D. 1969. Production studies in the Strait of Georgia. Part II. Secondary production under the Fraser River plume, February to May 1967. *J. Exp. Mar. Biol. Ecol.* 3:39–50
148. Parsons, T. R., Stephens, K., LeBrasseur, R. J. 1969. Production studies in the Strait of Georgia. Part I. Primary production under the Fraser River plume. *J. Exp. Mar. Biol. Ecol.* 3:27–38
149. Pearcy, W. G., Theilacker, G. H., Lasker, R. 1969. Oxygen consumption of *Euphausia pacifica:* The lack of a diel rhythm or light-dark effect, with a comparison of experimental techniques. *Limnol. Oceanogr.* 14:219–23
150. Peruyeva, Ye. G. 1971. Some quantitative feeding patterns exhibited by the copepod *Calanus. Oceanology* 11: 232–39
151. Porter, K. G. 1972. A method for the *in situ* study of zooplankton grazing effects on algal species composition and standing crop. *Limnol. Oceanogr.* 17:913–17
152. Porter, K. G. 1973. Selective grazing and differential digestion of algae by zooplankton. *Nature London* 244: 179–80
153. Poulet, S. A. 1973. Grazing of *Pseudocalanus minutus* on naturally occurring particulate matter. *Limnol. Oceanogr.* 18:564–73
154. Pratt, D. M., Campbell, D. A. 1956. Environmental factors affecting growth in *Venus mercenaria. Limnol. Oceanogr.* 1:2–17
155. Provasoli, L., Shiraishi, K., Lance, J. R. 1959. Nutritional idiosyncrasies of *Artemia* and *Tigriopus* in monoxenic culture. *Ann. N.Y. Acad. Sci.* 77: pt. 2. 250–61

156. Purchon, R. D. 1971. Digestion in filter feeding bivalves—a new concept. *Proc. Malacol. Soc. London* 39:253–62
157. Reeve, M. R. 1963. The filter feeding of *Artemia* I–III. *J. Exp. Biol.* 40:195–221
158. Richman, S. 1966. The effect of phytoplankton concentration on the feeding rate of *Diaptomus oregonensis. Verh. Int. Ver. Limnol.* 16:392–98
159. Richman, S., Rogers, J. N. 1969. The feeding of *Calanus helgolandicus* on synchronously growing populations of the marine diatom *Ditylum brightwellii. Limnol. Oceanogr.* 14:701–9
160. Rigler, F. H. 1961. The relation between concentration of food and feeding rate of *Daphnia magna* Straus. *Can. J. Zool.* 39:857–68
161. Riley, G. A., Stommel, H., Bumpus, D. F. 1949. Quantitative ecology of the plankton of the western North Atlantic. *Bull. Bingham Oceanogr. Coll.* 12: pt. 3, 1–169
162. Rotthauwe, H.-W. 1958. Untersuchungen zur Atmungsphysiologie und Osmoregulation bei *Mytilus edulis* mit einem kurzen Anhang über die Blutkonzentration von *Dreissena polymorpha* in Abhängigkeit vom Elektrolytgehalt des Aussenmediums. *Veröff. Inst. Meeresforsch. Bremerhaven Sonderb.* 5:143–59
163. Salánki, J. 1966. Comparative studies on the regulation of the periodic activity in marine lamellibranchs. *Comp. Biochem. Physiol.* 18:829–43
164. Salánki, J., Véró, M. 1969. Diurnal rhythm of activity in freshwater mussel *Anodonta cygnea* L. under natural conditions. *Ann. Biol. Tihany* 36:95–107
165. Schindler, J. E. 1971. Food quality and zooplankton nutrition. *J. Anim. Ecol.* 40:589–95
166. Schmidt, G. W. 1968. Zur Ausnützung des Nahrungsstickstoffs durch *Daphnia magna* Straus. Ein Beitrag zur Problematik der Sekundärproduktion. *Arch. Hydrobiol.* 65:142–86
167. Sheldon, R. W., Parsons, T. R. 1967. *A Practical Manual on the Use of the Coulter Counter in Marine Research.* Toronto: Coulter Electronics
168. Sleigh, M. A., Aiello, E. 1972. The movement of water by cilia. *Acta Protozool.* 11:265–77
169. Sorokin, Ju. I. 1965. On the trophic role of chemosynthesis and bacterial biosynthesis in water bodies. *Mem. 1st. Ital. Idrobiol.* 18:Suppl., 187–205
170. Strickland, J. D. 1972. Research on the marine planktonic food web at the Institute of Marine Resources: a review of the past seven years of work. *Oceanogr. Mar. Biol. Ann. Rev.* 10:349–414
171. Sushchenya, L. M. 1970. Food rations, metabolism and growth of crustaceans. See Ref. 99, 127–41
172. Takano, H. 1971. Breeding experiments of a marine littoral copepod *Tigriopus japonicus* Mori. *Bull. Tokai Reg. Fish Res. Lab.* 64:71–79
173. Tammes, P. M. L., Dral, A. D. G. 1955. Observations on the straining of suspensions by mussels. *Arch. Néer. Zool.* 11:87–112
174. Taniguchi, A. 1973. Phytoplankton-zooplankton relationships in the western Pacific Ocean and adjacent areas. *Mar. Biol.* 21:115–21
175. Tenore, K. R., Dunstan, W. M. 1973. Comparison of feeding and biodeposition of three bivalves at different food levels. *Mar. Biol.* 21:190–95
176. Tenore, K. R., Dunstan, W. M. 1973. Comparison of rates of feeding and biodeposition of the American oyster, *Crassostrea virginica* Gmelin, fed different species of phytoplankton. *J. Exp. Mar. Biol. Ecol.* 12:19–26
177. Tenore, K. R., Goldman, J. C., Clarner, J. P. 1973. The food chain dynamics of the oyster, clam, and mussel in an aquaculture food chain. *J. Exp. Mar. Biol. Ecol.* 12:157–65
178. Tezuka, Y. 1971. Feeding of *Daphnia* on planktonic bacteria. *Jap. J. Ecol.* 21:127–34
179. Theede, H. 1963. Experimentelle Untersuchungen über die Filtrationsleistung der Miesmuschel *Mytilus edulis. Kiel. Meeresforsch.* 19:20–41
180. Thompson, R. J., Bayne, B. L. 1972. Active metabolism associated with feeding in the mussel *Mytilus edulis* L. *J. Exp. Mar. Biol. Ecol.* 9:111–24
181. Trevallion, A., Ansell, A. D. 1967. Studies on *Tellina tenuis* Da Costa. II. Preliminary experiments in enriched sea water. *J. Exp. Mar. Biol. Ecol.* 1:257–70
182. Trevallion, A., Johnston, R., Finlayson, D. M., Nicoll, N. T. 1973. Studies in the bivalve, *Tellina tenuis* Da Costa. IV. Further experiments in enriched sea water. *J. Exp. Mar. Biol. Ecol.* 11:189–206
183. Ussing, H. H. 1938. The biology of some important plankton animals in the fjords of East Greenland. *Medd. Grønland* 100:1–108
184. Vahl, O. 1972. Efficiency of particle re-

tention in *Mytilus edulis* L. *Ophelia* 10:17–25

185. Vahl, O. 1972. Particle retention and relation between water transport and oxygen uptake in *Chlamys opercularis* (L.) (Bivalvia). *Ophelia* 10:67–74
186. Vahl, O. 1973. Porosity of the gill, oxygen consumption and pumping rate in *Cardium edule* (L.) (Bivalvia). *Ophelia* 10:109–118
187. Vahl, O. 1973. Pumping and oxygen consumption rates of *Mytilus edulis* L. of different sizes. *Ophelia* 12:45–52
188. Verduin, J. 1969. Hard clam pumping rates: Energy requirements. *Science* 166:1309–10
189. Wallengren, H. 1905. Zur Biologie der Muscheln. I. Die Wasserströmungen. *Lunds Univ. Årsskr. Afd. 2* 1(2):1–64
190. Walne, P. R. 1965. Observations on the influence of food supply and temperature on the feeding and growth of the larvae of *Ostrea edulis* L. *Fish. Invest. London Ser. II* 24(1):1–45
191. Walne, P. R. 1970. Studies on the food value of nineteen genera of algae to juvenile bivalves of the genera *Ostrea, Crassostrea, Mercenaria* and *Mytilus. Fish. Invest. London Ser. II* 26(5):1–62
192. Walne, P. R. 1970. Present problems in the culture of the larvae of *Ostrea edulis. Helgoländer Wiss. Meeresunters.* 20: 514–25
193. Walne, P. R. 1972. The influence of current speed, body size and water temperature on the filtration rate of five species of bivalves. *J. Mar. Biol. Assoc. U.K.* 52:345–74
194. Walne, P. R. 1973. Growth rates and nitrogen and carbohydrate contents of juvenile clams, *Saxidomus giganteus,* fed three species of algae. *J. Fish. Res. Bd. Can.* 30:1825–30
195. Ward, M. E., Aiello, E. 1973. Water pumping, particle filtration, and neutral red absorption in the bivalve mollusc *Mytilus edulis. Physiol. Zool.* 46:157–67
196. Weel, P. B. van 1961. Comparative physiology of digestion in molluscs. *Am. Zool.* 1:245–52
197. White, W. R. 1968. A method for measuring the pumping rate of mussels (*Mytilus edulis* (L.)). *Lab. Note Cent. Elect. Res. Lab.* RD/L/N 116/68
198. Widdows, J. 1973. Effects of temperature and food on the heart beat, ventilation rate and oxygen uptake of *Mytilus edulis. Mar. Biol.* 20:269–76
199. Widdows, J., Bayne, B. L. 1971. Temperature acclimation of *Mytilus edulis* with reference to its energy budget. *J. Mar. Biol. Assoc. U.K.* 51:827–43
200. Wilson, D. S. 1973. Food size selection among copepods. *Ecology* 54:909–14
201. Winter, J. E. 1969. Über den Einfluss der Nahrungskonzentration and anderer Faktoren auf Filtrierleistung und Nahrungsausnutzung der Muscheln *Arctica islandica* und *Modiolus modiolus. Mar. Biol.* 4:87–135
202. Winter, J. E. 1970. Filter feeding and food utilization in *Arctica islandica* L. and *Modiolus modiolus* L. at different food concentrations. See Ref. 99, 196–206
203. Winter, J. E. 1973. The filtration rate of *Mytilus edulis* and its dependence on algal concentrations, measured by a continuous automatic recording apparatus. *Mar. Biol.* 22:317–28
204. Yonge, C. M. 1926. Structure and physiology of the organs of feeding and digestion in *Ostrea edulis. J. Mar. Biol. Assoc. U.K.* 14:295–386
205. Yonge, C. M. 1960. *Oysters.* London: Collins
206. Zillioux, E. J., Wilson, D. F. 1966. Culture of a planktonic calanoid copepod through multiple generations. *Science* 151:996–98

Copyright 1975. All rights reserved

CIRCULATING GASTRIN[1] ❖1124

John H. Walsh
Department of Medicine, UCLA Center for Health Sciences,
Los Angeles, California 90024

This review is concerned with regulation of gastrin in the circulation. The subject was reviewed in part recently along with the other known gastrointestinal hormones (1). Insofar as possible an effort will be made to relate circulating concentrations of gastrin with gastric acid secretion. This field is changing rapidly at the moment because of the recognition of previously unsuspected heterogeneity of gastrin peptides in the circulation. Much of the recent information has been obtained by use of radioimmunoassay (RIA) combined with techniques that permit separation of different gastrin peptides on the basis of size and charge distinctions. Progress has been made in purification and structural analysis of different gastrin peptides. Some of these have been prepared in pure form in quantities sufficient to permit analysis of metabolic clearance and biological activity in the intact animal. Analytical studies of serum and of tissue extracts have allowed identification of the principal forms stored in tissues and found in the circulation. There has been some progress in identification of organs that remove gastrin from the circulation. Enzymatic mechanisms for degradation of gastrin peptides into biologically inactive fragments have been described. As usual there has been much study of the release of gastrin by different mechanisms and of autoregulation of gastrin release.

The general topic of regulation of gastric secretion of acid and pepsin is considered as it relates to gastrin. The complexities of the interrelationships between neural and humoral control of gastric secretion are discussed in detail elsewhere (46, 108). The spectrum of biological activities of gastrin and other gastrointestinal hormones also has been reviewed recently (47). Only the acid-stimulating properties of gastrin are considered in this review.

MOLECULAR HETEROGENEITY OF GASTRIN

Until 1970, it was assumed that gastrin in the circulation was identical to the pair of heptadecapeptide amides (sulfated and nonsulfated) isolated from gastric antral mucosa by Gregory & Tracy (40). Yalow & Berson then demonstrated that the

[1]This study was supported in part by US Public Health Service Grants 1 R01 AM 17294 and 1 P17 AM 17328.

major circulating form of gastrin detected by RIA in humans with hypergastrinemia was larger and less negatively charged than the heptadecapeptide form (115). Plasma gastrin immunoreactivity had slower electrophoretic mobility at pH 8.4 and eluted earlier from Sephadex G-50 columns than heptadecapeptide mixed with normal plasma. They named the new component BG or "basic gastrin" or "big gastrin" and heptadecapeptide-like gastrin was called H-LG. Further studies by the same workers (116) revealed that BG was the predominant form in plasma from patients with pernicious anemia (who have gastric achlorhydria but intact antral mucosa) and in patients with gastrinoma (Zollinger-Ellison syndrome). Only H-LG was found in the urine of a patient who had both BG and H-LG in the plasma. They demonstrated that trypsinization of BG converted it to a molecule with the properties of H-LG. Plasma concentrations of both BG and H-LG increased in patients with pernicious anemia who were fed a protein meal. In one patient with pernicious anemia, whose fasting plasma contained only BG, gastric acidification produced a fall in concentration of this fraction.

Berson & Yalow (10) also demonstrated immunoreactive materials with properties identical to those of plasma BG and H-LG in tissue extracts from mucosa of human antrum, duodenum, and jejunum, as well as in gastrinoma tissue. They showed that the proportion of BG increased from antrum to duodenum to jejunum, although the total extractable immunoreactive gastrin concentration decreased progressively with increasing distance from the antrum. The proportion of BG in antral extracts varied widely, from almost 0 to more than 60% (average about 20%). In duodenum about half was BG; in jejunum almost all of the extractable gastrin was in this form.

Gregory & Tracy succeeded in purifying from gastrinoma tissue a pair of gastrin peptides having the size and charge characteristics of BG (42, 43). BG peptides I and II were found to contain the same amino acids; apparently, like the heptadecapeptides, they differ only in the presence or absence of a sulfated tyrosine. Tryptic digestion of BG released a peptide with the amino acid composition of H-LG. By subtraction the remainder of the 34 amino acid BG molecule was found to have the following amino acid composition: Ala_1, Asp_1, Glx_2, Gly_2, His_1, Leu_2, Lys_2, Pro_3, Ser_2, Val_1. Two similar BG peptides isolated from hog antral mucosa had amino acid composition similar to but not identical with the human BG peptides. It was concluded that human BG contains the heptadecapeptide amide as a C-terminal sequence linked to the remainder of the molecule by a lysylglutaminyl peptide bond. The calculated molecular weights of the larger gastrins are around 3900. Gastric physiologists and gastrin immunoassayists are eagerly awaiting the completion of amino acid sequencing and synthesis of the N-terminal peptide of this larger gastrin molecule and the availability of synthetic BG.

Elucidation of the amino acid composition of BG gives us now a pair of gastrins with 17 amino acids and another pair with 34 amino acids. During the remainder of this review these gastrins are abbreviated G-17 and G-34 with designations I and II for nonsulfated and sulfated varieties respectively.

Other immunoreactive gastrin molecules now have been reported in the circulation. Yalow & Berson (118) found that a minor component of immunoreactive gastrin in plasma of patients with gastrinoma eluted in the void volume of Sephadex G-50 columns and thus appeared to have considerably higher molecular weight than G-34. This material was named "big-big gastrin" (BBG). BBG comprised a major fraction of total plasma gastrin immunoreactivity in fasting samples obtained from man, dog, and hog (119). It was the only form identified in plasma from one patient with previous antral resection, suggesting an extragastric source for BBG, possibly intestine. No change in plasma BBG was observed after feeding. It was not possible to absorb BBG completely onto charcoal or onto an anion exchange resin that completely removes G-17 and G-34 from plasma. The residual BBG fraction may account for the difficulty in or impossibility of preparing "gastrin-free plasma" by absorption and dialysis of normal plasma. Such gastrin-free plasma is desirable for preparation of RIA standards in order to prove that inhibition curves are identical in plasma and in the diluent used for the assay. Although BBG comprised a major fraction of immunoreactive gastrin in fasting plasma of normal subjects, it accounted for less than 2% of immunoreactivity in patients with gastrinoma.

The chemical nature of BBG remains undetermined. Trypsinization of material with the properties of BBG obtained from gastrinoma tissue did not result in apparent complete conversion to G-17 (119), but gave a heterogeneous pattern of immunoreactivity that eluted between the void volume and G-17 area on Sephadex G-50 chromatography. BBG may be some type of gastrin that is tightly bound to a larger protein. Little progress is likely in chemical analysis of BBG until an abundant source can be found.

Other workers have found even more evidence for molecular heterogeneity of immunoreactive gastrin. Rehfeld analyzed, by gel filtration, postprandial serum from normal subjects and sera from patients with pernicious anemia, and identified three immunoreactive components (80). Component I eluted between the void volume and the G-34 region, was present in 19 of 22 sera, and comprised 18% of total serum gastrin immunoreactivity. Component II, corresponding in position to G-34, comprised 73%, and component III, corresponding to G-17, made up an average of 9% but was identified in only half the sera studied. Incubation with trypsin converted both components I and II to a molecule with the elution pattern of G-17. In a subsequent study, sera from 15 patients with gastrinoma were subjected to gel filtration on Sephadex G-50 superfine columns (82). The average concentrations of components I, II, and III were 10, 58, and 27% of total immunoreactivity. An additional peak, component IV, eluted immediately before the salt peak and constituted approximately 5–6% of immunoreactive material. It was noted that Gregory had found an additional small component in gastrinoma extracts and had shown it to consist of the C-terminal tridecapeptide amide of G-17 in sulfated and nonsulfated forms (43). Since the behavior of component IV is identical with the C-terminal tridecapeptide amides of G-17, it is called G-13 hereafter in this review. It is also identical with "minigastrin." Subsequently Rehfeld & Stadil have reported that components II, III, and IV can be resolved by anion exchange resins into double peaks corresponding to sulfated and nonsulfated counterparts, while component I always behaves as a single peak (83). The molecular forms identified by use of antibodies with C-terminal specificity are illustrated in Figure 1.

In our laboratory we recently used different antibodies with selective specificity for the C-terminal and N-terminal regions of G-17 to characterize serum gastrin from patients with gastrinoma (31). Through use of an antibody with C-terminal specificity, the principal circulating forms of gastrin were identified as G-34 and G-17; minor and inconsistent peaks corresponding to BBG, component I, and G-13 also occurred. The antibody with N-terminal specificity did not detect G-34, since the N-terminal region of G-17 is not exposed in this molecule. G-17 was detected in equivalent amounts with the two antibodies. An additional major peak was found and tentatively identified by its chromatographic properties as the 1–13 amino terminal tridecapeptide of G-17. The 1–13 fragment of gastrin has been identified in hog antrum by Gregory (43). We called this fragment NT-G-17 to signify that it is an N-terminal fragment of G-17. NT-G-17 comprised a major fraction of fasting total serum immunoreactive gastrin in gastrinoma patients tested with this antiserum. The concentration of NT-G-17 in serum increased rapidly along with that of G-34 and G-17 when gastrin release was stimulated in gastrinoma patients

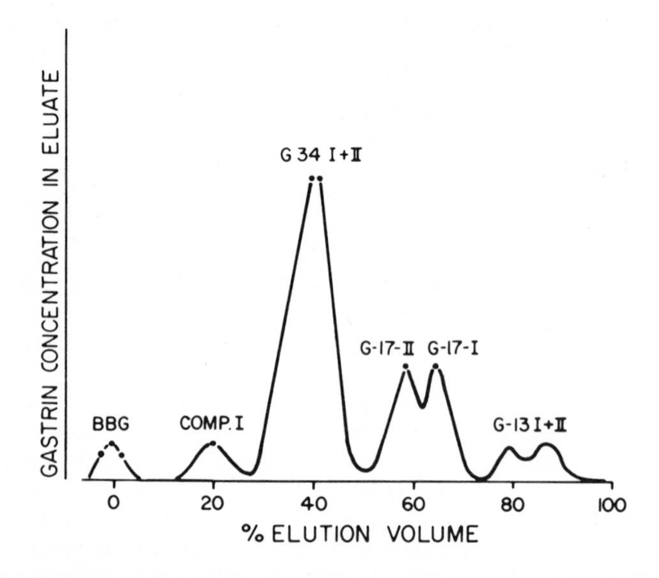

Figure 1 Idealized elution diagram for Sephadex G-50 superfine gel filtration of serum gastrin components. Concentration of gastrin in eluates determined by radioimmunoassay using antibody with specificity for C-terminal region of the gastrin molecule. Elution volume expressed as percent between void volume (albumin marker) and salt peak. BBG = "big-big gastrin" of Yalow & Berson; Comp-I = Component I of Rehfeld; G-34 I and II = nonsulfated and sulfated "big gastrin"; G-17 I and II = nonsulfated and sulfated heptadecapeptide gastrins; G-13 I and II = nonsulfated and sulfated C-terminal tridecapeptides of G-17 or "minigastrins."

by intravenous injection of secretin. It was not generated by incubation of G-17 or G-34 in serum. NT-G-17 is unlikely to have any major effect on gastric secretion because it lacks the biologically active C-terminal region of G-17. Its presence in serum may indicate the presence of its counterpart, the C-terminal tetrapeptide amide, which does have biological activity. None of the antisera presently available for gastrin RIA are inhibited sufficiently by the tetrapeptide to make likely the identification of this molecule in serum, even if it circulates in high concentrations.

The array of molecular variants of gastrin now identified in the serum makes simple analysis of total gastrin immunoreactivity relatively unrewarding unless further characterization is performed. However, the only forms found in significant amounts which are known to have biological activity are G-34 and G-17. Both of these molecules exist as sulfated and nonsulfated pairs; sulfation does not appear to influence biological activity. Thus efforts undoubtedly will be made to measure G-34 and G-17 specifically. Hopes that this could be done with antibodies with N-terminal specificity for G-17 (71) have been thwarted by the finding of large amounts of N-terminal gastrin fragment in serum. Antibodies will probably be developed against the N-terminal portion of G-34, but before these can be used for specific measurement of circulating G-34 it will be necessary to show that there are no circulating N-terminal G-34 fragments that cross-react in the assay system. At present the only satisfactory methods for determining concentrations of individual components of gastrin in the circulation are fractionation by molecular sieving, ion exchange chromatography, or starch gel electrophoresis.

GASTRIN IN TISSUES

Nilsson et al performed extensive analysis of immunoreactive gastrin extractable from human, dog, cat, and hog tissues (76). No gastrin was found in liver, kidney, heart, and lung (less than 50 pg/g tissue). Highest gastrin concentrations were found in the antral mucosa of all species. A concentration gradient of gastrin was found in the intestines of all species, with the highest concentrations occurring in the mucosa of the proximal duodenum. Gastrin immunoreactivity also was detected in the jejunum and ileum of all four species. The immunoreactive jejunal material was shown to be distinct from cholecystokinin. The amounts of gastrin extracted from the whole duodenum of man, dog, cat, and hog were respectively 97, 1.5, 1.9, and 0.1% of those found in the antrum. The corresponding values in the remaining small intestine of the four species were 0.7, 1.4, 1.2, and 0.1%. Thus man has notably more duodenal gastrin than other species. Evidence has been obtained that duodenal gastrin can be released by food in man (95). The extra-antral portions of the stomach contained less than 1–4% of the immunoreactivity present in the antrum. Minute concentrations of immunoreactive material were found in buccal mucosa, tongue, and esophagus. Immunoreactive gastrin was obtained in human pancreatic extracts in low concentrations (400 pg/g tissue), but could not be identified with certainty in other species.

Zelenkova & Gregor have studied the development of antral gastrin activity in newborn rats by bioassay methods (120). No gastrin activity could be found during the first 21 days of life while the animals were fed exclusively on mother's milk. Gastrin activity appeared during the weaning period when solid foods were eaten. Despite the absence of extractable gastrin, hydrochloric acid was secreted immediately after birth and during the nursing period. Similar results recently have been obtained by Lichtenberger et al who used RIA to measure antral gastrin concentrations (63). They found that gastrin was present at birth, increased modestly from less than 1 to about 3 $\mu g/g$ mucosa during suckling then increased dramatically to between 15 and 20 $\mu g/g$ on the 21st day, at the time of weaning. They postulated that this rapid increase in antral gastrin contributed to major developmental changes in gastrointestinal function occurring approximately at the same time. It was demonstrated previously that pentagastrin has trophic effects on both gastric and duodenal mucosa. McGuigan originally showed by immunohistologic techniques that gastrin is localized in special endocrine cells (G cells) situated in the midportion of the pyloric glands (65, 69); this has been confirmed by many others. It is beyond the scope of this review to discuss whether special staining procedures are capable of revealing G cells by nonimmunologic light or electron microscopy (8, 91). Electron micrographs of G cells have shown a typical granule, described as 150–200 nm in diameter with moderate electron density (45). Solcia also reported that G cells possess a microvillous luminal neck that communicates with the lumen of the pyloric gland (90). It would appear that this luminal structure is likely to contain receptors both for chemical substances that cause gastrin release when present in the stomach and for hydrogen ions that inhibit gastrin release. Such receptors have not yet been demonstrated directly.

The question of whether gastrin is present in the pancreas has not been resolved. Some investigators have been able to extract small amounts of immunoreactive gastrin from normal pancreas, while others have not. Grieder & McGuigan reported identification of a small number of cells that reacted directly with fluorescenated antibody to synthetic human gastrin (44), while Creutzfeldt et al were unable to observe gastrin immunofluorescence in normal human pancreas (18). On the other hand, gastrinomas most often arise in pancreas. In those instances in which gastrinoma cells are sufficiently differentiated to be classified, their electron-microscopic characteristics are quite similar to those of antral G cells. Gastrinoma cells have been shown to contain gastrin by direct biochemical analysis of tumor extracts (41), as well as by extraction of immunoreactive gastrin and by immunofluorescence of tumor cells.

STRUCTURE-FUNCTION RELATIONSHIPS OF GASTRIN PEPTIDES

The structures of heptadecapeptide gastrins of man, hog, cat, dog, cow, and sheep are known (58). There are minor amino acid differences, but all species share the same C-terminal heptapeptide amide sequence. Morley examined a large number of synthetic analogs of the C-terminal region and found that the C-terminal tetrapeptide amide possessed all the biological actions of the G-17 molecule; he considered this portion to be the minimal fragment with significant biological activity (75). He also found that amino acid substitutions in this tetrapeptide (Trp-Met-Asp-Phe-NH_2) were tolerated in most positions, but that substitutions by natural amino acid residues in the aspartic acid position always led to inactivity. He concluded that the other residues were binding sites while the Asp residue contained the functional site.

Recently Trout & Grossman (103) reported that substitution of alanine for aspartic acid in the pentultimate position of the C-terminal octapeptide of cholecystokinin, which has a C-terminal pentapeptide sequence identical with that of gastrin, and which possesses gastrin-like activity, did not eliminate gastric acid-stimulating activity. No acid-stimulating activity could be demonstrated in the analog of gastrin tetrapeptide in which alanine was substituted for aspartic acid. They concluded that either aspartic acid or a sulfated tyrosine group (present in the octapeptide) was necessary for acid stimulation, but that the aspartyl residue was not an absolute requirement for biological activity. However, the potency of the alanyl-substituted octapeptide was less than 1% of the aspartyl peptide.

In another study, desulfation of caerulein, a peptide very similar to the octapeptide of cholecystokinin, reduced acid-stimulating potency in dogs approximately 6-fold (56). Apparently the position of the sulfated tyrosyl residue is of critical importance. In gastrin II peptides the sulfated tyrosyl residue is one position closer to the C-terminus than in the caerulein and cholecystokinin peptides. The acid-stimulating potency of gastrin II does not differ from that of nonsulfated gastrin I.

Lin has reported that it is not necessary for the whole C-terminal tetrapeptide amide sequence of gastrin to be present for acid-stimulating activity (64). He found that the C-terminal tripeptide amide, Met-Asp-Phe-NH_2, stimulated acid secretion, pancreatic secretion, pyloric and duodenal motility, and gallbladder contraction in the dog. The potency of this peptide was less than 1/1000th that of the tetrapeptide amide. Debas & Grossman recently reported that the tripeptide amides Leu-Asp-Phe-NH_2 and Nle-Asp-Phe-NH_2 also possess acid-stimulating activity (24).

The above studies illustrate that the determinants for biological activity are located in the carboxyl-terminal region of gastrin peptides. However, they indicate neither the relationship between length of the molecule and biological activity nor the relationship between circulating gastrin concentrations and biological activity. Studies along these lines have recently been made possible by development of RIA techniques for accurate measurement of physiological concentrations of circulating gastrin, by purification of natural gastrins from antral and gastrinoma tissue extracts, and by synthesis of a number of structural analogs of G-17.

We recently completed a comparison of the acid-stimulating properties of G-34 I and II, G-17 I and II, and G-13 I and II in dogs (28, 111). Maximal rates of acid secretion in the dog produced by G-17, G-34, and G-13 were similar. No differences in potency or in maximal effect were found between sulfated and nonsulfated forms of any of these gastrins. Because of changes in molar concentration of circulating immunoreactive gastrins, it was necessary to increase serum gastrin five times higher with G-34 than with G-17 to produce a given rate of acid secretion. The potency ratios of circulating gastrins were 1.0:0.5:0.2 for G-17, G-13, and G-34 respectively. G-13 and G-17 have approximately equal metabolic clearance rates, so differences in endogenous potency were reflected in responses to the exogenous dose. However, the clearance rate of G-17 was approximately six times that of G-34, so equimolar exogenous doses of G-34 actually produced slightly higher acid secretion rates than G-17 produced. Thus the potency ratios of exogenous gastrins were 1.0:0.5:1.2 for G-17, G-13, and G-34 respectively. The above studies indicate that if increases in serum gastrin are solely responsible for stimulation of acid secretion in dogs, such responses could be predicted accurately only if the molecular composition responsible for the increase were known.

Gastrin appears to be the sole significant driving force for stimulation of acid secretion only in the vagally denervated antral pouch dog and in people with gastrin-secreting tumors. Vagal and other reflex nervous mechanisms, parietal cell responsiveness, and other circulating agents such as enterogastrones, all play major roles in control of gastric secretion after a meal (46). The measurement of total immunoreactive gastrin cannot be expected to reveal much about gastric secretion in an individual without a good bit of other knowledge. One exception to this rule is the patient with severe peptic ulcer disease and gastric acid hypersecretion who has serum gastrin immunoreactivity 20 or 50 times normal; the hypersecretion can be assumed to be based on hypergastrinemia probably due to gastrinoma.

ANTIBODY SPECIFICITY, SPECIES DIFFERENCES, AND BIOLOGICALLY INACTIVE DERIVATIVES OF GASTRIN

Since gastrins in the circulation are a relatively heterogeneous mixture of different molecular sizes, values obtained for total serum gastrin concentration depend in large part on the relative inhibitory potencies of the various molecular forms of gastrin on the particular antibody used in the RIA system. Ideally, total immunoreactive gastrin should be measured by an antibody with which equimolar amounts of all forms of gastrin containing the biologically active C-terminal region produce equal degrees of inhibition of binding between labeled gastrin and antigastrin. The ideal antibody should not detect other related molecules such as cholecystokinin, or be influenced by nonspecific factors such as salt or protein concentration. Some of the gastrins found in the circulation have been prepared in pure form suitable for preparation of RIA standards [G-34 I and II, G-17 I and II, G-13 I and II (28, 111)], while others have not been suitably purified (BBG and component I). Few antibodies have been completely characterized with a battery of these standards. Thus laboratories using different antibodies may obtain different results for total immunoreactive gastrin on identical serum specimens if their antibodies differ in patterns of specificity. At the present time true quantification of serum gastrin is possible only after prior separation into component forms, identified by their characteristic elution patterns, combined with assays in which separate standards are used for each component. For example, after separation of a serum sample from a patient with gastrinoma on Sephadex G-50 columns, peaks may be obtained in the characteristic areas in which G-34, G-17, and G-13 are known to elute (Figure 1). Pure G-34, G-17, and G-13 then can be used to prepare separate standard curves from which molar concentrations of gastrin present in each peak can be determined.

Concentrations of BBG and component I must be expressed as molar equivalents of one of the other standards, since pure standards are not available for these materials. Even more difficulty would be expected if the antibody had specificity for either sulfated or nonsulfated gastrins. Fortunately, most antibodies that have been tested for such specificity have reacted equally well with the sulfated and nonsulfated varieties.

The above comments should not be interpreted to mean that studies of total immunoreactive gastrin are not fruitful. However, it is apparent that values obtained should be interpreted cautiously. The limited studies that have been done to date on fractionation of gastrin components in normal serum indicate that changes measured in serum total immunoreactive gastrin are due principally to changes in G-34 and G-17 (116, 119). These include stimulation with food in normal and pernicious anemia patients and inhibition by intragastric acidification in achlorhydric hypergastrinemic patients. Since G-17 and G-34 may increase or decrease in varying proportions, it is important to know whether variations in the ratio of G-17 to G-34 might be of biological importance. Such determinations can be made by comparison of molar increments in serum gastrin concentrations produced by infusions of pure solutions of these gastrins with changes in rates of acid secretion. If basal gastrin concentrations are not altered by such infusions, molar increments in serum gastrin can be determined by use of the infused gastrin as the RIA standard and by subtraction of basal gastrin.

Measurement of serum gastrin immunoreactivity in different species may be complicated by antibody specificity for substitutions in the glutamic acid residues in positions 8 and 10 of G-17, such as exist in dog, cat, sheep, and cow. As a general rule, antibodies prepared in guinea pigs by immunization with crude gastrin extracts have shown higher affinity for gastrins from species whose gastrins were not substituted in these positions, i.e. human and porcine (84, 112, 117). Use of human or porcine standards when gastrins from these species are measured leads to underestimation of circulating gastrin concentrations. Antibodies prepared in rabbits by use of gastrin conjugated to albumin by carbodiimide tend to have similar immunoreactivity with gastrins from all these species. A likely explanation is that conjugation probably occurs through one of the five consecutive glutamic acid residues, rendering this portion of the molecule unavailable for immunologic stimulation. Such differences in specificity appear to be responsible for the observation that sheep gastrin had lower immunoreactivity than human or porcine gastrin as determined by RIA with a guinea pig antibody, but these gastrins were about equally potent as stimulants of acid secretion in the dog (112).

Cholecystokinin (CCK) is not a very potent stimulant of acid secretion in man or dog. Gastrin antibodies tend to be inhibited very poorly by CCK (54, 66, 81, 114), so that concentrations of this hormone are not reflected in total serum gastrin immunoreactivity. This fact has some advantage in the measurement of gastrin. If CCK acts as a circulating inhibitor of acid secretion under some circumstances, its contribution along with secretin and other circulating enterogastrones will have to be determined by separate specific RIA's for these compounds.

Another compound that would not be detected in the ordinary gastrin RIA is gastrin tetrapeptide amide or tetragastrin. Recently evidence has accumulated that the N-terminal 1–13 fragment of gastrin circulates in high concentrations in patients with gastrinoma (31). This material is devoid of acid-stimulating activity. However, the remaining portion of the G-17 molecule after the 1–13 fragment has been split off is tetragastrin, which has considerable acid-stimulating potency. It has not been detected in the serum, but its low order of cross-reactivity with gastrin antibodies (0.1 to 0.001%) make its detection extremely difficult.

Deamidation of the C-terminal amide group of G-17 removes at least 99% of its acid-stimulating activity (71). This compound has not been identified in the circulation, but might not show up if most antibodies resemble McGuigan's and have very low affinity for the deamidated gastrin. It would be detected by antibodies with N-terminal specificity of the type described by Dockray (31).

METABOLIC CLEARANCE AND DISAPPEARANCE HALF-TIMES OF GASTRINS

The predominant molecular form of gastrin extractable from antral mucosa and from most gastrinomas is G-17. The major form identified of the circulation of hypergastrinemic and stimulated normal subjects has been G-34. BBG is a major fraction of normal fasting plasma gastrin but does not appear to be secreted in response to a meal (119). The discrepancy between apparent tissue concentrations and circulating concentrations could reflect failure to extract all forms with equal efficiency, or it could indicate that tissue concentrations do not reflect the rate at which different forms of gastrin are secreted. For example, G-17 may be the form in which gastrin is stored in granules, while G-34 may be synthesized and released without significant conversion into a storage form. We have obtained some evidence that G-17 is available for immediate release in patients with gastrinoma by demonstrating that rapid injection of secretin, a hormone known to release gastrin from tumors, leads to a peak in serum G-17 within 5 min and a later and more prolonged G-34 peak (31). Similarly, Yalow & Berson found in achlorhydric subjects that the early peak in plasma gastrin obtained after feeding was comprised mainly of G-17. There is no evidence to support inefficient extraction of G-34 from tissues, since re-extraction of tissue extracts reportedly yields the same G-17/G-34 ratios obtained in the original extraction (10).

The other major possibility in accounting for relatively higher concentrations of G-34 in blood than in tissue is a slower rate of metabolism of this form of gastrin. In the dog we found that the metabolic clearance rates (MCR) for G-17 I and II were approximately six times those for G-34 I and II [54 vs 9 ml kg^{-1} min^{-1} (111)]. MCR for G-13 was approximately the same as for G-17 (28). If G-17 and G-34 release into the circulation is proportional to relative abundance in antral mucosa, the differences in MCR could account only partially for the predominance of G-34 in the circulation. In general, extractable G-34 has represented 10% or less of total tissue gastrin, while G-34 has been the major form of circulating gastrin. Thus both factors probably are operative: slower metabolism of G-34 and higher relative release of G-34 from tissues.

There are several reported studies on half-life and metabolic clearance of G-17 in dog and man in which synthetic human G-17 I (SHG I) was infused and serum gastrin determined by RIA. Reeder et al found a double exponential decay curve with fast and slow components producing calculated half-lives of 1.4 and 6.3 and an average model half-life of 2.1 min (79). McGuigan et al calculated a half-life from measured increases in steady state gastrin during infusion of SHG I at different rates by assigning estimated spaces of distribution of 19.2% and 28.5%; they obtained half-life values of 4.2 and 6.3 min (70). Schrumpf & Semb obtained a single exponential decay curve with a half-life of 4.2 min in the dog (86). Our own values of G-17 I and II in the dog have been approximately 3 min (111). In similar studies we found that the half-lives of G-34 I and II in the dog were 15–16 min (111). The half-life of G-13 was similar to that of G-17 (28). Straus & Yalow measured rates of degradation of different molecular forms of gastrin following pulse injections of labeled and unlabeled peptides (97). They obtained disappearance half-times of approximately 3, 9, and 90 min for G-17, G-34, and BBG respectively. The half-times of labeled G-17 were slightly longer than for unlabeled G-17 I and II (4–5 min vs 3 min). Labeled N-terminal tridecapeptide of G-17 had a half-time of 3 min, while labeled C-terminal tridecapeptide of G-17 had a half-time of 5 min.

Schrumpf et al found that the disappearance curve in man, unlike that obtained in dog, was at least biexponential (87). They calculated disappearance half-times of 7.5 and 12.6 min for SHG I in man. The differences in MCR between dog and man were even greater, 73 vs 9 ml kg^{-1} min^{-1}, reflected by much higher increments in serum gastrin obtained in man. The reason for the discrepancy between the 2:1 ratio of half-lives and the 8:1 ratio of MCR's is not clear, although it can be explained away superficially by assuming a fourfold difference in apparent space of distribution.

SITES AND MECHANISMS OF GASTRIN CATABOLISM

It is apparent from the short half-life and high rate of metabolic clearance that some of the body organs must have the capacity to remove G-17 rapidly from the circulation. Earlier biological studies indicated that the liver was not a likely site for removal of G-17 since portal and systemic infusions of gastrin produced similar acid secretory responses in the dog (39). On the other hand, pentagastrin and tetragastrin are removed rapidly by passage through the liver (98). Debas & Grossman have reported in preliminary form an analysis of the relationship between chain length of gastrin peptides and hepatic inactivation (25). They used dogs with complete portocaval transposition in which peptides could be infused into the liver through a catheter placed into a hind leg vein, while introduction through a front leg vein permitted infusion into the systemic circulation. Pentagastrin and the C-terminal heptapeptide of gastrin were more than 90% inactivated by passage through the liver, while the C-terminal decapeptide, the C-terminal tridecapeptide, and G-17 were progressively less inactivated. Secretin and CCK were not significantly affected by liver passage.

Thompson and co-workers earlier had found a 40% diminution in Heidenhain pouch acid secretion in dogs when SHG-I was infused through the portal vein rather than the inferior vena cava (100). They also determined posthepatic recoveries of gastrin, pentagastrin, and histamine in the left hepatic vein by use of inulin as a dilution marker. The loss of gastrin (SHG-I) across the liver, measured by RIA and corrected with the inulin marker, was 46%. Another group found that portal vein gastrin was 1.7 times higher than that in hepatic vein blood obtained simultaneously in the dog during antral stimulation by acetylcholine (67). In this study it was appreciated that significant dilution of hepatic vein blood by hepatic artery flow accounted for a major portion of this apparent dilution. Beger and co-workers found significantly less acid secretion in man when porcine G-17 II was administered through a catheter in the portal vein as compared with peripheral infusion (7).

The conclusion to be drawn from these and other studies on hepatic clearance of gastrin peptides is that inactivation of G-17 probably occurs to a minor extent, whereas tetragastrin is almost competely inactivated by liver passage. There is little direct information on the effect of hepatic transit on G-34. A major difference between G-17 and G-34 seems unlikely in view of the report of Dencker and co-workers that the relative concentrations of G-17 and G-34 were very similar in portal and peripheral serum (29).

The mechanisms for hepatic inactivation of tetragastrin and pentagastrin have been investigated in vitro and in vivo. Laster & Walsh demonstrated that homogenates of rat liver catalyzed hydrolysis of the C-terminal amide group from acylated tetrapeptide amide (61). This hydrolysis had the characteristics of an enzymatic reaction with a pH optimum of approximately 6.7. This amidase activity was identified in liver, small intestine mucosa, and stomach mucosa in rat, hamster, cat, and dog (110). Seelig studied in detail the amidase activity in rat liver homogenates, and prepared a partially purified enzyme preparation by gel filtration of the soluble supernatant obtained after 104,000 × g centrifugation of crude homogenates (88). This material demonstrated amidase activity when either pentagastrin or G-17 II was utilized as substrate. Significant degradation of G-17 was produced by incubation of G-17 with human serum.

Stagg and co-workers used ^{14}C labeled pentagastrin in dogs to demonstrate uptake of this compound by the liver and excretion of approximately 60% of the administered dose in the bile (94). Only one third of the labeled material recovered in the bile was biologically active, suggesting that a significant fraction of the pentagastrin had been inactivated by passage through liver cells or in the bile. Varro and co-workers performed similar studies in rats with ^{14}C labeled acylated C-terminal pentapeptide of gastrin and used chromatographic methods to identify both the amide and the free acid in the bile (106). The ratio of amide to free acid was 5:1, indicating that excretion was the most important mechanism for hepatic elimination of this peptide, although deamidation also occurred. Similar studies have not been performed with G-17 and it is not known whether this peptide is excreted in the bile in significant amounts.

Gastric acid hypersecretion occurs after portocaval anastamosis in dogs. The possibility that this hypersecretion might be due to a defect in gastrin inactivation was not supported by the finding that fasting and postprandial gastrin concentrations were diminished after this operation (102).

Other workers have obtained evidence that a gastric secretagogue normally inactivated by the liver is released by the presence of food in the jejunum (77). In dogs with normal portal circulation the presence of food in the jejunum contributed significantly to postprandial acid secretion from innervated fundic pouches in dogs (16). Slaff has reported in preliminary form that infusion of liver extract into the small intestine of antrectomized dogs augments maximal Heidenhain pouch response to exogenous pentagastrin without causing an increase in serum immunoreactive gastrin (89). In appears likely that some agent other than gastrin is released by food from intestinal mucosa and that this material potentiates the actions of gastrin. These observations provide an explanation for the previously described phenomenon that maximal Heidenhain pouch response to a meal is considerably higher than the maximal response achieved with exogenous gastrin (107).

The kidney appears to be a major site of gastrin inactivation. Booth and co-workers demonstrated renal extraction of gastrin by measuring differences in gastrin concentration in renal artery and vein of dogs during antral perfusion with acetylcholine (15). The same group demonstrated that bilateral nephrectomy in dogs increased the half-life and decreased the metabolic clearance rate approximately twofold as measured by RIA during and after intravenous infusion of G-17 (17). In rats, nephrectomy produced a marked increase in serum gastrin activity. Bilateral ureteral ligation produced no significant increase in serum gastrin, although the degree of azotemia produced was equivalent to that following nephrectomy (21). This study provided evidence that the kidney has a role in degradation of endogenous gastrin independent of urinary excretion. Thompson and co-workers demonstrated that less than 1% of gastrin extracted by the kidney could be detected in the urine (102). Enzymatic mechanisms responsible for renal inactivation of gastrin have not been identified with certainty. An activity that causes cleavage of C-terminal glycinamide from vasopressin and oxytocin has been identified in isolated perfused rat kidney (113). We found enzymatic activity in rat kidney homogenates that appeared to split off the C-terminal dipeptide amide from acylated gastrin tetrapeptide amide (110).

Evidence also has been obtained demonstrating that the small bowel may play an important role in gastrin metabolism. Small bowel mucosa contains enzymes capable of hydrolyzing the C-terminal amide and internal peptide bonds in acylated tetrapeptide amide (110). Degradation of G-17 by intestinal mucosal extracts has been shown (88). Temperley et al found that infusion of G-17 into mesenteric artery of dogs resulted in smaller acid secretory responses than when the peptide was infused in the external jugular vein (98). Becker and co-workers demonstrated significantly higher immunoassayable gastrin in the abdominal aorta than in a mesenteric vein in dogs during endogenous stimulation of gastrin release (4). Marked hypergastrinemia was found in 4 patients with extensive small bowel resections both in the fasting state and after meals (96). The predominant form of gastrin identified in the plasma of these subjects was G-34. The time course of appearance and disappearance of plasma gastrin did not support a role of decreased catabolism, but suggested increased release of gastrin in these patients.

Isolated perfused lung preparations had no effect on plasma gastrin, as measured by RIA, during infusion of G-17 (30). However, when interstitial pulmonary edema was produced, transudation of gastrin into the edema fluid could be demonstrated. The same investigators confirmed renal uptake of gastrin in isolated kidney perfusions. Other organs could contribute to gastrin inactivation, but there have been no convincing demonstrations of gastrin uptake by other tissues.

BASAL GASTRIN CONCENTRATIONS

As a general rule, measurement of basal gastrin concentration produces little information about the rate of basal acid secretion. Markedly increased serum gastrin concentrations in man usually are associated with one of two conditions: 1. atrophic gastritis of the acid-secreting portion of the stomach that spares the antrum and is associated with achlorhydria and hyperplasia of the G cells, or 2. marked gastric acid hypersecretion due to prolonged stimulation of the gastric mucosa by gastrin secreted from a gastrinoma, usually originating in the pancreas (Zollinger-Ellison syndrome) (11). Most of the information available on this subject has been obtained in man. When patients with gastrinoma have been omitted from consideration, the only correlation between serum gastrin and acid secretion has been a negative one due to inclusion of subjects with very low rates of acid secretion and hypergastrinemia. In subjects who are normal secretors of acid, there is little or no correlation between basal gastrin and rate of basal acid secretion (38, 60, 105). This is not surprising in view of the heterogeneity of circulating gastrin molecules and the complex interrelationship between nervous and humoral factors that control gastric secretion.

There are at least two published investigations of circadian rhythm of gastrin in subjects allowed to eat four meals during a 24 hr period. Ganguli & Forrester reported that mean serum gastrin concentrations were approximately 10% above the daily mean at midnight and 10% below the mean at 4:00 A.M. (37). Feurle and co-workers measured serum gastrin concentrations hourly in normal subjects and in patients with peptic ulcer disease (35). In normal subjects they found peaks after each meal, with highest values obtained in mid-afternoon, and a gradual decline after 8:00 P.M. to lowest values in the early morning before breakfast.

GASTRIN RELEASE BY FOOD AND OTHER LOCAL AGENTS

Almost every report of successful development of a gastrin RIA has included a demonstration that a protein meal is an effective method for increasing serum gastrin concentrations (12, 68). Until recently there have been no studies of the relationship between acid secretion stimulated by a meal and gastrin release in man. A method has been developed by which the rate of net gastric acid secretion in human subjects fed a normal meal can be measured by use of sodium bicarbonate infusion to control intragastric pH (36). The rate of bicarbonate infusion required to maintain pH constant is equal to the rate of acid secretion. This method was used to demonstrate that a steak meal induced peak rates of acid secretion similar to peak rates produced by subcutaneous histamine, confirming the earlier observations of Rune based on calculation of base excess in arterial blood during the first hour after a meal (85). In normal and ulcer subjects there was poor correlation between rates of acid secretion and changes in serum gastrin. In this study, as in several other published reports (72, 109), patients with peptic ulcer disease showed moderately higher increments in serum gastrin following a standard test meal.

Although amino acids cause release of gastrin, responses obtained with amino acid solutions are less than those obtained with a protein meal. There has been a question also of the mechanism by which whole protein in food, which presumably contains few small peptides and free amino acids, can cause prompt increases in serum gastrin after ingestion. One clue may have been provided in a recent report that large polypeptides were effective releasers of gastrin (22). It was found that bovine serum albumin was ineffective as a gastrin releaser until it was partially digested with pepsin, but that dialysis of the pepsinized albumin did not remove the gastrin releasing ability. Similarly, dialyzed liver extract retained its ability to release gastrin. In dogs with antral pouches, distension also is a potent mechanism for release of gastrin. All experiments done in dogs with this preparation must include control periods performed under identical conditions of distension but in the absence of chemical gastrin releasers. Evidence for release of gastrin by large peptides previously had been obtained by Elwin, who demonstrated some activity in the fraction that eluted with largest molecular weight when a protein hydrolysate had been subjected to gel filtration on Sephadex G-25 columns (32).

Intravenous calcium exerts a mild stimulatory effect on serum gastrin concentrations, dependent on an increase in serum calcium concentrations (1). This effect is obtained in man and has been shown in cats (2), but never has been obtained in dogs. Oral calcium carbonate stimulates acid secretion in man. We found that single oral doses of 2 g calcium carbonate produced significant increases in serum gastrin and in acid secretion without measurable changes in serum calcium concentration (62). Equal doses of sodium bicarbonate failed to stimulate acid secretion or to increase serum gastrin. It was concluded that gastrin release was produced by a local effect on gastric or duodenal mucosa. Grossman found that removal of calcium from milk decreases its acid-stimulating effect (48).

Csendes & Grossman reported that the D- and L-isomers of serine and alanine were equally effective as releasers of gastrin (19). This finding was contrasted with the observation that L-phenylalanine releases CCK but D-phenylalanine does not (74). It was observed that one of the few known biological systems that fails to distinguish between D- and L-isomers of amino acids is the so-called sarcosine carrier involved in intestinal transport of amino acids. Interestingly, amino acids that are effective releasers of gastrin also show high affinity for the sarcosine carrier.

EFFECT OF pH ON GASTRIN RELEASE

The inhibitory effect on gastrin release exerted by low antral pH was discussed in the last review of this subject (1). Berkowitz and co-workers observed that changes in antral permeation of charged ions at lower pHs could not account completely for inhibition of gastrin release caused by antral acidification, particularly when the stimulants are distension, vagal impulses, or ethanol (9).

The possibility that antral alkalinization causes release of gastrin was tested in dogs with isolated antral pouches (22). Raising the pH of antral perfusate from 4 to 7 or 10 failed to increase gastrin release or Pavlov pouch acid secretion in response to antral pouch distension with graded volumes of buffer. Responses were partially inhibited at pH 2.3 and completely inhibited at pH 1. Perfusion of similar pouches under conditions of minimal distension with buffers of pH 3, 5, 7, 9, and 11 failed to demonstrate evidence for gastrin release by antral alkalinization. This study suggests that antral pH in the dog exerts a permissive effect on gastrin release, but that alkali per se is not a gastrin-releasing agent.

CIRCULATING STIMULANTS OF GASTRIN RELEASE

Insulin-induced hypoglycemia is a time-honored standard method for production of gastrin release and has until recently been thought to act entirely by stimulation of the vagus nerve. Evidence for the direct vagal release of gastrin has been obtained during experiments employing sham feeding and by direct electrical stimulation of the nerve. This evidence was discussed in the last review on secretion of gastrointestinal hormones (1). Also discussed was the evidence that gastrin release is mediated through a cholinergic mechanism in the antral mucosa. It was pointed out that release of gastrin by a meal in intact dog or man is atropine resistant and may be noncholinergic. The release of gastrin by insulin hypolycemia in the dog was partially resistant to atropine, but could be prevented by quite high doses of atropine (20). In a recent preliminary report it was found that moderate doses of atropine (15 μg/kg) in man failed to prevent and actually enhanced serum gastrin response to insulin under conditions where intragastric pH was maintained at a constant level (34).

Stadil has reported in man that truncal vagotomy failed to abolish the increase in gastrin obtained after insulin injection (93). Similar responses were obtained after selective gastric vagotomy and after highly selective vagotomy of the acid-secreting portion of the stomach. Jaffe and co-workers also obtained significant gastrin responses to insulin after the same surgical procedures (55). Several groups have also reported that basal gastrin concentrations are increased after vagotomy (93, 95). The findings in man are in contrast to those in the dog, in which truncal vagotomy failed to increase serum gastrin concentrations (107). In the dog, antral denervation abolished the serum gastrin response to sham feeding and to insulin hypoglycemia (99).

Stadil & Rehfeld proposed that insulin may release gastrin through liberation of circulating adrenergic agents (93). Stimulation of gastrin release by catecholamines was suggested by Hayes et al, who found elevated plasma gastrin in two patients with pheochromocytoma (51). Administration of phenoxybenzamine and later resection of the adrenal tumors reduced plasma gastrin concentrations to normal. They also found that epinephrine infusions in dogs at rates of 0.25–4 $\mu g\ kg^{-1}\ min^{-1}$ caused significant increases in plasma gastrin. Stadil & Rehfeld found that lower doses in man, 25–75 $ng\ kg^{-1}\ min^{-1}$, caused an increase in serum gastrin concentration, while higher doses appeared to inhibit (92). Prior administration of a beta adrenergic blocking agent prevented the increase in gastrin concentration. The same workers reported that adrenergic blocking agents reduced the insulin-induced gastrin rise in vagotomized patients (93).

Recently a new peptide, bombesin, with gastric acid-stimulating properties was isolated from skin of two species of European frogs *Bombina bombina* and *Bombina variegata variegata* by Erspamer and co-workers, who previously had isolated caerulein from other species of frogs (13, 33). The amino acid sequence of this tetradecapeptide (Pyr-Gln-Arg-Leu-Gly-Asn-Gln-Trp-Ala-Val-Gly-His-Leu-Met-NH_2) bears no resemblance to gastrin. Injection of this peptide into dog or man produced a conspicuous increase in plasma gastrin (73). The effects on gastric acid secretion were inhibited by atropine and by metiamide (a histamine H-2 site blocking agent), but the rise in plasma gastrin was not affected. The gastrin response to bombesin was inhibited by antral acidification and markedly reduced by antrectomy. Although this peptide was isolated from frog skin it is not unlikely that biologically similar peptides exist in mammals. For example, the peptide caerulein, which was extracted from a different species of frogs, bears striking similarity to cholecystokinin. If such a peptide can be identified in man it is tempting to speculate that it could play some role in the atropine-resistant mechanism for gastrin release. Bombesin is the only peptide described to date that releases gastrin when administered intravenously.

CIRCULATING INHIBITORS OF GASTRIN ACTION AND RELEASE

Atropine is not the only compound that causes inhibition of acid secretion both by direct antagonism of the effects of gastrin on the oxyntic gland and by inhibition of gastrin release. At least three different peptide hormones have been reported to have similar effects. Hansky and co-workers reported that intravenous injections of secretin lowered basal gastrin concentrations in normal man (50). Thompson et al reported that secretin diminished postprandial rises in serum gastrin in normal subjects and in patients with duodenal ulcer (101). Similar effects have been found after injection or during infusion of glucagon, a peptide with structural similarity to secretin (3, 49). Large doses of calcitonin were found to inhibit gastrin responses to food in normal man (6). On the other hand, smaller doses of calcitonin inhibited gastric acid secretion stimulated by a meal in man, without any appreciable change in gastrin response (14). All of these peptides are known to inhibit the effect of exogenous gastrin on acid secretion. The inhibitory effect of secretin on gastrin release may provide a dual mechanism for inhibition of acid secretion occurring when the upper intestine is acidified: a combination of direct inhibition of the oxyntic glands and diminution of stimulation provided by gastrin release. Another chemical present in the body which is known to inhibit acid secretion is prostaglandin E_1. Infusion of this material in dogs decreased Heidenhain pouch acid response to food but led to significantly increased serum gastrin responses (5).

INTERACTION OF GASTRIN WITH OTHER STIMULANTS OF ACID SECRETION

At least four factors are known to enhance the action of gastrin on the innervated dog stomach. These are vagal stimulation, activation of reflexes in the gastric wall, direct chemical stimulation of the oxyntic glands, and release of an intestinal factor immunochemically distinct from gastrin (46). The effects of vagal stimulation are illustrated by diminished responses to gastrin obtained after vagal denervation of the oxyntic gland area and by the decrease in acid response to sham feeding after antrectomy, the response being restored to normal by infusions of subthreshold doses of gastrin (1). Local reflexes initiated by distension of denervated oxyntic gland pouches potentiate acid responses to gastrin (2). Recently Debas and coworkers reported a pyloro-oxyntic reflex that caused stimulation of acid secretion in dogs (26). When innervated antral pouches were distended with acid, secretion from innervated, but not from denervated, oxyntic mucosa was stimulated without an increase in serum gastrin. The response to distention was abolished by denervation of the antral pouch. Conversely, an oxynto-pyloric reflex has been reported in preliminary form (27). Distention of the vagally innervated oxyntic gland area released gastrin from the vagally innervated antral pouch; the release was blocked by acidification of the antrum.

Chemical stimulation of the oxyntic mucosa was demonstrated by instillation of peptide solutions into vagally denervated oxyntic pouches (23). Acid secreted by the pouch, determined by titration of the infused solution, was much greater with infusion of peptide solutions than of equal amounts of buffer. Serum gastrin was unchanged and acid secretion was not stimulated in the remaining vagally innervated oxyntic gland portion of the stomach. These findings indicate that the gastric phase of acid secretion consists of a complex interplay of direct effects of food on oxyntic and antral mucosa and reflexes originating in the wall of the stomach.

As mentioned earlier, the intestinal phase of acid secretion in the dog appears to involve release of a hormone, distinct from gastrin, which potentiates the effect of gastrin on denervated oxyntic mucosa (57, 89). The nature of this hormone is unknown. Its existence in man has not been demonstrated. Human duodenum, unlike dog, contains large amounts of immunoreactive gastrin (76). Evidence has been presented that this duodenal gastrin can be released by food in man (95), but the biological significance of duodenal gastrin in man has not been established.

EFFECTS OF GASTRIC OPERATIONS ON SERUM GASTRIN

Vagotomy, distal gastric resection, or combinations of the two are commonly performed for treatment of peptic ulcer disease. All operations produce marked reductions in acid secretion, but the greatest effect is obtained when vagotomy is combined with gastric resection. The effects of these operations on serum gastrin concentrations recently have been summarized by Stadil (93). Partial or total gastrectomy produces a reduction in circulating gastrin, but significant concentrations can still be measured. The proportion of BBG may be increased in such patients. Vagotomy, on the other hand, appears to produce an increase in basal gastrin. It does not seem to matter whether the vagotomy is truncal, selective gastric, or highly selective. In patients with vagotomy and no gastric resection, the diminution in oxyntic responsiveness to gastrin appears to have greater biological effect than the increase in gastrin, since acid secretion is markedly reduced.

ZOLLINGER-ELLISON SYNDROME (GASTRINOMA)

Gastrinoma in man produces a natural experiment involving the prolonged release of physiologically abnormal amounts of gastrin with loss of normal autoregulatory mechanisms. This subject has been reviewed recently (53). Fasting hypergastrinemia can be demonstrated in most patients with gastrinoma. The predominant circulating form usually is G-34, but significant amounts of G-17 and of a biologically inactive N-terminal fragment of G-17 are found routinely. Prolonged stimulation of the gastric mucosa by gastrin causes sustained high gastric acid secretion associated with hypertrophy of the gastric mucosa, probably due to the trophic action of gastrin on this tissue.

Two factors may accentuate release of gastrin in patients with gastrinoma. Hypercalcemia is only a moderate stimulant of gastrin release in normal subjects but is a very potent stimulant of gastrin release from gastrinoma tissue. There is a high incidence of associated hyperparathyroidism in these patients. Thus high rates of gastrin release are promoted by hypercalcemia in patients who have both tumors. Often correction of hypercalcemia leads to at least temporary decrease in serum gastrin concentrations and acid secretion rates. Increased responsiveness to exogenous calcium has been demonstrated in patients with gastrinoma (104). Calcium infusion has been utilized as a provocative test in patients with equivocal serum gastrin concentrations.

Secretin has a paradoxical effect in patients with gastrinoma, causing release of tumor gastrin in contrast to its normal inhibitory effect on gastrin release from the antrum (52). The opposite effects of secretin on tumor and normal antrum have been used to distinguish patients with gastrinoma from a patient with physiologic hypergastrinemia due to the presence of an isolated excluded gastric antrum after previous gastric operation (59). It is possible that secretin plays a role in pathogenesis of the Zollinger-Ellison syndrome. Acidification of the upper intestine causes release of secretin, which in turn may accentuate release of tumor gastrin.

Hypergastrinemia in patients with gastrinoma usually is not further increased after ingestion of a meal since the meal has no contact with the site of gastrin release (11). A separate population of patients with gastric acid hypersecretion and moderately increased basal gastrin concentrations has been identified in which test meals cause marked hypergastrinemia. Berson & Yalow defined this condition as hypergastrinemic hyperchlorhydria without gastrin-secreting tumor (11). It is likely that such patients have overactivity and hyperplasia of gastrin-secreting cells of the gastrointestinal mucosa, with a defect in autoregulation of gastrin release. A similar group of patients with gastric acid hypersecretion, peptic ulcer, hypergastrinema, and antral G-cell hyperplasia has been described (78). They may correspond to the hypergastrinemic hyperchlorhydric patients of Yalow & Berson. The pathophysiology of antral hyperactivity has not been defined further.

Literature Cited

1. Andersson, S. 1973. Secretion of gastrointestinal hormones. *Ann. Rev. Physiol.* 35:431–52
2. Becker, H. D., Konturek, S. J., Reeder, D. D., Thompson, J. C. 1973. Effect of calcium and calcitonin on gastrin and gastrin secretion in cats. *Am. J. Physiol.* 225:277–80
3. Becker, H. D., Reeder, D. D., Thompson, J. C. 1973. Effect of glucagon on circulating gastrin. *Gastroenterology* 65:28–35
4. Becker, H. D., Reeder, D. D., Thompson, J. C. 1973. Extraction of circulating endogenous gastrin by the small bowel. *Gastroenterology* 65:903–6
5. Becker, H. D., Reeder, D. D., Thompson, J. C. 1973. The effect of prostaglandin E_1 on the release of gastrin and gastric secretion on dogs. *Gastroenterology* 63:1148–51
6. Becker, H. D., Reeder, D. D., Scurry, M. T., Thompson, J. C. 1974. Inhibition of gastrin release and gastric secretion by calcitonin in patients with peptic ulcer. *Am. J. Surg.* 127:71–75
7. Beger, H. G., Meves, M., Witte, C., Kraas, E. 1972. The effect of the liver on the gastric secretion stimulated with gastrin II and gastrin-like substances in humans. *Acta Hepato-Gastroenterol.* 19:14–19
8. Bencosme, S. A., Lechago, J. 1973. Staining procedures for the endocrine cells of the upper gastrointestinal mucosa: light-electron microscopic correlation for the gastrin-producing cell. *J. Clin. Pathol.* 26:427–34
9. Berkowitz, J. M., Buetow, G., Walden, M., Praissman, M. 1971. Molecular factors in antral permeation: their proposed role in gastrin release. *Am. J. Physiol.* 221:259–65
10. Berson, S. A., Yalow, R. S. 1971. Nature of immunoreactive gastrin extracted from tissues of gastrointestinal tract. *Gastroenterology* 60:215–22
11. Berson, S. A., Yalow, R. S. 1972. Radioimmunoassay in gastroenterology. *Gastroenterology* 62:1061–84
12. Berson, S. A., Walsh, J. H., Yalow, R. S. 1973. *Frontiers in Gastrointestinal Hormone Research,* 57–66. Stockholm, Sweden: Almqvist & Wiksell
13. Bertaccini, G., Erspamer, V., Impicciatore, M. 1974. The action of bombesin on gastric secretion of the dog and the rat. *Brit. J. Pharmacol.* In press
14. Bieberdorf, F. A., Gray, T. K., Walsh, J. H., Fordtran, J. S. 1974. Effect of calcitonin on meal-stimulated gastric acid secretion and serum gastrin concentration. *Gastroenterology* 66:343–46
15. Booth, R. A. D., Reeder, D. D., Hjelmquist, U. B., Brandt, E. N. Jr., Thompson, J. C. 1973. Renal inactivation of endogenous gastrin in dogs. *Arch. Surg.* 106:851–54
16. Buxton, B., Wassuna, A. E. O., Bedi, B. S., Gillespie, I. E. 1972. Role of the jejunum and the ileum in the acid response of dogs to a meal. *Gastroenterology* 63:270–72
17. Clendinnen, B. G., Reeder, D. D., Brandt, E. N. Jr., Thompson, J. C. 1973. Effect of nephrectomy on the rate and pattern of the disappearance of exogenous gastrin in dogs. *Gut* 14:462–67
18. Creutzfeldt, W., Arnold, R., Creutzfeldt, C., Feurle, G., Ketterer, H. 1971. Gastrin and G-cells in the antral mucosa of patients with pernicious anaemia, aeromegaly and hyperparathyroidism and in a Zollinger-Ellison tumour of the pancreas. *Eur. J. Clin. Invest.* 1:461–79
19. Csendes, A., Grossman, M. I. 1972. D- and L-isomers of serine and alanine equally effective as releasers of gastrin. *Experientia* 28::1306
20. Csendes, A., Walsh, J. H., Grossman, M. I. 1972. Effects of atropine and of antral acidification on gastrin release and acid secretion in response to insulin and feeding in dogs. *Gastroenterology* 63:257–63
21. Davidson, W. D., Moore, T. C., Shippey, W., Conovaloff, A. J. 1974. Effect of bilateral nephrectomy and bilateral ureteral ligation on serum gastrin levels

in the rat. *Gastroenterology* 66: In press
22. Debas, H. T., Csendes, A., Walsh, J. H., Grossman, M. I. 1974. *Endocrinology of the Gut,* 222–32. Thorofare, N.J.: Charles B. Slack, Inc.
23. Debas, H. T., Grossman, M. I. 1974. Active analogs of the C-terminal tripeptide of gastrin. *Gastroenterology* 66:A–182/836 (Abstr.)
24. Debas, H. T., Grossman, M. I. 1974. Chemicals bathing oxyntic gland area stimulate acid secretion. *Gastroenterology* 66:A–182/836 (Abstr.)
25. Debas, H. T., Grossman, M. I. 1974. *5th World Congress of Gastroenterology, Mexico, October 13–19.* In press (Abstr.)
26. Debas, H. T., Konturek, S. J., Walsh, J. H., Grossman, M. I. 1974. Proof of a pyloro-oxyntic reflex for stimulation of acid secretion. *Gastroenterology* 66: In press
27. Debas, H. T., Walsh, J. H., Grossman, M. I. 1974. *Gastroenterology* 66: In press (Abstr.)
28. Debas, H. T., Walsh, J. H., Grossman, M. I. 1974. Pure human minigastrin: secretory potency and disappearance rate. *Gut.* In press
29. Dencker, J. et al 1974. Immunoreactive gastrin in portal and peripheral vanous blood during and after feeding in man. *Gut.* In press
30. Dent, R. I., Levine, B., James, J. H., Hirsch, H., Fischer, J. E. 1973. Effects of isolated perfused canine lung and kidney on gastrin heptadecapeptide. *Am. J. Physiol.* 225:1038–44
31. Dockray, G. J., Walsh, J. H. 1974. Amino terminal gastrin fragment in serum of Zollinger-Ellison syndrome patients. *Gastroenterology.* In press
32. Elwin, C. E. 1973. See Ref. 12, 177–82
33. Erspamer, V., Falconieri, V., Erspamer, G., Negri, L., Inselvini, M. 1972. Occurrence of bombesin and alytesin in extracts of the skin of three European discoglossid frogs and pharmacological actions of bombesin on extravascular smooth muscle. *Brit. J. Pharmacol.* 45:333–48
34. Farooq, O., Walsh, J. H. 1974. Atropine increases serum gastrin response to insulin in man. *Clin. Res.* 22:171A
35. Feurle, G., Ketterer, H., Becker, H. D., Creutzfeldt, W. 1972. Circadian serum gastrin concentrations in control persons and in patients with ulcer disease. *Scand. J. Gastroenterol.* 7:177–83
36. Fordtran, J. S., Walsh, J. H. 1973. Gastric acid secretion rate and buffer content of the stomach after eating. *J. Clin. Invest.* 52:645–57
37. Ganguli, P. C. 1972. Circadian rhythm in plasma level of gastrin. *Nature New Biol.* 235:127–28
38. Gedde-Dahl, D. 1974. Radioimmunoassay of gastrin. Fasting serum levels in humans with normal and high gastric acid secretion. *Scand. J. Gastroenterol.* 9:41–47
39. Gillespie, I. E., Grossman, M. I. 1962. Gastric secretion of acid in response to portal and systemic venous injection of gastrin. *Gastroenterology* 43:189–92
40. Gregory, R. A., Tracy, H. J. 1966. Isolation of two gastrins from human antral mucosa. *Nature* 209:583
41. Gregory, R. A., Tracy, H. J., Agarwal, K. L., Grossman, M. I. 1969. Amino-acid constitution of two gastrins isolated from Zollinger-Ellison tumour tissue. *Gut* 10:603–8
42. Gregory, R. A., Tracy, H. J. 1972. isolation of two "big gastrins" from Zollinger-Ellison tumour tissue. *Lancet* 2: 797–98
43. Gregory, R. A. 1974. The gastrointestinal hormones: a review of recent advances. *J. Physiol.* In press
44. Greider, M. H., McGuigan, J. E. 1971. Cellular localization of gastrin in the human pancreas. *Diabetes* 20(6): 289–96
45. Greider, M. H., Steinberg, V., McGuigan, J. E. 1972. Electron microscopic identification of the gastrin cell of the human antral mucosa by means of immunocytochemistry. *Gastroenterology* 63:572–83
46. Grossman, M. I. 1967. *Handbook of Physiology - Alimentary Canal,* 835–63. Washington, D.C.: Am. Physiol. Soc.
47. Grossman, M. I. 1973. See Ref. 12, 17–25
48. Grossman, M. I. 1974. Removal of calcium from milk decreases its acid-stimulating effect. *Gastroenterology* 66:A–219/873 (Abstr.)
49. Hansky, J., Soveny, C., Korman, M. G. 1973. The effect of glucagon on serum gastrin. *Gut* 14:457–61
50. Hansky, J., Soveny, C., Korman, M. G. 1971. Effect of secretin on serum gastrin as measured by immunoassay. *Gastroenterology* 61:62–68
51. Hayes, J. R., Kennedy, T. L., Ardill, J., Shanks, R. G., Buchanan, K. D. 1972. Stimulation of gastrin release by catecholamines. *Lancet* 1:819–21
52. Isenberg, J. I., Walsh, J. H., Passaro, E. Jr., Moore, E. W., Grossman, M. I.

1973. Unusual effect of secretin on serum gastrin, serum calcium, and gastric acid secretion in a patient with suspected Zollinger-Ellison syndrome. *Gastroenterology* 62:626–31
53. Isenberg, J. I., Walsh, J. H., Grossman, M. I. 1973. Zollinger-Ellison syndrome. *Gastroenterology* 62:140–65
54. Jackson, B. M., Reeder, D. D., Thompson, J. C. 1972. Dynamic characteristics of gastrin release. *Am. J. Surg.* 123:137–42
55. Jaffe, B. M., Clendinnen, B. G., Clarke, R. J., Williams, J. A. 1974. The effect of selective and proximal gastric vagotomy on serum gastrin. *Gastroenterology* 66: In press
56. Johnson, L. R., Stening, G. F., Grossman, M. I. 1970. Effect of sulfation on the gastrointestinal actions of caerulein. *Gastroenterology* 58:208–16
57. Jordan, P. H., de la Rosa, C. 1964. The regulatory effect of the pyloric gland area of the stomach on the intestinal phase of gastric secretion. *Surgery* 56:121–34
58. Kenner, G. W., Sheppard, R. C. 1973. See Ref. 12, 137–42
59. Korman, M. G., Scott, D. F., Hansky, J., Wilson, H. 1972. Hypergastrinaemia due to an excluded gastric antrum: a proposed method for differentiation from the Zollinger-Ellison syndrome. *Aust. NZ J. Med.* 3:266–71
60. Kronborg, O., Stadil, F., Rehfeld, J., Christiansen, P. M. 1973. Relationship between serum gastrin concentrations and gastric acid secretion in duodenal ulcer patients before and after selective and highly selective vagotomy. *Scand. J. Gastroenterol.* 8:491–96
61. Laster, L., Walsh, J. H. 1968. Enzymatic degradation of C-terminal tetrapeptide amide of gastrin by mammalian tissue extracts. *Fed. Proc.* 27:1328–30
62. Levant, J. A., Walsh, J. H., Isenberg, J. I. 1973. Stimulation of gastric secretion and gastrin release by single oral doses of calcium carbonate in man. *N. Engl. J. Med.* 289:555–58
63. Lichtenberger, L., Johnson, L. R., 1974. A possible role of gastrin in the ontogenic development of the small intestine. *Am. J. Physiol.* In press
64. Lin, T. M. 1972. Gastrointestinal actions of the C-terminal tripeptide of gastrin. *Gastroenterology* 63:922–23
65. McGuigan, J. E. 1968. Gastric mucosal intracellular localization of gastrin by immunofluorescence. *Gastroenterology* 55:315–27
66. McGuigan, J. E. 1969. Studies of the immunochemical I specificity of some antibodies to human gastrin. *Gastroenterology* 56:429–38
67. McGuigan, J. E., Jaffe, B. M., Newton, W. T. 1970. Immunochemical measurements of endogenous gastrin release. *Gastroenterology* 59:499–504
68. McGuigan, J. E., Trudeau, W. L. 1970. Studies with antibodies to gastrin. *Gastroenterology* 58:139–50
69. McGuigan, J. E., Greider, M. H. 1971. Correlative immunochemical and light microscopic studies of the gastrin cell of the antral mucosa. *Gastroenterology* 60:223–36
70. McGuigan, J. E., Isaza, J., Landor, J. H. 1971. Relationships of gastrin dose, serum gastrin, and acid secretion. *Gastroenterology* 61:659–66
71. McGuigan, J. E., Thomas, H. F. 1971. Physiological and immunological studies with desamidogastrin. *Gastroenterology* 62:553–57
72. McGuigan, J. E., Trudeau, W. L. 1973. Differences in rates of gastrin release in normal persons and patients with duodenal-ulcer disease. *N. Engl. J. Med.* 288:64–66
73. Melchiorri, P. et al 1974. Gastrin release by bombesin in the dog. *Brit. J. Pharmacol.* In press
74. Meyer, J. H., Grossman, M. I. 1972. Comparison of D- and L-phenylalanine as pancreatic stimulants. *Am. J. Physiol.* 222:1058–63
75. Morley, J. S. 1971. Gastrin and related peptides. In *Structure-Activity Relationships of Protein and Polypeptide Hormones,* Pt. 1 Rep., *Proc. 2nd Int. Symp. Liage, September 28-October 1, 1971,* ed. M. Margoulies, F. C. Greenwood, Vol. 1, 11–17. Amsterdam: Excerpta Medica
76. Nilsson, G., Yalow, R. S., Berson, S. A. 1973. See Ref. 12, 95–101
77. Orloff, M. J., Villar-Valdes, H., Abbott, A. G., Williams, R. J., Rosen, H. 1970. Site of origin of the hormone responsible for gastric hypersecretion associated with portacaval shunt. *Surgery* 68:202–8
78. Polak, J. M., Stagg, B., Pearse, A. G. E. 1972. Two types of Zollinger-Ellison syndrome: immunofluorescent, cytochemical and ultrastructural studies of the antral and pancreatic gastrin cells in different clinical states. *Gut* 13:501–12

79. Reeder, D. D., Jackson, B. M., Brandt, E. N. Jr., Thompson, J. C. 1972. Rate and pattern of disappearance of exogenous gastrin in dogs. *Am. J. Physiol.* 222:1571–74
80. Rehfeld, J. F. 1972. Three components of gastrin in human serum. Gel filtration studies on the molecular size of immunoreactive serum gastrin. *Biochem. Biophys. Acta* 285:364–72
81. Rehfeld, J. F., Stadil, F., Rubin, B. 1972. Production and evaluation of antibodies for the radioimmunoassay of gastrin. *Scand. J. Clin. Lab. Invest.* 30:221–32
82. Rehfeld, J. F., Stadil, F. 1973. Gel filtration studies on immunoreactive gastrin in serum from Zollinger-Ellison patients. *Gut* 14:369–73
83. Rehfeld, J. F., Stadil, F., Vikelse, J. 1974. Immunoreactive gastrin components in human serum. Evidence by gel filtration and cellulosic ion exchange chromatography that gastrin circulates as one large and three smaller, paired components. *Gut.* In press
84. Rosenquist, G. L., Holmquist, A. M. 1974. The specificity of antibodies directed to porcine gastrin. *Immunochemistry.* In press
85. Rune, S. J. 1966. Comparison of the rates of gastric acid secretion in man after ingestion of food and after maximal stimulation with histamine. *Gut* 7:344–50
86. Schrumpf, E., Semb, L. S. 1973. The metabolic clearance rate and half-life of synthetic human gastrin in dogs. *Scand. J. Gastroenterol.* 8:203–7
87. Schrumpf, E., Semb, L. S., Vold, H. 1973. Metabolic clearance and disappearance rates of synthetic human gastrin in man. *Scand. J. Gastroenterol.* 8:731–34
88. Seelig, H. P. 1972. *Gastrin.* Stuttgart, Germany: George Thieme
89. Slaff, G. F. 1974. Intestinal phase of gastric acid secretion: augmentation of maximal response of Heidenhair pouch to gastrin. *Gastroenterology* 66:A-2/656 (Abstr.)
90. Solcia, E., Vassallo, G., Sampietro, R. 1967. Endocrine cells in the antropyloric mucosa of the stomach. *Z. Zellforsch. Mikrosk. Anat.* 81:474–86
91. Solcia, E., Vassallo, G., Capella, C. 1970. *Origin, Chemistry, Physiology and Pathophysiology of the Gastrointestinal Hormones,* ed. W. Crentzfeldt, 10–15. Stuttgart, New York: F. K. Schattauer
92. Stadil, F., Rehfeld, J. F. 1973. Release of gastrin by epinephrine in man. *Gastroenterology* 65:210–15
93. Stadil, F. 1974. Gastrin and insulin hypoglycaemia. *Scand. J. Gastroenterol.* 9:1–49
94. Stagg, B. H., Temperley, J. M., Wyllie, J. H. 1971. The fate of pentagastrin. *Gut* 12:825–29
95. Stern, D. H., Walsh, J. H. 1973. Gastrin release in postoperative ulcer patients: evidence for release of duodenal gastrin. *Gastroenterology* 64:363–69
96. Straus, E., Gerson, C. D., Yalow, R. S. 1974. Hypersecretion of gastrin associated with the short bowel syndrome. *Gastroenterology* 66:175–80
97. Straus, E., Yalow, R. S. 1974. Studies on the distribution and degradation of heptadecapeptide, big, and big-big gastrins. *Gastroenterology* 66:936–43
98. Temperley, J. M., Stagg, B. H., Wyllie, J. H. 1971. Disappearance of gastrin and pentagastrin in the portal circulation. *Gut* 12:372–76
99. Tepperman, B. L., Walsh, J. H., Preshaw, R. M. 1972. Effect of antral denervation on gastrin release by sham feeding and insulin hypoglycemia in dogs. *Gastroenterology* 63:973–80
100. Thompson, J. C. et al 1969. Effect of hepatic transit of gastrin, pentagastrin, and histamine measured by gastric secretion and by assay of hepatic vein blood. *Ann. Surg.* 170:493–503
101. Thompson, J. C., Reeder, D. D., Bunchman, H. H., Becker, H. D., Brandt, E. N. 1972. *Ann. Surg.* 176:384–93
102. Thompson, J. C., Reeder, D. D., Davidson, W. D., Jackson, B. M., Clendinnen, B. G. 1973. See Ref. 12, 111–33
103. Trout, H., Grossman, M. I. 1971. Penultimate aspartyl unnecessary for stimulation of acid secretion by gastrin-related peptide. *Nature New Biol.* 234:256
104. Trudeau, W. L., McGuigan, J. F. 1969. Effects of calcium on serum gastrin levels in the Zollinger-Ellison syndrome. *N. Engl. J. Med.* 281:862–66
105. Trudeau, W. L., McGuigan, J. E. 1971. Relations between serum gastrin levels and rates of gastric hydrochloric acid secretion. *N. Engl. J. Med.* 284:408–12
106. Varró, V. et al 1973. Hepatic and mesenteric metabolism of C-terminal pentapeptide of gastrin in the rat. Part 1. Biliary excretion of labelled glycine-pentapeptide. *Acta Hepato-Gastroenterol.* 20:507–12

107. Walsh, J. H., Csendes, A., Grossman, M. I. 1972. Effect of truncal vagotomy on gastrin release and Heidenhain pouch acid secretion in response to feeding in dogs. *Gastroenterology* 63: 593–600
108. Walsh, J. H. 1973. *Gastrointestinal Disease,* 144–62. Philadelphia, Pennsylvania: Saunders
109. Walsh, J. H., Grossman, M. I. 1973. Circulating gastrin in peptic ulcer disease. *Mt. Sinai J. Med.* 11:374–81
110. Walsh, J. H., Laster, L. 1973. Enzymatic deamidation of the C-terminal tetrapeptide amide of gastrin by mammalian tissues. *Biochem. Med.* 8:432–49
111. Walsh, J. H., Debas, H. T., Grossman, M. I. 1974. Pure human big gastrin: immunochemical properties, disappearance half-time and acid stimulating action in dogs. *J. Clin. Invest.* In press
112. Walsh, J. H., Trout, H. H. III, Debas, H. T., Grossman, M. I. See Ref. 22, 277–89
113. Walter, R., Bowman, R. H. 1973. Mechanism of inactivation of vasopressin and oxytocin by the isolated perfused rat kidney. *Endocrinology* 92: 189–93
114. Yalow, R. S., Berson, S. A. 1970. Radioimmunoassay of gastrin. *Gastroenterology* 58:1–14
115. Yalow, R. S., Berson, S. A. 1970. Size and charge distinctions between endogenous human plasma gastrin in peripheral blood and heptadecapeptide gastrins. *Gastroenterology* 58:609–15
116. Yalow, R. S., Berson, S. A. 1971. Further studies on the nature of immunoreactive gastrin in human plasma. *Gastroenterology* 60:203–14
117. Yalow, R. S., Berson, S. A. 1971. *Structure-Activity Relationships of Protein and Polypeptide Hormones,* 48–56. Amsterdam, The Netherlands: Excerpta Medica
118. Yalow, R. S., Berson, S. A. 1972. And now, "big, big" gastrin. *Biochem. Biophys. Res. Commun.* 48:391–95
119. Yalow, R. S., Wu, N. 1973. Additional studies on the nature of big big gastrin. *Gastroenterology* 65:19–27
120. Zelenkova, J., Gregor, O. 1971. Development of gastrin activity. *Scand. J. Gastroenterol.* 6:653–56

Copyright 1975. All rights reserved

SOMATOSENSORY RECEPTORS AND THEIR CNS CONNECTIONS

❖1125

Bruce Lynn
Department of Physiology, University College London, London, WC 1, England

INTRODUCTION

This review deals with recent findings concerning the properties of receptor units in the somatosensory system and the connections of their afferents in the central nervous system. Frequent references are made to articles in the recently published Volume II of the Handbook of Sensory Physiology (72). I have divided this review into four main sections, corresponding roughly to the subdivisions of kinesthesis, touch and pressure, warm and cold, and pain.

LIMB MOVEMENT AND POSITION

Three main groups of receptors send information to the central nervous system about the position of the limb and about changes in its position. These are the stretch receptors in skeletal muscles and tendons, the mechanoreceptors in the joints, and certain of the skin mechanoreceptors. Cutaneous mechanoreceptors, which appear to play only a small part in kinesthesis (34) and are not usually considered as proprioceptors, are dealt with in the next section. However, it is worth noting that many hair receptors must fire during limb movements and that slowly adapting Type II receptors are excited by joint movements and must be capable of transmitting information about both movements and the fixed position of a limb (30, 84).

Afferent Inflow from Joints

The discharge characteristics of single afferent fibers from joint receptors have been reviewed recently by Matthews (103) and Skoglund (145). A number of recent studies have emphasized the relative lack of activity from slowly adapting afferents when the joint is held near its midposition, compared with activity near the limits of movement. Out of 278 single myelinated fibers running from the knee joint of the cat, only 4 fired best when the joint was held at an intermediate position, while 199 fired best when the limb was held at extreme flexion, extension, or both (23). These results, particularly the finding of many units activated at both extreme flexion and extension, are quite dissimilar from previous studies; some possible reasons for the differences are considered by Skoglund (145). One fact pointed out by Burgess & Clark (23) is that, for technical reasons, earlier studies of knee joint afferents did not systematically test units at full flexion and full extension. All slowly adapting afferents from the intercostal-vertebral joints of cats and rabbits were found to respond best at one of the extreme joint positions but never at both (50). Most units (72% of 48) fired with movements in the expiratory direction, while 28% fired best with inspiratory movements. However, units were active over most of the range of normal movement of these joints, and responded in a cyclical manner during spontaneous respiration. Recordings from the elbow joint nerve of the cat showed that greatest activity occurred at full extension, with much less activity at the midposition or at full flexion (107, 108).

The dynamic responses of slowly adapting receptor units from the cat's knee have been examined using small, low frequency, sinusoidal displacements (105). Responses have been related to the static sensitivity functions, which were usually monotonic over the limited range of movements studied. Changes in phase and gain with frequency were found to fit a "fractional-order differentiator" model (105).

A substantial minority of joint afferents are rapidly adapting: 10% from the intercostal-vertebral joints (50) and 16% from the knee joint (23). At the knee joint these were subdivided into two categories by Burgess & Clark (23); 1. Pacinian corpuscle-like units that fired to distant taps and 2. generally less rapidly adapting units that did not respond to distant taps but could often be fired tonically by combined extension and outward rotation of the lower limb.

Joint afferents from the cat's elbow were found to respond to muscle contraction even in the absence of joint movement. They also respond to 100 Hz vibration applied to muscles inserting and originating at the elbow (108). A small number of muscle spindle afferents were found to run in the posterior articular nerve from the cat's knee (23).

Central Connections of Joint Afferents

Cells activated by slowly adapting joint afferents have been reported by a number of workers in the dorsal column nuclei (DCN), and it had appeared that such units were activated via primary afferent collaterals in the dorsal columns (145). For the forelimbs such an arrangement has been confirmed by recent studies. The funiculus cuneatus contains many fibers responding with a slowly adapting discharge following forelimb joint rotation in the squirrel monkey (166). Also, cortical evoked potentials following electrical stimulation of the elbow joint nerve of the cat are largely abolished by dorsal column section (33). However, a quite different situation is found for the hind limb. No slowly adapting joint afferents are present in the cervical funiculus gracilis of either cat (15, 24, 32) or monkey (166). Many of the rapidly adapting joint afferents from the hindlimb, particularly those from Pacinian corpuscle-like receptors, do contribute axons to the cervical dorsal columns of the cat (24, 32).

Joint afferents from the forelimb weakly excite some of the postsynaptic fibers in the dorsal columns. Uddenberg (154) and Skoglund (145) suggested that such fibers may carry the information from slowly adapting (SA) hindlimb receptors. However, no such units have been reported in samples of cervical dorsal column units (166), even those which concentrated on postsynaptic units (122).

A recent study of cells in the gracile nucleus that are excited from the cat's knee joint failed to find any SA units, but found 59 units that responded with a rapidly adapting discharge following limb movement (168). Williams et al (168) suggested that previous studies of joint units in the DCN may also have been looking at this same population since criteria for classifying units into slowly adapting (SA) and rapidly adapting (RA) were not comparable with those used in studies of primary afferents. This may be the case for some joint units in the DCN, but it is not true for claw units that respond with a high frequency discharge for many seconds when the terminal phalangeal joint is held at a suitable, fixed angle (54). It may be significant that slowly adapting discharges following hindlimb claw displacement were observed in the thoracic dorsal columns (24).

In agreement with the unit studies, it has been found that cortical evoked potentials following electrical stimulation of the axons of the SA joint afferents are usually not reduced by dorsal column section (33), although those from RA afferents are substantially diminished. However, section of the dorsolateral funiculus (DLF) ipsilateral to the stimulus (contralateral to the cortical recording site) did substantially reduce potentials from SA afferent stimulation (33). A number of ascending systems run in the dorsolateral funiculus, including the spinocervical tract (SCT) and the dorsal spinocerebellar tract (DSCT). However, the DLF was sectioned at C1, above the lateral cervical nucleus, in the experiments of Clark et al (33). Also, no cells giving a discharge related to limb position have been found in the SCT or the lateral cervical nucleus (119). Thus the SCT does not appear to be involved in detecting limb position.

The DSCT, or a parallel system of relay neurones from the Clarke's column area, appear to be much more likely candidates. Clark (32) showed that SA joint afferents did run in the cat dorsal columns, but only as far as L3-Th13 segments in most instances. In agreement with this, cells in Clarke's column that receive a monosynaptic input from the SA joint afferents have recently been described (87, 96, 97). Such cells often responded only to one direction of movement in two joints and some also received cutaneous and/or muscle inputs (87). Many units only fired over the last 15–20° of a joint movement (97) like many of the primary afferents (23). Joint cells in Clarke's column resembled muscle cells in having a relatively regular discharge pattern and rather large excitatory post-synaptic potentials (EPSPs) (88). It therefore appears probable (33) that the information from SA joint afferents projects via a similar path to that from muscle stretch receptors (92).

Muscle Stretch Receptors

Three types of stretch receptors are found in mammalian muscle: the Golgi tendon organs and the primary and secondary endings of spindles. The afferent discharges from these endings have been studied for two generations (102, 103). An extensive account of the properties of mammalian muscle receptors has recently been published (103) and they will not be considered further here. The synaptic effects of the different types of muscle afferents on neurones that project to the cerebellum have also been examined in detail (118).

The classical view that muscle, as well as joint, receptors play a part in producing sensations of limb movement and position (kinesthesis) has recently been revived by experiments using tendon vibration as a means of specifically exciting muscle spindle primary endings (51). However, vibration also excites two other types of receptors: those in adjacent joints (108) and Pacinian corpuscles throughout the limb (69). Goodwin et al (51) also claimed that, in contradiction to previous studies (106), complete finger anesthesia does not cause movements of the fingers to pass undetected. Direct stretching of the tendons of the forearm muscles that cause finger flexion has also recently been found to give rise to sensations of finger movement (104), another result that conflicts with an earlier study (49). The lack of any serious loss in sense of limb position following total hip replacement would also appear to indicate that the muscle receptors play an important role (51). Since the majority of SA joint afferents may only fire within 10–20° of extreme flexion or extension (23) it would be interesting to have the sense of limb position tested for extremes of movement in patients with surgical joint replacements.

Central Connections of Muscle Stretch Receptors

The cortical projection pathways from muscle stretch receptors now clearly take on a more "normal" appearance, since it had appeared that this projection might represent a cortical receptor pathway with no parallel in conscious sensation (103).

Recent work on the central pathways carrying information from forelimb muscle receptors has been reviewed by Rosen (134). The connections of afferents of Golgi tendon organs and primary spindle endings have so far received most attention. Cells in the main cuneate nucleus that send axons in the contralateral medial lemniscus are excited only by primary ending afferents and not by tendon organ afferents (135). 72% of such cells were fired from only 1 of 4 wrist extensor muscles tested, and 21 cells tested from both wrist flexors and extensors were never excited by both (136). In the specificity of their afferent connections, these cells resemble those in both the external cuneate nucleus and Clarke's column that project to the cerebellum (135, 136). The muscle afferents that terminate in the cuneate nucleus appear to run via the cervical fasciculus cuneatus (135, 166).

The pathways for muscle afferent information from the hindlimb are more complex. Afferent fiber collaterals run for a short distance in the lumbar dorsal columns and terminate on cells in Clarke's column. These cells in turn send axons to nucleus Z in the medulla (13, 92). The pattern of highly specific connections displayed by cells in Clarke's column is repeated in nucleus Z. For example, 21 cells were excited by group I volleys from only one out of the three muscle nerves tested (92). Some cells were also fired by cutaneous (sural) nerve stimulation. The similarities of the projection patterns and properties of the relay from hindlimb muscle afferents to nucleus Z and to the cerebellum raises the possibility that axons in the DSCT divide to terminate in both regions. It also seems likely that hindlimb joint afferent information follows a similar route (33).

A group of cells in medial lamina 6 of the upper cervical cord receives an excitatory monosynaptic input from muscle stretch receptors in the lower limb (133). These cells also receive an excitatory cutaneous input (133). A number of reports of cells in the lumbosacral cord that respond to limb movements have appeared (157, 159, 160, 169). Such cells are found in the most ventral part of the dorsal horn (lamina 6) and in the intermediate and ventral gray matter. Some of these cells send axons to the contralateral thalamus (169), while others project in the ipsilateral DLF (4). These latter cells were found in the medial parts of laminae 5, 6, and 7 in segments L5–6 and were monosynaptically excited from a number of muscle nerves, and also sometimes from joint and skin nerves (4).

NON-NOXIOUS MECHANICAL EVENTS ON THE SKIN

Properties of Afferent Mechanoreceptor Fibers

Studies in the 1960s established the basic properties of cutaneous mechanoreceptor afferents in mammalian hairy skin and subdivided these into a number of categories according to the caliber of their axons (and whether myelinated or unmyelinated), the nature of any macroscopic structures associated with their terminations (e.g. hairs), their rate of adaptation to a constant displacement, the form of their receptive fields, and other factors (10, 18, 28). Because much of this work has recently been reviewed in depth by Burgess & Perl (27), I will concentrate on work that has appeared subsequently.

The encapsulated Ruffini corpuscle has been identified as the receptor ending for Type II slowly adapting afferents in cat hairy skin (30), and its fine structure has been examined using the electron microscope (3, 30). Further details of the responses of Type II endings to controlled skin indentation and to skin stretch are also given in this study, including quantitative data on input–output relations and on rates of adaptation.

Disagreements continue about the classification of hair afferents with large myelinated axons. The T (for tylotrich hair) and G (for guard hair) classification developed by Brown & Iggo (18) appears to correlate well with regional differences in the fur of rabbits (17). Burgess and associates (25, 27, 28), however, continue to treat all large hairs as alike, calling them guard (G) hairs, and prefer to classify afferents according to their velocity thresholds. The original subdivision into G_1 (high velocity threshold) and G_2 (low velocity threshold) (28) has been extended to include an intermediate category called "intermediate hair" (27). For the sural nerve, this category has been found to include many units previously classified as Pacinian corpuscles (25). There are, however, a very small number of genuine Pacinian corpuscles with axons in the sural nerve (69), but they comprise much less than the 4% of myelinated afferents claimed previously (28).

A further hair unit classification has been used by Tapper et al (148). These workers subdivided the afferents from the larger hairs into G (low velocity threshold) and G' (stiffest hairs, high velocity threshold), and suggested that their G class included the G_2 and intermediate classes of Burgess & Perl (27) and their G' class the G_1 (27) and T (18) classes.

The continued failure of different laboratories to agree on one classification scheme produces a certain skepticism towards all the published schemes. However, the demonstration that central cells may be excited by only one category of hair afferent (20, 110, 148) suggests that important functional differences may be involved.

A recent study in monkeys (167) examined the responses of myelinated hair afferents on proximal leg skin to tangential brushing along straight lines across the receptive fields. No differences were reported between different types of hairs. The patterns of response did not depend upon the direction of brushing, although directional properties were observed for some cortical neurones studied using the same stimuli (167).

Tapper et al (148) have provided some useful data on the innervation density of hair receptors in cat skin. They have counted the myelinated fibers in the posterior femoral cutaneous nerve and the numbers of down and guard (including tylotrich?) hairs per unit skin area, and have determined the numbers of hairs innervated by single afferent fibers and the areas over which these were spread. From such data they have been able to make estimates of the minimal numbers of fibers of each type innervating unit skin areas. They found at least 2.5 G units and 2.9 D (down hair) units for each cm^2. A similar analysis was presented for Type 1 slowly adapting units (innervating touch corpuscles), and once again a minimum figure of approximately 2.5 units/cm^2 was found. Complete maps of all the touch corpuscles on the posterior femoral skin have been published by Burgess et al (29) in connection with a study of the factors determining the pattern of regeneration following nerve injury. Burgess et al (29) noted that touch corpuscles are almost never found within 1 mm of each other in normal skin, a situation that would not occur if they were distributed at random.

The large sinus hairs of the face and wrist continue to receive attention. The slowly adapting terminations on the sinus hairs have been subdivided into two categories corresponding to the Type I and II categories for SA receptors in hairy skin (55). Two types of rapidly adapting endings, one with a high velocity threshold and Pacinian corpuscle-like behavior and one with a lower velocity threshold, have been found associated with the facial sinus hairs (including the true vibrissae) (55). From microdissection experiments and comparison with the anatomical data of Andres (2) and Nillson (115), the following structure–function correlations are proposed (55): Type I SA = Merkel cell–neurite complexes in the outer root sheath; Type II SA = lanceolate nerve terminals outside the glassy membrane surrounding the outer root sheath; Pacinian corpuscle-like units = lamellated Golgi-Mazzoni corpuscles. No structure could be assigned with any certainty to the relatively uncommon, low velocity RA units.

These correlations fit well with other studies. For example, Sakada (140) found that the rapidly adapting, vibration-sensitive receptors in the periostea of the cat's jaw were also Golgi-Mazzoni corpuscles. Also Merkel cell–neurite complexes are known to be SA receptors in touch corpuscles (Type I receptors) from mammalian hairy skin (70, 73). Merkel cell–neurite complexes have also been found at the locations of SA receptors in cat (76) and raccoon (111) glabrous skin. High velocity threshold units are not found in the carpal sinus hairs (55, 115), nor are Golgi-Mazzoni corpuscles (115). The many Pacinian corpuscles situated close to the carpal hairs (116) presumably perform the same function (55).

The receptor categories recognized by Gottschaldt el al (55) in cat vibrissae bear a close resemblance to the four categories defined by Zucker & Welker (170) in the rat. It is more difficult, however, to relate to these categories the data from studies using sinusoidal vibration of cat whiskers (57, 113, 114).

A detailed study of the responses of rapidly adapting afferent units with intracutaneous receptors (i.e. not from Pacinian corpuscles) in monkey glabrous skin has been made by Johnson (77). The thresholds for different patterns of activation by a 40 Hz sinusoidal displacement have been determined for different positions in receptive fields. Changes in threshold appear to follow a simple pattern, apparently determined largely by mechanical factors. From the distribution of thresholds over the population as a whole and the form of receptive fields, Johnson (77) has computed the population input–output relations for his particular stimulus using a computer model. Total impulse firing over the whole population is calculated to rise linearly with stimulus intensity, despite the nonlinear relation for individual units. These findings, and the general approach, have much in common with the more extensive studies by Gray and his colleagues (5, 6, 48, 56, 99) of rapidly adapting mechanoreceptor units from the glabrous skin of the cat's plantar cushion (large foot pad). These earlier workers were able to check the validity of their model of the system by measuring the summed activity from the pad nerves (6, 48). It would clearly be useful if some similar recordings could be made from the monkey preparation of Johnson (77).

Four types of mechanoreceptor with large myelinated axons have been distinguished by Pubols & Pubols (131) in a study of afferent fibers from the glabrous skin of the raccoon forepaw. The four categories are Pacinian corpuscles, rapidly adapting, moderately slowly adapting (MSA), and very slowly adapting (VSA). This classification supersedes an earlier one of just RA and SA (130).

Recent studies of afferent C-fibers from human skin (151, 155a) have failed to find any sensitive "C-mechanoreceptors" similar to those reported in cat hairy skin (10). Torebjörk & Hallin (151) studied nerves (including saphenous) that innervate both hairy and glabrous skin of the hand and foot. This situation contrasts with the abundance of such units in cat hairy skin (10, 11), including that supplied by the saphenous nerve (58). However, C-mechanoreceptors are not found in the glabrous skin of the cat's foot pads (8, 11). The situation in monkey appears to lie, appropriately, between cat and man. No C-mechanoreceptors are found in glabrous skin, but some are present in hairy skin, particularly on the proximal limb [T. Kumazawa and E. R. Perl, unpublished results cited by Burgess & Perl (27)]. These species and area differences may be correlated with the grooming behavior of the animals, since Bessou & Perl (10) noted that these receptors were ideal "bug" detectors.

As noted above, additional quantitative data on input–output relations for Type II SA units has been provided by Chambers et al (30). The relation between increase in firing frequency and static displacement has often fit a classic semilogarithmic relation (i.e. $F = A + K \log S$, where F = frequency of nerve impulses, S =

stimulus displacement, and A and K are constants). However, Chambers et al (30) also found that the data have often fit a power function (i.e. $\log F = A + K \log S$). The whole business of fitting functions to neural input–output is critically and perceptively reviewed by Kruger & Kenton (85). These authors showed how various normalization procedures, including corrections to exclude subthreshold parts of the input–output relations, can substantially alter the form of the best-fitting function. Kruger & Kenton (85) also passed a critical eye over previous attempts to apply information theory to neural data, particularly attempts to assess channel capacity for SA cutaneous mechanoreceptors units (165). For example, they claimed (81, 85) that measured information transmission usually exceeds 4–5 bits if care is taken in assigning stimulus and response categories. Channel capacity must always exceed this figure and therefore earlier claims of equivalence between the channel capacity of single afferent neurones and that of human subjects in psychophysical tests (165) appear unjustified.

Central Connections of Mechanoreceptor Afferents in Spinal Cord

The pattern of connections made in the spinal cord by different types of afferents from the skin has been reviewed recently (15, 162, 163). In discussing spinal cord cells, I often refer to laminae 1–10; these are the cytoarchitectonic laminae of spinal gray matter described by Rexed (132).

A detailed study of connections from myelinated afferents in the posterior femoral cutaneous nerve onto dorsal horn cells in decerebrate, spinal cats has been made by Tapper and his colleagues (19, 148). They studied only the hair receptors and touch corpuscles (Type I SA), and only those cells receiving short latency connections and lying in laminae 3–6. A few cells appeared to be excited by stimulation of just one receptor type (N.B. hairs were classified as G, G', and D, see above), although other cells received a convergent input from all possible combinations of the four receptor types. The pattern of convergence over the population was not significantly different from what would be expected if all entering fibers made their connections independently. However, only stimuli that would excite hair or touch corpuscle receptors were used, and many of these units may also receive input from higher threshold receptors and from heat-sensitive receptors (158, 159).

In contrast to the independence of convergence of connections of different types, units showed a high degree of spatial interdependence. Thus when a unit received connections from receptors of more than one type, these always originated from the same skin area. Spinal cord cells examined by Tapper et al (148) had much larger receptive fields (30–80 times larger in area) than those of primary afferent units.

The responses of dorsal horn cells to single spikes along single Type I axons were examined by Brown et al (21). The pattern of response of a given cell varied for different afferent fibers: some afferents produced short latency excitation followed by long latency inhibition, while others produced only excitation or only inhibition. Different cord cells were also tested from the same touch corpuscle, and again different effects were found on different cells, with no clear pattern emerging. It appears, therefore, that neither individual cells nor individual afferents have a stereotyped pattern of synaptic response. There were also no systematic variations in the responses to stimulating single corpuscles at different distances from the centers of the receptive field for a cord cell. This contrasts with the effects of descending inhibition from the pyramidal tract, which is less effective on touch corpuscle input from the edge of the receptive field than on input from the field center (79).

A series of papers on the location and properties of the cells of origin of the spinothalamic tract (STT) in both cat and monkey has established that many of these cells transmit information from skin mechanoreceptors (1, 41, 93, 94, 152, 153, 169). Spinal cord cells in the cat rarely send axons to the contralateral thalamus, and those that do are often situated deep in the spinal gray matter and do not receive excitation from cutaneous mechanoreceptors (93, 153). In the monkey, however, such cells are more plentiful and many are found in the first few laminae of the dorsal horn and are fired by sensitive cutaneous mechanoreceptors (94, 169). Willis et al (169) carefully characterized the responses of their cells to various sorts of stimuli, and related these responses to the anatomical location of the cells. Of their sample of STT cells, 38% were activated by gentle hair movement. These were mostly located in the lateral half of laminae 4 and 5. Responses to hair movement were rapidly adapting and receptive fields were often small, especially on the feet. Another 21% of cells were excited by small skin movements, but not by hair movement. Some of these cells were tonically activated by maintained displacements, while others adapted rapidly. Many of these STT cells, like other non-STT cells in the same region, were excited by noxious heating.

Eighty dorsal horn neurones with axons in the spinocervical tract and terminating in the lateral cervical nucleus have been examined in the monkey lumbar spinal cord (22). These mostly responded to low threshold mechanical skin stimulation with a relatively rapidly adapting discharge. Their location lay predominantly in laminae 4–6. They did not differ much from nearby non-SCT cells, including presumably the STT cells described above. The monkey SCT thus closely resembles that of the cat, which had previously received most of the attention (15, 16).

Connections of Mechanoreceptor Afferents in the Trigeminal Nucleus

A study of the responses following stimulation of the large sinus hairs (vibrissae) recorded from cells in the anterior part of the rat's trigeminal nucleus has revealed a considerable degree of specialization (143). Tonic (T) units were never excited from more than one vibrissa and showed marked directional sensitivity. No subdivision of T units is made by Shipley (143), but different illustrations show both a unit with marked dynamic firing (which resembles a Type I receptor) (55) and one with a linear displacement response like that found for Type II receptor units (55). However, it is not clear at present whether the cat classification can be carried over to rats. Phasic (P) units were also found in the rat trigeminal nucleus (143). These were often fired by movements of more than one vibrissa, unlike the primary afferents (170). Two types of phasic units were distinguished. One type (PS) had a low velocity threshold and fired steadily during constant velocity movements (143). The other type (PV) had a velocity-dependent threshold that was generally higher than for the PS units, but fired only one spike, or one brief burst of spikes, at the start of a constant velocity stimulus. These two types therefore bear a close resemblance to the two RA types of receptor afferents found in cat, with the PV unit acting as though it received input only from Golgi-Mazzoni corpuscles and the PS unit resembling the other RA receptor unit with lower velocity threshold. PV units were the ones most commonly fired from more than one vibrissa. Usually a group of adjacent vibrissae were effective, as found by Nord (117).

In the cat, Mosso & Kruger (110) described only two types of cell excited by vibrissal movement in the caudal spinal trigeminal nucleus. One type had a low velocity threshold, was directionally polarized, and sometimes showed tonic firing to a maintained displacement. Another 33% of units responded to rapid hair movements. Most spinal trigeminal units were only excited from one vibrissa (110). Convergence of afferents from all types of hair within the receptive field onto cells in the cat in nuclei caudalis and oralis has been reported (137).

I have found the literature on vibrissal units difficult to deal with as nearly every investigator has used different types of stimuli and different classification criteria. This has meant that potentially interesting comparisons about convergence onto central cells and about differences between species cannot be made.

Apart from vibrissal units, a number of other cells driven by hair or skin movements were found in the caudal spinal nucleus in cat (110). Most appeared to be driven by only one afferent receptor type, according to a classification scheme like that of Burgess & Perl (27). The degree of specialization of response patterns revealed by Mosso & Kruger (110) is striking, and extends to thermal and noxious stimuli. It is clearly important for the mechanoreceptor input running in the trigeminal nerve from structures other than the vibrissae to be firmly established so that studies in the nucleus can have a firmer base. Surprisingly, we know more about trigeminal thermoreceptor afferents than about the mechanoreceptors.

As well as finding a much higher degree of specificity than in previous studies, Mosso & Kruger (110) also found that many of the units that could be excited into a slowly adapting discharge during a maintained skin displacement produced a very regular pattern of firing. A previous study by Darian-Smith et al (38) found only rather variable firing by SA units in the caudal trigeminal nucleus. It seems likely that this difference may arise at least in part from the differing types of preparation used. The conclusion of Darian-Smith et al (38) and Darian-Smith (36) that the caudal part of the trigeminal nucleus had a very poor ability to transmit information about skin identation certainly seems premature in the light of recent findings (110).

Mechanically Excited Units in the Dorsal Columns, Dorsal Column Nuclei, and Medial Lemniscus

Most of the rapidly adapting cutaneous mechanoreceptor afferents with large myelinated axons from monkey fore- and hindlimbs (166) and raccoon forepaw (131) send collaterals to upper cervical levels in the dorsal columns. This is similar to the situation discovered earlier for cat (14, 15, 123). A proportion of slowly adapting afferents from the glabrous skin of the raccoon forepaw also project by this route (131), but none do so in the monkey (166). The raccoon is therefore more like the cat, since in the cat both Type I and II units project, at least in part, from the forelimb (155) and trunk (15).

Postsynaptic fibers ascending in both the dorsal columns and the dorsolateral funiculus to the dorsal column nuclei carry a wider range of information. Although usually excited by sensitive mechanoreceptors, they are also fired by high threshold receptors from both skin and, in the dorsal columns at least, muscle (40, 122, 154). Physiological and anatomical studies agree that postsynaptic fibers in both the DC and DLF terminate principally in rostral and basal parts of the nucleus and not on the "cell clusters" in the center of the nucleus where many of the primary afferent collaterals terminate (40, 53, 138, 149).

A study of fibers in the medial leminiscus close to the thalamus has confirmed and extended earlier observations on the specificity of connections of cells in the DCN that project by this route (20). The bulk of axons fired spontaneously in the absence of stimulation, thus showing that this activity had not been caused by damage when it had been recorded in the DCN themselves. The bulk of axons had small forelimb receptive fields, sometimes restricted to one point only. Axons having fields restricted to one point, or in other cases to a few touch corpuscles or a few tylotrich hairs, must receive a powerful input from only one receptor axon, thus indicating an amazing restriction of connections.

Two important reviews on the dorsal column system have challenged classical assumptions about the role and organization of what was thought to be a system of secure relays carrying high resolution tactile information to the forebrain. Gordon (52) has stressed the anatomical and physiological complexity of the DCN. He pointed out that the discovery of inputs from outside the dorsal columns (see above) and of the descending effects from DCN onto spinal cord cells (19, 39, 40) make the interpretation of the effects of dorsal column lesions very difficult. Wall (161) has argued that the dorsal column–lemniscal system does not function as a sensory relay at all. He has proposed that we look for a more sophisticated role for this system, and suggested that this role may be control of the activities of other input pathways such that optimal attention is paid to appropriate (e.g. changing) parts of the input. Wall & Dubner (163) have reviewed some of the more recent evidence on this matter.

Since that review, Vierck (156) has shown that a long-lasting deficit of some nonexploratory tactile tasks can occur following dorsal column lesions. Monkeys were trained to discriminate the size of discs pressed against their feet. After a unilateral dorsal column (DC) lesion they could not make this discrimination for 70–90 days. After this period the performance gradually improved until at 120–180 days it was back to where it had been preoperatively. Vierck (156) also pointed out that the motor deficits recover over a similar, very long, time scale.

Other tactile tasks (e.g. two-point discrimination) (95) recover much more quickly following DC lesions. None of the present hypotheses concerning DC function appear to be able to explain this difference between two very similar, passive, tactile tasks.

An important finding reported by Wall (161) was that rats with only their dorsal columns intact did not behave as though they could feel stimuli applied distal to the lesion. Cats with very similar lesions have, however, recently been found to have normal thresholds for electrical stimulation of mixed peripheral nerves below the section (112). At first sight these two studies appear completely incompatible. There are, though, major differences in methods (e.g. different species; cutaneous test in one, electric shock to mixed nerve in the other; etc). In particular, it would be interesting to know if the cats of Myers et al (112) reacted to cutaneous stimuli of the type used by Wall (161) in a normal manner.

SKIN TEMPERATURE: WARM AND COLD

Three useful reviews have been published recently by Hensel. Two deal with the structure and function of cutaneous thermoreceptors (63, 64a) and one deals with the peripheral and central events involved in thermoregulation (64).

Afferent Thermoreceptor Units Responding to Skin Cooling

A new attempt has been made to determine the histological structure of the cold receptor by examining pieces of nose skin that have been shown electrophysiologically to contain such an ending (63, 64, 80). A characteristic nerve termination located in the most superficial layer of the dermis, and with fine processes in close contact with the basal cells of the epidermis, was found at the marked sites. The fine structure of these receptors has been examined using both light and electron microscopy (63). Attempts to locate warmth receptors using similar techniques have not yet proved successful (63).

A number of recent studies have examined quantitatively the responses of primate cold receptors from tongue (125, 127, 128), face (44), and hand (36, 78, 98). Poulos & Lende (127, 128) recorded with a microelectrode in the trigeminal ganglion, while warming and cooling the tongue. They found many units responding to cooling and divided these into two classes, depending upon whether they responded to innocuous mechanical stimuli as well (T + M units) or not (T units). The majority of T + M units fired only when the temperature of the tongue was lowered fairly quickly. Another study of trigeminal afferent units found only T + M units, and most of these units gave slowly adapting mechanical responses (137, 142). It seems unlikely that such discharges play an important role in generating cold sensations (71, 78). The cold sensitivity of SA mechanoreceptors from limb skin has been studied quantitatively in cats (45) and monkeys (45, 78).

The cold afferents from the glabrous skin of monkey hands have been studied using controlled cooling and warming pulses of short (usually 4 sec) duration (37, 78). Similar stimuli have been utilized for a parallel psychophysical study of thermal sensitivity in human glabrous skin (78). Conduction velocities of cold units from monkey hand ranged from 5–35 m/sec (average 15 m/sec); cold units with unmyelinated fibers, such as have been found from primate hairy skin (65, 71), were not studied. Best static firing occurred at 19–31°C (average 25°C) and receptive fields were punctate. Moving the stimulator only 2 mm from the sensitive spot rendered the unit inexcitable even by a 10°C drop in skin temperature. Following rapid cooling, most, but not all, receptors gave a marked dynamic response that subsided over a few seconds as the unit adapted towards a steady firing frequency. This steady firing was characterized by the burst pattern described for some other cold units, particularly at low temperatures (37, 63, 71, 127). Stimulus repetition rates of greater than 2–3/min gave rise to a cumulative depression of responsiveness, and the extent of this temporal depression was analyzed for pairs and triplets of cold "pulses" (37). Input-output relations for single fibers (37) and the variability of successive responses to a fixed stimulus (78) were also determined.

The responses of primate cold receptors to heating the skin to noxious levels (above 45°C) have been examined for hairy skin of the face (44) and for glabrous skin of the hand (98). Facial cold receptors required heating to over 55°C initially before "paradoxical" firing (43) occurred, but were more sensitive on subsequent trials, with thresholds often dropping below 50°C (44). Immediately following the application of a heat stimulus, cold units fired little, but after a few seconds activity built up and could reach levels greater than those encountered during slow cooling (44). "Paradoxical" firing of cold units in glabrous skin of the hand was found to be markedly dependent upon rectal temperature (98). At a rectal temperature of 39°C, 90% of cold units were excited by skin heating to 53°C, while at 37°C rectal temperature only 20% of units fired for a similar stimulus. The mechanism by which cold-fiber heat sensitivity increases when rectal temperature rises is not clear. However, sympathetic effects may be involved. Recently it has been shown (146) that, in frogs, discharges in cutaneous nerves following cooling are enhanced by sympathetic stimulation or by local application of epinephrine or norepinephrine. It should be noted, however, that Long (98) found the "orthodox" (cold) excitation to be unaffected by rectal temperature changes. It is not clear whether glabrous skin units show any sensitization following noxious heating comparable to that found for units from facial hairy skin (44).

Afferent Thermoreceptor Units Responding to Skin Warming

Many warmth fibers from monkey facial skin have been found to have thinly myelinated axons (44, 147), as have a very small number from glabrous skin of the monkey hand (37). This contrasts with all previously described warmth units that had unmyelinated axons (63). However, Sumino et al (147) pointed out that there is earlier evidence from psychophysical experiments using differential nerve block that warm sensations are due, in part at least, to activity in small myelinated axons (12). Recent studies of human sensations during pressure block, where the degree of block was monitored by nerve recording, have not examined this matter directly, but have confirmed that good warm sensations are still felt following moderate skin temperature rises even when all A fiber activity has been blocked (150).

Facial warmth fibers, both those with myelinated and those with unmyelinated axons, showed good dynamic sensitivity (147). Their adapted firing could conform to one of two patterns. One group of warmth units reached peak firing frequencies at 41–42°C, while the other group fired best at a temperature above 45°C (44, 147). In contrast, nearly all warmth units isolated from the median nerve in the monkey and innervating glabrous skin had unmyelinated axons and few showed any dynamic firing (37, 89).

A number of studies where microelectrodes have been used for recording from the trigeminal ganglion have failed to find any warmth units, although cold-sensitive units have been found (80, 127, 128, 137, 142). This is true even when areas have been stimulated that are known to have warmth receptors [e.g. the tongue (42, 127, 128) and the nose (66, 80]. In fact, all successful recordings from warmth fibers have been made by dissecting peripheral nerves, presumably because this technique allows greater bias towards minority groups, particularly those with fine afferent fibers. It is important to realize that microelectrode samples from CNS structures may be as limited as those from the ganglion and thus not to make too much of negative results.

Central Connections of Thermoreceptor Afferents

The presence of "specific" thermally sensitive units in the most superficial parts of the dorsal horn (lamina 1, marginal zone) (31) has been confirmed by Hellon & Misra (59) in the rat. A similar concentration also occurs in the analagous pericornual zone of the spinal trigeminal nucleus of the cat (47, 109, 110). Other cells excited by small cutaneous temperature changes are also found in the deeper parts of the dorsal horn (59, 129) and spinal trigeminal nucleus (110). Thermal units in the trigeminal nucleus respond at relatively long latency following electrical skin stimulation, thus indicating that they receive an input only from afferents of fine caliber (110).

Both "warmth" and "cold" units have been found in the trigeminal nucleus of the cat (47, 109, 110), and in the dorsal horn of monkey (35), cat (31), and rat (59). Warmth units appear to be relatively uncommon in the caudal spinal trigeminal nucleus (110). Thermal units were only found in the spinal nucleus and not in the main sensory nucleus of the trigeminal in anesthetized cats (47).

Cold units in the monkey trigeminal nucleus showed a similar pattern of static and dynamic firing, as did afferent fibers isolated from the ganglion (125, 128a). The static firing profile of some spinal cord cells in response to skin warming also resembles that of primary afferents (67, 129). However, spinal cord units in rat often showed quite different static sensitivity profiles from those of afferents from the same skin area (the scrotum) (59, 71). For spinal cord cells, the relation between firing frequency and temperature was usually monotonic over the temperature range of 15–45°C (59), whereas the afferents showed the usual unimodal, convex relation with a maximum at 25–30°C (cold units) or 43°C (one warmth unit) (71). Spinal cord warmth units also showed little dynamic firing following rapid temperature shifts, while cold units usually showed a good dynamic response (59). Trigeminal nucleus cold units also retained a good dynamic sensitivity like the primary afferents (125).

The degree of convergence from peripheral receptor units onto spinal cord cells is considerable in the rat, where most cells, including those in lamina 1, had bilateral receptive fields (62). The receptive fields of cold units in the cat spinal trigeminal nucleus were much smaller, being only 2–4 mm across (47). However, given the dense innervation of cat facial skin and the punctate nature of peripheral receptive fields, this still indicates a considerable amount of convergence. The degree of convergence from lingual cold receptors onto trigeminal nucleus cells must also be considerable since the characteristic bursting pattern of the primary afferents was barely apparent in the discharges of such cells (125).

The projection pathways for thermal information are not clear, although cells similar to those found in the trigeminal nucleus and spinal cord have also been found in ventrobasal thalamus (60, 91, 101, 125, 126) and somatosensory cortex (61, 90). Axons in the anterolateral tract of the spinal cord at segments C3–5 have been found that respond to either skin cooling or warming of the trunk and hind limbs (144). These were assumed to be spinothalamic axons (144), although their termination was not tested directly. Direct spinothalamic axons are rare in the cat (152), and a recent study in the monkey of 186 spinothalamic cells identified by antidromic excitation from the thalamus revealed no specific thermosensitive units (169). Specific thermoreceptor units are not found in the spinocervical tract or the dorsal columns (15).

The central projection pattern for thermal information is likely to be different from those for other somatic systems because cutaneous thermoreceptors are involved in thermoregulation in addition to their sensory role (64). One consequence of this duality is that information from cutaneous thermoreceptors may be transmitted to CNS neurons, which are themselves thermosensitive or are in receipt of information from thermosensitive neurones. Such a convergence has been shown for certain spinal cord cells (144).

NOXIOUS SKIN STIMULATION

This section is restricted to considering the input from the skin. A more extensive review on these matters, including a consideration of the input from noncutaneous somatic structures, is in preparation (100).

Receptor Units

HIGH THRESHOLD MECHANORECEPTOR UNITS Small myelinated afferent fibers responding only to damaging or potentially damaging cutaneous stimuli have been found with fields in hairy skin in cats (26) and in hairy and glabrous skin in monkeys (120). These units have distinctive receptive fields consisting of a number (3–20) of spots scattered over an area of 1–8 cm^2 (26). Some of these units may also be heat sensitive (8,44), but possibly only after prolonged heating to noxious levels (27). It is not clear if the receptive fields of the units examined in recent studies consisted of multiple spots or whether they were in fact polymodal-type receptors with small myelinated axons like those described by Iggo & Ogawa (74) (see next section).

A small proportion of units with unmyelinated fibers are also excited by intense mechanical stimuli but not by noxious heat (8, 10), although they sometimes fire following extreme cooling (10, 27). These units may not comprise a homogeneous group since the form of their receptive fields is very variable.

POLYMODAL NOCICEPTOR UNITS A large group of unmyelinated fibers responding to strong pressure, noxious heating, and irritant chemicals was described in detail by Bessou & Perl (10) and designated as "polymodal nociceptor units." Such units have a receptive field comprising one spot or small zone and have been found in cat hairy and glabrous skin (8, 10, 11), in primate skin (27, 44) including that of man (151, 155a), in rat skin (75), and in rabbit skin (B. Lynn and E. R. Perl, unpublished observations). In monkeys, polymodal nociceptor units comprise about 90% of all unmyelinated afferent units (27) and are therefore the most numerous of all receptor units, at least from limb skin, since unmyelinated afferent fibers outnumber myelinated ones. And there are also some polymodal nociceptors with very slowly conducting myelinated axons (4–7 m/sec) in monkeys (74).

SENSITIZATION AND SENSITIVITY TO IRRITANT CHEMICALS Repeated heating increases the firing of polymodal nociceptors and reduces their heat threshold. This phenomenon was examined by Bessou & Perl (10) and was termed "sensitization." Heat sensitization has also been reported for C-fiber units from the glabrous skin of the cat's foot pad (8) and for the paradoxical firing of cold receptors from monkey face with myelinated axons (44).

Some polymodal nociceptors are excited by intra-arterial injections of bradykinin, others are excited by injections of serotonin (5-HT), and some respond to both (7). However, many other receptor units, including SA mechanoreceptors with large myelinated axons, mechanoreceptors with unmyelinated axons, and high threshold mechanoreceptors with A-delta axons and with C-axons were also excited by these substances. Only the RA hair units remain unaffected (7). Bradykinin, but not serotonin, was found to enhance the heat responses of C-fibers. These data are consistent with earlier work using intra-arterial bradykinin and serotonin (46) and intracutaneous bradykinin (10).

RESPONSES OF MECHANORECEPTOR AND THERMORECEPTOR UNITS TO NOXIOUS STIMULATION A group of thermoreceptors that have thresholds of about 30°C and increase their firing rate monotonically up to temperatures about 47°C have been described in the monkey face (147). This high optimum distinguished these units from many other warmth receptors, including others on the monkey face, which reach peak firing at temperatures below 45°C (44, 63, 147). Other warmth units with best static firing about 45°C have been described from the skin of the cat's nasal area (66). It has been suggested that the group with the high optimum temperature in monkeys may be involved with signalling threshold pain (44). However, it is not clear if the discharge of such units is maintained for more than a few seconds during noxious heating, or whether, like cat receptors, their discharges adapt out completely at high temperatures (66).

The responses of a number of types of mechanoreceptors have been examined using both noxious and innocuous stimuli (11, 120, 121). It was always possible to mimic the firing patterns produced by noxious stimulation with a large innocuous stimulus (27), and so these units are unlikely to play a role in generating painful sensations.

Central Connections of Nociceptor Afferents

Cells in the most superficial layer of the monkey spinal cord (lamina 1; marginal cells) have been described that, like those originally found in the cat (31, 83), only respond to noxious cutaneous stimuli (86, 169). Similar cells are also found in the analogous pericornual zone of the caudal trigeminal nucleus of the cat (109, 110). In both cat and monkey some of these cells send axons via the contralateral, lateral funiculus to upper cervical levels (86). In monkeys, but not in cats, many of these cells project all the way to the contralateral thalamus (153, 169).

Some spinal cord cells situated deeper in the dorsal horn and in parts of the ventral horn and intermediate gray matter also respond to noxious mechanical or thermal stimuli, but not to innocuous stimuli (129, 169). Similar cells have also been found in the nucleus proprius of the caudal spinal trigeminal complex (82, 110).

As well as these "specific" nociceptor cells, the dorsal horn contains a large population of cells that have low thresholds, but require noxious stimulation before maximal or maintained firing is produced (158). Such cells are concentrated in lamina 5 (68, 159) and 20% were found to send axons to the contralateral thalamus in monkeys (1, 94). However, very few lamina 5 cells from cat lumbosacral cord project in this manner (93, 153), although more may do so from cervical cord (41). Axons of similar, wide-range neurons are also found in the spinocervical tract (16, 22) and in the dorsal columns (122). Many of these cells also receive input from muscle afferents and visceral afferents with small myelinated axons (Group III) (124, 141). Bradykinin, injected into a major limb artery, also produces vigorous firing in many lamina 5 cells (9).

The evoked discharges of lamina 5 cells are markedly reduced by anesthetics (159). In spinal cats, nitrous oxide and hyperventilation were found to reduce the spontaneous firing of lamina 5 cells, but not that of lamina 1 cells (83). Spontaneous firing of neurons in the trigeminal nucleus that responded best to noxious stimuli was also inhibited by inhalation of 75% nitrous oxide, whereas the firing of cells that responded best to innocuous stimulation was enhanced (82).

CONCLUDING REMARKS

This review has considered the somatosensory system in four parts, each concerned with a different stimulus set. There are many situations where interactions occur between these parts, and by treating the system in this manner, I am implicitly assuming a certain view of its organization (164). However, recent studies to a certain extent justify the approach adopted here. New examples of receptor specificity have been found and the anatomical structures associated with many of these functional classes have been identified. Further, this work on the afferents is paralleled in recent finds concerning the specificity of responses of second-order neurones. Large numbers of cells that relay information to distant parts of the central nervous system do, however, receive an input from a wide spectrum of afferents, although the "width" of the spectrum may be considerably restricted in the presence of suitable activity in descending pathways (16, 79, 159). Undoubtedly situations like those existing in parts of the DCN, where one afferent fiber can dominate the output of some second-order cells, are the exception and there are no simple "relays" in the somatosensory system (52).

Literature Cited

1. Albe-Fessard, D., Levante, A., Lamour, Y. 1974. Origin of spinothalamic tract in monkeys. *Brain Res.* 65:503–9
2. Andres, K. H. 1966. Uber die feinstruktur der rezeptoren an sinushaaren. *Z. Zellforsch.* 75:339–65
3. Andres, K. H., von Dureing, M. 1973. Morphology of cutaneous receptors. See Ref. 72, Chap. 1, 1–28
4. Aoyama, M., Hongo, T., Kudo, N. 1973. An uncrossed ascending tract originating from below Clarke's column and conveying group I impulses from the hindlimb muscles in the cat. *Brain Res.* 62:237–41
5. Armett, C. J., Hunsperger, R. W. 1961. Excitation of receptors in the pad of the cat by single and double mechanical pulses. *J. Physiol. London* 158:15–38
6. Armett, C. J., Gray, J. A. B., Hunsperger, R. W., Lal, S. 1962. Transmission of information in primary receptor neurones and second order neurones of a phasic system. *J. Physiol. London* 164:395–421
7. Beck, P. W., Handwerker, H. O. 1974. Bradykinin and serotonin effects on various types of cutaneous nerve fibres. *Pfluegers Arch.* 347:209–22
8. Beck, P. W., Handwerker, H. O., Zimmermann, M. 1974. Nervous outflow from cat's foot during noxious radiant heat stimulation. *Brain Res.* 67:373–86
9. Besson, J. M., Conseiller, C., Hamann, K. F., Maillard, M. C. 1972. Modifications of dorsal horn cell activities in the spinal cord, after intra-arterial injection of bradykinin. *J. Physiol. London* 221:189–205
10. Bessou, P., Perl, E. R. 1969. Response of cutaneous sensory units with unmyelinated fibers to noxious stimuli. *J. Neurophysiol.* 32:1025–43
11. Bessou, P., Burgess, P. R., Perl, E. R., Taylor, C. B. 1971. Dynamic properties of mechanoreceptors with unmyelinated (C) fibers. *J. Neurophysiol.* 34: 116–31
12. Bishop, G. H. 1960. The relation of nerve fiber size to modality of sensation. In *Advances in Biology of Skin,* ed. W. Montagna, Vol. 1, 88–98. Oxford: Pergamon
13. Brodal, A., Pompeiano, O. 1957. The vestibular nuclei in the cat. *J. Anat.* 91:438–54
14. Brown, A. G. 1968. Cutaneous afferent fibre collaterals in the dorsal columns of the cat. *Exp. Brain Res.* 5:293–305
15. Brown, A. G. 1973. Ascending and long spinal pathways: dorsal columns, spinocervical tract and spinothalamic tract. See Ref. 72, Chap. 10, 315–38
16. Brown, A. G., Franz, D. N. 1969. Responses of spinocervical tract neurones to natural stimulation of identified cutaneous receptors. *Exp. Brain Res.* 7:231–49
17. Brown, A. G., Hayden, R. E. 1971. The distribution of cutaneous receptors in the rabbit's hind limb and differential electrical stimulation of their axons. *J. Physiol. London* 213:495–506
18. Brown, A. G., Iggo, A. 1967. A quantitative study of cutaneous receptors and afferent fibres in the cat and rabbit. *J. Physiol. London* 193:707–33
19. Brown, A. G., Gordon, G., Kay, R. H. 1974. A study of single axons in the cat's medial lemniscus. *J. Physiol. London* 236:225–46
20. Brown, A. G., Martin, H. F. III. 1973. Activation of descending control of spinocervical tract by impulses ascending the dorsal columns and relaying through the dorsal column nuclei. *J. Physiol. London* 235:535–50
21. Brown, P. B., Moraff, H., Tapper, D. N. 1973. Functional organization of the cat's dorsal horn: spontaneous activity and central cell response to single impulses in single type I fibers. *J. Neurophysiol.* 36:827–39
22. Bryan, R. N., Coulter, J. D., Willis, W. D. 1974. Cells of origin of the spinocervical tract in the monkey. *Exp. Neurol.* 42:574–86
23. Burgess, P. R., Clark, F. J. 1969. Characteristics of knee joint receptors in the cat. *J. Physiol. London* 203:317–35
24. Burgess, P. R., Clark, F. J. 1969. Dorsal column projection of fibres from the cat knee joint. *J. Physiol. London* 203: 301–15
25. Burgess, P. R., Horch, K. 1973. Specific regeneration of cutaneous fibers in the cat. *J. Neurophysiol.* 36:101–14
26. Burgess, P. R., Perl, E. R. 1967. Myelinated afferent fibres responding specifically to noxious stimulation of the skin. *J. Physiol. London* 190:541–62
27. Burgess, P. R., Perl, E. R. 1973. Cutaneous mechanoreceptors and nociceptors. See Ref. 72, Chap. 2, 29–78
28. Burgess, P. R., Petit, D., Warren, R. M. 1968. Receptor types in cat hairy skin

supplied by myelinated fibers. *J. Neurophysiol.* 31:833–48
29. Burgess, P. R., English, K. B., Horch, K. W., Stensaas, L. J. 1974. Patterning in the regeneration of type I cutaneous receptors. *J. Physiol. London* 236:57–82
30. Chambers, M. R., Andres, K. H., Von Dureing, M., Iggo, A. 1972. The structure and function of the slowly adapating type II mechanoreceptor in hairy skin. *Quart. J. Exp. Physiol.* 57:417–45
31. Christensen, B. N., Perl, E. R. 1970. Spinal neurons specifically excited by noxious or thermal stimuli: marginal zone of the dorsal horn. *J. Neurophysiol.* 33:293–307
32. Clark, F. J. 1972. Central projection of sensory fibers from the cat knee joint. *J. Neurobiol.* 3:101–10
33. Clark, F. J., Landgren, S., Silfvenius, H. 1973. Projections to the cat's cerebral cortex from low threshold joint afferents. *Acta Physiol. Scand.* 89:504–21
34. Cohen, L. A. 1958. Contributions of tactile, musculo-tendinous and joint mechanisms to position sense in human shoulder. *J. Neurophysiol.* 21:563–68
35. Courtney, K., Brengelman, G., Sundsten, J. W. 1972. Evidence for spinal cord unit activity responsive to peripheral warming in the primate. *Brain Res.* 43:657–61
36. Darian-Smith, I. 1973. The trigeminal system. See Ref. 72, Chap. 9, 271–314
37. Darian-Smith, I., Johnson, K. O., Dykes, R. 1973. "Cold" fiber population innervating palmar and digital skin of the monkey: responses to cold pulses. *J. Neurophysiol.* 36:325–47
38. Darian-Smith, I., Rowe, M. J., Sessle, B. J. 1968. "Tactile" stimulus intensity: information transmission by relay neurones in different trigeminal nuclei. *Science* 160:791–94
39. Dart, A. M. 1971. Cells of the dorsal column nuclei projecting down into the spinal cord. *J. Physiol. London* 219:29P
40. Dart, A. M., Gordon, G. 1973. Some properties of spinal connections of the cat's dorsal column nuclei which do not involve the dorsal columns. *Brain Res.* 58:61–68
41. Dilly, P. N., Wall, P. D., Webster, K. E. 1968. Cells of origin of the spinothalamic tract in the cat and rat. *Exp. Neurol.* 21:550–62
42. Dodt, E., Zotterman, Y. 1952. Mode of action of warm receptors. *Acta Physiol. Scand.* 26:345–57
43. Dodt, E., Zotterman, Y. 1952. The discharge of specific cold fibres at high temperatures. *Acta Physiol. Scand.* 26:358–65
44. Dubner, R., Sumino, R., Starkman, S. 1974. Responses of facial cutaneous thermosensitive and mechanosensitive afferent fibers in the monkey to noxious heat stimulation. *Advan. Neurol.* 4: 61–71
45. Duclaux, R., Kenshalo, D. R. 1972. The temperature sensitivity of the type I slowly adapting mechanoreceptors in cat and monkey. *J. Physiol. London* 224:647–64
46. Fjallbrant, N., Iggo, A. 1961. The effect of histamine, 5-hydroxytryptamine and acetylcholine on cutaneous afferent fibres. *J. Physiol. London* 156:578–90
47. Fruhstorfer, H., Hensel, H. 1973. Thermal cutaneous afferents in the trigeminal nucleus of the cat. *Naturwissenschaften* 60:209
48. Fuller, D. R. G., Gray, J. A. B. 1966. The relation between mechanical displacements applied to a cat's pad and the resultant impulse patterns. *J. Physiol. London* 182:465–83
49. Gelfan, S., Carter, S. 1967. Muscle sense in man. *Exp. Neurol.* 18:469–73
50. Godwin-Austen, R. B. 1969. The mechanoreceptors of the costovertebral joints. *J. Physiol. London* 202:737–53
51. Goodwin, G. M., McCloskey, D. I., Matthews, P. B. C. 1972. The contribution of muscle afferents to kinaesthesia shown by vibration induced illusions of movement and by the effects of paralysing joint afferents. *Brain* 95:705–48
52. Gordon, G. 1973. The concept of relay nuclei. See Ref. 72, Chap. 5, 137–50
53. Gordon, G., Grant, G. 1972. Afferents to the dorsal column nuclei from the dorsolateral funiculus of the spinal cord. *Acta Physiol. Scand.* 84:30A–31A
54. Gordon, G., Jukes, M. G. M. 1964. Dual organisation of the exteroceptive components of the cat's gracile nucleus. *J. Physiol. London* 173:263–90
55. Gottschaldt, K. M., Iggo, A., Young, D. W. 1973. Functional characteristics of mechanoreceptors in sinus hair follicles of the cat. *J. Physiol. London* 235:287–315
56. Gray, J. A. B. 1962. Coding in systems of primary receptor neurons. *Soc. Exp. Biol. Symp.* 16:345–54
57. Hahn, J. F. 1971. Stimulus-response relationships in the first-order sensory fibres from cat's vibrissae. *J. Physiol. London* 213:215–26
58. Hahn, J. F. 1971. Thermal-mechanical stimulus interactions in low-threshold

C-fiber mechanoreceptors of cat. *Exp. Neurol.* 33:607–17
59. Hellon, R. F., Misra, N. K. 1973. Neurones in the dorsal horn of the rat responding to scrotal skin temperature changes. *J. Physiol. London* 232:375–88
60. Hellon, R. F., Misra, N. K. 1973. Neurones in the ventrobasal complex of the rat thalamus responding to scrotal skin temperature changes. *J. Physiol. London* 232:389–99
61. Hellon, R. F., Misra, N. K., Provins, K. A. 1973. Neurones in the somatosensory cortex of the rat responding to scrotal skin temperature changes. *J. Physiol. London* 232:401–11
62. Hellon, R. F., Mitchell, D. 1974. Convergence in a thermal afferent pathway. *J. Physiol. London* 239:61P–62P
63. Hensel, H. 1973. Cutaneous thermoreceptors. See Ref. 72, Chap. 3, 79–110
64. Hensel, H. 1973. Neural processes in thermoregulation. *Physiol. Rev.* 53: 948–1017
64a. Hensel, H. 1974. Thermoreceptors. *Ann. Rev. Physiol.* 36:233–49
65. Hensel, H., Iggo, A. 1971. Analysis of cutaneous warm and cold fibres in primates. *Pfluegers Arch.* 329:1–8
66. Hensel, H., Kenshalo, D. R. 1969. Warm receptors in the nasal region of cats. *J. Physiol. London* 204:99–112
67. Hensel, H., Iggo, A., Witt, I. 1960. A quantitative study of sensitive cutaneous thermoreceptors with C afferent fibres. *J. Physiol. London* 153:113–26
68. Hillman, P., Wall, P. D. 1969. Inhibitory and excitatory factors influencing the receptive fields of lamina 5 spinal cord cells. *Exp. Brain Res.* 9:284–306
69. Hunt, C. C. 1961. On the nature of vibration receptors in the hind limb of the cat. *J. Physiol. London* 155:175–86
70. Iggo, A. 1962. Specific sensory structures in hairy skin. *Acta Neuroveg.* 24:175–80
71. Iggo, A. 1969. Cutaneous thermoreceptors in primates and sub-primates. *J. Physiol. London* 200:403–30
72. Iggo, A., Ed. 1973. Somatosensory System. *Handbook of Sensory Physiology,* Vol. II. Berlin: Springer. 851 pp.
73. Iggo, A., Muir, A. R. 1969. The structure and function of a slowly adapting touch corpuscle in hairy skin. *J. Physiol. London* 200:763–96
74. Iggo, A., Ogawa, H. 1971. Primate cutaneous thermal nociceptors. *J. Physiol. London* 216:77P–78P
75. Iriuchijima, J., Zotterman, Y. 1960. The specificity of afferent cutaneous C fibres in mammals. *Acta Physiol. Scand.* 49:267–78
76. Janig, W. 1971. Morphology of rapidly and slowly adapting mechanoreceptors in the hairless skin of the cat's hind foot. *Brain Res.* 28:217–31
77. Johnson, K. O. 1974. Reconstruction of population response to a vibratory stimulus in quickly adapting mechanoreceptive afferent fiber population innervating glabrous skin of the monkey. *J. Neurophysiol.* 37:48–72
78. Johnson, K. O., Darian-Smith, I., LaMotte, C. 1973. Peripheral neural determinants of temperature discrimination in man: a correlative study of responses to cooling skin. *J. Neurophysiol.* 36:347–70
79. Kasprzak, H., Mann, M. D., Tapper, D. N. 1970. Pyramidal modulation of responses of spinal neurons to natural stimulation of cutaneous receptors. *Brain Res.* 24:121–24
80. Kenshalo, D. R., Hensel, H., Graziadei, P., Fruhstorfer, H. 1971. On the anatomy, physiology and psychophysics of the cat's temperature-sensing system. In *Oro-Facial Sensory and Motor Mechanisms,* ed. R. Dubner, Y. Kawamura, 23–44. New York: Appleton-Century-Crofts
81. Kenton, B., Kruger, L. 1971. Information transmission in slowly adapting mechanoreceptor fibers. *Exp. Neurol.* 31:114–39
82. Kitahata, L. M., McAllister, R. G., Taub, A. 1973. Identification of central trigeminal nociceptors and the effects of nitrous oxide. *Anesthesiology* 38:12–19
83. Kitahata, L. M., Taub, A., Sato, I. 1971. Lamina-specific suppression of dorsal horn unit activity by nitrous oxide and by hyperventilation. *J. Pharmacol. Exp. Ther.* 176:101–8
84. Knibestöl, M., Vallbo, A. B. 1970. Single unit analysis of mechanoreceptor activity from human glabrous skin. *Acta Physiol. Scand.* 80:178–95
85. Kruger, L., Kenton, B. 1973. Quantitative neural and psychophysical data for cutaneous mechanoreceptor function. *Brain Res.* 49:1–24
86. Kumazawa, T., Perl, E. R., Burgess, P. R., Whitehorn, D. 1971. *Proc. Int. Union Physiol. Sci.* 9:328 (Abstr.)
87. Kuno, M., Munoz-Martinez, E. J., Randic, M. 1973. Sensory inputs to neurones in Clarke's column from muscle,

cutaneous and joint receptors. *J. Physiol. London* 228:327–42
88. Kuno, M., Munoz-Martinez, E. J., Randic, M. 1973. Synaptic action on Clarke's column neurones in relation to afferent terminal size. *J. Physiol. London* 228:343–60
89. LaMotte, C., Johnson, K., Darian-Smith, I., Goswell, M., Long, R. 1972. *Proc. Ann. Meet., Soc. Neurosci.* 2:188 (Abstr.)
90. Landgren, S. 1957. Cortical reception of cold impulses. *Acta Physiol. Scand.* 40:202–9
91. Landgren, S. 1960. Thalamic neurons responding to cooling of the cat's tongue. *Acta Physiol. Scand.* 48:255–67
92. Landgren, S., Silfvenius, H. 1971. Nucleus Z, the medullary relay in the projection path to the cerebral cortex of group I muscle afferents from the cat's hind limb. *J. Physiol. London* 218: 551–71
93. Levante, A., Albe-Fessard, D. 1972. Localisation dans les couches VII et VIII de Rexed des cellules d'origine d'un faisceau spino-reticulaire croise. *C.R. Acad. Sci. D* 274:3007–10
94. Levante, A., Lamour, Y., Albe-Fessard, D. 1973. Localisation dans la couche V de Rexed de cellules d'origine d'un faisceau spino-thalamique croise chez le macaque. *C.R. Acad. Sci. D* 276: 1589–92
95. Levitt, M., Schwartzmann, R. J. 1966. Spinal sensory tracts and two-point tactile sensitivity. *Anat. Rec.* 154:377
96. Lindstrom, S., Takata, M. 1971. *25th Int. Physiol. Congr.* 9:374 (Abstr.)
97. Lindstrom, S., Takata, M. 1972. Monosynaptic excitation of dorsal spinocerebellar tract neurones from low threshold joint afferents. *Acta Physiol. Scand.* 84:430–32
98. Long, R. R. 1973. Cold fiber heat sensitivity: dependency of "paradoxical" discharge on body temperature. *Brain Res.* 63:389–92
99. Lynn, B. 1970. *Factors in the transmission of information by a population of mechanosensitive neurones.* PhD thesis. Univ. London, London
100. Lynn, B. 1975. Physiology of the activation of pain. *Progr. Neurol. Surg.* 8:In press
101. Martin, H. F. III, Manning, J. W. 1971. Thalamic "warming" and "cooling" units responding to cutaneous stimulation. *Brain Res.* 27:377–81
102. Matthews, B. H. C. 1933. Nerve endings in mammalian muscle. *J. Physiol. London* 78:1–53
103. Matthews, P. B. C. 1972. *Mammalian Muscle Receptors and Their Central Actions.* London: Arnold
104. Matthews, P. B. C., Simmonds, A. 1974. *J. Physiol. London* 239:27P–28P
105. McCall, W. D., Farias, M. C., Williams, W. J., BeMent, S. L. 1974. Static and dynamic responses of slowly adapting joint receptors. *Brain Res.* 70:221–43
106. Merton, P. A. 1964. Human position sense and sense of effort. *Soc. Exp. Biol. Symp.* 18:387–400
107. Millar, J. 1972. Joint afferent discharge following muscle contraction in the absence of joint movement. *J. Physiol. London* 226:72P
108. Millar, J. 1973. Joint afferent fibres responding to muscle stretch, vibration and contraction. *Brain Res.* 63:380–83
109. Mosso, J. A., Kruger, L. 1972. Spinal trigeminal neurons excited by noxious and thermal stimuli. *Brain Res.* 38:206–10
110. Mosso, J. A., Kruger, L. 1973. Receptor categories represented in spinal nucleus caudalis. *J. Neurophysiol.* 36: 472–88
111. Munger, B. L., Pubols, L. M., Pubols, B. H. 1971. The Merkel rete papilla—a slowly adapating sensory receptor in mammalian glabrous skin. *Brain Res.* 29:47–61
112. Myers, D. A., Hostetter, G., Bourassa, C. M., Swett, J. E. 1974. Dorsal columns in sensory detection. *Brain Res.* 70:350–55
113. Nier, K. 1972. Phasenfrequenzgang neuraler impulsmuster von vibrissenreceptoren. *Pfluegers Arch.* 334:357–66
114. Nier, K. 1974. Effects of different ionic components on afferent responses of vibrissa receptors. *Pfluegers Arch.* 347:27–38
115. Nilsson, B. Y. 1969. Structure and function of the tactile hair receptors on the cat's foreleg. *Acta Physiol. Scand.* 77:396–416
116. Nilsson, B. Y. 1969. Hair discs and Pacinian corpuscles functionally associated with the carpal tactile hairs in the cat. *Acta Physiol. Scand.* 77:417–28
117. Nord, S. G. 1968. Receptor field characteristics of single cells in the rat trigeminal complex. *Exp. Neurol.* 21:236–43
118. Oscarsson, O. 1973. Functional organization of spinocerebellar paths. See Ref. 72, Chap. 11, 339–80

119. Oswaldo-Cruz, E., Kidd, C. 1964. Functional properties of neurons in the lateral cervical nucleus of the cat. *J. Neurophysiol.* 27:1–14
120. Perl, E. R. 1968. Myelinated afferent fibres innervating the primate skin and their response to noxious stimuli. *J. Physiol. London* 197:593–615
121. Perl, E. R. 1971. Is pain a specific sensation? *J. Psychiat. Res.* 8:273–87
122. Petit, D. 1972. Postsynaptic fibres in the dorsal columns and their relay in the nucleus gracilis. *Brain Res.* 48:380–84
123. Petit, D., Burgess, P. R. 1968. Dorsal column projection of receptors in cat hairy skin supplied by myelinated fibres. *J. Neurophysiol.* 31:849–55
124. Pomeranz, B., Wall, P. D., Weber, W. V. 1968. Cord cells responding to fine myelinated afferents from viscera, muscle and skin. *J. Physiol.* 199:511–32
125. Poulos, D. A. 1971. Trigeminal temperature mechanisms. See Ref. 80, 47–72
126. Poulos, D. A., Benjamin, R. M. 1968. Response of thalamic neurons to thermal stimulation of the tongue. *J. Neurophysiol.* 31:28–43
127. Poulos, D. A., Lende, R. A. 1970. Response of trigeminal ganglion neurones to thermal stimulation of oro-facial regions. I. Steady state response. *J. Neurophysiol.* 33:508–17
128. Poulos, D. A., Lende, R. A. 1970. Response of trigeminal ganglion neurones to thermal stimulation of oro-facial regions. II. Temperature change response. *J. Neurophysiol.* 33:518–26
128a. Poulos, D. A., Strominger, N., Pelletier, V., Gabriele, T. 1970. Response of medullary neurons to thermal stimulation of the tongue. *Fed. Proc.* 29:392 (Abstr.)
129. Price, D. D., Browe, A. C. 1973. Responses of spinal cord neurons to graded noxious and non-noxious stimuli. *Brain Res.* 64:425–29
130. Pubols, L. M., Pubols, B. H. 1973. Modality composition and functional characteristics of dorsal column mechanoreceptive afferent fibers innervating the raccoon's forepaw. *J. Neurophysiol.* 36:1023–37
131. Pubols, L. M., Pubols, B. H., Munger, B. L. 1971. Functional properties of mechanoreceptors in glabrous skin of the raccoon's forepaw. *Exp. Neurol.* 31:165–82
132. Rexed, B. 1952. The cytoarchitectonic organisation of the spinal cord of cat. *J. Comp. Neurol.* 96:415–95
133. Rosen, I. 1969. Afferent connexions to group I activated cells in the main cuneate nucleus of the cat. *J. Physiol. London* 205:209–36
134. Rosen, I. 1972. Projection of forelimb group I muscle afferents to the cat cerebral cortex. *Int. Rev. Neurobiol.* 15: 1–25
135. Rosen, I., Sjölund, B. 1973. Organisation of group I activated cells in the main and external cuneate nuclei of the cat: identification of muscle receptors. *Exp. Brain Res.* 16:221–37
136. Rosen, I., Sjölund, B. 1973. Organisation of group I activated cells in the main and external cuneate nuclei of the cat: convergence patterns demonstrated by natural stimulation. *Exp. Brain Res.* 16:238–46
137. Rowe, M. J., Sessle, B. J. 1972. Responses of trigeminal ganglion and brain stem neurones in the cat to mechanical and thermal stimulation of the face. *Brain Res.* 42:367–84
138. Rustioni, A. 1973. Non-primary afferents to the nucleus gracilis from the lumbar cord of the cat. *Brain Res.* 51:81–95
139. Deleted in proof
140. Sakada, S. 1971. Response of Golgi-Mazzoni corpuscles in the cat periostea to mechanical stimuli. See Ref. 80, 105–22
141. Selzer, M., Spencer, W. A. 1969. Convergence of visceral and cutaneous afferent pathways in the lumbar spinal cord. *Brain Res.* 14:331–48
142. Sessle, B. J., Rowe, M. J. 1967. Temperature sensibility of the face of the cat. *J. Dent. Res.* 46:1305–6
143. Shipley, M. T. 1974. Response characteristics of single units in the rat's trigeminal nuclei to vibrissae displacements. *J. Neurophysiol.* 37:73–90
144. Simon, E. 1972. Temperature signals from skin and spinal cord converging on spinothalamic neurons. *Pfluegers Arch.* 337:323–32
145. Skoglund, S. 1973. Joint receptors and kinaesthesis. See Ref. 72, Chap. 4, 111–36
146. Spray, D. C. 1974. Characteristics, specificity and efferent control of frog cutaneous cold receptors. *J. Physiol. London* 237:15–38
147. Sumino, R., Dubner, R., Starkman, S. 1973. Responses of small myelinated "warm" fibers to noxious heat stimuli applied to the monkey's face. *Brain Res.* 62:260–63

148. Tapper, D. N., Brown, P. B., Moraff, H. 1973. Functional organisation of the cat's dorsal horn: connectivity of myelinated fiber systems of hairy skin. *J. Neurophysiol.* 36:817–26
149. Tomasuolo, K. C., Emmers, R. 1972. Activation of neurons in the gracile nucleus by two afferent pathways in the rat. *Exp. Neurol.* 36:197–206
150. Torebjörk, H. E., Hallin, R. G. 1973. Perceptual changes accompanying controlled preferential blocking of A and C fibre responses in intact human skin nerves. *Exp. Brain Res.* 16:321–32
151. Torebjörk, H. E., Hallin, R. G. 1974. Identification of afferent C units in intact human skin nerves. *Brain Res.* 67:387–403
152. Trevino, D. L., Coulter, J. D., Willis, W. D. 1973. Location of cells of origin of spinothalamic tract in lumbar enlargement of the monkey. *J. Neurophysiol.* 36:750–61
153. Trevino, D. L., Maunz, R. A., Bryan, R. N., Willis, W. D. 1972. Location of cells of origin of the spinothalamic tract in the lumbar enlargement of cat. *Exp. Neurol.* 34:64–77
154. Uddenberg, N. 1968. Functional organisation of long second-order afferents in dorsal funiculus. *Exp. Brain Res.* 4:377–82
155. Uddenberg, N. 1968. Differential localisation in dorsal funiculus of fibres originating from different receptors. *Exp. Brain Res.* 4:367–76
155a. Van Hees, J., Gybels, J. M. 1972. Pain related to single afferent C fibres from human skin. *Brain Res.* 48:397–400
156. Vierck, C. J. 1973. Alterations of spatiotactile discrimination after lesions of primate spinal cord. *Brain Res.* 58:69–79
157. Wagman, I. H., Price, D. D. 1969. Responses of dorsal horn cells in M. mulatta to cutaneous and sural nerve A and C fiber stimuli. *J. Neurophysiol.* 32:803–17
158. Wall, P. D. 1960. Cord cells responding to touch, damage and temperature of skin. *J. Neurophysiol.* 23:197–210
159. Wall, P. D. 1967. The laminar organisation of dorsal horn and effects of descending impulses. *J. Physiol. London* 188:403–23
160. Wall, P. D. 1968. Organisation of cord cells which transmit sensory cutaneous information. In *The Skin Senses,* ed. D. R. Kenshalo, 512–30. Springfield: C. C. Thomas
161. Wall, P. D. 1970. The sensory and motor role of impulses travelling in the dorsal columns towards cerebral cortex. *Brain* 93:505–24
162. Wall, P. D. 1973. Dorsal horn electrophysiology. See Ref. 72, 253–270
163. Wall, P. D., Dubner, R. 1972. Somatosensory pathways. *Ann. Rev. Physiol.* 34:315–36
164. Wall, P. D., Melzack, R. 1962. Neural mechanisms which discriminate events on the skin. *Trans. IRE Info. Theory* IT8:120–125
165. Werner, G., Mountcastle, V. B. 1965. Neural activity in mechanoreceptive cutaneous afferents: stimulus-response relations, Weber functions and information transmission. *J. Neurophysiol.* 28: 359–97
166. Whitsel, B. L., Petrucelli, L. M., Sapiro, G. M. 1969. Modality representation in the lumbar and cervical fasciculus gracilis of squirrel monkeys. *Brain Res.* 15:67–78
167. Whitsel, B. L., Roppolo, J. R., Werner, G. 1972. Cortical information processing of stimulus motion on primate skin. *J. Neurophysiol.* 35:691–717
168. Williams, W. J., BeMent, S. L., Yin, T. C. T., McCall, W. D. 1973. Nucleus gracilis responses to knee joint motion: a frequency response study. *Brain Res.* 64:123–40
169. Willis, W. D., Trevino, D. L., Coulter, J. D., Maunz, R. A. 1974. Responses of primate spinothalamic tract neurons to natural stimulation of hindlimb. *J. Neurophysiol.* 37:358–72
170. Zucker, E., Welker, W. I. 1969. Coding of somatic sensory input by vibrissae neurons in the rat's trigeminal ganglion. *Brain Res.* 12:138–56

Copyright 1975. All rights reserved

VESTIBULAR MECHANISMS[1]

❖1126

Jay M. Goldberg and César Fernández
Departments of Pharmacological and Physiological Sciences and of Surgery (Otolaryngology), University of Chicago, Chicago, Illinois 60637

In this review we have attempted to describe recent advances in our understanding of the mechanisms of hair-cell action and the physiology of the vestibular endorgans. There has been an explosion of interest in central vestibular mechanisms and this has necessitated a more selective coverage. Important topics not dealt with include vestibulospinal and vestibulocerebellar relations and the organization of forebrain vestibular pathways. Psychophysical experiments are considered only when they have a direct bearing on physiological mechanisms. Several of these topics are covered in recent reviews and symposia (26, 33, 39, 86, 306).

PHYSIOLOGY OF HAIR-CELL SYSTEMS

Recent studies of hair-cell action are best discussed in the context of Davis's mechanoelectrical theory (46). A steady potential exists across the lumenal surface of the hair cell. The potential may have two sources: an intrinsic polarization of the serosal membrane of the hair cell and an extrinsic (or endolymphatic) potential. The two potentials taken together result in a current flow directed through the hair cell from its lumenal to its basal surface. An adequate stimulus results in a shearing displacement of the sensory hairs. The displacement is envisioned as modulating the resistance of the lumenal surface and hence the current flow. A decrease in resistance should increase current flow and depolarize the receptor cell. An increase should have the opposite effect. Which effect occurs depends on the direction of displacement and the functional polarization of the hair cell. Depolarizing receptor currents are excitatory and may affect afferent nerve activity either by controlling the release of excitatory transmitter or, in selected cases, by direct action on the afferent terminal.

[1]Preparation of this review was supported by NIH Grant NS 01330 and NS 05237 and by NASA Grant NGR-14-001-225.

Steady Potentials and Electrical Characteristics of Hair Cells

The endolymphatic potential (EP) reflects the electrogenic transport mechanisms responsible for the peculiar electrolyte composition of endolymph, viz. a high K^+ and a low Na^+ concentration (22, 150, 215, 258, 259, 263, 269). Cochlear and vestibular endolymph are similar, though the latter has a somewhat higher Na^+ content (149, 258, 259). Active transport processes in the cochlea most likely involve cells of the stria vascularis and spiral prominence; in the vestibular labyrinth, specialized epithelial cells associated with the sensory endorgans are implicated (2, 55, 156, 265, 267).

The EP of the mammalian cochlea is approximately +80 mV relative to perilymph (10). The source of the EP has been localized to the stria vascularis (47, 291). The positive potential (+EP) is not directly related to ionic gradients between endolymph and perilymph (23, 149, 161–163, 290), and falls to negative values within a few minutes after the start of anoxia (11, 27, 160). Most likely, the negative potential (–EP) represents a K^+ diffusion potential (147, 149, 160), which diminishes as the aforementioned ionic gradients run down. As for the +EP, a commonly held view is that it represents the sum of a negative K^+ diffusion potential and a positive component, the latter reflecting an electrogenic Na^+–K^+ pump located in the stria vascularis (149, 155).

There is no general agreement regarding the magnitude of the vestibular EP, though it is clearly smaller than the corresponding cochlear potential. One group of investigators (65, 96, 268) found that the EPs recorded from the sacculus, utriculus, or semicircular canals in guinea pig seldom exceeded +5 mV, whereas Trincker (296) reported values of +40 mV for the canals. In the bird semicircular canals, Schmidt (252) observed an average EP of +4 mV, and Dayal (48) an average of +28 mV. Values of +2 to +8 mV are reported in reptiles (253). In mammals and birds, the vestibular EP falls to –15 mV during oxygen deprivation, while in reptiles the EP, like many other processes, is insensitive to anoxia (253). Johnstone & Sellick (149) proposed that the utricular EP has near-zero values because it represents the sum of a negative K^+ diffusion potential and a positive electrogenic component of similar magnitude. The saccular EP falls to –12 mV following cochlear damage and parallels the cochlear EP during anoxia (258), suggesting that the saccular EP reflects the cochlear potential via an access resistance. As an alternative the saccular potential may be associated with specialized cells found adjacent to the macula (267).

The second DC potential, one presumably present in all hair-cell systems, is the membrane potential of the receptor cell itself. Early workers encountered a negative potential on penetration of the organ of Corti (10, 290) or the vestibular epithelium (296). Though doubts have been expressed concerning the nature of the potential (27, 169, 291), it is now commonly considered to have an intracellular origin (44, 170, 271). Intracellular potentials have been recorded from lateral-line organs (78), from electroreceptors (14), and from an auditory organ (the basilar papilla) in the lizard (221). Potentials are similar in elements histologically identified as either supporting or receptor cells. In the lateral lines, intracellular potentials may reach –65 mV (78). Similar potentials, typically –75 mV, are recorded from the lizard acoustic organ (221). The ionic basis of the potentials has not been explored in intracellular studies. Earlier work in the cochlea (27) indicated that a K^+ diffusion potential is involved.

The difficulties in recording from mammalian receptor cells are emphasized by Fex (75). He was able to record stable DC potentials from the organ of Corti. These were probably derived from supporting cells; in any case, expected inhibitory postsynaptic potentials (IPSPs) were not observed on stimulation of auditory efferents. Such IPSPs were rarely recorded and, when they were, the associated DC potential was lost within seconds.

Flock et al (78) have studied the passive electrical properties of cells in the lateral-line organs. The estimated specific resistance was 100–1000 ohm cm^2. Time constants were short (<0.2 msec). The corresponding capacitance was 0.3 $\mu F\ cm^{-2}$, a surprisingly small value. Lateral-line receptors showed no signs of electrical excitability: oppositely directed transmembrane currents resulted in symmetric voltage variations with no detectable impedance changes (78). Similar behavior has been observed in tonic electroreceptors of catfish (14). In contrast, the phasic electroreceptors of teleosts (13, 240) and the receptors of the Lorenzinian ampullae (226) exhibit oscillatory or regenerative responses to applied currents. Whether electrical excitability is an adaptation peculiar to electroreceptors remains to be seen.

Receptor Potentials

Stimulus-related potentials, routinely recorded extracellularly, have now been studied with intracellular techniques. Intracellular receptor potentials recorded from the lateral lines are less than 1 mV (79, 120). Those obtained from the basilar papilla of the lizard are of similar magnitude and are superimposed on a DC shift or summating potential (221). The small size of the potentials raises a question as to whether they could effectively control transmitter release. Here, observations on tonic electroreceptors are relevant (14). In the latter organs, afferent nerve activity can be modulated over its entire dynamic range (0–250 spikes/sec) by induced polarizations of ±1 mV.

In the lateral lines, receptor-like potentials recorded from supporting cells are small or absent. Remarkably, both microphonic and summating potentials are obtained from supporting elements in the lizard acoustic organ (221, 300). Though the responses recorded from receptor and supporting cells differ in some details, they are of comparable magnitude. This raises the intriguing possibility that the supporting cells respond directly to natural stimulation. Alternately, the hair cells might act as current sources for the supporting-cell potentials. Since the latter are larger than extracellular potentials, it would seem necessary to suppose a specialized coupling between elements. Gap junctions involving supporting cells have been described in the goldfish sacculus (117). Similar junctions have not been seen in the lizard papilla or other acousticolateralis organs.

According to the electromechanical theory, receptor potentials should be accompanied by impedance changes in hair cells. Further, the direction of current flow and hence the polarity of the response should be determined by the potential difference across the lumenal surface of the hair cell. Indirect support comes from studies in the mammalian cochlea. There is a fall in the input impedance of the scala media during high-intensity acoustic stimulation (130, 148, 167). Cochlear microphonics and summating potentials are affected in predictable ways by induced polarizations (131) or other procedures that reduce the +EP or the presumed DC potential of the hair cells (27); similar observations have been made in the goldfish sacculus (201).

One set of results is inconsistent with the theory. Konishi & Nielsen (164) studied the response of auditory nerve fibers to static deflections of the basilar membrane. Most fibers responded in an excitatory manner during deflections directed towards scala tympani and in an inhibitory manner during oppositely directed displacements. Significantly, excitation was accompanied by an increase in +EP, and inhibition by a decrease. The results of Zwislocki & Sokolich (315) lead to similar conclusions. These observations are precisely the reverse of those theoretically expected. An admittedly ad hoc explanation may be offered for the discrepancy. Potentials recorded in the intact cochlea largely arise from outer hair cells (45), whereas most auditory nerve fibers are thought to innervate inner hair cells (277). Conceivably, displacements of the cochlear partition could have opposite effects on the two sets of hair cells.

Functional Polarization and Directional Selectivity

Each hair cell possesses a morphological polarization determined by the relative positions of the kinocilium and sterocilia (303). Even in the hair cells of the adult mammalian cochlea, where the kinocilium is lacking, a polarization axis can be defined by the position of the basal body.

Lowenstein & Wersäll (189) first pointed out the relation between the morphological and functional polarization of the hair cells. In each of the semicircular canals of the ray *(Raja clavata),* accelerations that bend the hairs toward the kinocilium result in an increase in afferent discharge, oppositely directed stimuli in a corresponding decrease. The principle has now been extended to the canals of a wide variety of species ranging from cyclostomes (182, 188) to mammals (101). The theory is also applicable to otolith (70, 177, 188) and lateral-line organs (76, 104).

Implicit in the Lowenstein-Wersäll theory is the notion that displacements of the hair bundles orthogonal to the polarization axis should be ineffective. Results obtained from lateral-line organs are consistent with this suggestion (76, 104). The problem has now been explored in otolith-related neurons. In the vestibular nuclei (211), discharge rate was trigonometrically related to the direction of an imposed linear acceleration. Firing rate of peripheral neurons was similarly related to head-tilt angle (70, 177), indicating that response is, to a first approximation, linearly related to the force acting in a prescribed direction. The relation, it must be emphasized, is only approximate. A response asymmetry is commonly observed, the maximum excitatory response being larger than its inhibitory counterpart. Similar asymmetries have been seen in the microphonic responses obtained from many receptor organs (76, 89, 221) and may be a general feature of hair-cell systems. In otolith organs the asymmetry does not originate in the mechanics of the otolithic membrane (70).

Static-tilt data can be used to calculate a functional-polarization vector for each otolith neuron (70, 177). Fernández et al (70) compared the vectors characterizing utricular and saccular units. Results were consistent with the commonly held idea that the otolith organs are mainly affected by shearing forces.

The relation between morphological and functional polarization should provide clues as to the morphological basis of the sensory transduction process. Hillman & Lewis (128) have described a filamentous attachment between the kinocilium and neighboring stereocilia. Evidence is presented suggesting that, because of this attachment, bending of the hair bundles results in a plunger-like action of the kinocilium on the membrane of the cuticular notch. Deflections toward the kinocilium are described as dimpling the membrane, and oppositely directed deflections as distending it. These deformations are envisioned as controlling ionic conductances. Lewis & Nemanic (172) offer two additional observations. First the kinocilium is also attached to strands of filamentous matted material connecting the supporting cells to the otolithic membrane. Second, the hair bundle seems to be more compliant when it is displaced away from the kinocilium, rather than towards it. On this basis, it is suggested that during excitatory deflections the kinocilium is pulled taut by the opposing actions of its connections with the stereocilia and the matted material. During inhibitory deflections, the stereocilia collapse and the kinocilium slackens. Transduction would reflect the deformation of the kinocilium itself or an indirect effect of the deformation on the cuticular notch. Malcolm (193) offers an ingenious theory of hair-cell action. A universal feature of hair bundles is the stepwise arrangement of the stereocilia. Excitatory stimuli are directed towards the longer hairs and will result in a fanning out of the bundle. The increase in spacing between hairs should, in and of itself, decrease the lumenal resistance of the receptor cell. The theory does not postulate a key role for the kinocilium and hence is as applicable to the mammalian cochlea as to other endorgans.

Transmission at Afferent Synapses

The synapse between the hair cell and afferent terminal has a morphology suggesting chemical transmission (77). Presynaptically there is a dense synaptic bar (or body) surrounded by vesicles. Pre- and postsynaptic membranes are separated by a typical synaptic cleft. Intracellular recordings have now been obtained from afferent terminals in several endorgans, including the goldfish sacculus (88, 90, 138, 139), lateral-line organs (79, 81, 82), tonic electroreceptors in catfish (14), and the Lorenzinian ampulla (226). Excitatory postsynaptic potentials (EPSPs), not unlike those seen at other synapses, have been observed. Results are consistent with a chemical mode of transmission.

Particularly pertinent are studies in the goldfish sacculus (88, 90, 138, 139). This endorgan functions in these fish as a hearing organ. Acoustic stimulation evokes microphonic potentials, reflecting hair-cell activity. Intracellular recording has been facilitated by the large size of some of the afferents. The critical firing level of the terminal is 15 mV. After spikes are blocked by tetrodotoxin, uncontaminated EPSPs as large as 30 mV are observed. There is a synaptic delay of 0.5–0.7 msec between the microphonic potential and the EPSP. The relationship between the amplitudes of the microphonics and the EPSPs may be highly nonlinear. Polarization experiments indicate an EPSP reversal potential of 0 mV. Finally, spontaneous miniature EPSPs have been recorded, and evoked EPSPs show fluctuations suggestive of a quantal release mechanism.

Confirmatory evidence comes from studies in electroreceptors. Transmission in the Lorenzinian ampulla requires Ca^{2+} and is blocked by Mg^{2+} (282). Interestingly, in some mormyrid phasic receptors (281) and in lateral-line organs (242) the dependence on divalent cations is more complex. In electroreceptors, excitatory stimuli result in a depolarization of the terminal and inhibitory stimuli in a hyperpolarization (14, 226). It may be supposed that the depolarization results from an increase in excitatory transmitter release and the hyperpolarization from a decreased release. The hyperpolarization should then be accompanied by an increase in the impedance of the terminal. Critical evidence is lacking. Obara & Bennett (226) have, nevertheless, observed appropriate changes in the height of antidromic spikes recorded during synaptic activity.

Transmission at some synapses may be electrical. The evidence is most compelling for the large phasic electroreceptors of mormyrids (14, 281). Impulse transmission in the orthodromic direction involves brief delays (<0.3 msec); antidromic spikes invade the receptor cell in a manner consistent with the presence of an electrotonic junction; and afferent transmission is unaffected by high Mg^{2+} concentrations. Roth (239) has presented circumstantial evidence that, in tonic electroreceptors of catfish, the receptor cells merely serve to channel currents to the terminal. The arguments are not entirely convincing and the conclusion is at variance with intracellular observations (14). A coupling potential, indicating an electronic spread of currents from hair cells to afferent terminals, is observed in the goldfish sacculus; the potential is small and, by itself, does not lead to afferent discharge (139).

There is no morphological evidence, even in the large phasic receptors of mormyrids, for closely apposed synaptic contacts (49). Such contacts have, however, been described in the calyceal terminals surrounding Type-I vestibular hair cells in mammals (118, 276, 304). Though electrical transmission across the calyceal synapse is suggested, physiological corroboration is lacking.

Evidence concerning the identity of afferent transmitter(s) is at best incomplete and contradictory. Thornhill (295) presented pharmacological observations indicating that the synaptic bars might be storage sites for catecholamines. Steinbach & Bennett (281, 282) tested the effects of several agents on afferent transmission in electroreceptors. Only glutamate and related compounds altered activity. Flock & Lam (80) have reported that gamma-aminobutyric acid (GABA) is synthesized in the sensory epithelium of various organs and that transmission is blocked by picrotoxin. Significantly, GABA has no effects, even in high concentrations, on afferent activity in the Lorenzinian ampulla (282).

Efferent Systems

Endorgans of the auditory (3, 66, 157, 235, 278), vestibular (270, 302), and lateral-line systems (76, 116) receive an efferent innervation. Two modes of termination have been observed. Most commonly, efferents synapse onto hair cells. Innervation of the afferent terminal occurs in Type-I vestibular receptors (270, 302, 304) and on cochlear afferents supplying inner hair cells (266).

Efferent activation invariably inhibits afferent transmission. The inhibition has been most thoroughly studied in the mammalian cochlea (72, 292, 305), but has also been described in vestibular (176, 245) and lateral-line organs (81, 82, 241, 243). Efferent stimulation may also result in an enhancement of microphonic potentials and a negative variation in the EP; Fex (73) has cogently argued that these effects are consequences of the postsynaptic action of efferents on hair cells. The two effects have been seen in the cochlea (72, 73, 165, 292) and lateral-line organs (81, 82). Microphonic enhancement has not been investigated in the vestibular apparatus. Sala (245) did observe a labyrinthine DC potential evoked by presumed stimulation of vestibular efferents, but his recording arrangement precludes comparison with results obtained in other systems. All studies emphasize the relatively slow time course of efferent action. Significant effects are usually seen only on repetitive stimulation and are characterized by long buildup and decay times.

Flock & Russell (81, 82) have described the intracellular events taking place in lateral-line hair cells during efferent stimulation. Large, hyperpolarizing IPSPs are recorded, accompanied by a fall in transmembrane impedance. During the IPSP, the peak-to-peak height of the intracellularly recorded microphonic potential increases. At the same time, the absolute depolarization attained is reduced, since the microphonic potential, even when enhanced, is much smaller than the superimposed IPSP. Stimulus-evoked EPSPs, recorded from the afferent terminal, are diminished. Inhibition of afferent transmission is viewed as resulting from hair-cell hyperpolarization and especially from the shunting of depolarizing receptor currents through the efferent subsynaptic membrane.

Evidence is accumulating that acetylcholine (ACh) is the efferent transmitter. ACh can mimic efferent action in both the cochlea (20, 21, 98) and lateral-line organs (242), and the action can be blocked by anticholinergic drugs (21, 74, 75, 241, 242). Studies in the lateral lines indicate that the cholinergic receptor is muscarinic (242). Preliminary evidence suggests that ACh is synthesized in the efferents (75, 80) and released upon efferent stimulation (75, 115).

THE PERIPHERAL VESTIBULAR APPARATUS

General Considerations

RESTING DISCHARGE A common feature of all vestibular afferents is their resting discharge. The most obvious function of the resting discharge is that it permits a bidirectional response. Accelerations in one direction increase discharge, those in the opposite direction decrease it. Though the latter response is termed "inhibitory," there is no reason to suppose that an active inhibitory process is involved. A simpler view is that the hair cells exert a tonic excitatory influence on the afferents, presumably mediated by an excitatory transmitter. Movements of sensory hairs in one direction result in increased transmitter release, those in the opposite direction in a decreased release.

Two other functions may be ascribed to the resting discharge. First, it provides the basis for the tonic influence exerted by the labyrinth on the central nervous system. Second, the resting discharge may serve to decrease the sensory threshold. A spontaneously active fiber could conceivably respond to even the smallest deflections of the cupula or otolithic membrane. Observations in both canal (101) and otolith neurons (70, 177) support this view. Indeed, any threshold exhibited by the afferents is most likely attributable to mechanical factors, e.g. static friction (297).

DIVERSITY OF RECEPTOR TYPES Wersäll (301) first described the two kinds of hair cells and demonstrated that they had different nerve supplies. The Type-I hair cell, peculiar to higher vertebrates, is innervated by a calycoid ending derived from a single, usually thick afferent. Type-II hair cells, common to all vertebrates, receive bud-shaped endings from several afferents. The innervations of the two hair-cell systems are not independent (67, 174, 178, 301). The largest afferents, besides innervating two to five neighboring Type-I cells, may emit collaterals supplying Type-II receptors. Intermediate-sized fibers provide endings to several hair cells of both varieties. Thin fibers are thought to make bouton-type contacts with many widely separated Type-II cells. Thick fibers are distributed mainly to central regions of the sensory epithelium, thinner fibers more peripherally.

The identification of the distinctive physiology of the various afferent populations remains a key problem. A clue is provided by steady-state discharge patterns. Most vestibular nerve fibers in both mammals (70, 102, 177, 254, 297, 299) and birds (41) are characterized by a regular spacing of action potentials; fewer fibers show an irregular discharge. Walsh et al (299) compared discharge patterns in various parts of the superior vestibular nerve. The anterior part largely supplies the superior and horizontal semicircular canals, while the posterior part supplies the utriculus (91, 246). Proportionately more irregular units were encountered anteriorly. Since this part of the nerve contains a higher percentage of large-diameter fibers (91, 299), Walsh et al (299) suggested that irregular units correspond to thick afferents innervating Type-I hair cells, while regular units correspond to thin fibers supplying Type-II receptors. Confirmatory evidence comes from a comparison of discharge patterns of canal and otolith units (70).

The tentative correlation between discharge pattern and fiber diameter has implications for the mechanisms of repetitive discharge. Thick fibers, given their restricted innervation zone, should have a single spike-initiating or trigger site. The situation is less clear in thin fibers since they may supply widely separated receptor cells. An afferent characterized by multiple trigger sites might be expected to have irregular discharge patterns. The expectation is borne out in lateral-line afferents;

these fibers are characterized by irregular patterns (119, 121) and probably possess multiple sites (222). On this basis, the thin vestibular afferents, if indeed they are regularly discharging, should have a single trigger zone. Walsh et al (299) suggested that the degree of regularity is determined by the number of hair cells innervated by the afferent, rather than by the fiber diameter per se or the kind(s) of hair cell contacted. Interesting in this regard is Lowenstein's observation (184) that both regular and irregular units are found in lower vertebrates, even though only one kind of hair cell is present.

Regular and irregular units, including those innervating canals and otolith organs, differ in several of their other discharge characteristics, at least in mammals. In regular units there is a positive correlation between resting discharge and sensitivity to natural stimulation (70, 102). No such relation is apparent in irregular units. The latter are also distinguished in that their response dynamics deviate most markedly from the predicted mechanical behavior of the endorgan (70, 102, 103, 254). To a first approximation, regular units may be considered static receptors, response being closely related to expected displacement of the cupula or otolithic membrane. Irregular units (and by inference thick afferents) may be thought of as dynamic receptors; they show conspicuous adaptation and may be sensitive to both mechanical displacement and to the velocity of the displacement.

Variations in response dynamics may reflect differences in the physiology of hair cells and afferent terminals, in the modes of coupling of the sensory hairs to the accessory membrane, or in both. Unfortunately, little is known concerning the modes of coupling. It is not clear, for example, whether a subcupular space is interposed between the sensory epithelium and the membrane. Many workers (56, 128, 137, 146, 173) consider the space a normal feature; others (174, 175) suggest that it is a fixation artifact. Several investigators (56, 137, 173), in describing the space, deny that the sensory hairs are in direct contact with the membrane. How then could motion of the membrane be communicated to the hairs? There is a fine filamentous network, extending from the supporting cells to the membrane (56, 128, 172). The sensory hairs are envisioned as being enclosed in fluid-filled compartments bounded by the meshwork. Motion could be imparted to the hairs either by their making direct contact with the meshwork or indirectly by viscous coupling through the fluid. Alternatively, the hairs may extend across the subcupular space (assuming it exists) and insert into channels in the membrane (128, 172, 174). The channels may be broader than the hair bundles and, again, coupling may be viscous or elastic. Physiological evidence suggests that thick afferents function as dynamic receptors. It might be supposed then that Type-I hair bundles would be more loosely coupled to the membrane than would Type-II bundles. Lindeman et al (174, 175) have observed regional variations in the morphology of the sensory hairs and of the otolithic membrane, consistent with this suggestion.

Semicircular Canals

The semicircular canals have classically been thought to respond only to angular accelerations. Recent studies suggest that these organs may also respond to linear forces. Their chief role, nevertheless, is the detection of head rotations.

MECHANICS OF THE CUPULA-ENDOLYMPH SYSTEM Early work (64, 110, 283, 284) provided evidence that the cupula-endolymph, in its response to angular accelerations, could be described as a heavily damped torsion pendulum. The angular displacement of the endolymph $\xi(t)$ was related to the angular acceleration of the head $\alpha(t)$ by the differential equation

$$\Theta\frac{d^2\xi}{dt^2} + \Pi\frac{d\xi}{dt} + \Delta\xi = \Theta\alpha(t) \qquad 1.$$

Θ is the effective moment of inertia, Π a viscous damping couple, and Δ an elastic-restoring factor. The angular motion of the cupula should be linearly related to endolymph displacement (214, 227, 293). The original formulation of the torsion-pendulum model was based on relatively simple reasoning. Essentially the same equation arises from a more rigorous hydrodynamic treatment (279).

The heavy damping has two important consequences. First, the dynamics of motion should be governed by two time constants, a long one, $\tau_1 = \Pi/\Delta$, and a short one, $\tau_2 = \Theta/\Pi$. Second, though the physical stimulus is angular acceleration, the cupular displacement will more closely parallel the angular velocity of brief head movements. Indeed, the canal should function as a reasonably faithful velocity transducer over the frequency range $1/\tau_1 < \omega < 1/\tau_2$ (202, 210). The sensitivity with respect to velocity is directly related to τ_2; the time course of endolymph displacement during and following unidirectional accelerations is governed by τ_1. The value of τ_2 can be deduced from hydrodynamic principles and has a typical value of 0.005 sec (69, 217, 279). Unfortunately, τ_1 cannot be similarly deduced since the value of Δ—presumably reflecting the elastic-restoring properties of the cupula—has not been experimentally determined.

Offhand, a measurement of Δ would seem straightforward. The cupula can be visualized (54, 283, 284). What would then be required is a determination of the relation between the static displacement of the cupula and the pressure differential across it. Here theoretical calculations are relevant (227). Under physiological conditions, the pressure differential should range from 10^{-4} to 5×10^{-2} dyne cm^{-2}, and the corresponding deflections, measured at the midpoint of the cupula, from 10^{-6} to 5×10^{-4} cm. The figures emphasize the mechanical sensitivity of the hair cells and the experimental difficulties involved in a direct evaluation of Δ. Most workers have therefore been content with indirect measures.

One approach has been to study the dynamics of the vestibulo-ocular reflex (109, 209, 224). Values of τ_1 so obtained range from 10–20 sec. But the dynamics of the reflex are determined as much by central mechanisms as they are by peripheral factors (237, 264). A more direct measure is provided by studies of peripheral afferents. Such studies have now been performed in the vestibular nerve of several species (41, 69, 231, 254) and also in the mammalian vestibular nuclei (213, 254, 260). Estimates of τ_1 range from 2–8 sec. Even these values must be interpreted cautiously since the response dynamics of peripheral afferents depart significantly from those of a torsion pendulum. Nevertheless, taking a value of 5 sec as typical, the computed bandwidth over which the cupula-endolymph system functions as a velocity transducer extends from 0.025–25 Hz, a range encompassing the bandwidth of physiological head movements. The value of Δ may be estimated to be approximately 10^{-3} dyne cm radian^{-1}.

Dohlman (54), in his study of the displacement of the cupula, observed it to slide across the surface of the crista. Of necessity, the pressures and displacements used by Dohlman exceeded physiological limits. Because of this, the question as to how the cupula moves under normal conditions must be considered unsettled. The various possibilities have been summarized (293). The cupula could slide over a subcupular layer, much as envisioned by Dohlman; it could bend around its base in the manner of a cantilever beam; or it could be bowed, the maximum displacement occurring at its center. Obviously the mode of motion depends on the degrees of cupular attachment to the crista and the vault of the ampulla. The second possibility has been theoretically investigated (293). The calculations provide an estimate of the Young's modulus for the cupula of 10^3 dyne cm^{-2}, a value similar to that characterizing the softer gelatins.

The various parameters of the torsion-pendulum model are simply related to canal dimensions. It has been suggested (214) that these dimensions might vary so that the sensitivity and bandwidth of the cupula-endolymph system would match the motor capacities of individual animals. Large animals tend to be sluggish in their movements and might require a more sensitive peripheral apparatus and one characterized by longer time constants. Several studies (135, 136, 203, 293, 294) have investigated this problem, either by comparing canal dimensions across species or in a single species during growth. Many of the results are consistent with the original suggestion. ten Kate et al (293, 294) have critically examined the assumptions underlying the approach and have presented data at variance with the theory. They propose that physiological sensitivity is determined by the ratio G/h_c^2, where G is the mechanical sensitivity deduced from canal dimensions and h_c is the cupular height. Examination of a wide variety of animals (including fish, birds, and mammals) indicates that G/h_c^2 remains relatively constant. Why sensitivity should be inversely proportional to h_c^2 is not entirely clear. About all that can be concluded is that the mechanical sensitivity G is similar in animals with similarly sized cupulae. Another reservation stems from single-unit studies in the vestibular nerve (69, 101). Within a single species, indeed in a single preparation, there may be a tenfold variation in the sensitivity of individual afferents and considerable variations in response dynamics. Further, it seems unlikely that the physiological sensitivity of hair cells and afferents would be similar in warm- and coldblooded animals. Viewed in this light, only limited inferences can be drawn solely from a consideration of canal dimensions and their relation to the mechanical operation of the endorgan.

RESPONSE TO ANGULAR ACCELERATIONS Peripheral canal neurons in warmblooded animals have a remarkably high resting discharge, averaging some 65 spikes/sec in gerbils (254) and some 90 spikes/sec in pigeons (41) and squirrel monkeys (101). Lower resting discharges are found in coldblooded animals (187, 231). The afferents exhibit a bidirectional response. The directions of excitatory and inhibitory accelerations are identical for all afferents innervating a single canal and are consistent with Ewald's First Law (41, 101, 186, 231, 254). We have examined several thousand canal neurons in the squirrel monkey and have found no exceptions to these rules. An occasional unit in the frog did not respond in this stereotyped way; such units were interpreted as efferents (231). In the mammalian vestibular nerve, typical sensitivities with respect to angular velocity are 0.6 spikes/sec per deg/sec (69, 254). Slightly higher values are reported for the vestibular nuclei (212, 254).

Traditionally, the response dynamics of peripheral neurons were thought to mirror the dynamics of the cupula-endolymph system. Even in early work, though, there were indications that the afferents exhibited a form of sensory adaptation (110, 181). Adaptation has now been observed in the response of both peripheral (101, 231) and central vestibular neurons (29, 97, 244). In mammalian peripheral neurons (101), adaptation is reflected by preacceleratory response declines and postacceleratory secondary responses. The effects are most conspicuous in irregular units (102). The results are of interest because of their obvious similarity to the adaptation seen in the overall response of the vestibular system. The similarity is reinforced by the fact that the peripheral adaptation can be described by the same model that was originally developed to account for the adaptation observed in human psychophysical and nystagmus studies (194, 285, 314). It would, nevertheless, be a mistake to assume that the response adaptation of the entire system is solely determined by peripheral events. That nystagmus adaptation depends on the vigilance of the subject (114) argues for an interplay of peripheral and central mechanisms.

The response dynamics of peripheral neurons deviate in a second way from those of the torsion-pendulum model. The effect, which is again most conspicuous in irregular units, is best seen during sinusoidal rotations and involves a high-frequency gain enhancement and a corresponding phase lead (41, 69, 254). In the squirrel monkey (69) these high-frequency effects were interpreted as indicating that response was directly proportional to both cupular displacement and the velocity of the displacement. Studies in other species (41, 254), while confirming the presence of velocity-sensitive dynamics, demonstrate that response need not be simply proportional to cupular velocity. It has been proposed (69, 264) that the high-frequency effects might provide a means by which the peripheral apparatus could compensate for the dynamic loads represented by various reflex pathways. Further, similar effects have been observed in studies of vestibular nystagmus (15) and vestibular-controlled postural adjustments (223). Despite these considerations, the functional significance of the velocity-sensitive dynamics is unclear. The failure to observe such dynamics in studies of central neurons is pertinent (213, 254).

RESPONSE TO CONSTANT LINEAR FORCES Ledoux (171) noted that canal afferents in the frog could respond to static head tilts. His observations have recently been confirmed in the ray (183). Canal neurons in the monkey, particularly those arising from the superior canal, respond in a bidirectional manner to head tilts and centrifugal force (Goldberg & Fernández, unpublished results). The response most likely arises because of density differences between cupula and endolymph. The requisite density differences are so small (on the order of 10^{-4} g cm^{-3}) that they could easily arise from experimental perturbations. In the monkey, for example, we suspect that thermal gradients are responsible for the response. Such gradients are unlikely in coldblooded preparations. But here another explanation is possible. Most work in poikilotherms involves isolated preparations. After death, there is an equilibration of perilymph and endolymph, and this could cause the endolymph to become less dense than normal. Interestingly, results in the ray (183) could be explained if the cupula were denser than the endolymph.

The considerations suggest that the canals, in an intact preparation, would not respond in a consistent manner to constant linear forces. Despite this, the fact that the canals are potentially sensitive to such forces has both clinical and experimental implications. First, a small and unpredictable positional nystagmus is commonly observed in seemingly normal subjects (8, 216). The etiology of the nystagmus is undoubtedly complex, but small density differences between the cupula and endolymph may be contributory. Second, such density differences are implicated in the large positional nystagmus following drug intoxication (218, 219). And third, in studies of central vestibular neurons, it is usually assumed that units responding to static tilts receive an otolith input. The most common pattern of convergence described in the vestibular nuclei involves individual neurons receiving a canal and a presumed otolith input (62, 199). The conclusion is based on the observation that the same neuron responds to angular accelerations and slow head tilts. Both the conclusion, and the assumption upon which it is based, may be unwarranted.

RESPONSE TO ROTATING LINEAR FORCES There are profound differences in the reactions of the entire vestibular system to rotations about earth-vertical and earth-horizontal axes (17, 113). A constant-velocity rotation about a vertical axis does not lead to maintained responses. When the subject is rotated about a horizontal axis, as on a barbecue spit, there is a persistent undirectional nystagmus and a corresponding sensation of turning. The effects, which can also be produced by counter-rotation in a centrifuge, depend on the continual reorientation of the head relative to a linear force. Superimposed on the persistent component of the barbecue nystagmus is a sinusoidal or direction-changing component.

Conflicting views have been expressed as to whether the persistent component of barbecue nystagmus reflects stimulation of otolith organs (16, 113) or of semicircular canals (17, 279). Concerning the latter possibility, it has been hypothesized that linear forces deform the membranous canal and thereby produce a pressure differential across the cupula (17, 279). A constant force will be ineffective since the pressure on the two sides of the cupula will equalize within a few milliseconds. In contrast, a rotating force could, by a roller-pump action, result in a maintained cupular deflection.

Evidence that the semicircular canals can respond to rotating linear forces was provided by Benson et al (18). Canal-related central neurons were studied in animals counter-rotated on a centrifuge. The discharge of most neurons increased during counter-rotation in either direction. Nevertheless, without exception, units were more active when the centrifugal-force vector was rotated around the head in the direction of excitatory endolymphatic flow than when the vector was rotated in the opposite direction. The differential effects are consistent with the direction of the persistent component of barbecue nystagmus. Many units showed cyclic variations in activity, but these could not be related to the direction of the force vector.

Otolith organs may also contribute to the persistent component. Janeke et al (145) reported an elimination of the nystagmus after bilateral section of the utricular nerve and destruction of the sacculus. Their operative techniques, however, can be criticized (18). Correia & Money (42) plugged all six canals and observed a reduction, but not elimination, of the nystagmus. Since it was assumed that plugging totally inactivates the canals, the conclusion was drawn that the persistent component could be maintained solely by otolith activation. Our unpublished observations in the monkey are somewhat at variance with Correia & Money's assumption. Canal plugging, consistent with behavioral observations (220), abolishes the response of peripheral neurons to angular accelerations without obviously affecting resting activity. Significantly, the procedure does not eliminate the canal response to constant linear forces. The responses seen in the plugged preparation cannot be explained by the existence of thermal gradients, and they resemble in several respects the responses described by Benson et al (18) for rotating forces. It should be noted that, in a plugged canal, deformation of the membranous duct by a nonrotating force could lead to a maintained cupular deflection since occlusion of the canal would prevent pressure equalization.

Though the results are hardly conclusive, they suggest that the persistent component of barbecue nystagmus largely, if not solely, depends on canal activation. A recent clinical study on a patient with loss of canal function was consistent with this view (107). What about the sinusoidal component? Here the evidence would favor an otolithic origin for the response. First, the fact that the sinusoidal component is unattenuated at rotation rates as high as 30 rpm (40,286) would seem incompatible with the slow dynamics of the cupula-endolymph system. Further, there are similarities between the sinusoidal component and the nystagmus produced on a linear track by oscillating accelerations (225). The latter response is almost certainly attributable to otolith activation (16, 311).

Otolith Organs

The otolith organs are sensors of linear accelerations (and inertial forces). It has also been suggested (16, 183, 312) that the organs respond to angular accelerations, since the latter could cause a torsional motion of the otolithic membrane. In our experience, however, otolith neurons are virtually unaffected by even intense angular accelerations. Why this is so is not entirely clear. Conceivably the torsional rigidity of the membrane might be high. Alternatively, the lack of response may reflect the geometric arrangement of the hair cells. Torsional movements would deflect most sensory hair bundles in a direction perpendicular to their polarization axes. Such orthogonal shears are presumably ineffective.

RESTING DISCHARGE AND RESPONSE TO STATIC TILTS Otolith neurons, like other acousticolateralis afferents, should possess a resting discharge. Gualtierotti et al (112) have confirmed the presence of such a discharge by recording the activity of frog otolith neurons during orbital flight. A somewhat simpler approach was taken by Fernández et al (70). It was reasoned that, were response a linear function of effective force, the resting (or zero-force) activity should be given by the average discharge obtained from tilt positions 180° apart. In the squirrel monkey (70), otolith neurons have a typical resting discharge of some 60 spikes/sec. The sensitivity (the estimated static response to a 1 g force) averages about 40 spikes/sec. Most units are not silenced even in tilt positions leading to minimum discharge.

Each otolith neuron can be characterized by a functional-polarization vector presumably reflecting the morphological polarization of the hair cells innervated. Morphological-polarization maps have now been constructed for several species (174, 275), including man (238), and permit a comparison between morphological and physiological results. Functional-polarization vectors were determined for individual otolith neurons by Loe et al (177) in the cat and by Fernández et al (70) in the squirrel monkey. The vectors obtained by Loe et al (177) lay near the plane of the utricular macula and were presumably derived from this organ. Most units responded to both pitches and rolls. Units activated by either forward or backward pitches occurred in roughly equal numbers. There was a preponderance of units excited by ipsilateral rolls. A similar preponderance has been seen in other studies in the vestibular nerve (9, 70, 297) and vestibular nuclei (87, 229). Fernández et al (70) identified two classes of neurons: one whose vectors lay near the plane of the utricular macula, the other with vectors near the plane of the saccular macula. Independent evidence was presented that the second class arose from the sacculus. Tilt responses have also been obtained from saccular units in lower vertebrates (95, 185).

These last observations are of interest since the equilibrium function of the sacculus has often been questioned. Further evidence of its function comes from the observation that distinctive eye movements can be obtained upon focal electrical stimulation of either the utricular or saccular maculae (84, 85).

RESPONSE DYNAMICS The mechanics of the otolith organs are usually assumed to be governed by the equation

$$\frac{d^2x}{dt^2} + \frac{b}{m_e}\frac{dx}{dt} + \frac{k}{m_e}x = \alpha(t)\frac{\rho_o - \rho_e}{\rho_o + \rho_e}, \qquad 2.$$

relating otolith displacement $x(t)$ to input acceleration $\alpha(t)$. m_e is the effective mass of the otolith, ρ_o its density, and ρ_e the density of endolymph; b is a viscous-damping constant, and k a spring constant. System dynamics are determined by two parameters: a resonant frequency $f_o = [k(4\pi^2 m_e)^{-1}]^{0.5}$ and a damping factor $c = b(4m_e k)^{-0.5}$. The sensitivity s, expressed as the static displacement resulting from a 1 g acceleration, is given by $m_e g(\rho_o - \rho_e)[k(\rho_o + \rho_e)]^{-1}$. Direct observations made on the large saccular otolith of the ruff (52) provided estimates of $k = 1200$ dyne/cm, $f_o = 50$ Hz, and $s = 10^{-2}$ cm. The system was thought to be critically damped ($c = 1$). If the same value of k is assumed to hold for the smaller otoliths of mammals, the corresponding values would be on the order of $f_o = 400$ Hz and $s = 5 \times 10^{-5}$ cm. The human threshold for perception of linear acceleration is near 2×10^{-2} g (106), representing an estimated displacement of 10^{-6} cm. Again, the mechanical sensitivity of the vestibular endorgans is emphasized.

The relatively high value of the resonant frequency would suggest that the otolithic membrane could follow even quite rapid head movements. Confirmation comes from studies of afferent discharge. In some otolith neurons (103, 177), discharge faithfully reflects variations in effective force. For other neurons, however, the response deviates from presumed otolith motion. Dynamic responses have been observed in the vestibular nerve (95, 112, 185, 297) and vestibular nuclei (255). Goldberg & Fernández (103) have compared the response dynamics of regular and irregular otolith neurons in the monkey. Centrifugal force was used and the response to both trapezoidal and sinusoidal stimuli studied. Regular units are characterized by stiff dynamics. The response to trapezoids parallels the force profile. Sinusoidal gains are relatively constant over a 0.006–4 Hz range; small phase leads at low frequencies may be replaced by similar (5–20°) phase lags at higher frequencies. From the phase lags, it is suggested that the mammalian otolith is heavily damped. Irregular units exhibit velocity-sensitive dynamics. There are phasic responses during rapid force transitions, and response declines during prolonged acceleration. Sinusoidal gains are an increasing function of frequency; phase leads of 20–50° are seen throughout the spectrum. The high-frequency gain enhancement can be approximated by an operator of the form $(1 + \tau s^k)$. The fractional exponent $k < 1$ demonstrates that response is not simply proportional to the velocity of otolith motion. These results, coupled with earlier findings, indicate that the otolith organs have both dynamic and static functions.

Several workers have attempted to estimate the dynamics of the otolith organs from oculomotor responses to varying linear forces. Responses include ocular counter-rolling (154, 204), the sinusoidal component of barbecue nystagmus (16, 17, 40, 279, 286), and the nystagmus produced by sinusoidal accelerations passing through the interaural axis (225). Results are, by and large, compatible with the response dynamics of peripheral otolith neurons. Sinusoidal gains are either constant or show a high-frequency enhancement. Phase leads are commonly noted. Results reported by Young & Meiry (313) would seem exceptional. Subjects were placed on a linear track and were asked to indicate turning points during sinusoidal accelerations. A progressive phase lag was observed above 0.15 Hz and was simulated by a first-order lag term with a corner frequency of 0.25 Hz. In contrast, Benson & Barnes (16) obtained a significant phase lead in a roughly similar situation. Young & Meiry (313) incorporated their observations into a dynamic otolith model. Whatever the merits of the model in describing human sensation, it is at variance with direct observations of otolith motion (52) and with more recent studies of peripheral neurons (103, 177).

The Efferent Vestibular System

ANATOMICAL CONSIDERATIONS Evidence that highly vesiculated endings form an efferent innervation comes from two sources. The vesiculated endings are selectively stained by AChE histochemical methods (126, 144), and this staining is lost after vestibular nerve section (94). Further, the endings themselves degenerate after central lesions (127, 270).

The efferent innervation differs, depending on the hair cell innervated (68, 302). There are no efferents ending on Type-I hair cells. Rather, the efferents exert their influence on the calyceal terminal, the associated afferent dendrite, or both. Direct contacts are made with Type-II hair cells. In most descriptions of the latter cells this is the only efferent innervation mentioned. The situation is most likely not this simple (143, 270).

Considerable confusion existed concerning the origin of the efferents in mammals. Gacek & Lyon (93), using a horseradish peroxidase method, have clarified the issue. Efferent neurons were localized in a circumscribed area interposed between the abducens and lateral vestibular nuclei. The efferent innervation of each labyrinth consists of crossed and uncrossed components of about equal size. In the frog, efferents may originate from both the cerebellum (127, 176) and the vestibular nuclei (232).

PHYSIOLOGICAL STUDIES Relatively few experiments have been conducted on the peripheral action of efferent vestibular stimulation. Studies in the rabbit (245) and the frog (176) indicated that the efferents exert a basically inhibitory influence on afferent transmission.

More attention has been devoted to the discharge characteristics of the efferents themselves. Most studies have involved the frog or goldfish; in the majority of these, the efferent nature of the discharge was assured by detaching the particular nerve branch from its peripheral connections. The efferents respond to labyrinthine stimulation, including activation of canals (32, 99, 231, 251) and otolith organs (158), and they are also influenced by nonlabyrinthine inputs (53, 231, 250, 251).

There are clear differences in the responses of efferents and peripheral afferents to rotational stimuli. Gleisner & Henriksson (99) noted that the threshold for efferent activation was considerably higher than the afferent threshold. The efferents were also observed to be more variable in their response properties, to exhibit a definite latent period, and to show response declines on repeated stimulation. All afferents from the horizontal canal are activated by ipsilateral rotations and inhibited by contralateral rotations. In contrast, efferents may be activated by horizontal rotations in the ipsilateral direction, the contralateral direction, or in both directions (32, 231). Efferents excited by ipsilateral rotations receive their afferent drive from the ipsilateral horizontal canal; those activated by contralateral rotations are under the influence of the contralateral horizontal canal (32, 228).

The nonlabyrinthine stimuli activating vestibular efferents have not been precisely specified. Efferents have been observed to respond to tactile stimuli (231), to deep pressure (251), to passive movement of extremities (231, 251), and during spontaneous movement (251). Perhaps the best studied extralabyrinthine influences involve brainstem motor systems. Efferents, in both goldfish and rabbit (53, 250), showed a modulation of activity correlated with eye movements. Evidence was presented that the efferents were driven from optomotor centers, rather than from eye proprioceptors.

Several somewhat speculative suggestions have been made concerning the function(s) of the efferent system. Precht et al (231) have pointed out that an ipsilateral efferent pathway might serve as a negative feedback system, whereas a crossed pathway might enhance afferent discharge. McCabe & Gillingham (206) have implicated the efferents in the mechanisms of vestibular habituation. Finally, efferents may control the sensitivity of the endorgans during spontaneous or reflex-induced movement. Indeed Klinke & Schmidt (159) have suggested that the peripheral apparatus functions much like the muscle spindle under gamma control. Efferent activation might keep afferent activity more or less constant during programmed body movements. The endorgans would then signal departures from intended motion. In this context, the response of vestibular efferents to nonlabyrinthine stimuli may be interpreted, as has been suggested for lateral-line efferents (236), in terms of their capacity to evoke movement.

CENTRAL VESTIBULAR PATHWAYS

Vestibular Nuclei

ANATOMICAL ORGANIZATION Recent anatomical studies of the mammalian vestibular complex (25, 91, 280, 298) confirmed earlier observations (179) that peripheral afferents from different endorgans terminate in circumscribed regions of the four main nuclei,[2] and that there are areas of the complex devoid of direct afferent input. The work of Stein & Carpenter (280) and of Gacek (91) demonstrates that the cristae and maculae have unique as well as common regions of representation. The canals provide the main innervation of the SVN; the superior and horizontal canals are represented rostrolaterally, the posterior canal caudomedially. A small utricular input may also be present (280). There is agreement that ventral LVN receives a utricular innervation, though Gacek (91) also described a minor projection from the canals and sacculus. There are major discrepancies concerning the remaining nuclei. The rostral MVN is said by Stein & Carpenter (280) to receive only canal inputs, while Gacek (91) considered the region a major projection zone for both canal and utricular fibers. The caudal MVN is reported as receiving canal afferents, but Stein & Carpenter (280) also described a utricular input. The DVN, according to Stein & Carpenter (280), receives a small contingent of canal fibers and is the major termination site for both utricular and saccular fibers. Gacek (91) characterized the DVN, particularly its rostral portion, as a zone of convergence for all endorgans. He further considered the *y* group as the only region receiving a major saccular input. Finally, Stein & Carpenter (280) traced fibers from all endorgans to the IN, whereas Gacek (91) insisted that it only receives canal inputs.

There is no evidence that vestibular afferents project to the contralateral vestibular complex (25, 91, 208, 280, 298). Commissural connections do exist (30, 71, 105,

[2]Abbreviations for the nuclei are as follows: superior vestibular nucleus (SVN); lateral vestibular nucleus (LVN); medial vestibular nucleus (MVN); descending vestibular nucleus (DVN); and interstitial nucleus (IN). Other abbreviations are: medial longitudinal fasciculus (MLF), and brachium conjuctivum (BC).

207), and their detailed organization has been studied (168). There is a heavy commissural projection arising in the SVN, passing through the dorsalmost part of the pontine reticular formation, and terminating throughout the contralateral SVN. Some of the fibers also innervate the ventral areas of the other vestibular nuclei. In contrast, the commissural projection from the LVN is scanty and mainly terminates in the contralateral LVN and DVN. The DVN commissural fibers end mainly in the opposite DVN with minor projections to the other three nuclei. The commissural projection from the MVN could not be defined in anatomical studies because lesions located in this nucleus interrupt fibers of passage. The existence of a topographically organized commissural system has been confirmed in the frog (111).

Golgi studies of the intrinsic organization of the nuclei (122, 195) confirm earlier observations (28, 179) that afferent fibers run parallel to the longitudinal axis of the complex and emit collaterals generally oriented at right angles to the parent fibers. The afferents end on the soma and dendrites both as *boutons terminaux* and *boutons en passage.* There is considerable overlap of dendritric fields, which tend to be oriented in planes parallel to the afferent collaterals (122). Some disagreement exists concerning the extent of the fields. Hauglie-Hanssen (122) reported that most dendrites remain within the territory of the corresponding nucleus. According to Mannen (195), dendritic ramifications are so extensive that any division of the complex based on Nissl or fiber stains is arbitrary and misleading. Physiological studies (233, 261) suggest the existence of interneurons. Substantial numbers of interneurons have not been seen in anatomical material (122, 195), but short axon collaterals are frequently observed (122) and might serve the same function.

Transmission between mammalian vestibular afferents and secondary neurons is for the most part chemically mediated (140, 153), though in a small percentage ($<$20%) of central neurons electrical transmissions may be involved (108, 134). There is no histological evidence in mammals that incoming afferents form mixed synapses. In the tangential nucleus of birds, however, such synapses have been described (24, 129), and physiological studies (309) indicate both chemical and electrical transmission following vestibular-nerve stimulation. In rat LVN, fibers of unknown origin form mixed synapses on the cell bodies and dendrites of giant cells (272), an observation supported by the finding of electrotonic coupling within the nucleus (166).

CONVERGENCE OF LABYRINTHINE INPUTS Secondary vestibular neurons receive inputs from several sources, including the labyrinth, spinal cord, cerebellum, reticular formation, and higher centers. Here we consider only labyrinthine inputs.

Desole & Pallestrini (50) reported that the majority of LVN units in guinea pig received inputs from two or more canals from each labyrinth. Indeed, units were described that could be influenced by stimulation of all six canals. Local warming of ampullae was used; unfortunately, it is not clear that the method selectively activates individual canals. In contrast, Curthoys & Markham (43, 199, 200), working in spinal cats, found that only 20% of horizontal canal units received vertical canal inputs. Many more units, as had previously been described (57, 58, 62), responded to both angular acceleration and head tilt. The results were interpreted as indicating a convergence of canal and otolith inputs. The possibility that the response to head tilts could arise from the canals has been discussed previously (see p. 141). Recent investigations (1, 247, 307) agree that there is a surprisingly small degree of convergence onto individual secondary neurons from different endorgans of the same labyrinth.

The findings have important implications for the organization of vestibular pathways. In some pathways there must be an integration of inputs from two or more endorgans of each labyrinth. Convergence of inputs could occur within the vestibular nuclei, on motoneurons and/or closely related interneurons, or conceivably even at the level of the muscle. A priori it would seem reasonable to suppose that the necessary integration would take place within the vestibular nuclei. But the work reviewed above, together with studies of neck motoneurons (308), suggests that much of the convergence occurs within individual motor nuclei.

COMMISSURAL PATHWAYS DeVito et al (51) were the first to study interactions between the vestibular nuclei of the two sides; labyrinthine polarization resulted in either excitation or inhibition of units located in the contralateral LVN. The role of commissural connections was defined by Shimazu & Precht (261). Observations were made on secondary neurons responding to natural stimulation of the horizontal canal. Type-I neurons, units activated by ipsilateral rotations, were excited by electrical stimulation of the ipsilateral vestibular nerve and inhibited by stimulation of the contralateral nerve. The latent period for the crossed inhibition was 4.0 msec. In contrast, Type-II neurons, units activated by contralateral rotations, were excited by contralateral nerve stimulation with a latent period of 3.2 msec. The crossed effects on both Type-I and Type-II neurons were abolished by a shallow, midline incision of the medulla, which should have interrupted commissural fibers. Following the incision, strong stimulation of the contralateral nerve produced excitation of both types of neurons, the excitation presumably being mediated via deeper vestibulo-reticular pathways. From these and other observations, Shimazu & Precht (261) proposed that Type-II neurons were excited mainly by commissural connections and served as inhibitory interneurons acting upon Type-I neurons. The crossed inhibitory pathway was envisioned as increasing the sensitivity of Type-I neurons to ipsilateral rotations. Similar observations have been made on central neurons related to the vertical canals (198). Recent studies in the MVN (151, 197, 310) indicated that some commissural fibers provide monosynaptic inhibitory inputs to Type-I cells, i.e. the inhibitory pathway need not require a Type-II inhibitory interneuron. The bilateral inputs to Type-I neurons are, for the most part, activated by stimulation of synergic (coplanar) canals on the two sides (152).

The vestibular system works by means of a balance between influences arising from the two labyrinths. Inhibitory commissural connections, besides enhancing the sensitivity of secondary neurons, provide a mechanism for achieving this balance. A second mechanism entails the balancing of the bilateral outputs from the vestibular nuclei. That the second mechanism is operative, even in neurons under inhibitory commissural control, is indicated by the fact that such units commonly exhibit a background discharge (198, 234, 261). Further, some neurons apparently do not receive crossed inhibitory inputs. This is so both for tilt-sensitive units in the cat LVN (262) and for Type-I canal-related neurons in the frog (228). In both cases, only crossed excitatory effects are seen and these could not obviously serve a balancing function.

Vestibulo-Ocular Reflex

The vestibular endorgans are connected to extraocular motoneurons via a three-neuron arc (180, 288). Second-order neurons arise from the SVN or MVN and ascend in the MLF. Other pathways involve the ascending tract of Deiters and the BC. The MLF pathways have been recently studied by Tarlov (289) and Gacek (92). The SVN projects by way of the ipsilateral MLF to the IVth nucleus ipsilaterally and the IIIrd nucleus bilaterally. Tarlov (289) also described a projection to the contralateral IVth nucleus. The MVN innervates the VIth nucleus bilaterally. Ascending MVN fibers pass via the contralateral MLF to the contralateral IVth nucleus and the IIIrd nucleus bilaterally. According to Tarlov (289), MLF fibers from both the SVN and MVN project bilaterally to all extraocular cell groups in the IIIrd nucleus. Gacek (92) believes that the only vestibular connections to inferior-rectus motoneurons arise in the ventral LVN and ascend in Deiters' tract. Fibers have been traced from the lateral cerebellar nucleus, through the BC, to the contralateral IIIrd nucleus (31). Since primary vestibular fibers terminate in the lateral cerebellar nucleus (25), the BC pathway is potentially disynaptic. There is physiological evidence that some of the BC fibers arise from the *y* group (123).

Stimulation of an individual ampullary nerve results in a primary excitatory action on one extraocular muscle in each eye and an inhibitory action on the antagonistic muscle (38, 83, 141, 142, 288). The pattern of muscle activation gives rise to compensatory eye movements and is mediated by disynaptic EPSPs and IPSPs (6, 7, 123–125, 230, 248). Stimulation of one vestibular nerve results in excitation of contralateral, and inhibition of ipsilateral, motoneurons in all extraocular motor nuclei. Medial-rectus motoneurons are exceptional in that mixed excitatory and inhibitory actions are produced by nerve stimulation (123). The inhibitory pathway to the VIth nucleus is relayed through the MVN (6, 124), and those to the other motor nuclei by way of the SVN (123, 125, 230). The SVN appears to exert only inhibitory actions on motoneurons. In contrast, the MVN, besides inhibiting the ipsilateral VIth nucleus, has an excitatory action on all contralateral motor nuclei (6, 123–125, 230) and also on ipsilateral medial-rectus motoneurons (123). Activity from the SVN and MVN is relayed through the MLF (123, 125). In addition, the BC pathway exerts excitatory effects on selected groups in the contralateral IIIrd nucleus (123, 125). Disynaptic excitatory pathways originating in the utriculus have been traced to the ipsilateral VIth (257) and contralateral IVth nuclei (7) and may be involved, respectively, in the horizontal nystagmus (225) and counter-rolling reactions (19, 154, 287) resulting from otolith stimulation. Physiological and anatomical results are in general agreement concerning the vestibulo-ocular connections to the IVth and VIth nuclei. Discrepancies exist concerning the IIIrd nucleus: anatomical findings (92, 289) lead to the prediction, contrary to physiological observation, that vestibular nerve stimulation would lead to mixed excitatory-inhibitory actions in most motoneurons, not only those supplying the medial rectus.

Recent studies have been concerned with the roles of the various vestibulo-ocular pathways in vestibular-induced nystagmus. Patterns of activity corresponding to slow and fast phases have been recorded from motoneurons innervating, respectively, agonist and antagonist muscles (4, 5, 132, 133, 192, 196, 249, 256). Intracellular studies (5, 133, 192) of agonist motoneurons reveal a slow depolarization followed by a rapid hyperpolarization. In antagonist motoneurons, there is a rapid depolarization succeeded by a slow hyperpolarizing shift. The depolarizations are the result of EPSPs augmented by disinhibition. The hyperpolarizations arise from IPSPs reinforced by disfacilitation. What determines the rhythmic EPSP-IPSP sequences? Rhythmic patterns, correlated with the two phases of nystagmus, have been recorded from neurons in the vestibular nuclei (61, 63, 132) and also from secondary axons within the motor nuclei (5, 191). These observations leave little doubt that the rhythmic inputs to motoneurons involve transmission over disynaptic vestibulo-ocular pathways.

Less clear are the mechanisms responsible for the generation of the rhythmic patterns in secondary neurons. Maeda et al (192) have suggested that both slow and fast phases arise from reciprocal inhibitory (commissural) connections between the two vestibular nuclei. There are several difficulties with this proposition. First, unilateral labyrinthectomy results in a nystagmus. The procedure silences homolateral secondary neurons (234) and, hence, should inactivate commissural pathways. Further, it is reported (35) that nystagmus can be elicited following section of commissural pathways. Finally, the possible role of the reticular formation cannot be ignored. Nystagmus-like patterns have been recorded from reticular neurons (59, 60, 132, 196). There is accumulating electrophysiological (34, 36, 190, 273) and behavioral evidence (12, 35, 37, 100, 205) that the pontine reticular formation plays a key role in the coordination of eye movements. Conceivably, reticular pathways could influence vestibular-induced nystagmus by projecting back to the vestibular nuclei or by direct projections to ocular motoneurons. Ironically, central vestibular research in the 1930's was dominated by a controversy between Lorente de Nó (180) and Spiegel (274) concerning the relative roles of the vestibular nuclei and reticular formation in the etiology of nystagmus. Though progress has been made, the problem is still with us.

Literature Cited

1. Abend, W. K. 1974. Organization of the superior vestibular nucleus of the squirrel monkey. *Proc. 4th Ann. Meet. Soc. Neurosci.* In press (Abstr.)
2. Bairati, A., Iurato, S. 1960. The ultrastructural organization of "Planum Seminulata." *Exp. Cell Res.* 20:77–83
3. Bairati, A., Iurato, S. 1962. Experimental data on the termination of the efferent fibers to the inner ear. In *Electron Microscopy,* ed. S. S. Breese Jr., Vol. 2: U–2. New York: Academic
4. Baker, R., Berthoz, A. 1971. Spontaneous nystagmus recorded in trochlear motoneurons following labyrinthine lesion. *Brain Res.* 32:239–45
5. Baker, R., Berthoz, A. 1974. Organization of vestibular nystagmus in oblique oculomotor system. *J. Neurophysiol.* 37:195–217
6. Baker, R. G., Mano, N., Shimazu, H. 1969. Postsynaptic potentials in abducens motoneurons induced by vestibular stimulation. *Brain Res.* 15:577–80
7. Baker, R., Precht, W., Berthoz, A. 1973. Synaptic connections to trochlear motoneurons determined by individual vestibular nerve branch stimulation in the cat. *Brain Res.* 64:402–6
8. Barber, H. O., Wright, G. 1973. Positional nystagmus in normals. *Advan. Oto Rhino Laryngol.* 19:276–85
9. Beerens, A. J. J. 1969. *Stimulus coding in the utricular nerve of the cat. A quantitative study of the response to static stimulation of the utricle as recorded from primary afferent fibres.* Thesis. Univ. Amsterdam. Amsterdam: Drukkerij Cloeck en Moedigh. 103 pp.
10. Békésy, G. von 1952. DC resting potentials inside the cochlear partition. *J. Acoust. Soc. Am.* 24:72–76
11. Békésy, G. von 1952. Gross localization of the place of origin of the cochlear microphonics. *J. Acoust. Soc. Am.* 24:399–409
12. Bender, M. B., Shanzer, S. 1964. Oculomotor pathways defined by electrical stimulation and lesions in the brainstem of monkey. In *The Oculomotor System,* ed. M. B. Bender, 81–140. New York: Hoeber
13. Bennett, M. V. L. 1967. Mechanisms of electroreception. In *Lateral Line Detectors,* ed. P. Cahn, 313–93. Bloomington: Univ. Indiana Press
14. Bennett, M. V. L. 1971. Electrolocation in fish. *Ann. NY Acad. Sci.* 188:242–69
15. Benson, A. J. 1970. Interactions between semicircular canals and gravireceptors. In *Recent Advances in Aerospace Medicine,* ed. D. E. Busby, 249–61. Dordrecht-Holland: D. Reidel
16. Benson, A. J., Barnes, G. R. 1973. Responses to rotating linear acceleration vectors considered in relation to a model of the otolith organs. In *5th Symposium on the Role of the Vestibular Organs in Space Exploration.* NASA SP-314:221–36. Washington D.C.: US GPO
17. Benson, A. J., Bodin, M. A. 1966. Interaction of linear and angular accelerations on vestibular receptors in man. *Aerospace Med.* 37:144–54
18. Benson, A. J., Guedry, F. E. Jr., Melvill Jones, G. 1970. Response of semicircular canal dependent units in vestibular nuclei to rotation of a linear acceleration vector without angular acceleration. *J. Physiol. London* 210:475–94
19. Berthoz, A., Baker, R., Precht, W. 1973. Labyrinthine control of inferior oblique motoneurons. *Exp. Brain Res.* 18:225–41
20. Bobbin, R. P., Konishi, T. 1971. Acetylcholine mimics crossed olivocochlear bundle stimulation. *Nature New Biol.* 231:222–23
21. Bobbin, R. P., Konishi, T. 1974. Action of cholinergic and anticholinergic drugs at the crossed olivocochlear bundle-hair cell junction. *Acta Oto Laryngol.* 77:56–65
22. Bosher, S. K., Warren, R. L. 1968. Observations on the electrochemistry of the cochlear endolymph of the rat. *Proc. Roy. Soc. B* 171:227–47
23. Bosher, S. K., Warren, R. L. 1971. A study of the electrochemistry and osmotic relationships of the cochlear fluids in the neonatal rat at the time of development of the endocochlear potential. *J. Physiol. London* 212:739–61
24. Brightman, M. W., Reese, T. S. 1969. Junctions between intimately apposed cell membranes in the vertebrate brain. *J. Cell Biol.* 40:648–77
25. Brodal, A., Høivik, B. 1964. Site and mode of termination of primary vestibulocerebellar fibres in the cat. An experimental study with silver impregnation methods. *Arch. Ital. Biol.* 102:1–21
26. Brodal, A., Pompeiano, O., Eds. 1972. *Progress in Brain Research. Vol. 37, Basic Aspects of Central Vestibular Mechanisms.* Amsterdam: Elsevier. 656 pp.

27. Butler, R. A. 1965. Some experimental observations on the DC resting potentials in the guinea-pig cochlea. *J. Acoust. Soc. Am.* 37:429–33
28. Cajal, S. R. 1909. *Histologie du Système Nerveux de l'Homme et des Vertébrés.* Paris: Maloine. Tome 1
29. Cappel, K. L. 1966. Determination of physical constants of the semicircular canals from measurements of single neural unit activity under constant angular acceleration. *2nd Symposium on the Role of the Vestibular Organs in Space Exploration.* NASA SP-115: 229–34. Washington, D.C.: US GPO
30. Carpenter, M. B. 1960. Fiber projections from the descending and lateral vestibular nuclei in the cat. *Am. J. Anat.* 107:1–22
31. Carpenter, M. B., Strominger, N. L. 1964. Cerebello-oculomotor fibers in the rhesus monkey. *J. Comp. Neurol.* 123:211–30
32. Caston, J. 1972. L'activité vestibulaire efférente chez la grenouille. *Pfluegers Arch.* 331:365–70
33. Clark, B. 1970. The vestibular system. *Ann. Rev. Psychol.* 21:273–306
34. Cohen, B., Feldman, M. 1968. Relationship of electrical activity in pontine reticular formation and lateral geniculate body to rapid eye movements. *J. Neurophysiol.* 31:806–17
35. Cohen, B., Henn, V. 1972. The origin of quick phase of nystagmus in the horizontal plane. In *Cerebral Control of Eye Movements and Motion Perception,* ed. J. Dichgans, E. Bizzi, 36–55. Bib. Ophthal. 82. Basel: Karger
36. Cohen, B., Henn, V. 1972. Unit activity in the pontine reticular formation associated with eye movements. *Brain Res.* 46:403–10
37. Cohen, B., Komatsuzaki, A. 1972. Eye movements induced by stimulation of the pontine reticular formation: evidence for integration in oculomotor pathways. *Exp. Neurol.* 36:101–17
38. Cohen, B., Suzuki, J.-I., Bender, M. B. 1964. Eye movements from semicircular canal nerve stimulation in the cat. *Ann. Otol. Rhinol. Laryngol.* 73:153–69
39. Copack, P., Dafny, N., Gilman, S. 1972. Neurophysiological evidence of vestibular projections to thalamus, basal ganglia, and cerebral cortex. In *Corticothalamic Projections and Sensorimotor Activities,* ed. T. L. Frigyesi, E. Rinvik, M. D. Yahr, 309–39. New York: Raven
40. Correia, M. J., Guedry, F. E. Jr. 1966. Modification of vestibular responses as a function of rate of rotation about an earth-horizontal axis. *Acta Oto Laryngol.* 62:297–308
41. Correia, M. J., Landolt, J. P. 1973. Spontaneous and driven responses from primary neurons of the anterior semicircular canal of the pigeon. *Advan. Oto Rhino Laryngol.* 19:134–38
42. Correia, M. J., Money, K. E. 1970. The effect of blockage of all six semicircular canal ducts on nystagmus produced by dynamic linear acceleration in the cat. *Acta Oto Laryngol.* 69:7–16
43. Curthoys, I. S., Markham, C. H. 1971. Convergence of labyrinthine influences on units in the vestibular nuclei of the cat. I. Natural stimulation. *Brain Res.* 35:469–90
44. Dallos, P. 1968. On the negative potential within the organ of Corti. *J. Acoust. Soc. Am.* 44:818–19
45. Dallos, P., Billone, M. C., Durrant, J. D., Wang, C.-y., Raynor, S. 1972. Cochlear inner and outer hair cells: functional differences. *Science* 177: 356–58
46. Davis, H. 1965. A model for transducer action in the cochlea. *Cold Spring Harbor Symp. Quant. Biol.* 30:181–89
47. Davis, H. et al 1958. Modifications of cochlear potentials produced by streptomycin poisoning and by extensive venous obstruction. *Larynogoscope* 68:596–627
48. Dayal, V. S. 1970. DC potentials in the semicircular canal of the pigeon. *Acta Oto Laryngol* 69:254–56
49. Derbin, C., Szabo, T. 1968. Ultrastructure of an electroreceptor (Knollenorgan) in the mormyrid fish *Gnathonemus petersii. J. Ultrastruct. Res.* 22:469–84
50. Desole, C., Pallestrini, E. A. 1969. Responses of vestibular units to stimulation of individual semicircular canals. *Exp. Neurol.* 24:310–24
51. DeVito, R. V., Brusa, A., Arduini, A. 1956. Cerebellar and vestibular influences on Deitersian units. *J. Neurophysiol.* 19:241–53
52. de Vries, H. 1950. The mechanics of the labyrinth otoliths. *Acta Oto Laryingol.* 38:262–73
53. Dichgans, J., Schmidt, C. L., Wist, E. R. 1972. Frequency modulation of afferent and efferent unit activity in the vestibular nerve by oculomotor impulses. See Ref. 26, 449–56
54. Dohlman, G. 1935. Some practical and

theoretical points in labyrinthology. *Proc. Roy. Soc. Med.* 28:1371–80

55. Dohlman, G. 1964. Secretion and absorption of endolymph. *Ann. Otol. Rhinol. Laryngol.* 73:708–23
56. Dohlman, G. F. 1971. The attachment of the cupulae, otolith and tectorial membranes to the sensory cell areas. *Acta Oto Laryngol.* 71:89–105
57. Duensing, F. 1968. Die Aktivität der von den vertikalen Bogengängen abhängigen Neurone im Hirnstamm des Kaninchens. I. Mitteilung. Drehbescheungigungen in Seitenlage. *Arch. Ohren. Nasen Kehlkopfheilk.* 192:32–50
58. Duensing, F. 1968. Die Aktivität der von den vertikalen Bogengängen abhängigen Neurone im Hirnstamm des Kaninchens II. Mitteilung. Drehbeschleunigungen in verschiedenen Positionen. *Arch. Ohren Nasen Kehlkopfheilk.* 192:51–62
59. Duensing, F., Schaefer, K.-P. 1957. Die Neuroneaktivität in der Formatio reticularis des Rhombencephalons beim vestibulären Nystagmus. *Arch. Psychiat. Nervenkr.* 196:265–90
60. Duensing, F., Schaefer, K.-P. 1957. Die "locker gekoppelten" Neurone der Formatio reticularis des Rhombencephalons beim vestibulären Nystagmus. *Arch. Psychiat. Nervenkr.* 196:402–20
61. Duensing, F., Schaefer, K.-P. 1958. Die Aktivität einzelner Neurone im Bereich der Vestibulariskerne bei Horizontalbeschleunigungen unter besonderer Berücksichtigung des vestibulären Nystagmus. *Arch. Psychiat. Nervenkr.* 198:225–52
62. Duensing, F., Schaefer, K.-P. 1959. Über die Konvergenz verschiedener labyrinthärer Afferenzen auf einzelne Neurone des Vestibulariskerngebietes. *Arch. Psychiat. Nervenkr.* 199:345–71
63. Eckel, W. 1954. Electrophysiologische und histologische Untersuchungen im Vestibulariskerngebiet bei Drehreizen. *Arch. Ohren Nasen Kehlkopfheilk.* 164:487–513
64. Egmond, A. A. J. van, Groen, J. J., Jonkees, L. B. W. 1949. The mechanics of the semicircular canals. *J. Physiol. London* 110:1–17
65. Eldredge, D. H., Smith, C. A., Davis, H., Gannon, R. P. 1961. The electrical polarization of the semicircular canals (guinea pig). *Ann. Otol. Rhinol. Laryngol.* 70:1024–36
66. Engström, H. 1958. On the double innervation of the sensory epithelia of the inner ear. *Acta Oto Laryngol.* 49:109–18
67. Engström, H., Ades, H. W., Hawkins, J. E. Jr. 1965. The vestibular sensory cells and their innervation. *Symp. Biol. Hung.* 5:21–41
68. Engström, H., Bergström, B., Ades, H. W. 1972. Macula utriculi and macula sacculi in the squirrel monkey. *Acta Oto Laryngol. Suppl.* 301:75–126
69. Fernández, C., Goldberg, J. M. 1971. Physiology of peripheral neurons innervating semicircular canals of the squirrel monkey. II. Response to sinusoidal stimulation and dynamics of peripheral vestibular system. *J. Neurophysiol.* 34:661–75
70. Fernández, C., Goldberg, J. M., Abend, W. K. 1972. Response to static tilts of peripheral neurons innervating otolith organs of the squirrel monkey. *J. Neurophysiol.* 35:978–97
71. Ferraro, A., Pacella, B. L., Barrera, S. E. 1940. Effects of lesions of the medial vestibular nucleus. An anatomical and physiological study in Macacus rhesus monkeys. *J. Comp. Neurol.* 73:7–36
72. Fex, J. 1962. Auditory activity in centrifugal and centripetal cochlear fibres in cat. A study of feedback system. *Acta Physiol. Scand. Suppl.* 189:1–68
73. Fex, J. 1967. Efferent inhibition of the cochlea related to hair-cell dc activity: study of postsynaptic activity of the crossed olivocochlear fibres in the cat. *J. Acoust. Soc. Am.* 41:666–75
74. Fex, J. 1968. Efferent inhibition in the cochlea by the olivo-cochlear bundle. In *Hearing Mechanisms in Vertebrates,* ed. A. V. S. De Reuck, J. Knight, 169–80. Boston: Little, Brown
75. Fex, J. 1973. Neuropharmacology and potentials of the inner ear. In *Basic Mechanisms in Hearing,* ed. A. Møller, 377–420. New York: Academic
76. Flock, Å. 1965. Electron microscopic and electrophysiological studies on the lateral line canal organ. *Acta Oto Laryngol. Suppl.* 199:1–90
77. Flock, Å. 1971. Sensory transduction in hair cells. In *Handbook of Sensory Physiology. Vol. I, Principles of Receptor Physiology,* ed. W. R. Lowenstein, 396–441. Berlin: Springer
78. Flock, Å., Jørgensen, J. M., Russell, I. J. 1973. Passive electrical properties of hair cells and supporting cells in the lateral line canal organ. *Acta Oto Laryngol.* 76:190–98
79. Flock, Å., Jorgensen, J. M., Russell, I. 1973. The physiology of individual hair cells and their synapses. See Ref. 75, 273–302

80. Flock, Å., Lam, D. M. K. 1974. Neurotransmitter synthesis in inner ear and lateral line sense organs. *Nature* 249:142–44
81. Flock, Å., Russell, I. 1973. Efferent nerve fibers: postsynaptic action on hair cells. *Nature New Biol.* 243:89–91
82. Flock, Å., Russell, I. 1973. The postsynaptic action of efferent fibres in the lateral line organ of the burbot *Lota lota*. *J. Physiol. London* 235:591–605
83. Fluur, E. 1959. Influences of semicircular ducts on extraocular muscles. *Acta Oto Laryngol. Suppl.* 149:1–46
84. Fluur, E., Mellström, A. 1970. Utricular stimulation and oculomotor reactions. *Laryngoscope* 80:1701–12
85. Fluur, E., Mellström, A. 1970. Saccular stimulation and oculomotor reactions. *Laryngoscope* 80:1713–21
86. Fredrickson, J. M., Schwarz , D. W. F. 1974. Vestibulo-cortical projection. In *The Vestibular System: Anatomical, Physiological and Clinical Aspects,* ed. R. Naunton, C. Fernández. New York: Academic. In press
87. Fujita, Y., Rosenberg, J., Segundo, J. P. 1968. Activity of cells in the lateral vestibular nucleus as a function of head position. *J. Physiol. London* 196:1–18
88. Furukawa, T., Ishii, Y. 1967. Neurophysiological studies on hearing in goldfish. *J. Neurophysiol.* 30:1377–1403
89. Furukawa, T., Ishii, Y., Matsuura, S. 1972. An analysis of microphonic potentials of the sacculus of goldfish. *Jap. J. Physiol.* 22:603–16
90. Furukawa, T., Ishii, Y., Matsuura, S. 1972. Synaptic delay and time course of postsynaptic potentials at the junction between hair cells and eighth nerve fibers in the goldfish. *Jap. J. Physiol.* 22:617–35
91. Gacek, R. R. 1969. The course and central termination of first order neurons supplying vestibular endorgans in the cat. *Acta Oto Laryngol. Suppl.* 254:1–66
92. Gacek, R. R. 1971. Anatomical demonstration of the vestibulo-ocular projections in the cat. *Acta Oto Laryngol. Suppl.* 293:1–63
93. Gacek, R. R., Lyon, M. 1974. The localization of vestibular efferent neurons in the kitten with horseradish peroxidase. *Acta Oto Laryngol.* 77:92–101
94. Gacek, R. R., Nomura, Y., Balogh, K. 1965. Acetylcholinesterase activity in the efferent fibers of the stato-acoustic nerve. *Acta Oto Laryngol.* 59:541–53
95. Gallé, H., Clemens, A. 1973. The sacculus of rana: an equilibrium organ. *Equilibrium Res.* 3:33–47
96. Gannon, R. P., Eldredge, D. H., Smith, C. A., Davis, H. 1958. DC potentials of the semicircular canals. *Physiologist* 1:4
97. Gillingham, K. K. 1970. The effect of cerebellectomy on vestibular nuclear adaptation. *Ann. Otol. Rhinol. Laryngol.* 79:124–37
98. Gisselsson, L. 1960. Effect on microphonics of acetylcholine injected into the endolymphatic space. Preliminary report. *Acta Oto Laryngol.* 51:636–38
99. Gleisner, L., Henriksson, N. G. 1964. Efferent and afferent activity pattern in the vestibular nerve of the frog. *Acta Oto Laryngol. Suppl.* 192:90–103
100. Goebel, H. H., Komatsuzaki, A., Bender, M. B., Cohen, B. 1971. Lesions of the pontine tegmentum and conjugate gaze paralysis. *Arch. Neurol.* 24:431–40
101. Goldberg, J. M., Fernández, C. 1971. Physiology of peripheral neurons innervating semicircular canals of the squirrel monkey. I. Resting discharge and response to constant angular accelerations. *J. Neurophysiol.* 34:635–60
102. Goldberg, J. M., Fernández, C. 1971. Physiology of peripheral neurons innervating semicircular canals of the squirrel monkey. III. Variations among units in their discharge properties. *J. Neurophysiol.* 34:676–84
103. Goldberg, J. M., Fernández, C. 1974. Response dynamics of peripheral otolith neurons in barbiturate-anesthetized squirrel monkey. *Proc. 4th Ann. Meet. Soc. Neurosci.* In press (Abstr.)
104. Görner, P. 1963. Untersuchungen zur Morphologie und Elektrophysiologie des Seitenlinienorgans vom Krallenfrosch (*Xenopus laevis* Daudin). *Z. Vergl. Physiol.* 47:316–38
105. Gray, L. P. 1926. Some experimental evidence on the connections of the vestibular mechanism in the cat. *J. Comp. Neurol.* 41:319–64
106. Graybiel, A., Patterson, J. L. 1955. Thresholds of stimulation of the otolith organs as indicated by the oculogravic illusion. *J. Appl. Physiol.* 7:666–70
107. Graybiel, A., Stockwell, C. W., Guedry, F. E. Jr. 1972. Evidence for a test of dynamic otolith function considered in relation to responses from a patient with idiopathic progressive vestibular degeneration. *Acta Oto Laryngol.* 73:1–3
108. Grey, E. J., Barnes, C. D. 1973. Some observations on the pathway of the ves-

tibular rapid transmission system. *Brain Res.* 57:213–17
109. Groen, J. J. 1957. Cupulometry. *Laryngoscope* 67:894–905
110. Groen, J. J., Lowenstein, O., Vendrik, A. J. H. 1952. The mechanical analysis of the responses from the end-organs of the horizontal semicircular canal in the isolated elasmobranch labyrinth. *J. Physiol. London* 117:329–46
111. Grofová, I., Corvaja, N. 1972. Commissural projection from the nuclei of termination of the VIIIth cranial nerve in the toad. *Brain Res.* 42:189–95
112. Gualtierotti, T., Bracchi, F., Rocca, E. 1972. *Orbiting Frog Otolith Experiment (OFO-A).* Milan, Italy:Piccin
113. Guedry, F. E. Jr. 1965. Orientation of the rotation axis relative to gravity: its influence on nystagmus and the sensation of rotation. *Acta Oto Laryngol.* 60:30–49
114. Guedry, F. E. Jr. 1965. Psychophysiological studies of vestibular function. In *Contributions to Sensory Physiology,* ed. W. D. Neff, 1:63–135. New York: Academic
115. Guth, P. S., Burton, M., Norris, C. H. 1972. Release of acetylcholine by the olivocochlear bundles. *J. Acoust. Soc. Am.* 52:143–44 (Abstr.)
116. Hama, K. 1965. Some observations on the fine structure of the lateral line organ of the japanese sea eel *Lyncozymba nystromi. J. Cell Biol.* 24:193–210
117. Hama, K. 1969. A study on the fine structure of the saccular macula of the goldfish. *Z. Zellforsch. Mikrosk. Anat.* 94:155–71
118. Hamilton, D. W. 1968. The calyceal synapse of Type I vestibular hair cells. *J. Ultrastruct. Res.* 23:98–114
119. Harris, G. G., Flock, Å. 1967. Spontaneous and evoked activity from *Xenopus laevis* lateral-line. See Ref. 13, 135–61
120. Harris, G. G., Frishkopf, L., Flock, Å. 1970. Receptor potentials from hair cells of the lateral line. *Science* 167:76–79
121. Harris, G. G., Milne, D. C. 1966. Input-output characteristics of the lateral-line sense organs of *Xenopus laevis. J. Acoust. Soc. Am.* 40:32–42
122. Hauglie-Hanssen, E. 1968. Intrinsic neuronal organization of the vestibular nuclear complex in the cat. A Golgi study. *Ergeb. Anat. Entwicklungsgesch.* 40:1–105
123. Highstein, S. M. 1973. The organization of the vestibulo-oculomotor and trochlear reflex pathways in the rabbit. *Exp. Brain Res.* 17:285–300
124. Highstein, S. M. 1973. Synaptic linkage in the vestibulo-ocular and cerebello-vestibular pathways to the VIth nucleus in the rabbit. *Exp. Brain Res.* 17:301–14
125. Highstein, S. M., Ito, M., Tsuchiya, T. 1971. Synaptic linkage in the vestibulo-ocular reflex pathway of rabbit. *Exp. Brain Res.* 13:306–26
126. Hilding, D., Wersäll, J. 1962. Cholinesterase and its relations to the nerve endings in the inner ear. *Acta Oto Laryngol.* 55:205–17
127. Hillman, D. E. 1969. Light and electron microscopical study of the relationships between the cerebellum and the vestibular organ of the frog. *Exp. Brain Res.* 9:1–15
128. Hillman, D. E., Lewis, E. R. 1971. Morphological basis for a mechanical linkage in otolithic receptor transduction in the frog. *Science* 174:416–19
129. Hinojosa, R., Robertson, J. D. 1967. Ultrastructure of the spoon type synaptic endings in the nucleus vestibularis tangentialis of the chick. *J. Cell Biol.* 34:421–30
130. Honrubia, V., Strelioff, D., Ward, P. H. 1971. The mechanism of excitation of hair cells in the cochlea. *Laryngoscope* 81:1719–25
131. Honrubia, V., Ward, P. H. 1969. Dependence of the cochlear microphonics and summating potential on the endocochlear potential. *J. Acoust. Soc. Am.* 46:388–92
132. Horcholle, G., Tyč-Dumont, S. 1968. Activités unitaires des neurones vestibulaires et oculomoteurs au cours du nystagmus. *Exp. Brain Res.* 5:16–31
133. Horcholle-Bossavit, G., Tyč-Dumont, S. 1969. Phénomènes synaptiques du nystagmus. *Exp. Brain Res.* 8:201–18
134. Horcholle-Bossavit, G., Tyč-Dumont, S. 1971. Evidence for a rapid transmission in the cat vestibulo-ocular pathway. *Exp. Brain Res.* 13:327–38
135. Howland, H. C., Masci, J. 1973. The functional allometry of semicircular canals, fins, and body dimensions in the juvenile centrarchid fish, *Lepomis gibbosus* (L.). *J. Embryol. Exp. Morphol.* 29:721–43
136. Howland, H. C., Masci, J. 1973. The phylogenetic allometry of the semicircular canals of small fish. *Z. Morphol. Tiere* 75:283–96
137. Igarashi, M., Kanda, T. 1969. Fine structure of the otolithic membrane in

the squirrel monkey. *Acta Oto Laryngol.* 68:43–52
138. Ishii, Y., Matsuura, S., Furukawa, T. 1971. Quantal nature of transmission at the synapse between hair cells and eighth nerve fibers. *Jap. J. Physiol.* 21:79–89
139. Ishii, Y., Matsuura, S., Furukawa, T. 1971. An input-output relation at the synapse between hair cells and eighth nerve fibers in goldfish. *Jap. J. Physiol.* 21:91–98
140. Ito, M., Hongo, T., Okada, Y. 1969. Vestibular-evoked postsynaptic potentials in Deiters neurones. *Exp. Brain Res.* 7:214–30
141. Ito, M., Nisimaru, N., Yamamoto, M. 1973. The neural pathways mediating reflex contraction of extraocular muscles during semicircular canal stimulation in rabbits. *Brain Res.* 55:183–88
142. Ito, M., Nisimaru, N., Yamamoto, M. 1973. The neural pathways relaying reflex inhibition from semicircular canals to extraocular muscles of rabbits. *Brain Res.* 55:189–93
143. Iurato, S., Luciano, L., Pannese, E. 1972. Efferent vestibular fibers in mammals: morphological and histochemical aspects. See Ref. 26, 429–43
144. Iurato, S., Luciano, L., Pannese, E., Reale, E. 1971. Acetylcholinesterase activity in the vestibular sensory areas. *Acta Oto Laryngol.* 71:147–52
145. Janeke, J. B., Jongkees, L. B. W., Oosterveld, W. J. 1970. Relationship between otoliths and nystagmus. *Acta Oto Laryngol.* 69:1–6
146. Johnsson, L.-G., Hawkins, J. E. 1967. Otolithic membranes of the saccule and utricle in man. *Science* 157:1454–56
147. Johnstone, B. M. 1965. The relation between endolymph and the endocochlear potential during anoxia. *Acta Oto Laryngol.* 60:113–20
148. Johnstone, B. M., Johnstone, J. R., Pugsley, I. D. 1966. Membrane resistance in endolymphatic walls of the first turn of the guinea-pig cochlea. *J. Acoust. Soc. Am.* 40:1398–1404
149. Johnstone, B. M., Sellick, P. M. 1972. The peripheral auditory apparatus. *Quart. Rev. Biophys.* 5:1–57
150. Johnstone, C. G., Schmidt, R. S., Johnstone, B. M. 1963. Sodium and potassium in vertebrate cochlear endolymph as determined by flame micro-spectrophotometry. *Comp. Biochem. Physiol.* 9:335–41
151. Kasahara, M., Mano, N., Oshima, T., Ozawa, S., Shimazu, H. 1968. Contralateral short latency inhibition of central vestibular neurons in the horizontal canal system. *Brain Res.* 8:376–78
152. Kasahara, M., Uchino, Y. 1971. Selective mode of commissural inhibition induced by semicircular canal afferents on secondary vestibular neurones in the cat. *Brain Res.* 34:366–69
153. Kawai, N., Ito, M., Nozue, M. 1969. Postsynaptic influences on the vestibular non-Deiters nuclei from primary vestibular nerve. *Exp. Brain Res.* 8:190–200
154. Kellogg, R. S. 1965. Dynamic counterrolling of the eye in normal subjects and in persons with bilateral labyrinthine defects. In *The Role of the Vestibular Organs in the Exploration of Space.* NASA SP–77:195–202. Washington, D.C.: US GPO
155. Keynes, R. D. 1969. From frog skin to sheep rumen: a survey of transport of salts and water across multicellular structures. *Quart. Rev. Biophys.* 2:177–281
156. Kimura, R., Lundquist, P.-G., Wersäll, J. 1964. Secretory epithelial linings in the ampullae of the guinea pig labyrinth. *Acta Oto Laryngol.* 57:517–30
157. Kimura, R., Wersäll, J. 1962. Termination of the olivocochlear bundle in relation to the outer hair cells of the organ of Corti in guinea pig. *Acta Oto Laryngol.* 55:11–32
158. Klinke, R., Schmidt, C. L. 1968. Efferente Impulse im Nervus vestibularis bei Reizung des kontralateralen Otolithenorgans. *Pfluegers Arch.* 304:183–88
159. Klinke, R., Schmidt, C. L. 1970. Efferent influence on the vestibular organ during active movements of the body. *Pfuegers Arch.* 318:325–32
160. Konishi, T., Butler, R. A., Fernández, C. 1961. Effect of anoxia on cochlear potentials. *J. Acoust. Soc. Am.* 33:349–56
161. Konishi, T., Kelsey, E. 1967. Effect of sodium deficiency on cochlear potentials. *J. Acoust. Soc. Am.* 43:462–70
162. Konishi, T., Kelsey, E. 1969. Effect of calcium deficiency on cochlear potentials. *J. Acoust. Soc. Am.* 47:1055–62
163. Konishi, T., Kelsey, E., Singleton, G. T. 1966. Effects of quimical alteration in the endolymph on the cochlear potentials. *Acta Oto Laryngol.* 62:393–404
164. Konishi, T., Nielsen, D. W. 1973. The relationship between the movement of the basilar membrane and the initiation

of nerve impulses in primary auditory nerve fibers. *Commun. Sci. Lab. Quart. Rep. Univ. Fla.* 11:24–29

165. Konishi, T., Slepian, J. Z. 1971. Effects of the electrical stimulation of the crossed olivocochlear bundle on cochlear potentials recorded with intracochlear electrodes in guinea pigs. *J. Acoust. Soc. Am.* 49:1762–69
166. Korn, H., Sotelo, C., Crepel, F. 1973. Electrotonic coupling between neurons in the rat lateral vestibular nucleus. *Exp. Brain Res.* 16:255–75
167. Kurokawa, S. 1965. Experimental study on electrical resistance of basilar membraine in guinea pig. *Jap. J. Otol.* 68:1177–95
168. Ladpli, R., Brodal, A. 1968. Experimental studies of commissural and reticular formation projections from the vestibular nuclei in the cat. *Brain Res.* 8:65–96
169. Lawrence, M., Nuttall, A. L. 1970. Electrophysiology of the organ of Corti. In *Biochemical Mechanisms in Hearing and Deafness,* ed. M. M. Paparella, 83–96. Springfield, Illinois: Thomas
170. Lawrence, M., Nuttall, A. L., Clapper, M. P. 1974. Electrical potentials and fluid boundaries within the organ of Corti. *J. Acoust. Soc. Am.* 55:122–38
171. Ledoux, A. 1949. Activité électrique des nerfs des canaux semicirculaires du saccule et de l'utricule chez la grenouille. *Acta Oto Rhino Laryngol. Belg.* 3:335–49
172. Lewis, E. R., Nemanic, P. 1972. Scanning electron microscope observations of saccular ultrastructure in the mudpuppy (*Necturus maculosus*). *Z. Zellforschung. Mikrosk. Anat.* 123:441–57
173. Lim, D. J. 1973. Formation and fate of the otoconia. Scanning and transmission electron microscopy. *Ann. Otol. Rhinol. Laryngol.* 82:23–35
174. Lindeman, H. H. 1969. Studies on the morphology of the sensory regions of the vestibular apparatus. *Ergeb. Anat. Entwicklungsgesch.* 42:1–113
175. Lindeman, H. H., Ades, H. W., West, R. W. 1973. Scanning electron microscopy of the vestibular end organs. In *5th Symposium on the Role of the Vestibular Organs in Space Exploration.* NASA SP–314:145–56. Washington, D.C.: US GPO
176. Llinás, R., Precht, W. 1969. The inhibitory vestibular efferent system and its relation to the cerebellum in the frog. *Exp. Brain Res.* 9:16–29
177. Loe, P. R., Tomko, D. L., Werner, G. 1973. The neural signal of angular head position in primary afferent vestibular nerve axons. *J. Physiol. London* 230:29–50
178. Lorente de Nó, R. 1926. Études sur l'anatomie et la physiologie du labyrinthe de l'oreille et du VIIIe nerf. Deuxième partie. *Trav. Lab. Rech. Biol. Univ. Madrid* 24:53–153
179. Lorente de Nó, R. 1933. Anatomy of the eighth nerve. The central projection of the nerve endings of the internal ear. *Laryngoscope* 43:1–38
180. Lorente de Nó, R. 1933. Vestibulo-ocular reflex arc. *Arch. Neurol. Psychiat.* 30:245–91
181. Lowenstein, O. 1955. The effect of galvanic polarization on the impulse discharge from sense endings in the isolated labyrinth in the thornback ray *(Raja clavata). J. Physiol. London* 127:104–17
182. Lowenstein, O. 1970. The electrophysiological study of the responses of the isolated labyrinth of the lamprey *(Lampetra fluviatilis)* to angular acceleration, tilting and mechanical vibration. *Proc. Roy. Soc. London B* 174:419–34
183. Lowenstein, O. 1972. Physiology of vestibular receptors. See Ref. 26, 19–30
184. Lowenstein, O. 1974. The peripheral neuron. In *Neurotology: Anatomy, Physiology, and Disorders of the Vestibular System,* ed. R. Naunton, C. Fernández. New York: Academic. In press
185. Lowenstein, O., Roberts, T. D. M. 1948. Oscillographic analysis of the gravity and vibration responses from the labyrinth of the thornback ray *(Raja clavata). Nature* 162:852–54
186. Lowenstein, O., Sand, A. 1940. The individual and integrated activity of the semicircular canals of the elasmobranch labyrinth. *J. Physiol. London* 99:89–101
187. Lowenstein, O., Sand, A. 1940. The mechanism of the semicircular canal. A study of responses of single-fibre preparations to angular accelerations and to rotation at constant speed. *Proc. Roy. Soc. London B* 129:256–75
188. Lowenstein, O., Thornhill, R. A. 1970. The labyrinthe of *Myxine:* anatomy, ultrastructure and electrophysiology. *Proc. Roy Soc. London B* 176:21–42
189. Lowenstein, O., Wersäll, J. 1959. A functional interpretation of the electron-microscopic structure of the sensory hairs in the cristae of the elasmobranch *Raja clavata* in terms of directional sensitivity. *Nature* 184:1807–8

190. Luschei, E. S., Fuchs, A. F. 1972. Activity of brain stem neurons during eye movements of alert monkeys. *J. Neurophysiol.* 35:445–61
191. Maeda, M., Shimazu, H., Shinoda, Y. 1971. Rhythmic activities of secondary vestibular efferent fibers recorded within the abducens nucleus during vestibular nystagmus. *Brain Res.* 34: 361–65
192. Maeda, M., Shimazu, H., Shinoda, Y. 1972. Nature of synaptic events in cat abducens motoneurons at slow and quick phase of vestibular nystagmus. *J. Neurophysiol.* 35:279–96
193. Malcolm, R. 1974. A mechanism by which the hair cells of the inner ear transduce mechanical energy into a modulated train of action potential. *J. Gen. Physiol.* 63:757–72
194. Malcolm, R., Jones, G. M. 1970. A quantitative study of vestibular adaptation in humans. *Acta Oto Laryngol.* 70:126–35
195. Mannen, H. 1965. Arborisations dendritiques. Etude topographique et quantitative dan le noyau vestibulaire du chat. *Arch. Ital. Biol.* 103:197–219
196. Manni, E., Azzena, G. B., Casey, H., Dow, R. S. 1965. Influence of the labyrinth on unitary discharge of the oculomotor nucleus and some adjacent formations. *Exp. Neurol.* 12:9–24
197. Mano, N., Oshima, T., Shimazu, H. 1968. Inhibitory commissural fibers interconnecting the bilateral vestibular nuclei. *Brain Res.* 8:378–82
198. Markham, C. H. 1968. Midbrain and contralateral labyrinth influences on brain stem vestibular neurons in the cat. *Brain Res.* 9:312–33
199. Markham, C. H. 1972. Labyrinthine convergence on vestibular nuclear neurons using natural and electrical stimulation. See Ref. 26, 121–37
200. Markham, C. H., Curthoys, I. S. 1972. Convergence of labyrinthine influences on units in the vestibular nuclei of the cat. II. Electrical stimulation. *Brain Res.* 43:383–96
201. Matsuura, S., Ikeda, K., Furukawa, T. 1971. Effects of Na^+, K^+, and ouabain on microphonic potentials of the goldfish inner ear. *Jap. J. Physiol.* 21:563–78
202. Mayne, R. 1950. The dynamic characteristics of the semicircular canals. *J. Comp. Physiol. Psychol.* 43:309–19
203. Mayne, R. 1965. The "match" of the semicircular canals to the dynamic requirements of various species. In *The Role of the Vestibular Organs in the Exploration of Space.* NASA SP–77:57–67. Washington, D.C.: US GPO
204. Mayne, R. 1974. A system of the vestibular organ. In *Handbook of Sensory Physiology,* ed. H. H. Kornhuber, Vol. VI. In press
205. McCabe, B. F. 1965. The quick component of nystagmus. *Laryngoscope* 85: 1619–46
206. McCabe, B. F., Gillingham, K. 1964. The mechanism of vestibular suppression. *Ann. Otol. Rhinol. Laryngol.* 73:816–29
207. McMasters, R. E., Weiss, A. H., Carpenter, M. B. 1966. Vestibular projections to the nuclei of the extraocular muscles. Degeneration resulting from discrete partial lesions of the vestibular nuclei in the monkey. *Am. J. Anat.* 118:163–94
208. Mehler, W. R. 1972. Comparative anatomy of the vestibular complex in submammalian vertebrates. See Ref. 26, 55–67
209. Jones, G. M., Barry, W., Kowalsky, N. 1964. Dynamics of the semicircular canals compared in yaw, pitch and roll. *Aerosp. Med.* 35:984–89
210. Jones, G. M., Milsum, J. H. 1965. Spatial and dynamic aspects of visual fixation. *IEEE Trans. Bio-Med. Eng.* 12:54–62
211. Jones, G. M., Milsum, J. H. 1969. Neural response of the vestibular system to translation acceleration. In *System Analysis in Neurophysiology,* ed. C. Terzuolo, 8–20. Brainerd: Univ. Minnesota Press
212. Jones, G. M., Milsum, J. H. 1970. Characteristics of neural transmission from the semicircular canal to the vestibular nuclei of cats. *J. Physiol. London* 209:295–316
213. Jones, G. M., Milsum, J. H. 1971. Frequency-response analysis of central vestibular unit activity resulting from rotational stimulation of the semicircular canals. *J. Physiol. London* 219:191–215
214. Jones, G. M., Spells, K. E. 1963. A theoretical and comparative study of the functional dependence of the semicircular canal upon its physical dimensions. *Proc. Roy. Soc. London B* 157:403–19
215. Mendelsohn, M., Konishi, T. 1969. The effect of local anoxia on the cation content of the endolymph. *Ann. Otol. Rhinol. Laryngol.* 78:65–75

216. Miyata, H., Igarashi, M. 1973. Positional nystagmus in squirrel monkeys. *Equilibrium Res.* 3:63–72
217. Money, K. E. et al 1971. Physical properties of fluids and structures of vestibular apparatus of the pigeon. *Am. J. Physiol.* 220:140–47
218. Money, K. E., Johnson, W. H., Corlett, B. M. A. 1965. Role of semicircular canals in positional alcohol nystagmus. *Am. J. Physiol.* 208:1065–70
219. Money, K. E., Myles, W. S. 1974. Heavy water nystagmus and effects of alcohol. *Nature* 247:404–5
220. Money, K. E., Scott, J. W. 1962. Functions of the separate sensory receptors of nonauditory labyrinth in the cat. *Am. J. Physiol.* 202:1211–20
221. Mulroy, M. J., Altmann, D. W., Weiss, T. F., Peake, W. T. 1974. Intracellular electric responses to sound in a vertebrate cochlea. *Nature* 249:482–85
222. Murray, M. J., Capranica, R. R. 1973. Spike generation in the lateral-line afferents of *Xenopus laevis:* evidence favoring multiple sites of initiation. *J. Comp. Physiol.* 87:1–20
223. Nashner, L. M. 1970. *Sensory feedback in human posture control.* ScD thesis. MIT, Cambridge, Massachusetts
224. Niven, J. I., Hixson, W. C. 1961. *Frequency Response of the Human Semicircular Canals. I. Steady-State Ocular Nystagmus Response to High-Level Sinusoidal Angular Rotations.* Report No. 58. Pensacola, Florida:NSAM
225. Niven, J. I., Hixson, W. C., Correia, M. J. 1966. Elicitation of horizontal nystagmus by periodic linear acceleration. *Acta Oto Laryngol.* 62:429–41
226. Obara, S., Bennett, M. V. L. 1972. Mode of operation of ampullae of Lorenzini of the skate, *Raja. J. Gen. Physiol.* 60:534–57
227. Oman, C. M., Young, L. R. 1972. The physiological range of pressure difference and cupula deflections in the human semicircular canal. Theoretical considerations. *Acta Oto Largyngol.* 74:324–31
228. Ozawa, S., Precht, W., Shimazu, H. 1974. Crossed effects on central vestibular neurons in the horizontal canal system of the frog. *Exp. Brain Res.* 19:394–405
229. Peterson, B. W. 1970. Distribution of neural responses to tilting within vestibular nuclei of the cat. *J. Neurophysiol.* 33:750–67
230. Precht, W., Baker, R. 1972. Synaptic organization of the vestibulo-trochlear pathway. *Exp. Brain Res.* 14:158–84
231. Precht, W., Llinás, R., Clarke, M. 1971. Physiological responses of frog vestibular fibers to horizontal angular rotation. *Exp. Brain Res.* 13:378–407
232. Precht, W., Richter, A., Ozawa, S., Shimazu, H. 1974. Intracellular study of frog's vestibular neurons in relation to the labyrinth and spinal cord. *Exp. Brain Res.* 19:377–93
233. Precht, W., Shimazu, H. 1965. Functional connections of tonic and kinetic vestibular neurons with primary vestibular afferents. *J. Neurophysiol.* 28: 1014–28
234. Precht, W., Shimazu, H., Markham, C. H. 1966. A mechanism of central compensation of vestibular function following hemilabyrinthectomy. *J. Neurophysiol.* 29:996–1010
235. Rasmussen, G. L. 1946. The olivary peduncle and other fiber projections of the superior olivary complex. *J. Comp. Neurol.* 84:141–219
236. Roberts, B. L., Russell, I. J. 1972. The activity of lateral-line efferent neurones in stationary and swimming dogfish. *J. Exp. Biol.* 57:435–48
237. Robinson, D. A. 1971. Models of oculomotor neural organization. In *The Control of Eye Movements,* ed. P. Bach-y-Rita, C. C. Collins, 519–38. New York: Academic
238. Rosenhall, U. 1972. Vestibular macular mapping in man. *Ann. Otol. Rhinol. Laryngol.* 81:339–51
239. Roth, A. 1973. Ampullary electroreceptors in catfish: afferent fiber activity before and after removal of the sensory cells. *J. Comp. Physiol.* 87:259–75
240. Roth, A., Szabo, T. 1972. The receptor potential and its functional relationship to the nerve impulse analyzed in a sense organ by means of thermal and electric stimuli. *J. Comp. Physiol.* 80:285–308
241. Russell, I. J. 1968. Influence of efferent fibres on a receptor. *Nature* 219:177–78
242. Russell, I. J. 1971. The pharmacology of efferent synapses in the lateral-line system of *Xenopus laevis. J. Exp. Biol.* 54:643–58
243. Russell, I. J., Roberts, B. L. 1972. Inhibition of spontaneous lateral-line activity by efferent nerve stimulation. *J. Exp. Biol.* 57:77–82
244. Ryu, J. H., McCabe, B. F. 1973. Neural activity in the vestibular nuclei of the cat. *Ann. Otol. Rhinol. Laryngol.* 82:Suppl. 9, 1–28

245. Sala, O. 1965. The efferent vestibular system. Electrophysiological research. *Acta Oto Laryngol. Suppl.* 197:1–34
246. Sando, I., Black, F. O., Hemenway, W. G. 1972. Spatial distribution of vestibular nerve in internal auditory canal. *Ann Otol. Rhinol. Laryngol.* 81:305–15
247. Sans, A., Raymond, J., Marty, R. 1972. Projections des crêtes ampullaries et de l'utricule dans les noyaux vestibularies primaires. Étude microphysiologique et corrélations anatomo-fonctionnelles. *Brain Res.* 44:337–55
248. Sasaki, K. 1963. Electrophysiological studies on oculomotor neurons of the cat. *Jap. J. Physiol.* 13:287–302
249. Schaefer, K.-P. 1965. Die Erregungsmuster einzelner Neurone des Abducens-Kernes beim Kaninchen. *Pfluegers Arch.* 284:31–52
250. Schmidt, C. L., Wist, E. R., Dichgans, J. 1972. Efferent frequency modulation in the vestibular nerve of goldfish correlated with saccadic eye movements. *Exp. Brain Res.* 15:1–14
251. Schmidt, R. S. 1963. Frog labyrinthine efferent impulses. *Acta Oto Laryngol.* 56:51–64
252. Schmidt, R. S. 1963. Types of endolymphatic potentials. *Comp. Biochem. Physiol.* 10:83–87
253. Schmidt, R. S., Fernández, C. 1962. Labyrinthine DC potentials in representative vertebrates. *J. Cell Comp. Physiol.* 59:311–22
254. Schneider, L. W. 1973. *Responses of first and second order vestibular neurons to thermal and rotational stimuli.* PhD thesis. Univ. Michigan, Ann Arbor, Michigan
255. Schor, R. H. 1974. Response of cat vestibular neurons to sinusoidal roll tilt. *Exp. Brain Res.* 20:347–62
256. Schubert, G., Bornschein, H. 1962. Einzelfaseraktivität im N. oculomotorius bei vestibulärer Reizung. *Pfluegers Arch.* 275:107–16
257. Schwindt, P. C., Richter, A., Precht, W. 1973. Short latency utricular and canal input to ipsilateral abducens motoneurons. *Brain Res.* 60:259–62
258. Sellick, P. M., Johnstone, B. M. 1972. The electrophysiology of the saccule. *Pfluegers Arch.* 336:28–34
259. Sellick, P. M., Johnstone, J. R., Johnstone, B. M. 1972. The electrophysiology of the utricle. *Pfluegers Arch.* 336:21–27
260. Shimazu, H., Precht, W. 1965. Tonic and kinetic responses of cat's vestibular neurons to horizontal angular acceleration. *J. Neurophysiol.* 28:991–1013
261. Shimazu, H., Precht, W. 1966. Inhibition of central vestibular neurons from the contralateral labyrinth and its mediating pathway. *J. Neurophysiol.* 29: 467–92
262. Shimazu, H., Smith, C. M. 1971. Cerebellar and labyrinthine influences on single vestibular neurons identified by natural stimuli. *J. Neurophysiol.* 34: 493–508
263. Silverstein, H. 1966. Biochemical studies of the inner ear fluids in the cat. *Ann. Otol. Rhinol. Laryngol.* 75:48–63
264. Skavenski, A. A., Robinson, D. A. 1973. Role of abducens neurons in vestibuloocular reflex. *J. Neurophysiol.* 36:724–38
265. Smith, C. A. 1956. Microscopic structure of the utricle. *Ann. Otol. Rhinol. Laryngol.* 65:450–69
266. Smith, C. A. 1961. Innervation pattern of the cochlea. The inner hair cell. *Ann. Otol. Rhinol. Laryngol.* 70:504–27
267. Smith, C. A. 1970. The extrasensory cells of the vestibule. See Ref. 169, 171–85
268. Smith, C. A., Davis, H., Deatherage, B. H., Gessert, C. F. 1958. DC potentials of the membranous labyrinth. *Am. J. Physiol.* 193:203–6
269. Smith, C. A., Lowry, O. H., Wu, M. L. 1954. The electrolytes of the labyrinthine fluids. *Laryngoscope* 64:141–53
270. Smith, C. A., Rasmussen, G. L. 1967. Nerve endings in the maculae and cristae of the chinchilla vestibule, with a special reference to the efferents. In *3rd Symposium on the Role of the Vestibular Organs in Space Exploration.* NASA SP–152:183–201. Washington, D.C.: US GPO
271. Sohmer, H. S., Peake, W. T., Weiss, T. F. 1971. Intracochlear potential recorded with micropipets. I. Correlations with micropipet location. *J. Acoust. Soc. Am.* 50:572–87
272. Sotelo, C., Palay, S. L. 1970. The fine structure of the lateral vestibular nucleus in the rat. II. Synaptic organization. *Brain Res.* 18:93–115
273. Sparks, D. L., Travis, R. P. Jr. 1971. Firing patterns of reticular formation neurons during horizontal eye movements. *Brain Res.* 33:477–81
274. Spiegel, E. A. 1932. Physiopathology of the voluntary and reflex innervation of ocular movements. *Arch. Ophthalmol.* 8:738–53

275. Spoendlin, H. H. 1965. Ultrastructural studies of the labyrinth in squirrel monkeys. In *The Role of the Vestibular Organs in the Exploration of Space.* NASA SP–77:7–22. Washington, D.C.: US GPO
276. Spoendlin, H. H. 1966. Some morphofunctional and pathological aspects of the vestibular sensory epithelia. In *2nd Symposium on the Role of the Vestibular Organs in Space Exploration.* NASA SP–115:99–115. Washington, D.C.: US GPO
277. Spoendlin, H. H. 1973. The innervation of the cochlear receptors. See Ref. 75, 185–230
278. Spoendlin, H. H., Gacek, R. R. 1963. Electronmicroscopic study of the efferent and afferent innervation of the organ of Corti in the cat. *Ann. Otol. Rhinol. Laryngol.* 72:660–86
279. Steer, R. W. Jr. 1968. Progress in vestibular modeling. Part I: Response of semicircular canals to constant rotation in a linear acceleration field. In *4th Symposium on the Role of the Vestibular Organs in Space Exploration.* NASA SP–187:353–60. Washington, D.C.: US GPO
280. Stein, B. M., Carpenter, M. B. 1967. Central projections of portions of the vestibular ganglia innervating specific parts of the labyrinth in the rhesus monkey. *Am. J. Anat.* 120:281–318
281. Steinbach, A. B., Bennett, M. V. L. 1971. Effects of divalent ions and drugs on synaptic transmission in phasic electroreceptors in a mormyrid fish. *J. Gen. Physiol.* 58:580–98
282. Steinbach, A. B., Bennett, M. V. L. 1971. Presynaptic action of Ca and Mg and postsynaptic actions of glutamate at a sensory synapse. *Biol. Bull.* 141:403
283. Steinhausen, W. 1931. Über den Nachweis der Bewegung der Cupula in der intakten Bogengansampulle des Labyrinthes bei der natürlichen rotatorischen und calorischen Reizung. *Pfluegers Arch.* 228:322–28
284. Steinhausen, W. 1933. Über die Boebachtung der Cupula in den Bogengansampullen des Labyrinths des levenden Hechts. *Pfluegers Arch.* 232:500–12
285. Stockwell, C. W., Gilson, R. D., Guedry, F. E. Jr. 1973. Adaptation of horizontal semicircular canal responses. *Acta Oto Laryngol.* 75:471–76
286. Stockwell, C. W., Guedry, F. E. Jr., Turnipseed, G. T., Graybiel, A. 1972. The nystagmus response during rotation about a tilted axis. *Minerva Otorinolaringol.* 22:229–35
287. Suzuki, J.-I., Tokumasu, K., Goto, K. 1969. Eye movements from single utricular nerve stimulation in the cat. *Acta Oto Laryngol.* 68:350–62
288. Szentágothai, J. 1950. The elementary vestibulo-ocular reflex arc. *J. Neurophysiol.* 13:395–407
289. Tarlov, E. 1970. Organization of vestibulo-oculomotor projections in the cat. *Brain Res.* 20:159–79
290. Tasaki, I., Davis, H., Eldredge, D. H. 1954. Exploration of cochlear potentials in guinea pig with a microelectrode. *J. Acoust. Soc. Am.* 26:765–73
291. Tasaki, I., Spyropoulos, C. S. 1959. Stria vascularis as source of endocochlear potential. *J. Neurophysiol.* 22:149–55
292. Teas, D. C., Konishi, T., Nielsen, D. W. 1972. Electrophysiological studies on the spacial distribution of the crossed olivocochlear bundle along the guinea pig cochlea. *J. Acoust. Soc. Am.* 51:1256–64
293. ten Kate, J. H. 1969. *The oculo-vestibular reflex of the growing pike. A biophysical study.* Doctoral dissertation. Rijksuniversiteit te Groningen, Groningen, Netherlands.
294. ten Kate, J. H., van Barneveld, H. H., Kuiper, J. W. 1970. The dimensions and sensitivities of semicircular canals. *J. Exp. Biol.* 53:501–14
295. Thornhill, R. A. 1972. The effect of catecholamine precursors and related drugs on the morphology of the synaptic bars in the vestibular epithelia of the frog, *Rana temporaria. Comp. Gen. Pharmacol.* 3:89–97
296. Trincker, D. 1959. Electrophysiological studies of the labyrinth of the guinea pig. I. The DC resting potentials of the semicircular canal. *Ann. Otol. Rhinol. Laryngol.* 68:145–48
297. Vidal, J. et al 1971. Static and dynamic properties of gravity-sensitive receptors in the cat vestibular system. *Kybernetik* 9:205–15
298. Walberg, F., Bowsher, D., Brodal, A. 1958. The termination of primary vestibular fibers in the vestibular nuclei in the cat. An experimental study with silver methods. *J. Comp. Neurol.* 110:391–419
299. Walsh, B. T., Miller, J. B., Gacek, R. R., Kiang, N. Y. S. 1972. Spontaneous activity in the eighth cranial nerve of the cat. *Int. J. Neurosci.* 3:221–36

300. Weiss, T. F., Mulroy, M. J., Altmann, D. W. 1974. Intracellular response to acoustic clicks in the inner ear of the alligator lizard. *J. Acoust. Soc. Am.* 55:606–19
301. Wersäll, J. 1956. Studies on the structure and innervation of the sensory epithelium of the cristae ampullaris in the guinea pig. A light and electron microscopic investigation. *Acta Oto Laryngol. Suppl.* 126:1–85
302. Wersäll, J. 1968. Efferent innervation of the inner ear. In *Structure and Function of the Inhibitory Neuronal Mechanisms,* ed. C. von Euler, S. Skoglund, U. Söderberg, 123–39. Oxford: Pergamon
303. Wersäll, J., Flock, Å., Lundquist, P.-G. 1965. Structural basis for directional sensitivity in cochlear and vestibular sensory receptors. *Cold Spring Harbor Symp. Quant. Biol.* 30:115–32
304. Wersäll, J., Lundquist, P.-G. 1966. Morphological polarization of the mechanoreceptors of the vestibular and acoustic systems. In *2nd Symposium on the Role of the Vestibular Organs in Space Exploration.* NASA SP-115:57–71. Washington, D.C.: US GPO
305. Wiederhold, M. L., Kiang, N. Y. S. 1970. Effects of electrical stimulation of the crossed olivocochlear bundle in single auditory-nerve fibers in the cat. *J. Acoust. Soc. Am.* 48:950–65
306. Wilson, V. J. 1972. Physiological pathways through the vestibular nuclei. *Int. Rev. Neurobiol.* 15:27–81
307. Wilson, V. J., Felpel, L. P. 1972. Specificity of the semicircular canal input to neurons in the pigeon vestibular nuclei. *J. Neurophysiol.* 35:253–64
308. Wilson, V. J., Maeda, M. 1974. Connections between semicircular canals and neck motoneurons in the cat. *J. Neurophysiol.* 37:346–57
309. Wilson, V. J., Wylie, R. M. 1970. A short-latency labyrinthine input to the vestibular nuclei in the pigeon. *Science* 168:124–27
310. Wilson, V. J., Wylie, R. M. Marco, L. A. 1968. Synaptic inputs to cells in the medial vestibular nucleus. *J. Neurophysiol.* 31:176–85
311. Young, L. R. 1968. Effects of linear acceleration on vestibular nystagmus. In *3rd Symposium on the Role of the Vestibular Organs in Space Exploration.* NASA SP–152: 383–91. Washington, D.C.: US GPO
312. Young, L. R. 1974. Role of the vestibular system in posture and movement. In *Medical Physiology,* ed. V. B. Mountcastle, Vol. I, 704–21. St. Louis: Mosby
313. Young, L. R., Meiry, J. L. 1968. A revised dynamic otolith model. *Aerosp. Med.* 39:606–8
314. Young, L. R., Oman, C. M. 1969. Model of vestibular adaptation to horizontal rotations. *Aerosp. Med.* 40: 1076–80
315. Zwislocki, J. J., Sokolich, W. G. 1973. Velocity and displacement responses in auditory-nerve fibers. *Science* 182: 64–66

Copyright 1975. All rights reserved

ELECTROPHYSIOLOGY OF NEUROGLIA

❖1127

George G. Somjen
Department of Physiology and Pharmacology, Duke University, Durham, North Carolina 27710

INTRODUCTION

For many years the study of neuroglia was limited to microscopic examination of stained sections of healthy or diseased brains, and all inferences relating to its function were based on morphological observations. With the development of cultured explants of tissue, and of techniques of tissue fractionation, of microchemistry, and of microelectrophysiology, the observation of living instead of dead material became possible. Limitations of both available space and competence restrict the scope of this review to the electrophysiology of glia cells, but to provide background some of the more influential ideas concerning the functions of glia are first presented. For complementary reading a review by Watson (167) covers many of the topics omitted here. Earlier monographs, anthologies, and reviews may be consulted for complete coverage (20, 22, 26, 33, 35, 68, 83, 84, 88, 109, 169).

Historic Notes

Virchow's (159) discovery of neuroglia was not accidental, but was the fruit of a deliberate attempt to find the connective tissue of the central nervous system, prompted by dissatisfaction with the view prevalent in his time that the brain, alone amongst all organs, contains no such tissue. Being a pathologist, he was familiar with inflammations of the cerebral ventricular lining, and he set out to find, under the epithelial layer of the ependyma, the subethelial mesenchyma that could produce inflammatory reaction. Virchow's "Nervenkitt" ("nerve-putty") is today considered to be more nearly an epithelium (167) than connective tissue. In some respects it resembles both types of tissue and, of course, in other respects neither. The idea that glial fibers impart mechanical stability and firmness to the nervous tissue is today also the subject of doubt (171).

At one time or another the functions of supporting, protecting, clothing, and feeding nerve cells, and the removal of the offal of neural activity, have been attributed to neuroglia. Whether or not neurons could live without their supposedly symbiotic glial satellites is the subject of an unresolved debate (33). It has now been demonstrated that, in the leech ganglion at least, nerve cells suffer no immediate ill effects if stripped of their glial envelope (110). In cell cultures, neurons appear to thrive even if glia cells are absent (93, 113), but it could be argued that in the artificial millieu of an explant the experimenter provides the services normally rendered by glial satellites.

These supposed roles of neuroglia are subservient to the well-being of neurons. Some investigators, however, regard the two components of central nervous tissue as equal partners, and others attribute to glia functions 'higher" than those of neurons (32, 64, 65, 134, 147).

The history of our subject matter was ably reviewed more than once in the past (35, 84, 128). I select for brief mention the origins of only a few ideas that prevailed until this day.

To Golgi (40) we owe the suggestion that glia cells nourish neurons (for contemporary opinions, pro and con, see references 36, 170); to Nageotte (108) the thought that glia is an organ of internal secretion. Cajal (129) called attention to the fact that glia cells fill the void left by dead neurons in wounded brains. The suggestion that glial envelopes insulate one nerve cell from another is usually also attributed to Cajal, but he gives the credit to his brother (128). A new form was given to this idea by DeRobertis (19) and by Peters and Palay (117, 123), who proposed that glial barriers prevent the lateral diffusion of synaptic transmitter substances between adjacent synapses of differing functions. The first suggestion that glia cells produce myelin came from Jastrowitz (66; see also 121). Perhaps the most inspired seminal paper was one written by Lugaro (96). While commenting on the fact [discovered by Golgi (40)] that glial end feet (but never neurons) often surround capillaries, Lugaro (96) suggested that glia might filter unwanted components of blood plasma. The idea that the glial envelope constitutes the blood-brain barrier, popular for a period, is now generally rejected (84, 88, 89, 100), yet the ubiquitous presence of glial processes near capillaries still commands attention.

Lugaro (96) also suggested for the first time that glia cells may remove toxic byproducts of neural metabolism. What is even more remarkable, he proposed that at neuronal articulations (i.e. at synapses) nerve fiber endings influence dendrites and nerve cell bodies by elaborating specific chemical substances—a clear statement of chemical transmission at synapses. He then went on to say: "Protoplasmic extensions of glial cells which invariably penetrate to the vicinity of neural articulations serve to collect and to instantly break down any minimal residue of such chemical agents" [somewhat freely translated from (96)]. (For recent versions of this theory, consult references 21, 50–52, 63, 78, 82; for an opposing view, 106). Finally, Lugaro elaborated and modified a theme, originating with Hiss, that glia cells provide the framework within which neural processes can grow. He suggested that glial cells secrete the chemotactic stimuli that guide axons and dendrites to their destinations. It is interesting that a recent paper reported that glial tumor cells stimulate in vitro the growth of processes of cells derived from neuronal neoplasma (103). One is also reminded of the insistence of Loewenstein (94) that, for orderly growth of tissues, a chemical community must exist between cells, established through low-resistance gap junctions. In central nervous tissue, glia cells, but not neurons, are believed to be so joined. (See discussion later in this review.)

Remarks on the Multiformity of Glia

Hortega (133; see also 120) defined the classification of central glia that became the standard of textbooks. Fibrous and protoplasmic astrocytes, and oligodendrocytes, form the aboriginal glial population of central nervous territory, where microcytes probably are immigrants. Ependyma, Müller cells, Bergman glia, and the satellite cells in ganglia, are specialized forms found at special sites. It is known that oligodendrocytes form myelin (121), but there are oligodendrocytes also in regions where there are no myelinated fibers. The difference between myelin-forming and nonmyelin-forming oligodendrocytes is as yet obscure.

As far as one can judge today, whatever their specializations otherwise, all forms of "true" glia (with the possible exception of microglia) appear electrically equivalent. Almost indistinguishable intracellular recordings have been obtained from Müller cells in the retina (101), from satellite cells in sympathetic ganglia (4, 5), from reactive fibrous astrocytes in cortical scars (37, 47), from glia cells in invertebrate nervous systems (3, 86, 110), from the optic nerves of amphibians and mammals in vitro (14, 18, 116), and in normal gray matter of cortex (12, 46, 48, 82, 131, 135, 144) and spinal cord (137, 138, 142) of mammals. Intracellular markings (46, 74, 76, 144), however imperfect, make it probable that oligodendrocytes and protoplasmic astrocytes of neocortex have similar electrical properties. In culture, the electrical behavior of oligocytes and astrocytes is similar (60, 157, 165). Cultured glia generally has lower potassium content and correspondingly lower membrane potential than glia grown in normal tissue, but its responses, and the lack of them, to physical and chemical agents are similar (153, 157, 165, 173), and they are shared by in vitro ependyma (59). Through most of this review the various types of glia, because of the uniformity of their electrical properties, will be discussed as though they were one.

The Distinction of Glia from Neurons

Neurons usually are distinguishable from glia cells. There may be some uncertainty whenever only a small part of a cell falls within an electron micrograph, but not usually when the structures of a whole cell are visible. Nevertheless, disputes have arisen in some cases. For example, the horizontal and amacrine cells of the retina were considered to be glia cells by some (102, 147, 158), and neurons by others (24, 168). Their identification with glia was based on the absence of an axon, and the supposedly corresponding absence of spike potentials. As it now turns out, amacrine cells that do not have an axon do generate all-or-nothing type action potentials, whereas bipolar cells that do have anatomical axons do not (168). Horizontal cells, having neither axon nor impulses, nonetheless are joined one to another and to bipolar cells by true synapses. Ultrastructurally unmistakable synapses (24) that transmit signals in a way similar to other interneuronal junctions (168) should, it seems, decide the issue. Horizontal, bipolar, and amacrine cells should be regarded as neurons because they appear to be integral components in the neural circuit of the retina.

The last statement may justifiably be said to represent a partisan point of view. Yet the body of knowledge available today appears, to me at least, to indicate that input and output of information, as well as its immediate processing, are the functions of neurons, and of neurons alone. Some (64, 134) say that glia may have a long-term influence on neural function, and this may be true. If, however, glia indeed plays a part in the long-term storage of information (64), then retrieval of the same probably occurs by glia influencing synaptic transmission, and not by glia cells taking part in the actual circulation of signals.

Having stated a personal position, experimental findings henceforth will be presented impartially, so that the reader may draw conclusions that may differ from my own.

The Size of Glia

Neither the volume nor the mass of neuroglia is known, excepting a few special instances. Wolff (172) quoted data indicating that, in the striatum, glia tissue occupies 20% of the total tissue volume, in the pallidum 40%. Kuffler (83, 84) stated that "up to 50%" of the central nervous system may consist of glia; his estimate is based on measurements on a limited number of arbitrarily selected electron micrographs. There is a great need for statistically valid, systematic measurements of the magnitude of glial tissue in various regions of the central gray matter so that researchers will be able to calculate balance sheets of metabolism and apportion electrolytes and other chemical constituents among tissue "spaces."

While the total mass of neuroglia has not yet been determined, various other relevant measurements have been made. Published reports show that synapse-rich regions have relatively more glia than synapse-poor regions (172). The volume of the glial envelopes surrounding neurons of various sizes was also estimated (118). Furthermore, the relative areas of apposition between glia and dendritic surfaces (6), and the magnitude of the interface between intercellular space and glia [45–60% of the total surface of interstitial fluid (172)] have been estimated.

If determination of the relative volume of the glial "compartment" was neglected, more attention was paid to the relative numbers of cells in central gray matter. Neuronal and glial nuclei have been counted in tissue sections and in suspensions prepared from tissue homogenates (2, 10, 44, 49, 112). There is a wide variation of glia–neuron ratios both between regions of the brain and between species. For example, in the second layer of the neocortex of rats, glia cells are outnumbered by neurons one to three, whereas deeper in the tissue where nerve cells are of larger size, glia cells are in the majority by a ratio exceeding four to one (2). Man appears to be rich in glia compared to most other animals. Friede (31) related this observation to an older theory of Nissl, who believed that "Rindengrau," the supposedly amorphous ground substance of gray matter, was the substrate of the highest nervous functions, since it appeared to occupy more space in man's brain than in that of other animals. Friede substituted glial tissue for Nissl's ground substance. It later appeared, however, that whales and elephants have even more glia than people (49, 152), and Tower (152) demonstrated that the relative number of glial cells correlates to brain size, not to intelligence. It seems that the size of glia cells does not change with the size of the brain, but that the size of neuron perikarya increases with brain size, although not nearly proportionately. As the total number of nerve cells increases, the number of connections required to interconnect these elements increases out of proportion to the number of elements. To make these extra connections, the surface area of dendrites and the branching of axon terminals in neuropil must expand vastly. Where there is more neuropil, there also must be more glia, which always grows to fill the spaces between neural processes (171), presumably to segregate chemical transmitters (117). Tower & Young (152) made a convincing, albeit indirectly supported, claim (opposed by Wolff, 172) for a constant density of glia in the face of increasing brain size, coupled with a decreasing density of neurons.

Extracellular Space and the Ion Content of Glia

The distribution of ions and of fluid between the various "compartments" of central gray matter is an issue clearly relevant to the electrophysiology of neuroglia. It has been neglected in this review because there have been no very important new developments since it was last authoritatively and comprehensively discussed (15, 73, 155). Briefly stated, it now is agreed by almost all concerned that there exists a real extracellular space in the mammalian brain and that its size is between 12 and 20% of the total volume. The size of this "compartment" appears to vary between different tissues. It probably is larger in white matter than in gray, and also larger in neuropil than in nuclear regions of gray matter. How much larger is a matter still to be determined.

Extracellular fluid of the central nervous system communicates freely with cerebrospinal fluid, but is protected from free exchange with blood plasma by a true "barrier" of relatively low permeability (varying for different solutes). Some substrates appear to enter the brain either by active transport or by facilitated diffusion. The cellular substrate of the blood-brain barrier is probably not glia (84, 88, 89, 100).

Much of the following discussion hinges on the now generally accepted view that astrocytes have high internal K^+ content and correspondingly high membrane potential. However, since the calculated size of the sodium and chloride "spaces" still exceeds that of the extracellular space (77), the location of the excess Na^+ and Cl^- remains to be found. The unaccounted-for NaCl may be evenly dispersed in the intracellular fluid of all cellular elements. Perhaps less likely, but not yet excluded, is the possibility that some, though not all, glia cells have high Na^+, low K^+ intracellular fluid. Such cells would not be detected during exploration by roving intracellular microelectrodes.

MEMBRANE POTENTIAL AND DEPOLARIZING POTENTIAL RESPONSES OF GLIA CELLS

Ever since the first intracellular probe was sunk into a spinal cord and then into a brain, investigators encountered standing negative potentials that, though often larger and more stable than the membrane potentials of neurons, could not be induced to generate impulses or synaptic potentials. Little attention was paid to these at first, and in early reports they merited but a paragraph or two of small print (17, 27, 92, 99, 124). Phillips (124) assumed that these stable standing potentials were generated across the membrane of cells that he called "idle" (perhaps out of frustration engendered by finding so many of these sturdy but good-for-nothing cells instead of neurons). From the start it seemed possible to investigators that the idle resting potentials could be those of glial elements (17, 27, 92, 124), though to some it seemed less than plausible (99) that glia cells, which are small, should withstand microelectrode puncture more readily than neurons. Small cells can, however, be tough, as became obvious in microelectrode exploration of cell cultures where glia cells, also of smaller size, withstood puncture better than neurons (60).

The cells that Phillips had called idle others called "inexcitable," "silent," "unresponsive," or "presumed glia" (PG). Positive proof that they indeed belong to glia was rendered by Kelly, Krnjević & Yim (76), Grossman & Hampton (46), Sugaya et al (144), and Watanabe et al (166), who used the intracellular iontophoretic marking technique for histological verification. Recently Kelly & Van Essen (74) achieved the best staining with the fluorescent dye procion yellow.

These cells are inexcitable by all the usual modes of stimulation to which nerve cells readily respond. They do not emit the agonal howl of injury discharge, they do not respond with impulses nor with synaptic potentials to stimulation of nervous pathways, nor are they excited by electrical current delivered either by an intracellular or extracellular stimulating probe. As mentioned earlier, some short-axon neurons are also incapable of generating all-or-nothing propagated potentials of action (168). Nonspiking neurons, however, do generate synaptic potentials and synaptic "noise."

Eventually it became apparent that unresponsive cells, notwithstanding their confirmed failure to generate neuron-like signals, are not completely idle after all. Sugaya, Goldring & O'Leary (143) noticed that during seizure activity these cells underwent very slow waves of depolarization. Shortly thereafter, Karahashi & Goldring (71) reported depolarizing shifts of potential evoked by prolonged repetitive, but not by single-shock, stimulation of either the cortical surface or an appropriate afferent pathway. These depolarizing shifts could be distinguished from synaptic potentials not only by their substantially slower rise and fall, but also by the absence of a change of membrane resistance (131, 138) and the fact that they are invariably in the depolarizing direction, no matter what the input (137, 138). Other investigators have seen similar depolarizing shifts in glia cells of optic nerve of amphibia (116), in mammalian neocortex (12, 46, 58, 131, 135, 144) and spinal cord (137, 138, 142), in sympathetic ganglia (5), and in Müller cells of the retina (101). Depolarizing potential shifts are often followed, after cessation of stimulation, by a small but very prolonged hyperpolarization (132).

Glial depolarizations evoked by trains of repeated electrical pulses could be dismissed as artefacts of the laboratory. Neuronal input evoked by "natural" (adequate) stimulation of sensory receptors can, however, bring about similar phenomena. Orkand et al (116) reported depolarization of glia cells in optic nerve when light was flashed into the eye. Miller & Dowling (101) identified the generator of the so-called *b* wave of the eletroretinogram with Müller's glia. And, most intriguing, Kelly & Van Essen (74) were able to evoke depolarization of glia cells in primary visual cortex by projecting optical stimuli on a screen in front of the experimental animal. Moreover, glia cells shared the preference of their neural neighbors for stimulation by optical edges of a given orientation (tilt). These glia cells thus appeared to be yoked to the neurons of the functional cortical column in which they were located (74).

At about the time when Goldring and his associates (12, 71, 131, 143) began calling attention to the electrical properties of idle cells in the neocortex, Kuffler and his colleagues were publishing their systematic studies of glia of leech ganglia and of amphibian optic nerves in vitro. Their work deservedly became a classic in a very short time and has already been reviewed by the senior authors (83, 84) and others (89, 139, 167). Only a brief summary of their findings is therefore required now.

Electrical Behavior of Glia in Acutely Isolated Preparations in vitro and its Dependence on $[K^+]_o$

Ganglia of leech are readily maintained in vitro, and contain large glia cells that lend themselves to electrical recording (86, 110). Closer to the mammalian nervous system and yet well maintained under similar conditions is the optic nerve of *Necturus;* Kuffler and associates found that they could unambiguously recognize penetration of satellite (glia) cells by microelectrodes in this preparation (85, 116). Later, in the same laboratory, Dennis & Gerschenfeld (18) investigated glia cells in a similar preparation of optic nerves of rats in vitro.

In the nervous system of all three classes of animals (hirudinea, amphibia, mammalia) glia cells appeared to have resting membrane potentials comparable to, or higher than, nerve cells. The magnitude of the membrane potential appeared to be a linear function of the logarithm of internal over external potassium concentration. The slope of the function describing the dependence of membrane potential in potassium concentration closely conforms to the Nernst equation in the case of the poikilotherm organisms (85, 110), but not in mammalian glia (18). These observations suggest that glia, like neurons, have high internal potassium content, a fact confirmed by actual microanalysis, at least for the leech (111). It also suggests that the surface membrane of glia cells is much more permeable to potassium than to other ions.

When the nerve fibers or the nerve cells of which they are the satellites are excited, glia cells undergo the slow waves of depolarization that were described in the previous paragraph. Successive waves sum, so that the final magnitude of the depolarizing shift can, during repetitive nerve stimulation, be quite substantial. Orkand et al (116) and Baylor & Nicholls (3) have suggested that the depolarization of glia is caused by potassium ions released by nerve fibers and cells during activity, and accumulating in intercellular clefts. The evidence for this suggestion was circumstantial, yet convincing. Frankenhaeuser & Hodgkin (28) have already reasoned that potassium levels do rise transiently near active nerve fibers. The slow time course of glial depolarization, the absence of change of membrane resistance, the ability to sum successive waves of depolarization, and the demonstrable dependence of glial membrane potential on deliberate changes of extracellular K^+, are all in agreement with this proposition. In addition, it can be shown that the successively summing waves of depolarization have amplitudes that decrease logarithmically. Since membrane potential depends on the logarithm of external K^+, equal increments of $[K^+]_o$ are expected to cause logarithmically decreasing step-wise shifts of membrane potential.

Kuffler and associates (85, 110) have also demonstrated that diffusion through the available extracellular space is sufficient to account for the movement of ions in the leech nervous system, and that leech neurons survive and continue to function for several hours after being stripped of glial envelope by microdissection (111). In addition, they (86) measured the input resistance of leech glial cells, estimated their (specific) membrane resistance (see Table 1), and established the fact that glial cells

Table 1 Membrane resistance of glia cells; reported mean of values and/or their range

Tissue	Input Resistance meg Ω	Specific Resistance Ω × cm²	Time Constant μsec	Reference
Cat neocortex	48.4			82
Cat neocortex	10.5		385	154
	4.7–19.6	190–480	217–632	
Cat neocortex normal	12.4		482	37
Cat neocortex gliosis (scar)	2.0		255	37
Cat neocortex	22.0			166
	6–80			
Cat spinal cord	4.6			138
	1.2–12.2			
Cat sympathetic ganglion	<20		<3000	4
Leech ganglion	0.3–0.5	>1000		86
Tissue culture rat & kitten cerebellum	0.6–1.7	3–10		60
Tissue culture rabbit cerebellum	4.2			165
Tissue culture human embryo	2.6	95–325	310	153
Tissue culture hamster	5.2		294	153
Tissue culture rat ependyma	0.2–0.35	1.6–3.0		59
Tissue culture rat, cerebrum and cerebellum		8.0		174

in leech (86) as well as in amphibian (85) nervous systems are electrically coupled. Electrical coupling was shown by injecting current into one glia cell and recording a potential drop in another, sometimes at distances greater than 1 mm, demonstrating the existence of a true and extensive functional syncytium.

Glial Depolarization and Sustained Extracellular Potential Shifts

Investigators who used direct-coupled instruments in preference to condenser-coupled electrical recorders have noticed voltage variations of the brain that could last for seconds or more. To remain in line with the interpretations common in electroencephalography, these sustained shifts of potential were at first attributed by most authors to the activity of neurons. Alternatives, however, were also considered, such as electrogenic effects of metabolism, blood flow, or oxygen tension, and the activity of secretory cells of the blood-brain barrier (for review, see 139).

That glia cells might contribute to slow electrical phenomena was also suggested, at first without experimental evidence, by Galambos (32) and in 1963 by Roitbak (see 134). Laborit (87) also considered the role that glia might play in cerebral electrophysiology. He argued that, since the extracellular environment of neurons is restricted in volume, it must be controlled by the glia cells that line it. If the metabolic activity of glia influences the ionic millieu of neurons, then glia must be capable of controlling the level of membrane potential of neurons, and hence of modulating the electrical activity of nervous elements. A contribution by glia to the electrical activity of the retina was advocated by Svaetichin, Mitarai, and their associates (102, 147), but these investigators classified horizontal and amacrine cells as glia (see above).

Orkand et al (116) have suggested that glia cells could also contribute to the sustained shifts of electrical potential seen in mammalian brain, but their suggestion was based on their observations of amphibian optic nerve. Cohen (14) showed that when this nerve spans a sucrose gap, as much as 40% of the intracellular voltage drop generated by the glial syncytium can be recorded by extracellular leads.

An experimental foundation to the suspected relationship of glial depolarization to sustained potential shifts of mammalian brains was first laid by Karahashi & Goldring (71). Grossman & Hampton (46), who also recorded the slow depolarization of glia cells, at first rejected the idea, but Grossman now accepts the glial generation of sustained potentials. Others have raised doubts either on the grounds of (*a*) the low membrane resistance of glia cells (154; see discussion in 72, 139) or (*b*) because of the confusing multitude of current generators in central gray matter (115).

The relationship of membrane resistance to extracellular current (objection *a*) is discussed later. As far as objection *b* is concerned, central nervous tissue indeed contains many electrogenic elements, several of which are capable of sustained changes of membrane potential. The activity of neuronal pre- or postsynaptic elements does not appear to be predictably related to sustained extracellular potential shifts, whereas that of glia is closely correlated to such voltages (12, 137–140, 142). Undoubtedly, sustained changes of neuronal membrane potential must, to some degree, contribute to extracellular current flow, and under some circumstances this contribution may be significant. The lack of correlation demonstrated in the reports cited above proves only that, under the conditions of these particular experiments, the contribution of the sampled neuronal population was negligible.

Accepting the possibility of the generation of extracellular voltage gradients by glia cells, we now must examine the question of their mechanism. By the first rule of biological electrography we know that changes of membrane potential remain undetected by extracellular probes, unless current flows in the extracellular medium. A cell generates current if and only if one part of its membrane is at a potential different from another part, or if the intracellular medium of one cell is joined by a low-resistance electrical junction to that of another and the potential of the two is unequal. Glia cells therefore could generate extracellular currents if they had processes long enough to extend from regions of low to regions of high membrane potential, and if many such unequally polarized fibers were geometrically lined up in nonrandom arrays. The Müller cells of the retina and the Bergman fibers of the cerebellum conform to these morphological requirements. The former span the thickness of the retina (figure 186 in Vol. II of ref. 128); the latter are also oriented perpendicularly to the cerebellar surface, as is required by the distribution of potentials during sustained voltage shifts of the cerebellar cortex (156). Grossman (personal communication; see also 72) recently called attention to illustrations by Cajal (figures 80 & 81 in Vol. 1 of ref. 128) in which glial fibers are shown traversing long distances in the cerebral and cerebellar cortex. Green's (43) description of the hippocampal cortex supports a similar arrangement there. Lenhossék (91) described radial glial fibers extending from the central canal to the surface of the spinal cord. His material was from immature nervous systems, but he voiced the opinion that this architecture persists during maturation, though it is, for technical reasons, difficult to demonstrate it in adult specimens. 80 years after its publication his proposition is neither proven nor refuted.

But if in cortex and spinal cord individual glia cells turned out not to have the configuration required to generate extracellular current, they still could act as a current source if they were coupled electrically. Gap junctions that may provide pathways for intercellular current between glia cells have been described (9, 19, 42, 122). The reported electrical syncytium of glia of leech and mudpuppy were discussed already (85, 86; for the newt see 70). In the mammalian central nervous system low-resistance contact between glia cells has not yet been demonstrated. In cell cultures not only are glia cells coupled to other glia cells, but glia appears to be joined to neurons as well (162). There is at least one report of similar electrical continuity between glia cells and neurons in the nervous system of the newt (70). This finding is in urgent need of further study.

The properties of an electrotonic syncytium have been examined in a formal model, simulated by computer, by Joyner & Somjen (69, 139, 140). The model consisted of a row (or a sheet) of simulated "glia cells," the cytoplasm within each cell being considered at isopotential and of negligible resistance. The "glia cells" were assumed to be interconnected by fixed coupling resistances, and to communicate with the outside medium by fixed membrane resistances. The extracellular environment of one cell was assumed to be linked resistively to the environment of the others; the extracellular medium was assumed to be connected to a "ground" by arrays of parallel resistances. "Depolarization" of some of the "glia cells" was represented by batteries lying in series with the membrane resistances of some, but not all, cells. The model generated potential profiles not unlike those recorded in the spinal cord. The following results of the simulation are worth noting.

1. If other parameters are kept constant, the higher the "membrane resistance" of simulated glia cells, the farther the shifts of potential spread from the "depolarized" into the "inactive" zones. In other words, the relative magnitude of the membrane resistance determines the "space constant" of the syncytium. While lowering the membrane resistance confines the potential shifts within the "depolarized" zone, it also enhances the magnitude of both intracellular and extracellular voltage shifts within the "depolarized" focus. Conversely, the more current is drawn away (i.e. shunted) from the depolarized cells to the inactive cells (i.e. the farther the electrotonic spread), the smaller the measured change of voltages at the "active" site.

2. Increasing the coupling resistance between cells reduces the extracellular voltage shifts, but enhances intracellular shift. Infinite coupling resistance would insulate one cell from another and prevent the flow of extracellular current. This is the formal expression of what was called the "first rule of electrography" at the beginning of this section.

3. Reducing the extracellular resistances or, 4., the resistance of tissue to ground, would reduce the extracellular voltage drop and enhance the intracellular voltage drop. Clearly, if one could "ground" the entire extracellular medium, there would be no effective (longitudinal) outside current, and therefore no extracellular voltage gradient. It should be noted that intracellular and extracellular voltages vary in the same direction only when either the membrane resistance or the magnitude of the membrane batteries change. In the three other examples cited, intracellular and extracellular voltages vary in opposite directions. It should also be noted that in this model, as in conventional microelectrode recordings, voltages are referred to as "ground" potentials; the true membrane potential is given by the difference between intracellular and extracellular potentials (cf Figure 1).

Glial Response to Potassium and to Other Chemical Stimuli

Having discussed ways in which depolarization of glia cells could generate extracellular voltage gradients, we now must define the factors that might cause their depolarization.

Clues to the behavior of glia had been sought by challenging cultured glia cells with various physical and chemical stimuli. Hild & Tasaki (60) reported that strong electrical pulses caused depolarizing potentials; according to Chang & Hild (13) the pulses also caused a contractile response of glia cells in vitro. Electrical responses were also reported from glia stimulated in situ (151). These authors (60, 150) recognized, however, that the intensive stimulating current required to elicit such responses could never occur under natural conditions. Wardell (165) later argued that the Tasaki-Hild response is actually a breakdown of the dielectric properties of the glial membrane, unlike physiological reactions of excitable cells. Investigators who subsequently have sought to stimulate glia cells by electrical pulses agreed that these cells must be considered electrically inexcitable (82, 85, 138).

If not by electric current, the glial membrane nevertheless is influenced by relatively low concentrations of a variety of naturally occurring chemical substances. Depolarization, but not reduction of membrane resistance, is reportedly caused by acetylcholine and by gamma-aminobutyric acid, but not by glutamate (82). The motility of cultured glia cells is stimulated under the influence of 5-hydroxytryptamine (107); metabolic changes have been induced by exposure to catecholamines, cyclic AMP, and also adrenocortical hormones (22, 34, 65). Membrane potentials have not been recorded in these last mentioned experiments. Whether glia behaves in its natural habitat as it does in a glass dish is not clear at this time.

In spite of the demonstrated response of some glia cells under some conditions to several chemical agents, most investigators today assume that the depolarizing shifts of glia in situ are caused by elevation of extracellular potassium activity, which, in its turn, is the result of the release of potassium ions from activated neurons.

The dependence of glia of leech and of amphibian optic nerves on extracellular K^+ activity has already been described. Mammalian glia is also depolarized by $[K^+]_o$ but, unlike glia of leech and of mudpuppy, was said not to obey precisely the

Figure 1 The relationship of the depolarization of glia cells and sustained extracellular potential (SP) shifts to the level of extracellular potassium activity. *A:* Responses evoked in spinal gray matter by repetitive stimulation of afferent nerves. Recordings made with three-channel microelectrode assemblies. One electrode was lodged inside a glial cell; at a distance of about 30–50 μm, a double-barreled electrode recorded the extracellular electric potential and also the activity of potassium ions with the aid of a K^+ selective ion exchanger filling one of the electrode tips. Data are from 7 cells in 3 spinal cords. Vertical lines connect data points representing simultaneous measurements. Different symbols are used for measurements from different cells. Ordinate of the upper part of graph shows magnitude of depolarizing potential shift, recorded intracellularly, and referred to ground potential. Ordinate of lower graph indicates extracellular SP shifts. Abscissa indicates potassium level scaled logarithmically (unpublished observations of Somjen and Lothman). *B:* The membrane potential change of glial cells; i.e. the difference between intracellular and extracellular potential shifts, plotted against the logarithm of potassium levels. Calculated from the same data as part *A.* Continuous diagonal line indicates Nernst function at 37.5°C. *C:* The behavior of cortical glia and of cortical SP shifts. Upper part of graph shows theoretical function published by Ransom & Goldring to describe the intracellular potential of glia cells (referred to ground) as a function of extracellular potassium (130, figure 6). In the lower graph the open circles indicate the amplitude of extracellular SP shifts evoked by repetitive direct cortical stimulation, plotted against the logarithm of potassium level measured at the same site simultaneously with double-barreled microelectrodes. (Unpublished data of Lothman, Cordingley & Somjen). The smooth curve of the lower graph of part *C* was drawn according to the equation of Ransom & Goldring that was used in the upper graph, but scaled by dividing by a constant for best fit of extracellular measurements. Note the conformation of experimental points to the theo retical curve, notwithstanding the differences between the conditions under which Ransom & Goldring's observations and our own were made.

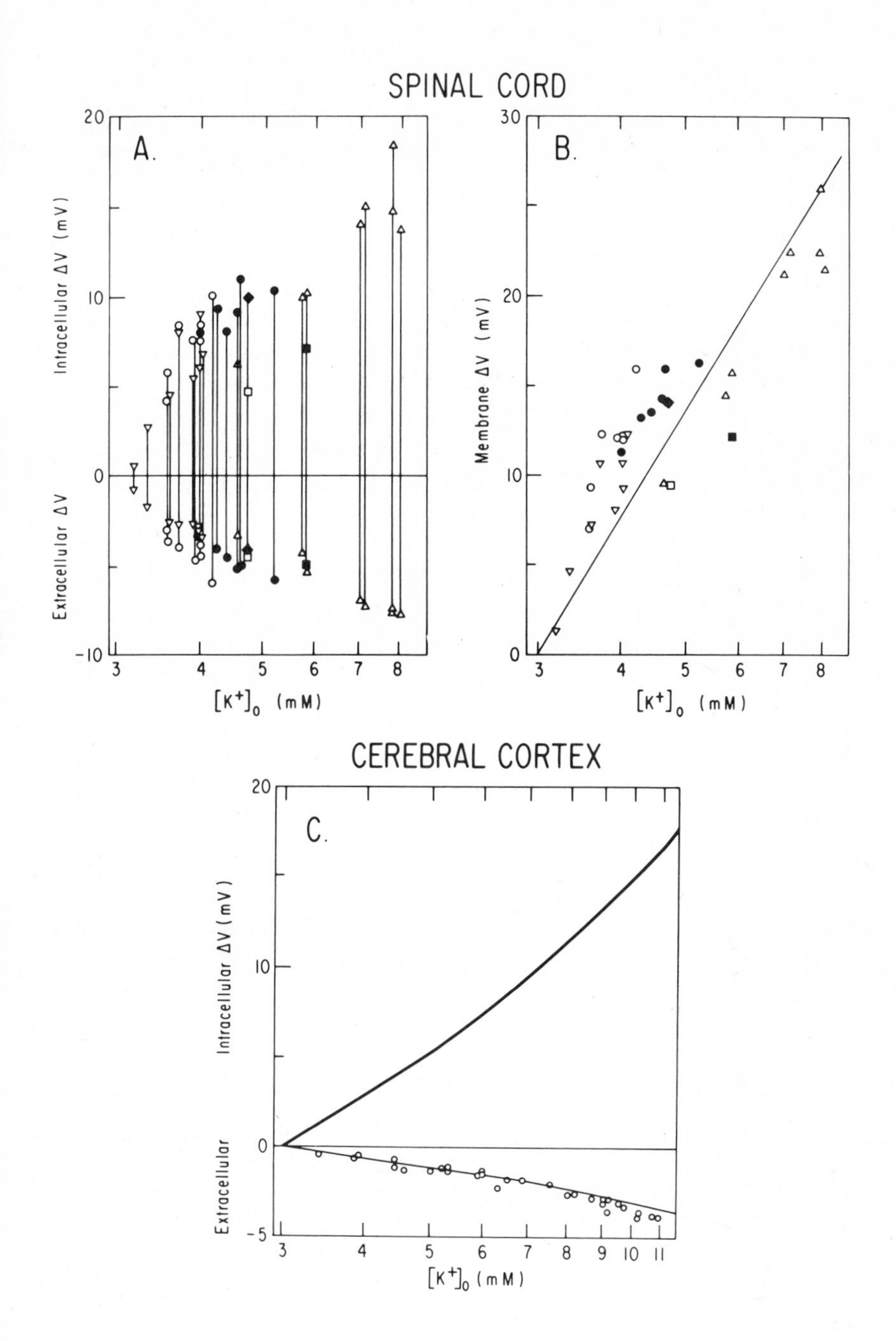

SPINAL CORD
A.
Intracellular ΔV (mV)
Extracellular ΔV
[K+]o (mM)
B.
Membrane ΔV (mV)
[K+]o (mM)
CEREBRAL CORTEX
C.
Intracellular ΔV (mV)
Extracellular
[K+]o (mM)

Nernst equation (18, 119, 130; however, see Figure 1B). The relationships among extracellular K^+ activity, extracellular potential shifts, and glia depolarization in mammalian spinal cord and neocortex are shown in Figure 1.

There are two plausible and not necessarily mutually exclusive reasons for the departure from the values of the Nernst equation in some cases of observed glial membrane potentials. I have already discussed one of them: electrotonic coupling between depolarized and resting cells (139). Glia either generates extracellular currents, or acts as a precise K^+ electrode, but cannot do both at the same time, especially if intracellular voltage is measured against ground (see previous section and Figure 1). A second reason may be the contribution of sodium conductance to the membrane potential. Ransom & Goldring (130) considered the latter the most significant cause. Further possible reasons for the deviation of observed from predicted values are also discussed and rejected by these authors.

POTASSIUM IN EXTRACELLULAR FLUID IN THE MAMMALIAN CENTRAL NERVOUS SYSTEM, AND THE POSSIBLE ROLE OF GLIA IN ITS CLEARANCE

After demonstrating that the membrane potential of glia is influenced by $[K^+]_o$, it remains to be proven that the level of K^+ changes to a noticeable degree under physiological conditions in extracellular fluid of the central nervous system. That K^+ levels may indeed rise as a consequence of neural activity was made plausible by theoretical calculations published by Lebovitz (90). What was a conjecture a few years ago has become a firmly established fact since Walker described the manufacture of ion-selective micropipette electrodes in 1971 (164). The first report of their use in nervous tissue, by Vyskočil et al, appeared in 1972 (161). Since then, reports on central nervous potassium levels have appeared from, or are being prepared in, laboratories in Prague, Montreal, Göttingen, Palo Alto, Seattle, New York, Durham, and Washington D.C. (61, 62, 79–81, 95, 97, 98, 104, 126, 141, 160; and Lewis & Schuette, personal communication). These reports agree that repetitive electrical stimulation of the cortical surface or of an afferent pathway causes a slow rise of the potassium level in extracellular fluid. After cessation of stimulation, the potassium level sinks exponentially to its resting level or below that in a matter of seconds. Krnjevic & Morris (80, 81) reported the similarity of the elevation of $[K^+]_o$ and the shift of potential in cuneate nucleus, and Somjen & Lothman (141) demonstrated in the spinal cord a statistically significant positive correlation between these two variables.

Since depolarizing potential shifts of glia cells are correlated to extracellular sustained potential shifts (138, 139, 142), and extracellular potential shifts to changes of extracellular K^+ levels (95, 141), it was to be expected, and has now been demonstrated experimentally, that glial depolarizations must also be correlated to increments of extracellular $[K^+]_o$ (Figure 1). Similar correlation is found not only when recordings are made from a fixed point in central gray matter, but also in the spatial distributions of these three variables (glial depolarization, extracellular potential shifts, and rise of $[K^+]_o$) found with roving probes within the substance of the spinal cord (79, 137, 138, 142; and Lothman & Somjen, unpublished). There is also a good correspondence between the hyperpolarization of glial cells observed following tetanic afferent stimulation (132, 149), post-stimulation positive shifts of extracellular potential (138), and a subsidance of potassium levels below the resting level often seen after cessation of stimulation (Lothman & Somjen, unpublished).

Of course, elevated potassium levels also have an effect on neural elements. At moderate levels, however, the membrane potential of nerve cells is much less sensitive to changing $[K^+]_o$ than is that of glia (84, 110). The lesser dependence of the nerve membrane on $[K^+]_o$ has been attributed to its greater conductance for Na^+ (84). Nevertheless, if synaptic transmission is to operate reliably and securely, both presynaptic terminals and post-synaptic dendrites must be protected against excessive increments of K^+ activity. Glia may have a role in such protection.

The idea that glia may have a role in protecting neurons from excessive accumulation of K^+ has its origin in the suggestion of Lugaro (96), already mentioned, that glia cells are the guardians of extracellular fluid. Currently the opinions are divided about the mechanism by which glia could limit the rise of K^+ levels in extracellular fluid. One theory regards glial tissue as a passive conduit, another assigns an active role to glial membrane ATPase. Kuffler and associates (83, 84, 116) proposed the following theory of clearance by passive diffusion: Since glia appears to be near equilibrium with respect to $[K^+]_i/[K^+]_o$, it presumably is highly permeable to this one species of ion and to no other. Therefore, any increase of K^+ activity in the vicinity of a glia cell would cause an inflow of K^+ into that cell; at the same time the cell would depolarize, hence its internal potential would rise above that of other cells not exposed to high $[K^+]_o$ to which it is electrotonically coupled. Thus current would flow and K^+ ions would move from the cytoplasm of the depolarized cells to that of the unaffected cells, until the now also somewhat depolarized distant cells would discharge an equivalent amount of K^+ from their cytoplasm into extracellular fluid. The glial syncytium would thus act as a conveyor of K^+ bypassing the narrow and tortuous intercellular clefts. In favor of this mechanism of "spatial buffering," Pollen & Trachtenberg (125) have pointed to the low specific membrane resistance of glia cells (see below).

It follows from the results of our computer simulation (69, 139) described earlier that the more efficient the glial syncytium in conveying K^+, the larger must be current flowing in extracellular fluid. For a given level of $[K^+]_o$, extracellular voltage shifts are consistently larger in spinal cord than in cerebral cortex (Figure 1); this could reflect the more effective clearance of K^+ from the former tissue. This, in turn, could explain the immunity of spinal gray matter from spreading depression (139). However, it is also expected that for a given level of extracellular K^+, glia cells should be less depolarized in the better protected tissue than in the susceptible one. For reliable comparisons, direct measurements, made upon both tissues in one laboratory, will be required.

Active Transport of K^+ by Glia

The alternative view, that glia cells may clear potassium by active transport, is supported by several teams of investigators (7, 51, 55). The first condition for accepting this theory is the demonstration of active transport of K^+ by the glial membrane. A Na^+-K^+ activated ATPase and oxygen-dependent as well as anaerobic energy-yielding enzyme systems have been described to occur in glia cells (55, 56). There can be little doubt that glia cells are indeed capable of accumulating K^+ against a gradient, for the electrophysiological observations already discussed indicate that the activity of K^+ inside glia cells exceeds that of their environment, and also that their membrane is permeable to this ion. Under such conditions a concentration gradient can only be maintained by active transport. The question then is not whether glia can take up K^+ from its environment, for patently it can do so, but whether the transport activity is influenced by the load, i.e. whether it depends on extracellular K^+ activity. In vitro this certainly seems to be the case (51, 54, 55). Moreover, in cell suspensions separated by density-gradient centrifugation, glia-rich cell fractions appear to accumulate K^+ more avidly than neuron-rich fractions (51), although it must be admitted that this observation may reflect simply the greater resistance of glia cells to the damage caused by their isolation.

Favoring the glial clearance of excess K^+, Tower & Young (152) pointed to the anaerobic glycolytic capability of glial cells. They suggested that the availability of energy-yielding reactions in the face of shortage of oxygen may be required for the removal of K^+ in hypoxic emergencies.

To the active transport of K^+ by glia, Hertz (53) not only attributed the function of the elimination of a potentially harmful waste product, but also the spatial patterning of excitation. Hertz (53) argued that the transportation of ions from one region to another could influence the distribution of excitation among neurons, and therefore the signalling function of nervous tissue.

The experiments explicitly designed to investigate glial response to a K^+ load in situ have remained inconclusive to date. There is good reason to believe that the overall energy turnover of cortical tissue is dependent on the load on the transport mechanism (95, 136), but it is by no means clear how the work of pumping K^+ is shared between neurons and glia.

Bourke et al (7) described swelling of cortical glia cells when exposed to high K^+ levels; they ascribed this to active uptake of K^+ accompanied by Cl^- and H_2O. Bracho & Orkand (8) found that the temperature coefficient of the decay time of glial depolarization is low, and therefore they thought it unlikely that K^+ clearance would be enzymic. But then Orkand, Bracho & Orkand (114) have measured the oxidative energy turnover of optic nerve by estimating the ratio of reduced/oxidized NADH/NAD by the fluorometric method of Jöbsis et al (67), which earlier was applied to intact cortex (67, 136). They repeated the experiment with optic nerves in which all nerve fibers were replaced by reactive glial tissue, consequent to degeneration following enucleation of the eye. When placed in a medium of excess potassium, the oxidative energy turnover of such "glia-nerve" was elevated to the same degree as that of normal nerve. This experiment demonstrated that glia cells increase their activity under a K^+ load, but did not show to what use the extra energy is put. In a somewhat similar experiment in our department (Cordingley et al, work in progress) we are exposing cortical glial scar tissue to elevated levels of K^+. Unlike normal cortex (136) and unlike the "glia-nerve" of Orkand et al (114), glial cortical scars do not appear to respond to high K^+ with increased oxidation of NADH. It would be tempting to conclude that this failure to respond is the cause of the epileptogenic property of healed old wounds of the brain, but available data do not permit an unequivocal conclusion.

Also addressing themselves to the clearance of K^+, Lux & Neher (98) measured the time constant of the clearance of a microbolus of K^+ that they deposited iontophoretically in the vicinity of a K^+-sensitive microelectrode. They found the coefficient of diffusion of potassium in cortex to be only about one sixth of that in a saline solution. This value suggests restriction of movement and is concordant with the estimated volume of extracellular fluid, which in mammalian central nervous system is now believed to be about 15% of the total volume (73, 155). If local accumulation of excess potassium was cleared by diffusion through extracellular space, then glia would have no significance in this respect either as a passive conduit or as an active transport system. Lux & Neher's (98) results could seem to point to this conclusion. The magnitude of several parameters is not precisely determined, however, including the size of extracellular space and also whether mobility of K^+ in the extracellular medium of brain is equal to that in a saline solution. Such uncertainties preclude settling the issue at this time.

A distinction must be made between the effect of excess $[K^+]_o$ derived from an extrinsic source and one that is intrinsic to the tissue. During the discharge of impulses, neurons not only lose K^+ but also gain Na^+. Their membrane-bound ATPase is thus stimulated on both counts. By contrast, K^+ deposited by the experimenter causes no uptake of Na^+ and, therefore, presumably less stimulation of the neuronal membrane transport system. From the point of view of glia, however, both K^+ derived from neurons and K^+ from an experimental source must appear equally extraneous. Since glia does not accumulate Na^+ it has little Na^+ to spare to exchange for K^+; therefore, if it acquires K^+, it must do so together with an anion. This would not be a requirement of the passive conduit theory since equivalent amounts to the K^+ entering in the depolarized region would be lost at the quiescent part of the electrotonic net. Thus there would not be a net gain, but only the flow of ions through the circuit. However, if there is a net gain of K^+, and if it is accompanied by Cl^-, then presumably water would also enter and the cells would swell. Bourke et al (7) have indeed reported that glia cells take up Cl^- and H_2O with K^+ when exposed to a potassium load, and they do so excessively during spreading depression.

Movement of water, without change of tissue water content, must be accompanied by change of extracellular fluid volume. Changes of extracellular tissue resistance said to accompany or follow electrical stimulation of the cerebral cortex (30) may reflect such water uptake by glia. Another class of small tissue impedance responses, on a time scale of milliseconds, have also been reported, but are too rapid to reflect glial events and therefore are not relevant to our discussion. Glia in tissue culture displays amoeboid movements that are enhanced in excess K^+ (148).

Whether such movements occur in situ is not known, but, in any event, their time course is too slow to account for tissue impedance responses.

REPORTED VALUES OF MEMBRANE POTENTIAL AND OF IMPEDANCE OF GLIAL CELLS

The upper limit of resting membrane potentials measured with microelectrodes in mammalian gray matter for both neurons and glia cells is around 85–95 mV. While the upper limit is similar, glia cells more frequently sustain a higher membrane potential than neurons; thus the mean values calculated for glia regularly exceed that of neurons (4, 45, 82). Whether this difference reflects the greater resistance of glia to mechanical damage or whether glia cells have truly higher average membrane potential cannot at this time be determined.

I have already discussed the dependence of the glial membrane potential on extracellular K^+. Bracho & Orkand (8) have also established that the membrane potential followed changes of temperature, as expected from the RT/F term of the Nernst equation. The authors reported that, besides acting as good K^+ electrodes, coldblooded glia cells also work as reliable though not very sensitive thermometers. Any thought of assigning to glia a role in temperature regulation would, however, be premature. A study of temperature effects in situ was conducted by Adey (1).

A quantity measured with relative ease during experimentation with micropipette electrodes is the "input resistance" of cells. It is defined as the apparent resistance between electrode tip and extracellular medium when the electrode is located within a cell. It is calculated from the voltage drop from electrode to extracellular fluid when a known current is injected into the cytoplasm.

A glance at Table 1 reveals that there are differences not only between the input resistance measurements made in different tissues, but also between the values reported for the same tissue by different investigators. Such discrepancies may reflect variations of samplings, or of technique, or both. Consistently, however, whenever one experimenter measured both input resistance of glia and neurons, the average value of the former always exceeded the latter. The reason for this difference probably is the smaller average size of glia cells. For theoretical considerations it would be of greater importance to know the specific membrane resistance of these cells.

If the configuration of glia was simple, its specific membrane resistance could be calculated from the input resistance and the surface area of cells. However, since cells have long, irregularly branched and bent tubular and sheet-like processes (171), complex sets of cable equations would be applicable for calculating the spread of current into the glial expansions. (For a differing point of view, see reference 154.) Furthermore, if glia cells are joined in an electrotonic syncytium, then current injected into one spreads to others, and calculations based on the geometry of individual cells would yield false results. In the case of single glia cells isolated in vitro, reasonably accurate surface area measurements can be made (153). Such cells may, however, differ from normal cells in significant ways.

Trachtenburg & Pollen (154) have sought to bypass the need for estimating the surface area of glia by calculating specific membrane resistance from the membrane time constant and the specific capacitance. For the latter value they had to rely on estimates made on cultured glia cells (153). Their calculation is valid, therefore, only if the membrane capacitance of the glial membrane in situ is equal to that of glia in explants, and, furthermore, only if their assumption that the apparent time constant equals the true membrane time constant proves correct (154, see also discussion of preceding paragraph).

Estimates of specific membrane resistance of glia reported for different tissues by different investigators vary from less than 10 $\Omega \times cm^2$ to over 1000 $\Omega \times cm^2$ (Table 1). This range is not surprising, considering the variations of cell types and the sources of error. The input resistance of glial cells does not change during depolarization caused by gamma-aminobutyric acid (GABA) (82) or K^+ (130, 131, 138). Extracellular application of Ca^{2+} or Mg^{2+} does, however, sometimes cause an increase of resistance of glia without changing the membrane potential (75).

SEIZURES, SPREADING DEPRESSION, POTASSIUM, AND GLIA CELLS

Sugaya, Goldring & O'Leary (143) first noticed that idle cells undergo waves of depolarization during seizure activity of cortical tissue. Several investigators made similar observations (23, 29, 38, 71, 126, 129, 149). That such depolarizing responses are associated with waves of increments of potassium activity in extracellular fluid was suspected (25), and has now been confirmed by the use of potassium-selective micropipette electrodes (61, 97, 104, 127, 140).

The elevation of $[K^+]_o$ during seizures may simply be the result of nerve discharges. Failure of K^+ clearance could, however, be a link in a vicious circle of self-reexcitation, and, therefore, a pathogenetic factor in some forms of epilepsy (25, 45, 97, 125). This theory requires that K^+ levels during seizures should rise above those seen during nonconvulsive neural activity. We found (140, 141, and Lothman & Somjen, unpublished) that spinal seizures caused by toxic doses of penicillin originate from ventral gray matter, and, also, that at this site potassium levels sometimes did indeed rise higher than during intensive afferent excitation of normal spinal cords. These results allow for, but do not prove, K^+ to be the cause rather than effect in this form of paroxysmal discharge.

Elaborating on the potassium theory of seizures, Pollen & Trachtenberg (125) suggested that in the epileptogenic foci the spatial buffering function of glia cells may fail. To test this suggestion, first Grossman & Rosman (47), then Glötzner (37), examined the properties of glia cells in epileptogenic foci. Grossman & Rosman (47) could not find evidence for failure of glial function in an epileptogenic cortical scar, but suggested that incapacitated glial cells may have eluded their search. Glötzner (37) reported, however, that in epileptogenic foci glial cells actually repolarize faster than in normal tissue; he therefore concluded that, instead of deficient clearance, the removal of potassium is in fact faster in the diseased site than it is in normal cortex. Glötzner (37) thus views the elevation of $[K^+]_o$ as an effect, and not as a cause, of seizures, a position shared by Prince and collaborators (104).

Potassium had been implicated in the pathogenesis of spreading cortical depression before it became suspect in seizures. Grafstein (41) suggested a theory in 1956, according to which the K^+ released during excessive activation of clusters of neurons may lead to depolarization of the same neurons and their neighbors, thus leading to further release of K^+ and the recruitment of ever widening circles of neural tissue into the process.

As expected by the potassium theory, glia cells as well as neurons do indeed undergo profound depolarization during spreading depression (11, 16, 39, 57, 58, 71, 105). Measurements with potassium-selective microelectrodes have now confirmed that during spreading depression potassium levels in the cortex rise to heights never seen normally, or even during seizure activity (95, 127, 161).

While these observations seem to add up to a coherent theory of spreading depression, two recent reports are not immediately explicable from the foregoing considerations. Sugaya, Takato & Noda (145, 146) demonstrated that application of high-potassium solution to cortex treated with tetrodotoxin (TTX) evoked a sustained shift of potential and glial depolarization similar to that seen during spreading depression, and, moreover, the process spread through the tetrodotoxin-treated area and into normal cortex, where it arrested electroencephalographic activity. In the TTX-treated area, impulse activity of neurons was abolished as expected, but glial depolarization did occur. It appears then, that a spreading wave of depolarization of many cells can be provoked without the mediation of nerve impulses. Perhaps the excess potassium could sufficiently depolarize nerve terminals to trigger the release of large quantities of transmitter substances. The transmitters released could evoke synaptic potentials, and, with the synaptic currents, the discharge of more potassium, which in turn could cause further depolarization of other presynaptic terminals and so spread the process. Low-resistance junctions between glia cells could facilitate its progression.

Even more intriguing is a report of Walker & Hild (163) of a spreading wave of negative surface potential, accompanied by a change of tissue impedance similar to that seen in cortical spreading depression, in cell cultures entirely composed of glia cells. It seems that in the absence of neurons, depolarized glia cells can discharge an agent that can cause depolarization of other glia cells. If confirmed, this datum will necessitate reconsidering more than one concept relating to pathological processes in brain.

CLOSING REMARKS

Glia cells, or most of them, appear to have in common with neurons and indeed with most other living cells an electronegative, potassium-rich cytoplasm. Presumably, this is the medium in which cytoplasmic enzymes can properly function. The standing negative potential of glia cells appears to be subject to change, reflecting the activity of the nerve cells that surround them. Concomitant with changes of membrane potential, the ion, and possibly also the water, content of these cells is presumably perturbed. The question is, do these perturbations influence the functioning of glia cells? As long as we remain ignorant of the functional role played by glia cells, it will be hard to discover the factors that influence their functioning. If, however, it proves true that glia cells aid neurons in their activity, be it by supplying substrates for metabolism or by taking up transmitters or other spilt materials, then changes of membrane potential may well be the signal governing the intensity of glial activity. The depolarization of glia cells is a reliable measure of the activity of neighboring nerve cells and hence, presumably, of the demand made on the supporting function provided by glial cells, whatever its nature might be.

I have already discussed in some detail the proposition that glial depolarization is associated with the removal of excess potassium from extracellular fluid. While it is by no means definitely proven that glia plays this part in potassium homeostasis, today the problem seems nearer to its solution than any one of the other questions raised about glial involvement.

The fact that neuroglia is electrogenic must be recognized in the interpretation of electrographic recordings from all central nervous tissue. From this recognition stems the next question we must consider; that is, whether glia cells by their electrical activity participate in the signalling of neural circuits. As indicated in another context, I find few arguments in favor and several against this proposition, but as before, final conclusions cannot be drawn at this time.

More than a hundred years of research brought us to this point where each proposition suggesting one or another function for neuroglia can be countered by a valid point of criticism or doubt. Yet as for glia tissue merely filling the spaces left vacant by neurons, I protest that it is far too alive, far too full of enzymes, and evidently too active when appropriately challenged. If we can offer hope that it will take less than another century to understand the significance of glia, it is because lately the balance between conjecture and factual observation has begun to shift in favor of the latter.

ACKNOWLEDGMENT

The author's research is supported by grants from the US Public Health Service and the Epilepsy Foundation.

Literature Cited

1. Adey, W. R. 1974. Biophysical and metabolic bases of cooling effects of cortical membrane potentials in the cat. *Exp. Neurol.* 42:113–40
2. Bass, N. H., Hess, H. H., Pope, A., Thalheimer, C. 1971. Quantitative cytoarchitectonic distribution of neurons, glia and DNA in rat cerebral cortex. *J. Comp. Neurol.* 143:481–90
3. Baylor, D. A., Nicholls, J. G. 1969. Changes in extracellular potassium concentration produced by neuronal activity in the central nervous system of the leech. *J. Physiol.* 203:555–69
4. Blackman, J. G., Crowcroft, P. J., Devine, C. E., Holman, M. E., Yonemura K. 1969. Transmission from preganglionic fibres in the hypogastric nerve to peripheral ganglia of male guinea pigs. *J. Physiol.* 201:723–43
5. Blackman, J. G., Purves, R. D. 1969. Intracellular recordings from ganglia of the thoracic sympathetic chain of the guinea pig. *J. Physiol.* 203:173–98
6. Blackstad, T. W. 1964. Ultrastructural studies on the hippocampal region. *Progr. Brain Res.* 3:122–48
7. Bourke, R. S., Nelson, K. M., Naumann, R. A., Young, O. M. 1970. Studies of the production and subsequent reduction of swelling in primate cerebral cortex under isosmotic conditions in vivo. *Exp. Brain Res.* 10:427–46
8. Bracho, H., Orkand, R. K. 1972. Neuron-glia interaction: dependence on temperature. *Brain Res.* 36:416–19
9. Brightman, M. W., Reese, T. S. 1969. Junctions between intimately apposed cell membranes in the vertebrate brain. *J. Cell Biol.* 40:648–77
10. Brizzee, K. R. 1973. Quantitative histological studies on aging changes in cerebral cortex of rhesus monkey and albino rat with notes on effects of prolonged low-dose ionizing irradiation in the rat. *Progr. Brain Res.* 40:141–60
11. Brožek, G. 1966. Changes in the membrane potential of cortical cells during spreading depression. *Physiol. Bohemoslov.* 15:98–103
12. Castellucci, V. F., Goldring, S. 1970. Contribution to steady potential shifts of slow depolarization in cells presumed to be glia. *Electroencephalogr. Clin. Neurophysiol.* 28:109–18
13. Chang, J. J., Hild, W. 1959. Contractile responses to electrical stimulation of glial cells from the mammalian central nervous system cultivated in vitro. *J. Cell Comp. Physiol.* 53:139–44
14. Cohen, M. W. 1970. The contribution by glial cells to surface recordings from the optic nerve of an amphibian. *J. Physiol.* 210:565–80
15. Cohen, M. W., Gerschenfeld, H. M., Kuffler, S. W. 1968. Ionic environment of neurones and glial cells in the brain of an amphibian. *J. Physiol.* 197:363–80
16. Collewijn, H., Van Harreveld, A. 1966. Membrane potential of cerebral cortical cells during spreading depression and asphyxia. *Exp. Neurol.* 15:425–36
17. Coombs, J. S., Eccles, J. C., Fatt, P. 1955. The electrical properties of the motoneurone membrane. *J. Physiol.* 130:291–325
18. Dennis, M. J., Gerschenfeld, H. M. 1969. Some physiological properties of identified mammalian neuroglial cells. *J. Physiol.* 203:211–22
19. DeRobertis, E. D. P. 1965. Some new electron microscopical contributions to the biology of neuroglia. *Progr. Brain Res.* 15:1–11
20. DeRobertis, E. D. P., Carrea, R., Eds. 1965. *Biology of Neuroglia. Progress in Brain Research,* Vol. 15. Amsterdam: Elsevier. 296 pp.
21. Desmedt, J. E., LaGrutta, G. 1957. The effect of selective inhibition of pseudocholinesterase on the spontaneous and evoked activity of the cat's cerebral cortex. *J. Physiol.* 136:20–40
22. DeVellis, J., Kukes, G. 1973. Regulation of glial cell functions by hormones and ions: a review. *Tex. Rep. Biol. Med.* 31:271–93
23. Dichter, M. A., Herman, C. J., Selzer, M. 1972. Silent cells during interictal discharges and seizures in hippocampal penicillin foci. Evidence for the role of extracellular K^+ in the transition from the interictal state to seizures. *Brain Res.* 48:173–83
24. Dowling, J. E., Boycott, B. B. 1966. Organization of the primate retina: electron microscopy. *Proc. Roy. Soc. B* 166:80–111
25. Fertziger, A. P., Ranck, J. B. 1970. Potassium accumulation in interstitial space during epileptiform seizures. *Exp. Neurol.* 26:571–85
26. Fleischhauer, K. 1973. Ependyma and subependymal layer. In *Structure and Function of the Nervous System,* ed. G. Bourne, 6:1–46. New York: Academic

27. Frank, K., Fuortes, M. G. F. 1955. Potentials recorded from the spinal cord with microelectrodes. *J. Physiol.* 130:625–54
28. Frankenhaeuser, B., Hodgkin, A. L. 1956. The after-effects of impulses in the giant nerve fibers of Loligo. *J. Physiol.* 131:341–76
29. Frederking, U., Glötzner, F., Grüsser, O. J. 1971. Some cellular aspects of the pathophysiology of epilepsia. Responses of single cortical nerve and glial cells during generalized and focal seizures. In *Special Topics in Stereotaxis,* ed. W. Umbach, 130–48. Stuttgart: Hippokrates
30. Freygang, W. H. R., Landau, W. M. 1955. Some relations between resistivity and electrical activity in the cerebral cortex of the cat. *J. Cell Comp. Physiol.* 45:377–92
31. Friede, R. 1954. Der quantitative Anteil der Glia an der Cortexentwicklung. *Acta Anat.* 30:290–96
32. Galambos, R. 1961. A glia-neural theory of brain function. *Proc. Nat. Acad. Sci. USA* 47:129–36
33. Galambos, R. 1964. Glial cells. *Neurosci. Res. Program Bull.* 2: Pt. 6
34. Gilman, A. G., Nirenberg, M. 1971. Effect of catecholamines on the adenosine 3':5'-cyclic monophosphate concentrations of clonal satellite cell of neurons. *Proc. Nat. Acad. Sci. USA* 68: 2165–68
35. Glees, P. 1955. *Neuroglia, Morphology and Function.* Springfield, Ill.: Thomas. 111 pp.
36. Globus, A., Lux, H. D., Schubert, P. 1973. Transfer of amino acids between neuroglia cells and neurons in the leech ganglion. *Exp. Neurol.* 40:104–13
37. Glötzner, F. L. 1973. Membrane properties of neuroglia in epileptogenic gliosis. *Brain Res.* 55:159–71
38. Glötzner, F., Grüsser, O. J. 1968. Membranpotential and Entladungsfolgen corticaler Zellen, EEG und corticales DC Potential bei generalisierten Krampfanfallen. *Arch. Psychiat. Nervenkr.* 210:313–39
39. Goldensohn, E. S. 1969. Experimental seizure mechanisms. In *Basic Mechanisms of the Epilepsies,* ed. H. Jasper, A. Pope, 289–98. Boston: Little, Brown
40. Golgi, C. 1903. *Opera Omnia.* Milano: U. Hoepli
41. Grafstein, B. 1956. Mechanism of spreading cortical depression. *J. Neurophysiol.* 19:154–71
42. Gray, E. G. 1961. Ultra structure of synapses of the cerebral cortex and certain specialization of neurglial membranes. In *Electron Microscopy in Anatomy,* ed. J. D. Boyd, F. R. Johnson, J. D. Lever, 54–73. London: Arnold
43. Green, J. D. 1960. Some recent electrophysiological and electron microscopic studies of Ammon's horn. In *Structure and Function of the Cerebral Cortex,* ed. D. B. Tower, J. P. Schadé, 266–71. Amsterdam: Elsevier
44. Griffin, R., Illis, L. S., Mitchell, J. 1972. Identification of neuroglia by light and electron microscopy. *Acta Neuropathol.* 22:7–12
45. Grossman, R. G. 1972. Alterations in the microphysiology of glial cells and neurons and their environment in injured brain. *Clin. Neurosurg.* 19:69–83
46. Grossman, R. G., Hampton, T. 1968. Depolarization of cortical glial cells during electrocortical activity. *Brain Res.* 11:316–24
47. Grossman, R. G., Rosman, L. J. 1971. Intracellular potentials of inexcitable cells in epileptogenic cortex undergoing fibrillary gliosis after local injury. *Brain Res.* 28:181–201
48. Grossman, R. G., Whiteside, L., Hampton, T. 1969. The timecourse of evoked depolarization of cortical glial cells. *Brain Res.* 14:401–15
49. Hawkins, A., Olszewski, J. 1957. Glia/nerve cell index for cortex of the whale. *Science* 126:76–77
50. Hemminki, K., Hemminki, E., Giacobini, E. 1973. Activity of enzymes related to neurotransmission in neuronal and glial fractions. *Int. J. Neurosci.* 5:87–90
51. Henn, F. A., Haljamäe, H., Hamberger, A. 1972. Glial cell function: active control of extracellular K^+ concentration. *Brain Res.* 43:437–43
52. Henn, F., Hamberger, A. 1971. Glial cell function: Uptake of transmitters substances. *Proc. Nat. Acad. Sci. USA* 68:2686–90
53. Hertz, L. 1965. Possible role of neuroglia: a potassium-mediated neuronal-neuroglial-neuronal impulse transmission system. *Nature* 206:1091–94
54. Hertz, L. 1966. Neuroglial localization of potassium and sodium effects on respiration in brain. *J. Neurochem.* 13: 1373–87
55. Hertz, L. 1973. *Ion effects on metabolism in the adult mammalian brain in vitro. Evidence of a potassium-induced*

stimulation of active uptake of KCl into neuroglial cells. Copenhagen: Fadl's Forlag. 207 pp.

56. Hess, H. H., Embree, L. J., Shein, H. M. 1972. Enzymic control of sodium and potassium active transport in normal and neoplastic rodent astroglia. *Progr. Exp. Tumor Res.* 17:308–17
57. Higashida, H., Mitarai, G., Watanabe, S. 1974. A comparative study of membrane potential changes in neurons and neuro glial cells during spreading depression in the rabbit. *Brain Res.* 65:411–25
58. Higashida, H., Miyake, A., Tarao, M., Watanabe, S. 1971. Membrane potential changes of neuroglial cells during spreading depression in the rabbit. *Brain Res.* 32:207–11
59. Hild, W., Takenaka, T., Walker, F. 1965. Electrophysiological properties of ependymal cells from the mammalian brain in tissue culture. *Exp. Neurol.* 11:493–501
60. Hild, W., Tasaki, I. 1962. Morphological and physiological properties of neurons and glial cells in tissue culture. *J. Neurophysiol.* 25:277–304
61. Hotson, J. R., Sypert, G. W., Ward, A. A. 1973. Extracellular potassium concentration changes during propagated seizures. *Exp. Neurol.* 38:20–26
62. Hubschmann, O., Grossman, R. B., Mehta, P., Abramson, M. 1973. Spreading depression of electrocortical activity studied with K^+ ion specific microelectrodes. *27th Ann. Meet. Am. EEG Soc.* 18, p. 25 (Abstr.)
63. Hutchison, H. T., Werrbach, K., Vance, C., Haver, B. 1974. Uptake of neurotransmitters by clonal lines of astrocytoma and neuroblastoma in culture. I. Transport of gamma-aminobutyrityric acid. *Brain Res.* 66:265–74
64. Hydén, H., Egyházi, E. 1963. Glial RNA changes during a learning experiment in rats. *Proc. Nat. Acad. Sci. USA* 49:618–24
65. Iversen, L. L. 1974. Biochemical aspects of synaptic modulation. In *The Neurosciences, Third Study Program,* ed. F. O. Schmidt, F. G. Worden, 905–15. Cambridge: MIT Press
66. Jastrowitz, M. 1871. Studien über die Encephalitis und Myelitis des ersten Kindesalters. *Arch. Psychiat.* 3:162–213
67. Jöbsis, F. F., O'Connor, M., Vitale, A., Vreman, H. 1971. Intracellular redox changes in functioning cerebral cortex. I. Metabolic effects of epileptiform activity. *J. Neurophysiol.* 34:735–49
68. Johnston, P. V., Roots, B. I. 1972. *Nerve Membranes. A Study of the Biological and Chemical Aspects of Neuron-Glia Relationships.* Oxford: Pergamon. 274 pp.
69. Joyner, R., Somjen, G. 1972. A model stimulating the contribution of glia to sustained potential shifts of central nervous tissue. *26th Ann. Meet. Am. EEG Soc.,* 3 (Abstr.)
70. Kanno, Y., Matsui, Y., Nomura, S. 1972. Intercellular communication between neurons and neuroglia in the newt. *Advan. Neurol. Sci. Tokyo* 16:97–100
71. Karahashi Y., Goldring, S. 1966. Intracellular potentials from "idle" cells in cerebral cortex of cat. *Electroencephalogr. Clin. Neurophysiol.* 20:600–7
72. Katchalsky, A., Rowland, V., Blumenthal, R. 1974. Dynamic patterns in brain cell assemblies. Report of an NRP work session, May 1972, *Neurosci. Res. Program Bull.* 12:1–187
73. Katzman, R., Pappius, H. M. 1973. *Brain Electrolytes and Fluid Metabolism.* Baltimore: Williams and Wilkins. 419 pp.
74. Kelly, J. P., Van Essen, D. C. 1974. Cell structure and function in the visual cortex of the cat. *J. Physiol.* 238:515–47
75. Kelly, J. S., Krnjevíc, K., Somjen, G. 1969. Divalent cations and electrical properties of cortical cells. *J. Neurobiol.* 1:197–208
76. Kelly, J. S., Krnjevíc, K., Yim, G. K. W. 1967. Unresponsive cells in cerebral cortex. *Brain Res.* 6:767–69
77. Koch, A. R., Ranck, J. B., Newman, B. L. 1962. Ionic content of neuroglia. *Exp. Neurol.* 6:186–200
78. Koelle, G. B. 1954. The histochemical localization of cholinesterases in the central nervous system of the rat. *J. Comp. Neurol.* 100:211–36
79. Kríž, N., Syková, E., Ujec, E., Vyklický, L. 1974. Changes of extracellular potassium concentration induced by neuronal activity in the spinal cord of the cat. *J. Physiol.* 238:1–15
80. Krnjević, K., Morris, M. E. 1972. Extracellular K^+ activity and slow potential changes in spinal cord and medulla. *Can. J. Physiol. Pharmacol.* 50:1214–17
81. Krnjević, K., Morris, M. E. 1973. Correlation between slow potentials and changes in extracellular K^+ concentration evoked by primary afferent activity. *Fed. Proc.* 32:444 (Abstr.)

82. Krnjević, K., Schwartz, S. 1967. Some properties of unresponsive cells in the cerebral cortex. *Exp. Brain Res.* 3:306–19
83. Kuffler, S. W. 1967. Neuroglial cells: physiological properties and a potassium mediated effect of neuronal activity on the glial membrane potential. *Proc. Roy. Soc. B* 168:1–21
84. Kuffler, S. W., Nicholls, J. G. 1966. The physiology of neuroglial cells. *Ergeb. Physiol.* 57:1–90
85. Kuffler, S. W., Nicholls, J. G., Orkand, R. K. 1966. Physiological properties of glial cells in the central nervous system of amphibia. *J. Neurophysiol.* 29: 768–87
86. Kuffler, S. W., Potter, D. D. 1964. Glia in the leech central nervous system: physiological properties and neuron-glia relationship. *J. Neurophysiol.* 27: 290–320
87. Laborit, H. 1964. Sur la participation de la névroglie a l'électrogénêse cérébrale. *Presse Méd.* 72:1047–51
88. Lasansky, A. 1965. Functional implications of structural findings in retinal glial cells. *Progr. Brain Res.* 15:48–72
89. Lasansky, A. 1971. Nervous function at the cellular level: Glia. *Ann. Rev. Physiol.* 33:241–56
90. Lebovitz, R. M. 1970. A theoretical examination of ionic interactions between neural and non-neural elements. *Biophys. J.* 10:423–44
91. Lenhossék, M. von 1891. Zur Kenntnis der Neuroglia des menschlichen Rückenmarkes. *Verh. Anat. Ges.* 5:193–221
92. Li, C. L. 1959. Cortical intracellular potentials and their reponses to strychnine. *J. Neurophysiol.* 22:436–50
93. Lodin, Z., Booher, J., Kasten, F. H. 1970. Long-term cultivation of dissociated neurons from embroyonic chick dorsal root ganglia in the Rose chamber. *Exp. Cell Res.* 59:291–98
94. Loewenstein, W. R. 1972. Cellular communication through membrane junctions. Special consideration of wound healing and cancer. *Arch. Intern. Med.* 129:299–305
95. Lothman, E., LaManna, J., Cordingley, G., Rosenthal, M., Somjen, G. 1974. Levels of potassium, NADH and extracellular potential in the cerebral cortex during electrical stimulation, seizures and spreading depression. *4th Ann. Meet. Soc. Neurosci.,* 315 (Abstr.)
96. Lugaro, E. 1907. Sulle funzioni della nevroglia. *Riv. Patol. Nerv. Ment.* 12:225–33
97. Lux, H. D. 1973. Kaliumaktivität im Hirngewebe; Untersuchungen zum Krampfproblem. *Mitt. Max Planck Ges.* 1:34–52
98. Lux, H. D., Neher, E. 1973. The equilibration time course of $[K^+]_o$ in cat cortex. *Exp. Brain Res.* 17:190–205
99. Martin, A. R., Branch, C. L. 1958. Spontaneous activity of Betz cells in cats with midbrain lesions. *J. Neurophysiol.* 21:368–79
100. Maynard, E. A., Schultz, R. L., Pease, D. C. 1957. Electron microscopy of the vascular bed of rat cerebral cortex. *Am. J. Anat.* 100:409–34
101. Miller, R. F., Dowling, J. E. 1970. Intracellular responses of the Müller (glial) cells of the mudpuppy retina: their relation to the b-wave of the electroetinogram. *J. Neurophysiol.* 33: 323–41
102. Mitarai, G. 1965. Glia-neuron interaction in carp retina, glia potentials revealed by microelectrode with lithium carmine. In *Intracellular Membraneous Structures,* ed. S. Seno, E. V. Cowdry, 549–58. Okayama: Jap. Soc. Cell. Biol.
103. Monard, D., Solomon, F., Rentsch, M., Gysin, R. 1973. Glia-induced morphological differentiation in neuroblastoma cells. *Proc. Nat. Acad. Sci. USA* 70: 1894–97
104. Moody, W. J., Futamachi, K. J., Prince, D. A. 1974. Extracellular potassium activity during epileptogenesis. *Exp. Neurol.* 42:248–62
105. Morlock, N. L., Mori, K., Ward, A. A. 1964. A study of single cortical neurons during spreading depression. *J. Neurophysiol.* 27:1192–98
106. Moucha, R. D., Jinga, V. V., Popescu, M. 1973. Observations préliminaries sur le comportment des cellules gliales en culture en présence de la noradrénaline la sérotonine et le virus neurotrope MM. *Rev. Roum. Physiol.* 10:85–89
107. Murray, M. R. 1958. Response of oligodendrocytes to serotonin. In *Biology of Neuroglia,* ed. W. F. Windle, 176–80. Springfield, Ill.: Thomas
108. Nageotte, J. 1910. Phénomènes de sécrétion dans le protoplasma des cellules névrogliques de la substance grise. *C. R. Soc. Biol.* 68:1068–69
109. Nakai, J., Ed. 1963. *Morphology of Neuroglia.* Tokyo: Igaku Shoin Ltd. 198 pp.
110. Nicholls, J. G., Kuffler, S. W. 1964. Extracellular space as a pathway for exchange between blood and neurons in the central nervous system of the leech:

ionic composition of glial cells and neurons. *J. Neurophysiol.* 27:645–71
111. Nicholls, J. G., Kuffler, S. W. 1965. Na and K content of glial cells and neurons determined by flame photometry in the central nervous system of the leech. *J. Neurophysiol.* 28:519–25
112. Nurnberger, J. I., Gordon, M. W. 1957. The cell density of neural tissues. Direct counting method and possible application as a biologic referent. *Progr. Neurobiol.* 2:100–38
113. Okun, L. M. 1972. Isolated dorsal root ganglian neurons in culture: cytological maturation and extension of electrically active processes. *J. Neurobiol.* 3:111–51
114. Orkand, P. M., Bracho, H., Orkand, R. K. 1973. Glial metabolism: alteration by potassium levels comparable to those during neural activity. *Brain Res.* 55:467–71
115. Orkand, R. K. 1969. Neuroglial-neuronal interactions. In *Basic Mechanism of the Epilepsies,* ed. H. Jasper, A. Ward, A. Pope, 737–46. Boston: Little, Brown
116. Orkand, R. K., Nicholls, J. G., Kuffler, S. W. 1966. Effect of nerve impulses on the membrane potential of glial cells in the central nervous system of amphibia. *J. Neurophysiol.* 29:788–806
117. Palay, S. L. 1966. The role of neuroglia in the organization of the central nervous system. In *Nerve as a Tissue,* ed: K. Rodahl, B. Issekutz, 3–10. New York: Hoeber
118. Pannese, E., Bianchi, R., Calligaris, B., Ventura, R., Weibel, E. R. 1972. Quantitative relationships between nerve and satellite cells in spinal ganglia. An electron microscopical study. I. Mammals. *Brain Res.* 46:215–34
119. Pape, L. G., Katzman, R. 1972. Response of glia in cat sensorimotor cortex to increased extracellular potassium. *Brain Res.* 38:71–92
120. Penfield, W. 1932. *Cytology and Cellular Pathology of the Nervous System,* Vol. II. New York: Hafner (1965 facsimile edition)
121. Peters, A. 1960. The formation and structure of myelin sheaths in the central nervous system. *J. Biophys. Biochem. Cytol.* 8:431–46
122. Peters, A. 1962. Plasma membrane contacts in the central nervous system. *J. Anat.* 96:237–48
123. Peters, A., Palay, S. L. 1965. An electron microscope study of the distribution and patterns of astroglial processes in the central nervous system. *J. Anat.* 99:419
124. Phillips, C. A. 1956. Intracellular records from Betz cells in the cat. *Quart. J. Exp. Physiol.* 41:58–59
125. Pollen, D. A., Trachtenberg, M. C. 1970. Neuroglia: Gliosis and focal epilepsy. *Science* 167:1252–53
126. Prince, D. A. 1971. Cortical cellular activities during cyclically occurring inter-ictal epileptiform discharges. *Electroencephalogr. Clin. Neurophysiol.* 31: 469–84
127. Prince, D. A., Lux, H. D., Neher, E. 1973. Measurement of extracellular potassium activity in cat cortex. *Brain Res.* 50:489–95
128. Ramón y Cajal, S. 1952. *Histologie du système nerveux de l'homme et des vertebrés.* (Transl. Azoulay). Madrid: Cons. Sup. Invest. Cientif. Vol. I: 986 pp., Vol. II: 993 pp.
129. Ransom, B. R. 1974. The behavior of presumed glial cells during seizure discharge in cat cerebral cortex. *Brain Res.* 69:83–99
130. Ransom, B. R., Goldring, S. 1973. Ionic determinants of membrane potential of cells presumed to be glia in cerebral cortex of cat. *J. Neuophysiol.* 36:855–68
131. Ransom, B. R., Goldring, S. 1973. Slow depolarization in cells presumed to be glia in cerebral cortex of cat. *J. Neurophysiol.* 36:869–78
132. Ransom, B. R., Goldring, S. 1973. Slow hyperpolarization in cells presumed to be glia in cerebral cortex of cat. *J. Neurophysiol.* 36:879–92
133. Río Hortega, P. del 1942. La neuroglia normal. *Arch. Histol. Norm. Pat.* 1:5–71
134. Roitbak, A. I. 1970. A new hypothesis concerning the mechanism of formation of the conditioned reflex. *Acta Neurobiol. Exp.* 30:81–94
135. Roitbak, A. I., Fanardzhyan, V. V. 1973. Intracellular potentials of cortical glial cells during electrical stimulation of the cortex. *Dokl. Akad Nauk SSSR, Biol. Sci. Sect.* 211:748–51. Transl. Consult. Bur. NY. *Dokl. Biol. Sci.* 211:340–43
136. Rosenthal, M., Somjen, G. 1973. Spreading depression, sustained potential shifts and metabolic activity of the cerebral cortex of cats. *J. Neurophysiol.* 36:739–49
137. Somjen, G. G. 1969. Sustained evoked potential changes of the spinal cord. *Brain Res.* 12:268–72
138. Somjen, G. 1970. Evoked sustained focal potentials and membrane potential

of neurons and of unresponsive cells of the spinal cord. *J. Neurophysiol.* 33:562–82

139. Somjen, G. 1973. Electrogenesis of sustained potentials. *Progr. Neurobiol. Oxford* 1:199–237
140. Somjen, G. 1974. Do potassium, glia, and neurons interact? Presented at UCLA Colloq. Behav. Sci. 1973. *Cellular Mechanisms Subserving Changes in Neuronal Activity,* ed. C. D. Woody et al. Los Angeles: Brain Inform. Ser. In press
141. Somjen, G. G., Lothman, E. W. 1974. Potassium, sustained focal potential shifts, and dorsal root potentials of the mammalian spinal cord. *Brain Res.* 69:153–57
142. Strittmatter, W. J., Somjen, G. G. 1973. Depression of sustained evoked potentials and of glial depolarization in the spinal cord by barbiturates and by diphenylhydantoin. *Brain Res.* 55:333–42
143. Sugaya, E., Goldring, S., O'Leary, J. L. 1964. Intracellular potentials associated with direct cortical response and seizure discharge in cat. *Electroencephalogr. Clin. Neurophysiol.* 17:661–69
144. Sugaya, E., Karahashi, Y., Sugaya, A., Haruki, F. 1971. Intra- and extracellular potentials from "idle" cells in cerebral cortex of cats. *Jap. J. Physiol.* 21:149–57
145. Sugaya, E., Takato, M., Noda, Y. 1971. Spreading depression under the effect of tetrodotoxine. *J. Physiol. Soc. Jap.* 33:591–92
146. Sugaya, E., Takato, M., Noda, Y. 1971. Glial membrane potential during spreading depression under the effect of tetrodotoxine. *J. Physiol. Soc. Jap.* 33:654–55
147. Svaetichin, G., Negishi, K., Fatehchand, R., Drujan, B. D., Selvin de Testa, A. 1965. Nervous function based on interactions between neuronal and non-neuronal elements. *Progr. Brain Res.* 15:243–66
148. Svanidze, I. K., Roitbak, A. I., Didimova, E. V. 1973. Effect of potassium ions on the motor activity of glia cells of the cerebral cortex under conditions of tissue culture. *Dokl. Akad. Nauk SSSR, Biol. Sci. Ser.* 211: 1450–52. Transl. Consult. Bur. NY. *Dokl. Biol. Sci.* 211:307–9
149. Sypert, G. W., Ward, A. A. Jr. 1971. Unidentified neuroglia potentials during propagated seizures in neocortex. *Exp. Neurol.* 33:239–55
150. Tasaki, I. 1965. Excitability of neurons and glial cells. *Progr. Brain Res.* 15:234–42
151. Tasaki, I., Chang, J. J. 1958. Electric response of glia cells in cat brain. *Science* 128:1209–10
152. Tower, D. B., Young, O. M. 1973. The activities of butyrylcholinesterase and carbonic anhydrase, the rate of anaerobic glycolysis, and the question of a constant density of glial cells in cerebral cortices of various mammalian species from mouse to whale. *J. Neurochem.* 20:269–78
153. Trachtenberg, M. C., Kornblith, P. L., Häuptli, J. 1972. Biophysical properties of cultured human glial cells. *Brain Res.* 38:279–98
154. Trachtenberg, M. C., Pollen, D. A. 1970. Neuroglia: biophysical properties and physiologic function. *Science* 167: 1248–52
155. Van Harreveld, A. 1966. *Brain Tissue Electrolytes.* London: Butterworth. 171 pp.
156. VanGilder, J. C., O'Leary, J., Ferguson, J. P. 1967. Steady potentials of cerebellar cortex. Results of direct olivo and pontocerebellar activation. *Electroencephalogr. Clin. Neurophysiol.* 22: 401–13
157. Vernadakis, A., Berni, A. 1973. Changes in the resting membrane potentials of glial cells in culture. *Brain Res.* 57:223–28
158. Villegas, G. M., Villegas, R. 1963. Neuron-glia relationship in the bipolar cell layer of the fish retina. *J. Ultrastruct. Res.* 8:89–103
159. Virchow, R. 1871. *Cellularpathologie in ihre Begründung auf physiologische und pathologische Gewebelehre.* Berlin: August Hirschwald. 4th ed. (First edition: 1858)
160. Vyklicky, L., Syková, E., Kríž, N., Ujeć, E. 1972. Post-stimulation changes of extracellular potassium concentration in the spinal cord of the rat. *Brain Res.* 45:608–11
161. Vyskočil, F., Kríž, N., Bureš, J. 1972. Potassium-selective microelectrodes used for measuring the extracellular brain potassium during spreading depression and anoxic depolarization in rats. *Brain Res.* 39:255–59
62. Walker, F. D., Hild, W. J. 1969. Neuroglia electrically coupled to neurons. *Science* 165:602–3
163. Walker, F. D., Hild, W. J. 1972. Spreading depression in tissue culture. *J. Neurobiol.* 3:223–35

164. Walker, J. L. 1971. Ion specific liquid ion exchanger microelectrodes. *Anal. Chem.* 43:89A–93A
165. Wardell, W. M. 1966. Electrical and pharmacological properties of mammalian neuroglial cells in tissue culture. *Proc. Roy. Soc. B* 165:326–61
166. Watanabe, S., Mitarai, G., Takenaka, S. 1968. The glial cell in the cerebral cortex of the cat. *Proc. Int. Union Physiol. Sci., 24th Int. Cong.* 7:459
167. Watson, W. E. 1974. Physiology of neuroglia. *Physiol. Rev.* 54:245–71
168. Werblin, F. S., Dowling, J. E. 1969. Organization of the retina of the mudpuppy, Necturus Maculosus: II. Intracellular recording. *J. Neurophysiol.* 32:339–55
169. Windle, W. F., Ed. 1958. *Biology of Neuroglia,* Springfield, Ill.: Thomas. 340 pp.
170. Wolfe, D. E., Nicholls, J. G. 1967. Uptake of radioactive glucose and its conversion to glycogen by neurons and glial cells in the leech central nervous system. *J. Neurophysiol.* 30:1593–1609
171. Wolff, J. 1965. Elektronenmikroskopische Untersuchungen über Struktur und Gestalt von Astrozytenforsätzen. *Z. Zellforsch.* 66:811–28
172. Wolff, J. 1966. Die Astroglia im Gewebsverband des Gehirns. *Acta Neuropathol. Suppl.* 4:33–39
173. Zhukovskaya, N. M., Chailakhyan, L. M. 1970. Changes of membrane potential related to ionic composition of external medium in different types of cells in nerve tissue culture: 1. The influence of potassium ions on membrane potential. Intracellular concentration of potassium ions. (Russian; Engl. abstr.) *Tsitologiia* 12:1248–54
174. Zhukovakaya, N. M., Kokina, N. N., Chailakhyan, L. M. 1970. Changes of the electrophysiological characteristics of the nervous tissue cells during their differentiation in tissue culture. (Russian: Engl. Abstr.) *Tsitologiia* 12: 1116–25

Copyright 1975. All rights reserved

NEURAL CONTROL OF THE POSTERIOR PITUITARY[1,2]

❖1128

James N. Hayward
Departments of Neurology and Anatomy, Reed Neurological Research Center, and Brain Research Institute, UCLA School of Medicine, Los Angeles, California 90024

INTRODUCTION

The subject of the neural control of the posterior pituitary (PP) encompasses cellular and subcellular aspects of magnocellular neuroendocrine cells and the neurohypophysis. It includes electrophysiological mechanisms of activation of neurosecretory neurons, the osmometric, volumetric, and behavioral reflex mechanisms of peptide hormone release, and the pharmacological and pathological aspects of neurohypophysial function. Comprehensive reviews of the neurohypophysis appeared in 1963 (64) and 1969 (37); more recent surveys have been limited to blood volume in 1970 (41) and body fluid regulation in 1972 (121). Another review of the neurohypophysis appears in Berde's 1968 *Handbook of Experimental Pharmacology* (8). There are other excellent if specialized reviews available (9, 13, 14, 19, 22, 23, 39, 48–50, 52, 96, 97, 118, 119, 124, 131). Space limitations dictate broad concepts of neural control of the PP; the material reviewed, with some exceptions, has appeared within the last three years. I apologize for the inevitable omissions.

POSTERIOR PITUITARY PEPTIDES

The mammalian PP has several peptides in addition to arginine vasopressin (lysine vasopressin in Suiformes) and oxytocin (molecular weight ∼1000). There is arginine vasotocin (molecular weight ∼1000), the basic "water balance principle" of all nonmammalian vertebrate PP (118) and also found in the PP of mammalian fetuses

[1]Preparation of this review was supported in part by NIH Grants NS–05638, NS–10129, NS–11443, and the Ford Foundation. I thank Ms. S. Curtis for editorial assistance.

[2]*Abbreviations:* ACTH: adrenocorticotropin; ADH: antidiuretic hormone or activity; AVP: arginine vasopressin; AVT: arginine vasotocin; BBB: blood-brain barrier; CSF: cerebrospinal fluid; CNS: central nervous system; DI: diabetes insipidus; INZ: internuclear zone of Greving; LVP: lysine vasopressin; MEA: milk-ejection activity; Np: neurophysin; NPV: paraventricular nucleus-neuron; NSO: supraoptic nucleus-neuron; PP: posterior pituitary gland; RIA: radioimmunoassay.

(97), coherin (molecular weight ~4000), with action on mammalian gastrointestinal motility (44), and the neurophysins (molecular weight ~10,000), a group of neurohypophysial "carrier proteins" or "prohormones."

The recent development of highly specific and sensitive (picogram levels) radioimmunoassays for vasopressin (59, 107, 110, 125), oxytocin (14, 110), and neurophysins (15, 16, 108–112, 146, 147) has provided exciting new approaches to the histochemical and physiological studies of the neural control of the PP.

CELLULAR AND SUBCELLULAR ASPECTS

Magnocellular Neuroendocrine Cells

Rechardt (101), with her improved light- and electron-microscopic techniques, confirmed the findings of earlier workers of a heterogeneous population of neurosecretory neurons in rat NSO. She found a dual population of magnocellular neuroendocrine cells, "dark" and "light" neurons, differing in the free ribosomes. Dehydration caused an increase in the dark cell ribosomes, but no effect on light cell ribosomes, suggesting that dark cells may be AVP secretors and light cells producers of oxytocin. In the only successful classical Golgi study of mammalian NSO and NPV, Leontovich (69) described a homogeneous population of Golgi type I neurons with thick, beaded, nonbranching axons rising from an elongated pole of these large bipolar cells. These results (69) conflict with other morphological, histochemical, and electrophysiological data that suggest heterogeneity (3, 51, 55, 56, 66, 147). One such study is that of Hayward (51) who found three morphological types of magnocellular neuroendocrine cells in procion yellow-filled cells of the preoptic nucleus of the goldfish. Cell type I was a large, multipolar neuron located away from the ependyma, with neural input and miltiple branched axons. Cell type II was a large, multipolar neuron, lying close to the ependyma, with neural and cerebrospinal input and limited branching of axons. Cell type III was small, multipolar, and otherwise undefined.

In a masterful study, Zimmerman and co-workers (147) utilized the relatively specific immunoperoxidase technique for localizing Np-I (an oxytocin-Np?) in bovine and monkey supraoptic nucleus, paraventricular nucleus, internuclear zone, the axons of these neurosecretory tracts, and the PP gland. These hypothalamic neurosecretory nuclei were heterogeneous with Np-I stained magnocellular neuroendocrine cells lying interspersed among Np-II unstained neurosecretory neurons. No Np-I was found in the pituicytes or in other CNS areas. These results indicate that neurophysin is present throughout the entire neurosecretory neuron: cell body, axon, and PP terminals. The authors further suggest that both Np-I and Np-II, linked to oxytocin and AVP respectively, are synthesized in both NSO and NPV, possibly in separate neurons (147). Somewhat similar results have been described in the rat hypothalamus and PP, with a slightly less discriminating immunofluorescence technique (144). In his excellent studies of ^{3}H-estradiol uptake by rat NPV, Stumpf (128) found heterogeneity: the anterior portion of NPV remained unlabeled, estrogen neurons existed in its central and caudal portion, and labeled neurons fanned out laterally toward the fornix and the zona incerta. These morphological data, when coupled with some of the electrophysiological results (see 50–56), suggest a cellular rather than a nuclear organization of magnocellular neuroendocrine cells in the hypothalamus.

Synaptic Input and Deafferentation of Neuroendocrine Cells

In confirmatory work, Rechardt (101) described three kinds of synaptic vesicles in rat NSO in axosomatic, axodendritic, and axo-axonal synapses: small agranular, small granular, and large granular vesicles. She also stated that the small granular vesicles, related to adrenergic transmission, were found in the axosomatic and axodendritic synapses (101). Others provide evidence for facilatatory input to NPV. After two days of deafferentation of NSO and NPV, only the NPV showed increased numbers of neurosecretory granules and increased milk-ejection activity (32).

Osmotic Stress on Neuroendocrine Cells

Rechardt (101) found that dehydration had no effect on the appearance or number of synaptic vesicles in the rat NSO. Because of swelling and hypertrophy of glial processes, the intimate contacts between the neurosecretory neurons NSO and the BBB type of capillaries decreased after dehydration. Autoradiographic studies with intraventricular ^{3}H-valine in the dehydrated cat (120) and with ^{3}H-cytidine systemically in the dehydrated mouse (42) revealed heavy uptake of precursor in NSO, in NPV, in medial portions of the arcuate nucleus, and in ependyma adjacent to the arcuate nucleus. Light- and electron-microscopic studies showed that within an hour the ^{3}H-valine was localized, first in the endoplasmic reticulum, later in the elementary granules in the usual sequence for protein synthesis (120). Since this amino acid does not participate in the AVP or oxytocin sequence, it may be involved in Np synthesis (120). In the dehydrated mouse, during osmotic stress the selective increase of ^{3}H-cytidine incorporation into RNA in the arcuate nucleus and adjacent ependyma may reflect stress-related release of corticotropin-releasing factor and ACTH. It can also indicate a reception and transmission of thirst-drinking activity (42).

There have been many other interesting studies indicating subcellular changes during osmotic stress in normal and Brattleboro-strain rats and in ducks. Enhanced protein synthesis was indicated by cell enlargement; increase in size of cell soma, nucleoli, endoplasmic reticulum, and Golgi complex; replication of nucleoli; and increase of anaerobic enzymes (34, 47, 61a, 87, 102, 144).

Section of the Median Eminence and Stalk

The median eminence, the proximal part of the neurohypophysis, contains an internal layer through which the unmyelinated axons of the supraoptico-hypophysial tract run, and an external layer containing the terminals of the tubero-hypophysial tract (releasing factors), ending on portal capillaries (8). We do not know whether axons from magnocellular neuroendocrine cells NPV, NSO, and INZ end on portal capillaries in the external layer and release neurohypophysial peptides into portal veins for release of adenohypophysial hormones such as ACTH and growth hormone.

Human stalk section results in portal vessel thrombosis and venous infarction of the stalk; the stump subsequently reorganizes with neurohemal contacts, i.e., axon terminals on fenestrated capillaries, but does not hypertrophy (21). In the hypophysectomized rat, Raisman (99,100) found an initial (2 days to 3 weeks) obstructive phase with NSO and axon terminals engorged with neurosecretory granules followed by a recovery phase, after 2 weeks, in which fenestrated capillaries proliferate and appear to promote neurite sprouting, transforming the median eminence into a miniature neural lobe. Because of greater cell loss in NSO than NPV, the regrowth of neurosecretory sprouts in the reconstituted median eminence neurohemal contact zone has predominantly electron-lucent vesicles (200 nm diam, oxytocin?). The suggested role of cervical sympathetics in formation of a miniature neural lobe after hypophysectomy in the rat (38) could not be confirmed by Raisman (100). These results indicate the plasticity of neurosecretory terminals and the influence of trophic capillary factors in sprout formation.

In similar studies of natural scrapie in sheep, Parry & Livett (95) found DI sheep with degeneration of the neural lobe, but hypertrophy of the external zone of median eminence with increased content of Np and AVP. This suggests compensatory hypertrophy in a previously unknown hypothalamic pathway from magnocellular neuroendocrine cells to portal capillaries of the median eminence; this pathway is probably used for release of neurohypophysial hormones. This exciting hypothesis was further supported by the definitive work of Zimmerman et al (146), who measured concentrations of AVP and Np in monkey portal veins much higher than those found in arterial blood, and who localized Np immunohistochemically in concentrated amounts around the portal capillaries in the external layer of the median eminence. One or more of the neurohypophysial peptides may act physiologically as a releasing hormone for the anterior pituitary.

Axonal Transport

AVP and oxytocin are synthesized together with the carrier peptides Np in the NSO, NPV, and INZ of the hypothalamus (114, 115). In these magnocellular neuroendocrine cells the neurosecretory material (AVP, oxytocin, Np) is packed in granules; they are ready for transport 1.5 hr from the start of synthesis (60, 88). AVP and oxytocin may be stored in complex with Np in separate neurosecretory granules. The neurosecretory material is transported along the neurotubles of the supraoptico-hypophysial axons and starts to accumulate in the nerve terminals in the PP 2 hr after the start of synthesis or 0.5 hr after transport has begun (60, 88). Of the three phases of axonal transport—rapid, intermediate, and slow—the rapid rate was unchanged by hemorrhage (88). Immunohistochemical evidence (1) shows movement of Np from hypothalamic magnocellular neuroendocrine cells to the PP of the dog: Np-specific fluorescence accumulated in axons proximal to stalk constriction, but not in axons immediately distal to the site of injury (1). The neurotubular poisons colchicine and vincristine may alter the ultrastructure of the microtubules (113), interrupting axonal flow in the magnocellular-neurohypophysial system (40), and thereby causing, paradoxically, the clinical syndrome of inappropriate secretion of antidiuretic hormone (20, 106), rather than the expected DI state.

Mechanisms of Peptide Release from Neural Lobe

The outstanding studies of Douglas and co-workers (see 22) and Dreifuss et al (see 23) have increased our understanding of peptide release from unmyelinated axons in the PP. First, there is impulse generation and propagation through the classical sodium-dependent and tetrodotoxin-sensitive spike mechanisms (22, 23, 131). Next, depolarization of the nerve terminal occurs, with the entry of calcium, leading to the induction of exocytosis and the extrusion of granule contents directly to the cell exterior (22, 23). Following exocytosis, the membranes of the neurosecretory granules now incorporated into the limiting membrane of the neuron appear to be recycled by a vesiculation process that produces coated microvesicles that subsequently lose their coats and become smooth (22). Leading as it does to synaptic vesicles, this sequence may be related to cell surface conservation (22).

Evidence is accumulating which refutes the hypothesis that synaptic vesicles play some role in the neurotransmission in the PP. In addition to the data of Douglas (22), Bridges et al (12) and Whitaker & LaBella (145) failed to identify cholinergic neurons in the PP, finding instead that the high levels of acetylcholine and specific acetylcholinesterase were localized to certain pituicytes and pituicyte-neuron junctions. The adrenergic fibers in the PP seem to innervate blood vessels (145), while the moderate amounts of histamine in the PP (126) probably reside in the mast cells (8). Strangely, rabbits exposed to hormone-releasing stimuli—intravascular $CaCl_2$ or vagal stimulation—or parasympathomimetic drugs (methacholine) developed a local increase in blood flow (^{133}Xenon) to the PP; this increase was blocked by atropine but was not affected by either sympathomimetic or sympathetic blocking drugs (127). The role of cholinergic and noradrenergic fibers in regulation of peptide release from PP needs clarification.

The functional role of the pituicyte in hormone release from PP remains unknown. Some pituicytes contain not only acetylcholine and specific cholinesterase, but also an efficient concentrating mechanism for triiodothyronine (5), which is localized within the membraneous elements in the cytoplasm, particularly the mitochondria, Golgi apparatus, and nuclear envelope. Other poorly understood PP cell types include the perivascular cells (91), which may be involved in phagocytosis of neurosecretory endings. The pituicyte develops more extensive contacts with neurosecretory fibers than with the perivascular cells. At times, typical synaptoid contacts are found between pituicytes and neurosecretory fibers (91, 92). Osmotic stress produces mitotic proliferation, cytoplasmic modifications progressing to eventual degeneration, and a shift to anaerobic metabolism in pituicytes (87, 92).

ELECTROPHYSIOLOGICAL STUDIES

Cross and Green (see 19) pioneered in the analysis of hypothalamic unit activity. They found single, extracellularly recorded anterior hypothalamic neurons in the urethane-anesthetized rabbit that responded to intracarotid osmotic stimuli and sensory stimuli. Since their work, improvements in hypothalamic unit recording techniques include the study of antidromically identified magnocellular neuroendocrine cells, intracellular recording from cells marked by dye, iontophoresis of neuropharmacological agents placed directly on the cell membrane during unit recording, correlation of unit activity with hormone release, and statistical analysis of unit activity in behaving nonanesthetized animals (see 9, 19, 23, 39, 48–50). Unless otherwise stated, all studies of single cells in NSO, NPV, and INZ refer to antidromically identified neurons.

Electrical Membrane Characteristics

Kandel (62) recorded intracellular potentials from the antidromically identified magnocellular neuroendocrine cells of the preoptic nucleus of the anesthetized goldfish. Preoptic neurosecretory cells fired with low frequency (2–8 spikes/sec), showed a long duration of action potential (3.5 msec) with a biphasic hyperpolarizing afterpotential, and received excitatory input (EPSPs) from olfactory tract stimulation. Subthreshold volleys to the pituitary gland elicited inhibitory potentials (IPSPs) in preoptic neurons. Lacking histological verification, Kandel could not absolutely localize these neurons to the magnocellular part of the preoptic nucleus, nor could he determine whether the axon of the antidromically identified cell ended on a blood vessel (neurohemal contact) or innervated an adenohypophysial cell (see 96). In his intracellular study with procion yellow-filled micropipettes, Hayward (51) confirmed these electrical membrane properties of histologically marked preoptic magnocellular neuroendocrine cells, as well as their orthodromic facilitation from olfactory tract stimuli. In addition, he found both physiological and morphological evidence for multiple axonal branching. Three identifiable neuroendocrine cell types were distributed within the anatomical limits of the preoptic nucleus, the pars magnocellularis, each type having specific input connections and unique output pathways. He concluded, as did Kandel, that magnocellular neuroendocrine cells show the electrical membrane properties of other central neurons, and, in addition, the three types of neuroendocrine cells may be related to the cellular secretion of specific neurohypophysial hormones and neurophysins (51).

In the isolated bullfrog hypothalamo-hypophysial system, Koizumi et al (65) found preoptic magnocellular neuroendocrine cells with both a low threshold, recurrent-collateral facilitatory influence and a high threshold, recurrent-collateral inhibitory connection between neuroendocrine cells. Their diagramatic interpretation of the synaptic connections of neurosecretory cells, (65) proposed to explain the facilitatory and inhibitory phenomena, resembles the postulated connections between respiratory neurons in the nucleus of the tractus solitarius (36).

By their intracellular recordings of cat and dog magnocellular neuroendocrine cells, Koizumi & Yamashita (66) confirmed Kandel's units in the fish. (62). In addition they found frequent dissociation between the early, small A-spike (initial segment spike) and the later, large B-spike (somatodendritic spike) types. Spike separations of up to 10 msec may reflect the magnocellular neuroendocrine cells' special anatomy: absence of a typical initial segment and presence of axo-axonal synapses. While confirming Kandel's finding of recurrent collateral inhibition (IPSPs) from pituitary gland stimulation, Koizumi & Yamashita felt this was indirect, possibly involving an interneuron. Furthermore, they described antidromic activation of small, high frequency (500–800/sec) cells which appeared to be prime candidates for the neuroendocrine "Renshaw" cells. Recently, Sakai et al (116, 117) described intracellular measurements in an in vitro 2–3 week organ culture of the neonatal puppy NSO.

Functional Cell Types and "Spontaneous Activity"

In the unanesthetized monkey three basic functional types of magnocellular neuroendocrine cells are present in NSO, INZ (53–56, 136), and NPV (57): "silent" cells, "burster" neurons, and "continuously active" cells. Two of these spontaneous discharge patterns are not unique to magnocellular neuroendocrine cells: silent and continuously active cells have been described elsewhere in the hypothalamus (9, 19, 39, 57). The burster magnocellular neuroendocrine cells have been associated with invertebrate neurosecretory systems (see 4a, 50) and have been described in the NSO and NPV in urethane-anesthetized rats (24, 27, 81, 141). While the functional importance of these discharge patterns for specific secretory activity is not known, evidence in the monkey (54, 57) suggests that magnocellular neuroendocrine cells shift from one phase to another in a regular sequence, i.e. from silent to continuously active to burster, with differing degrees of responsiveness to afferent input in each phase. Hayward & Jennings (54) speculated that the silent cell might be synthesizing and transporting but not releasing neurohypophysial hormone, the continuously active cell might be releasing basal amounts of hormone, and the burster cell might be discharging pulsatile packets of hormone.

Correlation of spontaneous activity of magnocellular neuroendocrine cells in the hypothalamus with blood levels of AVP and oxytocin remains unresolved. Ideally, an unanesthetized, freely moving, chronically prepared mammal should be analyzed for the activity of antidromically identified single magnocellular neuroendocrine cells and simultaneous radioimmunoassayable central blood levels of AVP and oxytocin. No such studies are available. Urethane, the most commonly used anesthetic in acute electrophysiological studies of the hypothalamus, produces high blood levels of ADH and MEA, possibly by a direct action on the neurosecretory nerve terminals in the PP (27, 29). It blocks reflex activation of magnocellular neuroendocrine cells to orthodromic stimuli, perhaps by a central monoaminergic inhibitory pathway (89), and converts continuously active NSO osmosensitive cells to silent phases in the unanesthetized monkey (58). Dyball and co-workers found that spontaneous firing patterns in NSO and NPV in urethane-anesthetized rats were poorly correlated with blood ADH and MEA (27, 30). Important factors other than anesthesia that influence spontaneous firing rates include operative stress, central monamine activity (89), animal strain (28), and levels of circulating gonadal hormones (83). Heterozygous Brattleboro rats (non-DI) showed higher firing rates in NSO than did control rats of the Long-Evans strain under urethane (28). Firing rates of NPV were increased by estrogen and decreased by progesterone (83) in urethane-anesthetized rats.

Osmometric-Volumetric Factors

In the waking monkey, Hayward & Vincent (58) described single nonidentified NSO cells that displayed excitatory-inhibitory sequences in response to intracarotid hypertonic sodium chloride, but did not respond to non-noxious sensory stimuli. These they labeled "specific" biphasic osmosensitive cells. Subsequently in conscious-monkey studies utilizing antidromically identified NSO and INZ (54, 56, 136, 137), these workers found the "specific" biphasic response to both hypertonic NaCl and to D-glucose (54, 56). Osmotic loading shifted "silent" cells to "continuously active," "continuously active" to "burster," and "burster" to "hyperburster" (56).

Osmosensitive cells in the perinuclear zone of NSO with nonphasic (excitatory or inhibitory) responses have been found in unanesthetized primates (58, 136). Osmosensitive cells unresponsive to non-noxious sensory stimuli (light, sound, touch), i.e. specific monophasic cells, were postulated to be the osmoreceptors of Verney, important in the regulation of AVP release (58, 136). Those osmosensitive cells responsive to non-noxious sensory stimuli (light, sound, touch) were designated the osmoreceptors of Sawyer (58, 136), important in drinking and behavioral aspects of osmoregulation (48–52).

In the urethane-anesthetized rat, Dyball (27) found accelerated NSO discharge and elevated ADH levels following acute osmotic stress, but hormone levels remained elevated well beyond the return of NSO units to control levels. In parallel studies of chronic osmotic stress, Dyball et al (28, 31) found enhanced firing rates in NSO and NPV in normal rats drinking 2% NaCl and in DI rats. In Bennett's allobarbital-urethane-anesthetized, osmotically stressed rats, nonidentified units in NSO showed elevated firing rates that decreased or increased with a further 2–3% reduction or elevation of plasma osmolality, respectively (7). Despite adverse effects of anesthesia, the osmoreceptor drive of NSO cells functions appropriately.

Electrophysiological correlates of volumetric regulation of PP AVP release (41, 121) were observed by Barker et al (3) in the pentobarbital-anesthetized cat NSO; the latter showed long-latency, multisynaptic unit discharge in response to stimulation of ipsi- and contralateral vagal and carotid sinus nerves. In the allobarbital-urethane-anesthetized cat, unit discharge rates in nonantidromically identified NSO and NPV increased with osmotic stress and slowed with left atrial stretch (74).

Behavioral Influences

The behavioral state of a mammal is a major determinant for release of AVP and oxytocin from the neurohypophysis (53, 135). Hayward and co-workers (54, 56–58) found that osmosensitive, antidromically identified NSO and NPV neuroendocrine cells did not respond to mildly arousing non-noxious sensory stimuli (light, touch, sound), but showed accelerated discharge in response to noxious cutaneous stimuli. Hayward & Murgas (57) found the three functional cell types could be driven by noxious sensory input depending upon the nature of the stimulus, the "meaning" of the stimulus to the animal, and the firing level of the cell. Sleep-waking behavior modifies certain continously active cells, leading to a periodic burster pattern (53).

Drinking, a potentially significant behavioral state for AVP release, should modify NSO unit activity in the unanesthetized mammal. In the waking monkey, Vincent et al (136) found inhibition of NSO units during water drinking. The specific osmoreceptors of Verney, in the vicinity of NSO, were either activated or inhibited by osmotic stress, with opposite responses to water drinking. The nonspecific osmoreceptors shifted discharge rates during drinking in parallel with arousal responses. Dorsolateral hypothalamic osmoreceptors were activated by arousal but inhibited by drinking. In the pentobarbital-anesthetized cat, Emmers (35) found nonantidromically identified NSO units phasically inhibited by stimulation of the gustatory nucleus of the ventrobasal thalamus. Osmotic stress activated NSO, NPV, and lateral hypothalamus. Destruction of gustatory thalamic nucleus did not change NSO or NPV osmotic responses. Denervation of the tongue and cord section markedly reduced lateral hypothalamic, but not NSO or NPV, responses to osmotic stress. Emmers confirmed the gustatory inhibitory effects on NSO found by Vincent et al (136), further suggesting a direct ventrobasal thalamic-NSO pathway in contrast to an indirect gustatory excitator pathway to NSO via the lateral hypothalamus (35). Further studies are needed to extend these interesting approaches to drinking and NSO activity.

Milk ejection, coitus, and parturition are the behavioral states of particular significance for the magnocellular neuroendocrine cells responsible for oxytocin release. Wakerley & Lincoln (142) recorded from NPV units in anesthetized rats during milk ejection reflex evoked by the natural suckling stimulus. During suckling, 58% of NPV units develop a 2–4 sec burst discharge (28–84 spikes/sec), followed by a period of silence (7–56 secs), the biphasic response, with milk ejection 15–20 sec after the burst. The authors' conclusion that this NPV burst discharge and delayed milk ejection are causally related seems justified. In an equally careful experiment on milk ejection in the rabbit, Novin & Durham (89) made the significant observation that urethane may block antidromic facilitation, but not antidromic inhibition at NPV. They also noted that the stress of operation activates a central monoamine inhibitory system that seems to block ascending excitatory afferents (milk ejection pathway) at the NPV. In a study of the relation of vaginal distention to activation of NPV units in urethane-anesthetized rats, Negoro et al (84) found that estrogren lowers and progesterone elevates the activation threshold. While most of Findlay's (39) cells were nonspecific and responded identically to vaginal stimulation and other arousing stimuli, he did find one nonantidromically identified NPV unit in the freely moving rabbit which specifically accelerated in response to vaginal distension. Limbic system sites in septum, amygdala, and areas in the brain stem (periaqueductal grey and midbrain reticular formation), produce activation/inhibition of NSO & NPV units (66, 84) and behavioral effects upon electrical stimulation (see 48).

Recurrent Collateral and Neuropharmacological Effects

Kandel (62) presented evidence for recurrent collateral inhibition of preoptic magnocellular neuroendocrine cells by recording IPSP's following subthreshold stimulation of the pituitary gland in the goldfish. Subsequent workers studying NSO (3, 24, 55, 66, 136) and NPV (3, 57, 66, 81) confirmed the inhibitory effects. Studies in rat (82), cat (56), and bullfrog (65) described trans-synaptically activated units that discharged repetitively in response to single shocks to the neural lobe, but with variable and long latencies. These postulated neuroendocrine "Renshaw" cells lie in or near the NSO, NPV, and preoptic nucleus, and are excited or inhibited by afferent volleys from reticular formation (66), amygdala, and septum (82). Evidence suggests that both recurrent and afferent inhibitory pathways to NSO-NPV may converge upon and be mediated by these interneurons. The analytic studies of Koizumi et al (65) in anesthesialess bullfrog organ culture indicated low threshold excitatory (no interneuron) and high threshold inhibitory (interneuron) collateral pathways.

Norepinephrine, β-adrenergic depression, acetylcholine muscarinic depression, and acetylcholine nicotinic excitation of antidromically identified NSO units were first demonstrated by Barker, Crayton & Nicoll (4) in urethane-anesthetized cat. Moss et al (73, 80) and Dreifuss & Kelly (25) confirmed these results (4), with the exception of the muscarinic inhibitory effects of acetylcholine. Sakai et al (117) reproduced all the findings of Barker et al (4) in organ-cultured puppy NSO. The acetylcholine concentration-response curve was bell-shaped, with initiation of spiking at lower concentrations and reduction of spike frequency at higher concentrations. The nicotine antagonist, dihydro-β-erythroidine, decreased the spiking of acetylcholine, while the muscarinic receptor blocker, atropine, increased NSO cell spiking. These studies indicate that NSO cell membranes contain excitatory nicotinic (4, 25, 78, 80), and inhibitory muscarinic cholinergic receptors (4, 117) and inhibitory β-adrenergic receptors (4, 78, 80, 117).

After systematically eliminating such putative transmitters for recurrent collateral inhibition as acetylcholine, glycine, gamma-aminobutyric acid, and norepinephrine, Nicoll & Barker (85) concluded that AVP was the transmitter involved. Moss et al (79) obtained equivocal effects with AVP. They found oxytocin excited most NPV units, but had no effect on nonantidromically identified NPV and NSO units. Dyball (28) further cast doubt on AVP as the recurrent collateral inhibitory synaptic transmitter when he demonstrated the presence of recurrent inhibition in DI rats with total vasopressin deficiency. The inhibitory synaptic transmitter for recurrent collateral inhibition remains unknown. AVP-induced bursting at the axon hillock of snail neurosecretory cells by a unique membrane effect is reported by Barker & Gainer (4a).

Angiotensin II, a peptide important in water balance and blood volume regulation (2, 121), accelerated NSO cell discharge after direct micro-iontophoretic application in the pentobarbital-anesthetized cat (86). In the organ-cultured puppy NSO, Sakai et al (116) elicited concentration-dependent spiking activity by superfusion with angiotensin II. Specific angiotensin antagonists, cysteine-8-angiotensin II and sarcosine-1-isoleucine-8-angiotensin II, blocked this activity, but did not block spiking initiated by glutamate or nicotine superfusion. NSO membranes must therefore contain specific angiotensin II receptors.

NEURAL MECHANISMS OF PEPTIDE RELEASE

Osmometric-Volumetric Aspects of Vasopressin Release

Verney (135) found osmotic, volumetric, and behavioral factors interacting to release ADH from the neurohypophysis. Andersson and co-workers (2, 93, 94), applying various hypertonic solutions to the CNS of the conscious goat from outside (intracarotid) and inside (intraventricular) the BBB and studying ADH release, challenged the validity of Verney's osmoreceptor theory (see 48, 49, 56). They found that the ability of hypertonic solutions to release ADH in the goat seemed to depend more upon the availability of sodium ions in the vicinity of the third ventricle than just upon osmolality. They presented an alternative to Verney's concept of osmoreceptors: sodium-sensitive cells located near the 3rd ventricle, which release ADH (2, 93, 94). Eggena & Polson's exposure of a cultured toad hypothalamo-hypophysial system to hypertonic NaCl, mannitol, and urea supported the osmoreceptor rather than the Na^{+} detector concept (33).

Osmometric-volumetric interactions in the regulation of AVP release have been studied repeatedly since Verney's time (2, 41, 48–50, 121, 135). With development of sensitive, specific radioimmunoassays (RIA) for AVP, studies of these interactions became more precise. The range of serum AVP in normal humans with ad lib fluid intake is 1–3 pg/ml (59, 107, 110, 125); after 12 hr dehydration the range is 4–10 pg/ml (59, 107, 110, 125). In unanesthetized rats, Dunn et al (26) manipulated volumetric and osmometric parameters independently. They concluded that AVP release is primarily regulated by blood osmolality, but that the responsiveness of this mechanism may be altered by changes in blood volume. Similarly, in man, Moses & Miller (76) found that a decrease in plasma volume by dehydration lowered the osmotic threshold for ADH release, while an increase in plasma volume by hypertonic saline infusion increased the threshold.

In the conscious dog, iso-osmotic blood volume expansion and contraction result in a decrease and increase, respectively, of ADH release, as well as a decrease or increase, respectively, of response to standard osmotic stimuli (129). The left vago-sympathetic trunk was found to contain the most sensitive receptors for blood volume effects on ADH release (130), as previously described (see 41, 121). In the morphine-chloralose-anesthetized dog, Lawrence et al (67) found left atrial distension produces diuresis by two mechanisms: an initial short-lived hemodynamic component and a second, prolonged inhibition of ADH release. In the continued search for the elusive volumetric-triggered natriuretic factor (see 121), Lichardus & Ponec (70) claimed that an oxytocin-like neurohypophysial factor can restore natriuresis to volume-expanded hypophysectomized rats.

Motivated-Reflex Reproductive Behavior and Oxytocin Release

Coitus, vaginal distension, and the complex exteroceptive stimuli associated with mating release oxytocin from the neurohypophysis, possibly augmenting uterine contractility and accelerating ascent of sperm. In the conscious goat, bioassayable oxytocin release from vaginal distension occurs seasonally (December to May), only in the presence of intact ovaries or estrogen, and is blocked centrally by progesterone (104, 105). In the estrous female goat, McNeilly et al (72) found that coitus is not a major stimulus for the release of bioassayable oxytocin. They did (72), however, observe that the individual exteroceptive oxytocin-releasing stimuli associated with mating could be classified in descending order of effectiveness: presence of another goat, smell of the male, sound of the male, and sight of the male. In diestrous gcats, in contrast, oxytocin release occurred in all animals in response to physical stimuli associated with coitus and simulated mating (72).

The development of sensitive, specific RIA for oxytocin, AVP, and Np (110) has made possible further understanding of the complex relationships between the events of parturition and the neurohypophysis (see 13, 14). During the second stage of labor in the goat, oxytocin and Np are elevated, with an abrupt further rise during the expulsive phase. There are elevated levels of oxytocin, AVP, and Np in animal and human fetal cord blood at parturition (14, 124). The factors of neural control and the function of oxytocin release during parturition remain to be explored (13).

The milk ejection reflex, the response of the myoepithelial cells of the mammary glands that produces a rise in intramammary ductal pressure and expulsion of milk, is generally considered to be under the control of spurts of circulating oxytocin release from the neurohypophysis (13). The close temporal relationship of suckling to milk ejection and of oxytocin injections to milk ejection has confirmed such a reflex relationship (13). In humans, milk ejection can be inhibited by such factors as cold, emotion, and pain (13). On the basis of pharmacological and nerve-cord section experiments in the urethane-anesthetized rat, Grosvenor et al (45) stated that blockade of the milk-ejection reflex occurs because of a central monoaminergic inhibition of NPV, in agreement with Novin & Durham (89), and a peripheral sympathetic and extrasympathetic inhibition of contractility of the mammary gland. Wakerley, Lincoln, and co-workers (71, 139, 140, 142) observed milk ejection in spurts in rats. Spurts were blocked by oxytocin-AVP antagonist and ADH levels were low, indicating suckling-induced specific oxytocin release (139). Surgical levels of anesthesia (tribromethanol, pentobarbital, urethane) did not block the milk ejection reflex (71). Milk ejection is associated with a unique behavioral response of the pups, i.e. a synchronized extensor reaction and a vigorous increase in suckling for 10 sec following intramammary pressure rise (142). These workers (71) concluded that the major variables involved were the number of suckling young, the degree of mammary distension, and time. Application of these data to NPV unit recording yielded some fascinating results (142).

Central Neural Pathways

Independent release of oxytocin and AVP from PP is well documented (see 48, 49). Oxytocin and AVP of PP originate in NPV and NSO, while oxytocin content of NPV is greater than NSO (see 8). The findings of Bisset et al (11), who used electrical stimulation of the brain in chloralosed cats, disagreed with this concept. Voloschin & Tramezzani (138) studied conscious lactating rats subjected to natural suckling stimuli after stereotaxically controlled discrete transections of afferent pathways in the diencephalon. They found that caudal afferents contain the major bundles of the milk ejection afferent pathway. The integrity of NPV or its afferents is not required. Voloschin & Tramezzani's carefully controlled studies support the concept of suckling-induced oxytocin release by both NSO and NPV.

Tindal & Knaggs (132) found a discrete ascending subthalamic reticular hypothalamic pathway for milk ejection afferents in the guinea pig. Urban et al (134), in the rabbit, and Richard (103), in the ewe, found a variable diffuse milk ejection pathway. Species differences, central monoaminergic inhibition (89), and parameters of electrical stimulation (133) may account for these discrepancies. For example, Tomas et al (133), in a study of hippocampal-induced ADH release in the rat, found facilitation at high frequencies and inhibition at low.

Neurophysin Release

Neurophysins (see 61) I, II, III, a class of carrier proteins synthesized in the NSO and NPV (114, 115, 144, 147) in association with AVP and oxytocin, are also found in the PP (15a, 111, 143, 144, 147), hypophysial portal blood (146), CSF and ependyma (111), systemic blood (14, 15, 16, 73, 110, 112), and tumors responsible for ectopic ADH in man (15a, 46). Np nomenclature is not yet standardized among laboratories (61, 110, 143, 144). Cheng & Friesen (15), employing a sensitive RIA for porcine Np, found elevated blood levels of Np in pigs following dehydration, ingestion of hypertonic saline, intravenous infusions of hypertonic solutions, and acute reduction in extracellular fluid volume, but not suckling. Hypophysectomy decreases Np levels to one third control values, and external jugular Np was fivefold greater than in the inferior vena cava (15). DI rats had elevated plasma Np but Np was virtually absent from the PP (16). Lesions in the median eminence of normal and DI rats lowered serum Np (16). In rat external jugular blood, Np was higher than the Np in inferior vena cava blood of both normal and DI rats (16).

Using more specific RIA, Robinson et al (112) found that, in the bovine, Np-I was elevated during oxytocin-related events and during AVP-related events, while Np-II was elevated only during AVP-related events. In the goat, McNeilly et al (73) found tonic and spurt release of Np in parallel with oxytocin during parturition. In humans, Cheng & Friesen (15a) and Robinson et al (108) found elevated values of Np-I in amniotic fluid and in cord blood during pregnancy, at parturition, and postpartum, and in the blood of patients with galactorrhea, acromegaly, inappropriate release of ADH, DI, and renal failure, without change during suckling or coitus. In the monkey, Robinson et al (109) described two types of Np that appear independently regulated: one is stimulated by estrogen and the other by nicotine. Legros & Louis (68) found in human pituitaries a Np-AVP and a Np-oxytocin.

The functional role of Np is enigmatic. The arresting discovery by Robinson & Zimmerman (111) and Zimmerman and co-workers (146, 147) of high levels of Np in CSF, in ependymal tanycytes, around the portal capillaries of the external zone of the median eminence, and in portal blood, suggests possible action of Np, associated AVP, or oxytocin on the adenohypophysis as a releasing hormone.

Neuropharmacological and Clinical Aspects

In mammals, angiotensin II may release AVP central natriuretic factor and initiate drinking (48, 49, 121). Andersson and co-workers (2, 94) found that intraventricular angiotensin II potentiates the hypertensive, dipsogenic, ADH, and natriuretic effects of intraventricular hypertonic NaCl in the conscious goat. They suggested that angiotensin II facilitates transport of Na^+ into brain cells regulating thirst and ADH, and that intracellular Na^+ concentration, rather than strictly osmotic factors, determines the activity of these cells. Share and co-workers found no ADH-releasing capacity of angiotensin II alone (18), but when they combined Angiotensin II with infusions of hypertonic saline they found significant potentiation of the expected osmotic ADH release (123). In humans they found a rise in renin in response to ambulation and sodium depletion, without change in plasma ADH (122). In their anesthetized dog preparation they found that the left atrial pressure drop accompanying hemorrhage triggered release of ADH and renin, with some dissociation of these responses according to the rate of bleeding (17).

Thorn (131) reviewed evidence for cholinergic and adrenergic mechanisms of ADH release. He suggested a monoaminergic synapse between osmoreceptor and interneuron and a cholinergic synapse between this interneuron and NSO. Oba (90) found the milk-ejection reflex in rats to be primarily cholinergic. The potential role of histamine in NSO activity is suggested by the high levels of histamine that occur there (10). Morphine has dose-dependent biphasic effects on ADH release: at low dosage there is inhibition, with higher doses, excitation (52).

Humans with DI show undetectable levels of plasma AVP by RIA (59, 107, 110, 125), while Np levels may be elevated (15a, 110). Several new compounds that stimulate ADH release may prove useful in treatment of partial DI. Chlorpropamide, a sulfonylurea and oral hypoglycemic agent, has ADH action, dependent upon both enhanced release of ADH from PP and augmentation of action of circulating AVP (77). The hypolipidemic agent clofibrate enhances AVP release without peripheral augmentation (75). Clofibrate induces ADH release in normal, but not in DI, rats (75). Carbamazepine, a potent anticonvulsant and analgesic used for trigeminal neuralgia, releases ADH from the neurohypophysis without peripheral augmentation (63). These drugs may release AVP inappropriately, and with a water load produce water intoxication. Humans with the syndrome of inappropriate ADH secretion show elevated levels of AVP (6, 106, 110, 125) and Np (15a, 46), whether the syndrome is due to tumor (43), CNS disease (6), or vincristine therapy (20, 106).

CONCLUSION

Recent studies of central neural control of the posterior pituitary have probed deeply into the cellular and subcellular mechanisms, electrophysiological activity, and mechanisms of peptide release. With increased use of sensitive and specific RIA for posterior pituitary peptides, combined with discriminating methods for study of individual magnocellular neuroendocrine cells in correlation with behavior, I expect further studies on the neural control of the neurohypophysis to answer many of the questions raised in this review.

Literature Cited

1. Alvarez-Buylla, R., Livett, B. G., Uttenthal, L. O., Hope, D. B., Milton, S. H. 1973. Immunochemical evidence for the transport of neurophysin in the hypothalamo-neurohypophysial system of the dog. *Z. Zellforsch.* 137:435–50
2. Andersson, B., Eriksson, L., Fernandez, O., Kolmodin, C. G., Oltner, R. 1972. Centrally mediated effects of sodium and angiotensin II on arterial blood pressure and fluid balance. *Acta Physiol. Scand.* 85:398–407
3. Barker, J. L., Crayton, J. W., Nicoll, R. A. 1971. Antidromic and orthodromic responses of paraventricular and supraoptic neurosecretory cells. *Brain Res.* 33:353–66
4. Barker, J. L., Crayton, J. W., Nicoll, R. A. 1971. Noradrenaline and acetylcholine responses of supraoptic neurosecretory cells. *J. Physiol. London* 218:19–32

4a. Barker, J. L., Gainer, H. 1974. Peptide regulation of bursting pacemaker activ-

ity in a molluscan neurosecretory cell. *Science* 184:1371–73
5. Bar-Sella, P., Stein, O., Gross, J. 1973. Electron microscopic radioautography of 125-I-triiodothyronine in rat posterior pituitary and median eminence. *Endocrinology* 93:1410–22
6. Baumann, G., Lopez-Amor, E., Dingman, J. F. 1972. Plasma arginine vasopressin in the syndrome of inappropriate antidiuretic hormone secretion. *Am. J. Med.* 52:19–24
7. Bennett, C. T. 1973. Activity of osmosensitive neurons: plasma osmotic pressure thresholds. *Physiol. Behav.* 11:403–6
8. Berde, B. 1968. Neuropophysial hormones and similar polypeptides. *Handb. Exp. Pharmacol.* 23:1–967
9. Beyer, C., Sawyer, C. H. 1969. Hypothalamic unit activity related to control of the pituitary gland. In *Frontiers in Neuroendocrinology, 1969,* ed. W. F. Ganong, L. Martini, 255–87. New York: Oxford
10. Bhargava, K. P., Kulshrestha, V. K., Santhakumari, G., Srivastava, Y. P. 1973. Mechanisms of histamine-induced antidiuretic response. *Brit. J. Pharmacol.* 47:700–6
11. Bisset, G. W., Clark, B. J., Errington, M. L. 1971. The hypothalamic neurosecretory pathways for the release of oxytocin and vasopressin in the cat. *J. Physiol. London* 217:111–31
12. Bridges, T. E., Fisher, A. W., Gosbee, J. L., Lederis, K., Santolaya, R. C. 1973. Acetylcholine and cholinesterases (assays and light- and electron microscopical histochemistry) in different parts of the pituitary of rat, rabbit and domestic pit. *Z. Zellforsch.* 136:1–18
13. Caldeyro-Barcia, R., Melander, S., Coch, J. A. 1971. Neurohypophyseal hormones. In *Endocrinology of Pregnancy,* ed. F. Fuchs, A. Klopper, 235–85. New York: Harper & Row
14. Chard, T. 1973. The posterior pituitary and the induction of labour. *Mem. Soc. Endocrinol.* 20:61–76
15. Cheng, K. W., Friesen, H. G. 1970. Physiological factors regulating secretion of neurophysin. *Metabolism* 19: 876–90
15a. Cheng, K. W., Friesen, H. G. 1973. Studies of human neurophysin by radioimmunoassay. *J. Clin. Endocrinol. Metab.* 36:553–60
16. Cheng, K. W., Friesen, H. G., Martin, J. B. 1972. Neurophysin in rats with hereditary hypothalamic diabetes insipidus (Brattleboro strain). *Endocrinology* 90:1055–63
17. Claybaugh, J. R., Share, L. 1973. Vasopressin, renin and carodiovascular responses to continuous slow hemorrhage. *Am. J. Physiol.* 224:519–23
18. Claybaugh, J. R., Share, L., Shimizu, K. 1972. The inability of infusions of angiotensin to elevate the plasma vasopressin concentration in the anesthetized dog. *Endocrinology* 90: 1647–52
19. Cross, B. A. 1973. Unit responses in the hypothalamus. See Ref. 9, 1973, 133–71
20. Cutting, H. O. 1971. Inappropriate secretion of antidiuretic hormone secondary to vincristine therapy. *Am. J. Med.* 51:269–71
21. Daniel, P. M., Prichard, M. M. L. 1972. The human hypothalamus and pituitary stalk after hypophysectomy or pituitary stalk section. *Brain* 95:813–24
22. Douglas, W. W. 1973. How do neurones secrete peptides? Exocytosis and its consequences, including "synaptic vesicle" formation, in the hypothalamo-neurohypophyseal system. In *Drug Effects on Neuroendocrine Regulation,* ed. E. Zimmerman, W. H. Gispen, B. H. Marks, D. DeWied, 21–38. Amsterdam: Elsevier
23. Dreifuss, J. J. 1973. Mécanismes de sécrétion des hormones neurohypophysaires. Aspects cellularies et sub-cellularies. *J. Physiol. Paris* 67:5A–52A
24. Dreifuss, J. J., Kelly, J. S. 1972. Recurrent inhibition of antidromically identified rat supraoptic neurones. *J. Physiol. London* 220:87–103
25. Dreifuss, J. J., Kelly, J. S. 1972. The activity of identified supraoptic neurones and their response to acetylcholine applied by iontophoresis. *J. Physiol. London* 220:105–18
26. Dunn, F. L., Brennan, T. J., Nelson, A. E., Robertson, G. L. 1973. The role of blood osmolality and volume in regulating vasopressin secretion in the rat. *J. Clin. Invest.* 52:3212–19
27. Dyball, R. E. J. 1971. Oxytocin and ADH secretion in relation to electrical activity in antidromically identified supraoptic and paraventricular units. *J. Physiol. London* 214:245–56
28. Dyball, R. E. J. 1974. Single unit activity in the hypothalamo-neurohypophysial system of Brattleboro rats. *J. Endocrinol.* 60:135–43
29. Dyball, R. E. J., Dyer, R. G. 1971. Plasma oxytocin concentration and paraventricular neurone activity in rats

with diencephalic islands and intact brains. *J. Physiol. London* 216:227–35
30. Dyball, R. E. J., McPhail, C. I. 1974. Unit activity in the supraoptic and paraventricular nuclei—the effects of anesthesia. *Brain Res.* 67:43–50
31. Dyball, R. E. J., Pountney, P. S. 1973. Discharge patterns of supraoptic and parventricular neurones in rats given a 2% NaCl solution instead of drinking water. *J. Endocrinol.* 56:91–98
32. Dyer, R. G., Dyball, R. E. J., Morris, J. F. 1973. The effect of hypothalamic deafferentation upon the ultrastructure and hormone content of the paraventricular nucleus. *J. Endocrinol.* 57:509–16
33. Eggena, P., Polson, A. X. 1974. Osmotic stimulation of vasotocin secretion by the toad's hypothalamo-neurohypophysial system in vitro. *Endocrinology* 94:35–44
34. Ellman, G. L., Gan, G. L. 1971. Responses of cells of the supraoptic nucleus: kinetic aspects. *Exp. Brain Res.* 14:1–8
35. Emmers, R. 1973. Interaction of neural systems which control body water. *Brain Res.* 49:323–47
36. Euler, C. von, Hayward, J. N., Marttila, I., Wyman, R. J. 1973. The spinal connections of the inspiratory neurons of the ventrolateral nucleus of the tractus solitarius of cat. *Brain Res.* 61:23–33
37. Farrell, G., Fabre, L. F., Rauschkolb, E. W. 1968. The neurohypophysis. *Ann. Rev. Physiol.* 30:557–88
38. Fendler, K., Vermes, I., Stark, A., Lissak, K. 1972. Effect of cervical sympathectomy on water balance in pituitary stalk-sectioned rats. *Acta Physiol. Acad. Sci. Hung.* 42:61–65
39. Findlay, A. L. R. 1972. Hypothalamic inputs: methods and five examples. In *Progress in Brain Research, Vol. 38, Topics in Neuroendocrinology,* ed. J. Ariens Kappers, J. P. Schade, 163–90. Amsterdam: Elsevier
40. Flament-Durand, J., Dustin, P. 1972. Studies on the transport of secretory granules in the magnocellular hypothalamic neurons. I. Action of colchicine on axonal flow and neurotubules in the paraventricular nuclei. *Z. Zellforsch.* 130:440–54
41. Gauer, O. H., Henry, J. P., Behn, C. 1970. The regulation of extracellular fluid volume. *Ann. Rev. Physiol.* 32:547–95
42. George, J. M. 1973. Localization in hypothalamus of increased incorporation of ^{3}H-cytidine into RNA in response to oral hypertonic saline. *Endocrinology* 92:1550–55
43. George, J. M., Capen, C. C., Phillips, A. S. 1972. Biosynthesis of vasopressin in vitro and ultrastructure of a bronchogenic carcinoma. *J. Clin. Invest.* 51:141–48
44. Goodman, I., Hiatt, R. B. 1972. Coherin: a new peptide of the bovine neurohypophysis with activity on gastrointestinal motility. *Science* 178:419–21
45. Grosvenor, C. E., DeNuccio, D. J., King, S. F., Maiweg, H., Mena, F. 1972. Central and peripheral neural influences on the oxtocin-induced pressure response of the mammary gland on the anesthetized lactating rat. *J. Endocrinol.* 55:299–309
46. Hamilton, B. P. M., Upton, G. V., Amatruda, T. T. 1972. Evidence for the presence of neurophysin in tumors producing the syndrome of inappropriate antidiuresis. *J. Clin. Endocrinol. Metab.* 35:764–67
47. Hatton, G. I., Walters, J. K. 1973. Induced multiple nucleoli, nucleolar margination and cell size changes in supraoptic neurons during dehydration and rehydration in the rat. *Brain Res.* 59:137–54
48. Hayward, J. N. 1972. The amygdaloid nuclear complex and mechanisms of release of vasopressin from the neurohypophysis. In *Neurobiology of the Amygdala,* ed. B. E. Eleftheriou, 685–749. New York: Plenum
49. Hayward, J. N. 1972. Hypothalamic input to supraoptic neurones. See Ref. 39, 145–61
50. Hayward, J. N. 1974. Neurohumoral regulation of neuroendocrine cells in the hypothalamus. In *Recent Studies of Hypothalamic Function,* ed. K. Lederis, K. E. Cooper. Basel: Karger. In press
51. Hayward, J. N. 1974. Physiological and morphological identification of hypothalamic magnocellular neuroendocrine cells in goldfish preoptic nucleus. *J. Physiol. London* 239:103–24
52. Hayward, J. N. 1974. Effects of drugs of abuse on motivated behavior and magnocellular neurodendocrine cells. In *Narcotics and the Hypothalamus,* ed. E. Zimmerman, R. George. New York: Raven. In press
53. Hayward, J. N., Jennings, D. P. 1973. Influence of sleep-waking and nociceptor-induced behavior on the activity of supraoptic neurons in the hypo-

thalamus of the monkey. *Brain Res.* 57:461–66

54. Hayward, J. N., Jennings, D. P. 1973. Osmosensitivity of hypothalamic magnocellular neuroendocrine cells to intracarotid hypertonic D-glucose in the waking monkey. *Brain Res.* 57:467–72
55. Hayward, J. N., Jennings, D. P. 1973. Activity of magnocellular neuroendocrine cells in the hypothalamus of unanesthetized monkeys. I. Functional cell types and their anatomical distribution in the supraoptic nucleus and the internuclear zone. *J. Physiol. London* 232:515–43
56. Hayward, J. N., Jennings, D. P. 1973. Activity of magnocellular neuroendocrine cells in the hypothalamus of unanesthetized monkeys. II. Osmosensitivity of functional cell types in the supraoptic nucleus and the internuclear zone. *J. Physiol. London* 232:545–72
57. Hayward, J. N., Murgas, K. 1973. Sensory input and firing patterns of antidromically identified supraoptic neurons in unanesthetized monkey. *Programs & Abstracts, III Meet. Soc. Neurosci.* 3:120
58. Hayward, J. N., Vincent, J. D. 1970. Osmosensitive single neurones in the hypothalamus of unanesthetized monkeys. *J. Physiol. London* 210:947–72
59. Husain, M. K., Fernando, N., Shapiro, M., Kagan, A., Glick, S. M. 1973. Radioimmunoassay of arginine vasopressin in human plasma. *J. Clin. Endocrinol. Metab.* 37:616–25
60. Jones, C. W., Pickering, B. T. 1972. Intra-axonal transport and turnover of neurohypophysial hormones in the rat. *J. Physiol. London* 227:553–64
61. Jongkind, J. F. 1972. Neurophysin. See Ref. 39, 59–66

61a. Kalimo, H., Rinne, U. K. 1972. Ultrastructural studies on the hypothalamic neurosecretory neurons of the rat. II. The hypothalamo-neurohypophysial system in rats with hereditary hypothalamic diabetes insipidus. *Z. Zellforsch.* 134:205–25

62. Kandel, E. R. 1964. Electrical properties of hypothalamic neuroendocrine cells. *J. Gen. Physiol.* 47:691–71
63. Kimura, T., Matsui, K., Sato, T., Yoshinaga, K. 1974. Mechanism of carbamazepine (Tegretol)-induced antidiuresis: evidence for release of antidiuretic hormone and impaired excretion of a water load. *J. Clin. Endorcinol. Metab.* 38:356–62
64. Kleeman, C. R., Cutler, R. E. 1963. The neurohypophysis. *Ann. Rev. Physiol.* 25:385–432
65. Koizumi, K., Ishikawa, T., Brooks, C.Mc. 1973. The existence of facilitatory axon collaterals in neurosecretory cells of the hypothalamus. *Brain Res.* 63:408–13
66. Koizumi, K., Yamashita, H. 1972. Studies of antidromically identified neurosecretory cells of the hypothalamus by intracellular and extracellular recordings. *J. Physiol. London* 221:683–705
67. Lawrence, M., Ledsome, J. R., Mason, J. M. 1973. The time course of the diuretic response to left atrial distension. *Quart. J. Exp. Physiol.* 58:219–27
68. Legros, J. J., Louis, F. 1973–74. Identification of a vasopressin-neurophysin and of an oxytocin-neurophysin in man. *Neuroendocrinology* 13:371–375
69. Leontovich, T. A. 1969. The neurons of the magnocellular neurosecretory nuclei of the dog's hypothalamus. A Golgi study. *J. Hirnforsch.* 11:499–517
70. Lichardus, B., Ponec, J. 1973. On the role of the hypophysis in the renal mechanism of body fluid volume regulation. *Endokrinologie* 61:403–12
71. Lincoln, D. W., Hill, A., Wakerley, J. B. 1973. The milk-ejection reflex of the rat: an intermittent function not abolished by surgical levels of anesthesia. *J. Endocrinol.* 57:459–76
72. McNeilly, A. S., Ducker, H. A. 1972. Blood levels of oxytocin in the female goat during coitus and in response to stimuli associated with mating. *J. Endocrinol.* 52:399–406
73. McNeilly, A. S., Martin, M. J., Chard, T., Hart, I. C. 1972. Simultaneous release of oxytocin and neurophysin during parturition in the goat. *J. Endocrinol.* 52:213–14
74. Menninger, R. P., Frazier, D. T. 1972. Effects of blood volume and atrial stretch on hypothalamic single-unit activity. *Am. J. Physiol.* 223:288–93
75. Moses, A. M., Howanitz, J., Van Gemert, M., Miller, M. 1973. Clofibrate-induced antidiuresis. *J. Clin. Invest.* 52:535–42
76. Moses, A. M., Miller, M. 1971. Osmotic threshold for vasopressin release as determined by saline infusion and by dehydration. *Neuroendocrinology* 7: 219–26
77. Moses, A. M., Numann, P., Miller, M. 1973. Mechanism of chlorpropamide-induced antidiuresis in man: evidence

for release of ADH and enhancement of peripheral action. *Metabolism* 22:59–66

78. Moss, R. L., Dyball, R. E. J., Cross, B. A. 1971. Responses of antidromically identified supraoptic and paraventricular units to acetylcholine, noradrenaline and glutamate applied iontophoretically. *Brain Res.* 35:573–75
79. Moss, R. L., Dyball, R. E. J., Cross, B. A. 1972. Excitation of antidromically identified neurosecretory cells of the paraventricular nucleus by oxytocin applied iontophoretically. *Exp. Neurol.* 34:95–102
80. Moss, R. L., Urban, I., Cross, B. A. 1972. Microelectrophoresis of cholinergic and aminergic drugs on paraventricular neurons. *Am. J. Physiol.* 223:310–18
81. Negoro, H., Holland, R. C. 1972. Inhibition of unit activity in the hypothalamic paraventricular nucleus following antidromic activation. *Brain Res.* 42:385–402
82. Negoro, H., Visessuwan, S., Holland, R. C. 1973. Inhibition and excitation of units in paraventricular nucleus after stimulation of the septum, amygdala and neurohypophysis. *Brain Res.* 57:479–83
83. Negoro, H., Visessuwan, S., Holland, R. C. 1973. Unit activity in the paraventricular nucleus of female rats at different stages of the reproductive cycle and after ovariectomy, with or without oestrogen or progesterone treatment. *J. Endocrinol.* 59:545–58
84. Negoro, H., Visessuwan, S., Holland, R. C. 1973. Reflex activation of paraventricular nucleus units during the reproductive cycle and in ovariectomized rats treated with oestrogen or progesterone. *J. Endocrinol.* 59:559–67
85. Nicoll, R. A., Barker, J. L. 1971. The pharmacology of recurrent inhibition in the supraoptic neurosecretory system. *Brain Res.* 35:501–11
86. Nicoll, R. A., Barker, J. L. 1971. Excitation of supraoptic neurosecretory cells by angiotensin II. *Nature New Biol.* 233:172–74
87. Norstrom, A., Eggertsen, G., Freden, H., Enestrom, S. 1972. A study of lactate dehydrogenase (LDH) in the supraopticohypophyseal system of the rat. *Exp. Neurol.* 37:502–9
88. Norstrom, A., Sjostrand, J. 1971. Effect of hemorrhage on the rapid axonal transport of neurohypophysial proteins of the rat. *J. Neurochem.* 18:2017–26
89. Novin, D., Durham, R. 1973. Orthodromic and antidromic activation of the paraventricular nucleus of the hypothalamus in the rabbit. *Exp. Neurol.* 41:418–30
90. Oba, T. 1971. Blockade by cholinergic and adrenergic blocking agents of the suckling-induced depletion of oxytocin from the neurohypophysis of the lactating rat. *Acta Endocrinol.* 68:707–14
91. Olivieri-Sangiocomo, C. 1972. On the fine structure of the perivascular cells in the neural lobe of rats. *Z. Zellforsch.* 132:25–34
92. Olivieri-Sangiocomo, C. 1972. Degenerating pituicytes in the neural lobe of osmotically stressed rats. *Experentia* 28: 1362–63
93. Olsson, K. 1973. Further evidence for the importance of CSF Na concentration in central control of fluid balance. *Acta Physiol. Scand.* 88:183–88
94. Olsson, K., Kolmodin, R. 1974. Accentuation by angiotensin II of the antidiuretic and dipsogenic responses to intracarotid infusions of NaCl and fructose. *Acta Endocrinol.* 75:333–41
95. Parry, H. B., Livett, B. G. 1973. A new hypothalamic pathway to the median eminence containing neurophysin and its hypertrophy in sheep with natural scrapie. *Nature* 242:63–65
96. Perks, A. M. 1969. The neurohypophysis. In *Fish Physiology, Vol. II, The Endocrine System,* ed. W. S. Hoar, D. J. Randall, 112–205. New York: Academic
97. Perks, A. M., Vissolyi, E. 1973. Studies of the neurohypophysis in feotal mammals. In *Foetal and Neonatal Physiology,* ed. K. S. Comline, K. W. Cross, G. S. Dawes, P. W. Nathanielsz, 430–38. London: Cambridge Univ. Press
98. Pickup, J. C., Johnston, C. I., Nakamura, S., Uttenthal, L. O., Hope, D. B. 1973. Subcellular organization of neurophysins, oxytocin, (8-lysine) vasopressin and adenosine triphosphatase in procine posterior lobes. *Biochem. J.* 132:361–71
99. Raisman, G. 1973. An ultrastructural study of the effects of hypophysectomy on the supraoptic nucleus of the rat. *J. Comp. Neurol.* 147:181–208
100. Raisman, G. 1973. Electron microscopic studies of the development of new neurohaemal contacts in the median eminence of the rat after hypophysectomy. *Brain Res.* 55:245–61
101. Rechardt, L. 1969. Electron microscopic and histochemical observations

on the supraoptic nucleus of normal and dehydrated rats. *Acta Physiol. Scand.* 329:1–79
102. Rhees, R. W., Abel, J. H., Frame, J. R. 1972. Effect of osmotic stress and hormone therapy on the hypothalamus of the duck (Anas platyrhynchos) *Neuroendocrinology* 10:1–22
103. Richard, P. H. 1972. The reticulo-hypothalamic pathway controlling the release of oxytocin in the ewe. *J. Endocrinol.* 53:71–83
104. Roberts, J. S. 1971. Progesterone-inhibition of oxytocin release during vaginal distention: evidence for a central site of action. *Endocrinology* 89:1137–41
105. Roberts, J. S. 1973. Functional integrity of the oxytocin-releasing reflex in goats: dependence on estrogen. *Endocrinology* 93:1309–14
106. Robertson, G. L., Bhoopalam, N., Zelkowitz, L. J. 1973. Vincristine neurotoxicity and abnormal secretion of antidiuretic hormone. *Arch. Int. Med.* 132:717–20
107. Robertson, G. L., Mahr, E. A., Athar, S., Sinha, T. 1973. Development and clinical application of a new method for the radioimmunoassay of arginine vasopressin in human plasma. *J. Clin. Invest.* 52:2340–52
108. Robinson, A. G., Archer, D. F., Tolstoi, L. F. 1973. Neurophysin in women during oxytocin-related events. *J. Clin. Endocrinol. Metab.* 37:645–52
109. Robinson, A. G., Ferin, M., Zimmerman, E. A. 1974. Neurophysin in monkey: correlation with mid-cycle estrogen and LH. *Program and Abstracts of the Endocrine Society. Endocrinol. Suppl.* 94:A196
110. Robinson, A. G., Frantz, A. G. 1973. Radioimmunoassay of posterior pituitary peptides: a review. *Metabolism* 22:1047–57
111. Robinson, A. G., Zimmerman, E. A. 1973. Cerebrospinal fluid and ependymal neurophysin. *J. Clin. Invest.* 52:1260–67
112. Robinson, A. G., Zimmerman, E. A., Frantz, A. G. 1971. Physiologic investigation of posterior pituitary binding proteins neurophysin I and neurophysin II. *Metabolism* 20:1148–55
113. Rufener, C., Rouiller, Ch., Orci, L. 1972. Effect of vincristine on the ultrastructure of rat neurohypophysis. *Experentia* 28:837–38
114. Sachs, H., Fawcett, P., Takabatake, Y., Portanova, R. 1969. Biosynthesis and release of vasopressin and neurophysin. *Recent Progr. Horm. Res.* 25:447–91
115. Sachs, H., Goodman, R., Osinchak, J., McKelvy, J. 1971. Supraoptic neurosecretory neurons of the guinea pig in organ culture. Biosynthesis of vasopressin and neurophysin. *Proc. Nat. Acad. Sci.* 68:2782–86
116. Sakai, K. K., Marks, B. H., George, J. M., Koestner, A. 1974. Specific angiotensin II receptors in organ-cultured canine supraoptic nucleus cells. *Life Sci.* In press
117. Sakai, K. K., Marks, B. H., George, J. M., Koestner, A. 1974. The isolated organ-cultured supra-optic nucleus as a neuropharmacological test system. *J. Pharmacol. Exp. Ther.* In press
118. Sawyer, W. H. 1971. Evolution of neurohypophysial peptides among the non-mammalian vertebrates. In *Neurohypophysial Hormones,* ed. G. E. W. Wolstenholme, J. Birch, 5–14. London: Churchill
119. Schreibman, M. P., Pang, P. K. T. 1973. The current status of fish endocrine systems. *Am. Zool.* 13:711–936
120. Scott, D. E., Dudley, G. K., Weindl, A., Joynt, R. J. 1973. An autoradiographic analysis of hypothalamic magnocellular neurons. *Z. Zellforsch.* 138:421–37
121. Share, L., Claybaugh, J. R. 1972. Regulation of body fluids. *Ann. Rev. Physiol.* 34:235–60
122. Share, L. et al 1972. Effects of change in posture and of sodium depletion on plasma levels of vasopressin and renin in normal human subjects. *J. Clin. Endocrinol. Metab.* 35:171–74
123. Shimizu, K., Share, L., Claybaugh, J. R. 1973. Potentiation by angiotensin II of the vasopressin response to an increasing plasma osmolality. *Endocrinology* 93:42–50
124. Skowsky, W. R., Bashore, R. A., Smith, F. G., Fisher, D. A. 1973. Vasopressin metabolism in the foetus and newborn. See Ref. 97, 439–47
125. Skowsky, W. R., Rosenbloom, A. A., Fisher, D. A. 1974. Radioimmunoassay measurement of arginine vasopressin in serum: development and application. *J. Clin. Endocrinol. Metab.* 38:278–87
126. Snyder, S. H., Taylor, K. M. 1972. Histamine in the brain: a neurotransmitter? In *Perspectives in Neuropharmacology,* ed. S. H. Snyder, 43–73. New York: Oxford
127. Sooriyamoorthy, T., Livingston, A. 1973. Blood flow changes in the pituitary neural lobe of the rabbit associa-

ted with neurohypophysial hormone-releasing stimuli. *J. Endocrinol.* 57: 75–85

128. Stumpf, W. E. 1970. Estrogen-neurons and estrogen-neuron systems in the periventricular brain. *Am. J. Anat.* 129:207–17
129. Szczepanska-Sadowska, E. 1972. The activity of the hypothalamo-hypophysial antidiuretic system in conscious dogs. I. The influence of isoosmotic blood volume changes. *Pflugers. Arch.* 335:139–46
130. Szczepanska-Sadowska, E. 1972. The activity of the hypothalamo-hypophysial antidiuretic system in conscious dogs. II. Role of the left vago-sympathetic trunk. *Pflugers Arch.* 335:147–52
131. Thorn, N. A. 1970. Antidiuretic hormone synthesis, release and action under normal and pathological circumstances. *Advan. Metab. Disord.* 4:40–73
132. Tindal, J. S., Knaggs, G. S. 1971. Determination of the detailed hypothalamic route of the milk-ejection reflex in the guinea-pig. *J. Endocrinol.* 50:135–52
133. Tomas, T., Traczyk, W. Z., Guzek, J. W. 1973. ADH release from cut pituitary stalk and intact pituitary gland during hippocampal stimulation of various frequencies in rats. *Neuroendocrinology* 11:257–67
134. Urban, I., Moss, R. L., Cross, B. A. 1971. Problems in electrical stimulation of afferent pathways for oxytocin release. *J. Endocrinol.* 51:347–58
135. Verney, E. B. 1947. The antidiuretic hormone and the factors which affect its release. *Proc. Roy. Soc. B* 135:25–106
136. Vincent, J. D., Arnauld, E., Bioulac, B. 1972. Activity of osmosensitive single cells in the hypothalamus of the behaving monkey during drinking. *Brain Res.* 44:371–84
137. Vincent, J. D., Arnauld, E., Nicolescu-Catargi, A. 1972. Osmoreceptors and neurosecretory cells in the supraoptic complex of the unanesthetized monkey. *Brain Res.* 45:278–81
138. Voloschin, L. M., Tramezzani, J. H. 1973. The neural input of the milk ejection reflex in the hypothalamus. *Endocrinology* 92:973–83
139. Wakerley, J. B., Dyball, R. E. J., Lincoln, D. W. 1973. Milk ejection in the rat: the result of a selective release of oxytocin. *J. Endocrinol.* 57:557–58
140. Wakerley, J. B., Lincoln, D. W. 1971. Intermittent release of oxytocin during suckling in the rat. *Nature New Biol.* 233:180–81
141. Wakerley, J. B., Lincoln, D. W. 1971. Phasic discharge of antidromically identified units in the paraventricular nucleus of the hypothalamus. *Brain Res.* 25:192–94
142. Wakerley, J. B., Lincoln, D. W. 1973. The milk ejection reflex of the rat: a 20- to 40-fold acceleration in the firing of paraventricular neurones during oxytocin release. *J. Endocrinol.* 57:477–93
143. Watkins, W. B. 1972. The tentative identification of three neurophysins from the rat posterior pituitary gland. *J. Endocrinol.* 55:577–89
144. Watkins, W. B., Evans, J. J. 1972. Demonstration of neurophysin in the hypothalamo-neurohypophysial system of the normal and dehydrated rat by the use of cross-species reactive anti-neurophysins. *Z. Zellforsch.* 131:149–70
145. Whitaker, S., LaBella, F. S. 1973. Cholinesterase in the posterior and intermediate lobs of the pituitary. *Z. Zellforsch.* 142:69–88
146. Zimmerman, E. A., Carmel, P. W., Husain, M. K., Ferin, M., Tannenbaum, M., Frantz, A. G., Robinson, A. G. 1973. Vasopressin and neurophysin: high concentration in monkey hypophyseal portal blood. *Science* 182: 925–27
147. Zimmerman, E. A., Hsu, K. C., Robinson, A. G., Carmel, P. W., Frantz, A. G., Tannenbaum, M. 1973. Studies of neurophysin secreting neurons with immunoperoxidase techniques employing antibody to bovine neurophysin. I. Light microscopic findings in monkey and bovine tissues. *Endocrinology* 92: 931–40

Copyright 1975. All rights reserved

THE REGULATION OF GROWTH BY ENDOCRINES[1]

❖1129

William H. Daughaday, Adrian C. Herington,[2] *and Lawrence S. Phillips*[3]
Department of Medicine, Metabolism Division, Washington University School of Medicine, St. Louis, Missouri 63110

Normal growth is the product of a complex interaction among nutrition, circulating hormones, and changing tissue responsiveness. Although malnutrition is probably the world's most common cause of poor growth, the greatest advances in our understanding of the growth process have come from studies of the function of endocrine factors in normal and disordered growth. Limitations of space have led us to give greatest attention to growth hormone and somatomedin because of the many recent developments in these areas. We have emphasized clinical research in many areas to take advantage of the increases in knowledge that have come from the application of modern immunoassay techniques to growth problems in man.

SOMATOMAMMOTROPINS

The importance of the pituitary growth hormone (GH) in the regulation of growth in most vertebrate species is generally accepted. Earlier studies have been extensively reviewed and will not be discussed here (34, 50, 60, 111, 132, 153, 215, 222, 274, 297).

Chemistry

Major advances have recently been made in the elucidation of the primary structure of many of the mammalian growth hormones and of the other somatotropic or lactogenic polypeptide hormones. Excellent reviews of these studies have been presented (182, 184, 195, 303).

[1]Supported by Research Grant #AM01526 and Training Grant #AM05027 from the National Institutes of Health, National Institute of Arthritis, Metabolism, and Digestive Diseases, Bethesda, Maryland.

[2]Medical Research Centre, Prince Henry's Hospital, Melbourne, Australia.

[3]Northwestern University Medical School, Ward Memorial Building, 303 East Chicago Avenue, Chicago, Illinois 60611.

GROWTH HORMONE Human growth hormone (hGH) is a single chain polypeptide of 191 amino acids with two intrachain disulfide bridges (184). Earlier, Li et al (148) had reported a slightly shorter sequence, which on careful reexamination (146, 181, 183, 184) was shown to be erroneous, principally due to the mislocation of a 17 amino acid fragment. It is of interest that chemical synthesis of the complete Li sequence produced a molecule having about 10% of the somatotropic and lactogenic activities of the native hormone (150), despite the sequence errors. This indicates that the entire primary structure of the GH molecule is not required for expression of biological activity.

Either complete or substantial portions of the amino acid sequences have now been determined for bovine (bGH) (64, 236, 296), ovine (oGH) (14, 149), equine (eGH) (310), and porcine (pGH) (169) growth hormones. As noted by Niall et al (183, 184), hGH, bGH, and oGH have considerable homology in their amino acid sequences. Bovine GH and oGH both show approximately 60% identity with hGH. Niall et al (183) also described several repeating areas of homologous amino acid sequence within the hGH molecule itself, and suggested that these may represent regions possessing the same biological activities. The observation of almost identical repeating homologous regions within the sequences of human chorionic somatomammotropin and ovine prolactin (see below) led to the hypothesis that these molecules evolved from a much smaller primordial peptide through a series of tandem gene duplications (183, 184).

CHORIONIC SOMATOMAMMOTROPIN Human chorionic somatomammotropin (hCS), also called human placental lactogen, is a placental polypeptide possessing both lactogenic and weak growth-promoting activity (69, 79, 122, 125). Many of the earlier chemical, biological, and immunological studies with hCS have been reviewed (80, 237, 244, 255).

The amino acid sequence of hCS (35, 147, 183, 184, 245) exhibits striking homology with hGH: 85% of its 191 amino acids are identically placed, and the nonhomologous amino acids occur mainly in the amino terminal two thirds of the molecule (184, 246). Recently, Niall (182) reported that the amino terminal sequence of monkey placental lactogen also shows a close structural homology with hGH and hCS.

Although hCS appears to have physiological roles in maternal metabolism and in the development and differentiation of the mammary gland (95, 237, 255), of particular relevance here is its weak growth-promoting activity, less than 10% of that possessed by GH. Early studies of the metabolic and growth activities of hCS have been well summarized (95, 123, 244). In more recent studies, hCS increased the body and organ weights of Snell-Bagg dwarf mice (6) and hCS treatment of hypophysectomized rats increased epiphyseal cartilage width (179) and stimulated the incorporation of tritiated thymidine into DNA of coastal cartilage and adipose tissue (32, 177). In contrast, the ability of hCS to act as a growth hormone was questioned by Beas et al (10), who found no increase in the growth or carcass composition of hCS-treated hypophysectomized rats.

Attempts to substitute hCS for hGH in the treatment of children with GH deficiency have not been successful (95, 123, 239, 240). In addition, Schultz &

Blizzard (239) were unable to induce nitrogen retention or hypercalciuria in two hypopituitary patients. Many of the apparent discrepancies with respect to the growth potential of hCS may be related to differences in doses employed (95).

HUMAN PROLACTIN Prior to 1971 the existence of a discrete human prolactin molecule was disputed, despite the clear observation of separate prolactin molecules in many nonprimate mammalian species. Studies on the isolation and metabolic role of the nonprimate prolactins have been reviewed by Bern & Nicoll (15). The isolation of human prolactin was achieved independently by Lewis et al (144) and Hwang et al (116), and subsequent studies on purification, measurement by bioassay and radioimmunoassay, biological properties, and clinical significance have been extensively reviewed (46, 74, 81, 94, 164).

On limited sequence analysis, amino acids 1–50 of human prolactin have 92% homology with ovine prolactin (143, 182, 184) and 48% homology with hGH (184). Prolactins have little growth-promoting activity in man (26). The lower homology between the human GH and prolactin molecules may account for this difference in function.

Active Fragments of Growth Hormone and Chorionic Somatomammotropin

Li (145) originally suggested that one or more "active cores" may exist within the GH molecule, each expressing one or more of the various metabolic actions of the hormone. This hypothesis has received support in recent years because of the close homology between certain regions of several mammalian growth hormones (see section above): similar metabolic activities may be due to sequence homology in these regions, with species specificity determined by the nonhomologous regions. In addition, since GH may have insulin-like activity under certain experimental conditions, yet act as an insulin antagonist in others (91, 153), different regions of the same molecule may produce different metabolic effects. These considerations led many investigators to study the effects of GH fragments on a variety of metabolic processes. Fragments have been isolated as such from biological fluids, produced by chemical or enzymic clevage of a purified GH, or chemically synthesized.

Early studies on the enzymic cleavage of bGH have been summarized (260). These and more recent studies with trypsin (261, 272, 273, 307), chymotrypsin (131, 258), papain (272), pepsin (131), an extract from streptomycete cells (219) or plasmin (168, 251, 304, 305), demonstrated that some of the resulting fragments retained significant amounts of biological activity, including in many cases growth-promoting activity.

The tryptic digests studied by Sonenberg and colleagues (261) have been the best characterized. From a limited tryptic digest of bGH they isolated two homogeneous components, one (designated A I) of molecular weight 16,000 and the second (A II) of molecular weight 5,000 (307). Fragment A II produced a significant increase in body weight and epiphyseal cartilage width when injected into hypophysectomized rats, but fragment A I had less activity. Neither peptide was as potent as the native bGH (261, 307). Only fragment A II was active in vitro, stimulating glucose uptake and oxidation to CO_2, incorporation of glucose into glyceride-glycerol, glycerol release, and the incorporation of histidine into protein (273). Fragment A II is a 37 amino acid peptide (306) almost identical to residues 96–132 of bGH (64, 296) and 95–133 of hGH and hCS (184). However, it has also been reported (184) that a synthetic peptide corresponding to the proposed A II sequence had no significant biological activity.

Although bGH itself has no activity when administered to man, chymotryptic digests (59, 258), tryptic digests (178, 259), or papain digests of bGH (257) all elicited metabolic effects typical of hGH in hypopituitary subjects. The bGH fragment A II also produced similar effects in hypopituitary children (142). In addition, fragment A II produced a conformational change in human erythrocyte membranes (256). Since this change was also caused by hGH but not by parent bGH, activity in the A II portion may have been masked in the full molecule (see below).

Of particular interest have been studies of plasmin cleavage of hGH (168, 251, 304, 305). Limited plasmin digestion appears to remove a small peptide (either amino acids 135–140 or 135–146) from hGH (251). The resulting molecule, with a very different tertiary structure from native hGH, had the same (168) or markedly increased (251, 304, 305) GH- or prolactin-like biological activity when tested in the rat or man. The GH-like effects reported in both hypopituitary and normal patients included a positive balance of nitrogen, phosphorus, sodium, and potassium, an increased body weight, and in two of three patients an impairment of glucose tolerance (168). The biologically active fragment A II of bGH (see above) is almost identical to the amino acid sequence 95–133 of hGH and is therefore immediately adjacent to the small peptide removed from hGH by plasmin digestion. The removal of such a peptide in vivo might expose the A II sequence and permit expression of its biological action. However, it is not known whether such cleavage of hGH is required for activity in vivo.

Growth hormone fragments have also been obtained by cyanogen bromide cleavage of bGH (187), pGH (188, 189), and hGH (189, 241). Of five bGH fragments and four corresponding fragments from pGH and hGH, only one fragment in each case exhibited any GH-like effects either in vivo or in vitro, and none of the cyanogen bromide fragments had growth-promoting activity (189). The active fragments stimulated the incorporation of amino acids into protein of diaphragm and liver in vivo and in vitro, but at a markedly reduced potency compared to the native hormones (187–189). Hypophysectomized rats treated with the fragments had neither an increase in serum somatomedin (SM) activity nor an increase of in vitro incorporation of thymidine into DNA of costal cartilage taken from the treated rats (186, 189). No SM activity has been found in the few GH fragments tested directly on isolated cartilage in vitro (65).

In addition to GH fragments obtained by enzymic or chemical cleavage, other portions of the known hGH sequence have been prepared by solid phase chemical synthesis (29, 37, 38). Two synthetic peptides corresponding to amino acids 81–121 and 122–153 of the original incorrect hGH sequence (148) showed activity in the tibial line bioassay for growth promoting activity, despite the sequence errors (38). Following the revisions in the hGH sequence (146, 181, 183), Chillemi & Pecile (37) resynthesized the correct peptides (amino acids 87–123 and 124–155) and again found weak tibial line activity in both peptides. The ability of these two peptides, which do have some internal homology, to show growth-promoting activity reinforces the suggestion by Niall et al (184) that internally homologous regions in hGH may represent multiple regions possessing the same biological activity.

Bornstein and colleagues have also reported synthesis of biologically active hGH fragments (27–30). They described the isolation and later synthesis of two peptides with many of the biological effects of GH on carbohydrate and lipid metabolism both in vivo and in vitro. One of these peptides (somantin) corresponds to the C-terminal sequence 166–190 of hGH and has been shown to have anti-insulin or diabetogenic actions. The second peptide (cataglykin) exhibited several insulin-like actions and reversed the anti-insulin action of somantin. Synthetic peptides corresponding to amino acids 1–16, 1–15, and 3–13 of the correct Niall sequence all showed cataglykin-like activity. Neither somantin nor cataglykin have any growth-promoting activity (30). A preliminary report by Lostroh et al (152) described the isolation of comparable peptides with similar biological actions. However, Schwartz (241) found no biological activity in similar, but not identical, peptides prepared by cyanogen bromide cleavage of hGH.

Studies of GH fragments have suggested that different metabolic functions may be due to activity of different regions of the GH molecule. In addition to the differentiation between growth-promoting and lipolytic activities observed by Bornstein and colleagues, separation of these effects was also noted after digestion of bGH with papain (257) or pepsin (131), and after chromatographic fractionation of hGH (185, 281). On the other hand, the biologically active tryptic peptide of bGH, A II (see above), possessed both growth-promoting and lipolytic actions (261, 273).

Many studies with GH fragments have yielded conflicting results in that similar fragments have not always shown comparable biological activity, and not all in vivo effects of GH could be reproduced. As a possible explanation, Niall (184) pointed out that many of these fragments are poorly soluble and may also have a shorter half-life than active GH components produced in vivo. Despite these problems, it is clear that different regions of the GH molecule do contain distinct metabolic activities. The region most likely to possess the growth-promoting activity of GH appears to be within the sequence 80–140 (184).

In direct contrast to the extensive study of GH fragments, much less attention has been paid to the biological activity of fragments of hCS. Breuer (32) noted that, while native hCS caused a small but significant stimulation of thymidine incorporation by costal cartilage of hypophysectomized rats, fragments arising from partial enzymatic digestion of hCS exhibited no biological activity. Chemical modification of hCS (partial reduction or dissociation from a dimeric to a monomeric form) resulted in a partial loss of activity (32).

More recently, Neri et al (179) reported changes in biological and immunological activity following chemical and enzymatic treatment of hCS. Alterations in lactogenic activity did not always parallel changes in growth-promoting activity, although all chemical modifications impaired immunoreactivity. Progressive tryptic digestion decreased immunological and lactogenic activity, but cleavage of up to four bonds did not significantly affect growth activity of hCS. They concluded that the growth-promoting region of hCS did not overlap with the regions possessing either lactogenic or immunologic activity.

SOMATOMEDIN

Despite intensive study of the structure and function of GH (above), the mechanism of GH stimulation of growth is still not well understood. Because of the ineffectiveness of GH in stimulating anabolic processes in cartilage from hypophysectomized rats in vitro and the effectiveness of normal serum, but not hypophysectomized rat serum, in restoring these anabolic processes, Salmon & Daughaday (230) originally proposed what is now termed the somatomedin hypothesis. This states that GH does not stimulate essential growth tissues directly but leads to the generation of a secondary hormonal agent, somatomedin (SM) (originally called sulfation factor), which acts at the cellular level. Previous reviews (44, 47, 292, 293) describe the early work in this field.

Somatomedin Assay

Serum SM Activity was originally measured by the stimulation of the incorporation of sulfate by costal cartilage obtained from hypophysectomized rats (53). More recently, the incorporation of H^3-thymidine has also been used (290). Yde (308) used cartilage from normal fasted rats with some loss of sensitivity; to avoid the large variance from animal to animal, assays were performed on cartilage segments from a single rat. Wiedemann & Schwartz (302) have used cartilage from a single hypophysectomized rat and have also reported improved precision. Alford et al (3) have described a procedural modification that they claim makes the rat cartilage assay simpler and more reproducible.

Van den Brande & Du Caju (289) reported an assay using porcine cartilage discs. Although somewhat less sensitive, this assay has greater precision than the rat cartilage methods. Phillips et al (200) confirmed the basic utility of pig cartilage discs, but indicated that satisfactory responsiveness requires cartilage from young animals, not always available from slaughter houses in the United States. Hall (99) has described a somatomedin assay system using pelvic rudiments from 12-day-old chick embryos. Results obtained with the chick cartilage assay confirmed earlier clinical results with the hypophysectomized rat assay.

Isolated chondrocytes may also prove useful for the assay of SM. Garland et al (84) measured thymidine incorporation in chondrocytes isolated from 15-day-old chick embryos and found that normal serum produced much greater stimulation than serum from a hypophysectomized individual. While this sytem is promising, it has not been successfully applied to the routine quantitation of somatomedin in human serum.

The demonstration that receptors present on adipocytes, chondrocytes, and liver membranes bind insulin and somatomedin (109) has encouraged workers to develop radioligand assays for measurement of SM in body fluids. Recently, Marshall et al (157) described a radioligand assay for SM based on the displacement of ^{125}I-labeled SM from receptors on placental membrane preparations. This system appears to be highly sensitive and can detect apparent SM-like activity in small aliquots (5–10μl) of plasma. In preliminary studies with this assay, SM levels were elevated in patients with acromegaly and depressed in patients with hypopituitarism.

Somatomedin Isolation and Characterization

Somatomedin activity in plasma is associated with a large molecular weight complex, "big" SM, that is nondialyzable, sedimentable by ultracentrifugation, and excluded from G-25 Sephadex (47). SM of smaller molecular size, "small" SM, can be extracted from plasma by the acid ethanol procedures used for insulin. This suggested that small SM is bound to a plasma protein to form big SM (290).

Direct evidence that a SM binding protein exists in plasma was provided by Hintz et al (110). Small SM was dissociated from big SM by gel filtration in 1% formic acid. Recombining small SM with a crude plasma fraction regenerated big SM, as confirmed by gel filtration at pH 8.1.

Based on the effectiveness of acid ethanol extraction of small SM from human plasma, large volumes of outdated plasma have been extracted with acid ethanol by A. B. Kabi Laboratories (Stockholm), with further SM purification and biologic characterization in the laboratories of Hall & Uthne, and of Van Wyk and his collaborators (101, 286, 293). Conventional techniques of gel filtration, ion absorption chromatography, and electrophoresis have led to highly purified peptide fractions of molecular weight about 6000–9000.

Hall (101) and Uthne (286) monitored their extraction procedure by the chick pelvic cartilage assay. A neutral peptide was isolated that had over a millionfold enrichment of biologic activity compared to the starting plasma (105). This peptide is now called somatomedin A.

A second biologically active peptide, somatomedin B, has more acidic properties. This peptide has little action on cartilage, but stimulates thymidine incorporation by fibroblasts and glial cells (286). Its effects on cultured cells are similar to those of a fibroblast-stimulating factor (MSA) isolated from plasma by Pierson & Temin (203); this factor also has somatomedin-like activity on rat cartilage (56). Van Wyk et al (291, 293), using a rat cartilage assay measuring incorporation of both thymidine and sulfate to monitor the products, obtained a highly purified basic peptide, somatomedin C (SM-C).

At the present time the physiological significance of these separate peptides remains obscure. Growth hormone dependence of SM-C is suggested by the studies of Marshall et al (157), who used a placental receptor assay (see above) to show increased SM levels in acromegalic plasma and decreased levels in hypopituitary plasma. There is no unequivocal evidence that somatomedin A and B are GH dependent; until this becomes available their designation as somatomedins must be provisional.

The biologic actions of SM on cartilage were initially evaluated by comparison of the effects of normal serum with that of serum from hypophysectomized animals or human beings. In addition to stimulating incorporation of sulfate by cartilage, normal serum promoted the conversion of proline to hydroxyproline, indicative of increased collagen synthesis (49), and after a delay of about 24 hr stimulated incorporation of ^{3}H-thymidine (52). Partially purified SM preparations increased the incorporation of leucine into protein-chondroitin sulfate complexes and of uridine into cartilage RNA (231, 232). These studies indicate a general action on many phases of cartilage matrix synthesis and cell replication.

SM also has effects on noncartilage tissues: stimulating glucose oxidation (104, 105), inhibiting lipolysis (284) in fat cells, and stimulating leucine incorporation into protein of rat diaphragm (228). SM effects on other tissues are less well established. Tell et al (276) reported that SM preparations depressed adenylate cyclase activity in membranes from splenic lymphocytes and hepatocytes as well as in membranes from adipocytes and chondrocytes. These findings, although fragmentary, suggest that SM may have significant actions on many tissues of the body.

The chemical and biologic properties of the somatomedins closely resemble those reported for the acid-ethanol soluble component of the nonsuppressible insulin-like activity (NSILA-S) that has been described by Jakob et al (119). This material inhibited lipolysis in adipocyte ghosts (218), stimulated fibroblasts in culture (172), and stimulated incorporation of sulfate and thymidine by cartilage (214). More recently it has been shown that this material can displace ^{125}I-insulin from liver cell membranes (162). Megyesi et al (163) have also used ^{125}I-NSILA-S in a radioligand assay to measure levels in human serum.

Somatomedin Generation

Although SM generation might theoretically occur by cleavage of the original GH molecule, most investigators have hypothesized that SM is a separate hormonal agent formed in response to GH action, and have attempted to recognize the tissue of origin by measuring SM activity in different body tissues. Hall & Bozovic (102) extracted skeletal muscle and obtained a substance that stimulated incorporation of sulfate into cartilage, but the relationship of this fraction to plasma SM has never been clarified. Salmon (228) found little SM activity in extracts of liver, pancreas, kidney, spleen, salivary gland, heart, thymus, adrenal, pituitary, and thyroid. These data and unpublished experiences from a number of laboratories have failed to establish any organ of the body with a high concentration of somatomedin.

Despite the lack of evidence of SM storage, there is accumulating evidence of hepatic generation of SM. Uthne & Uthne (287) reported a rapid decrease in serum SM activity following partial hepatectomy in rats, and a reappearance of SM activity associated with apparent liver regeneration. More direct evidence of hepatic synthesis of SM came from the studies of McConaghey & Sledge (159, 161). They perfused isolated liver with or without addition of bGH and subsequently tested the perfusate for its ability to stimulate incorporation of sulfate by hypophysectomized rat cartilage. The perfusate containing GH produced much greater stimulation than the perfusate not containing GH. In studies using rat liver slices, addition of bGH also led to the generation of apparent SM activity in the medium (159). No SM activity was generated in incubations using homogenized liver or frozen and thawed liver slices. In addition, Hall & Uthne (104) reported apparent generation of SM activity by rat liver microsomes incubated in a medium containing large amounts of GH.

SM production may not be limited to liver. McConaghey & Dehnel (160), in a preliminary report, claimed that addition of bGH to perfusions of normal and hypophysectomized rat kidneys also appeared to generate SM-like activity, but slices of hypophysectomized rat kidney produced a stimulatory medium even in the absence of bGH.

Somatomedin in Rat Serum

Hypophysectomy in rats leads to a rapid decrease in serum SM activity, with a half-life of 3–4 hr (44). The SM concentration of three pools of hypophysectomized rat serum assayed by the pig cartilage method in our laboratory ranged from 21 to 34% of the activity of normal rat serum (200).

SM activity can be restored to the serum of hypophysectomized rats by GH administration (230). Phillips et al (201) found that larger doses of GH are required to induce the restoration of serum SM than are required to stimulate incorporation of sulfate by the cartilage of the injected rat. These observations may be explained by preferential adsorption of newly formed SM by SM-deficient tissues. Alternatively, existing assays may not be sufficiently sensitive to detect changes of SM that are small but of biologic significance. Although supranormal levels of SM have not been observed in rats injected with large doses of GH, rats bearing the transplantable pituitary tumor MstTW15, a tumor which secretes massive amounts of GH and prolactin, had significant elevations of serum SM levels (194).

Somatomedin in Human Serum

Physiologic and pathologic influences on serum SM concentration have been extensively studied in man. Despite problems of standardization and specificity there has been surprising agreement between different assay systems. Almqvist (5) was the first to report that children under the age of four years had lower serum SM than older children and adults. This observation was confirmed by Van den Brande (288), who established a normal range and confidence limits of serum SM for children of various ages and for adults. No sex difference in SM activity has yet been claimed. There is little circadian variation (53, 288).

All workers have reported that SM activity in serum of hypopituitary subjects is low (20–40% of normal). Although radical hypophysectomy produces serum SM levels that are uniformly low (53), SM levels are more variable in patients with spontaneous, often incomplete, hypopituitarism (5, 103, 191, 288).

Growth hormone treatment of hypopituitary subjects increases serum SM, and investigators have studied the relationship between GH dose and SM response. Daughaday et al (48) found that administration of hGH [5 international units (IU) per day] to four hypopituitary dwarfs restored SM to the normal range in two days, with maximal values in four days. In another study, intravenous administration of 2 IU of GH led to a detectable rise in serum SM within 3 hr (100). A more detailed study of the short-term relationship between daily dose of GH and serum SM levels has been reported by Van den Brande (288), who studied two hypopituitary dwarfs and found that between 5 and 10 IU/day of GH were required for complete restoration of SM activity. He also noted that more hGH was required to restore SM than is needed to initiate "catch-up" growth in a previously untreated patient. This situation is similar to that described in rats by Phillips et al (201) (see above). In hypopituitary dwarfs treated for longer periods with hGH, Hall & Olin (103) established a good correlation between growth rate and SM concentration.

Serum SM is frequently elevated in pateints with acromegaly (5, 53, 101). The failure of all patients with acromegaly to exhibit elevated levels of SM is unexplained. Hall (101) has observed a poor correlation between hGH concentration and serum SM levels and suggested that in acromegaly, serum SM may be a better measure of disease "activity" than hGH levels.

DWARFISM DUE TO GROWTH HORMONE RESISTANCE

Laron and co-workers (137, 140) described a familial form of growth failure with clinical features of growth hormone deficiency despite elevated levels of serum GH. While the condition seems to be particularly common in Asiatic Jews, it has also been reported in other groups (137), and analysis of pedigrees has suggested transmission as a Mendelian recessive trait. It was shown by Daughaday et al (48) that despite the high GH levels, serum SM levels were low and did not rise following adminstration of large doses of GH. This observation was subsequently confirmed by others (180, 275, 288). In addition to the failure of SM generation, Laron et al (139) found that affected children had little nitrogen retention, urinary calcium excretion, phosphorus retention, and lipolysis after GH administration. Adminstration of GH also failed to stimulate skeletal growth.

Although it was initially hypothesized that these patients secreted an abnormal GH (140), several investigators have reported that serum GH from these patients has immunologic and electrophoretic behavior identical to that of hGH standards (58, 61, 288). In addition, Tsushima & Friesen (282) found that the serum of one affected child reacted normally in a GH radioreceptor assay. These findings support the hypothesis that refractoriness to GH is due to lack of tissue response to GH rather than an abnormality of the GH molecule (45).

PITUITARY DWARFISM IN MAN

The cause of pituitary dwarfism is generally undetermined. About 5–10% of cases have familial isolated GH deficiency. Studies of affected families indicate that the trait is transmitted as a Mendelian recessive gene (220, 243). Some of the nonfamilial cases have recognized craniofacial abnormalities that suggest a defect in hypothalamic or pituitary embryogenesis (115, 311). The possibility that birth injury might be responsible for damage to the pituitary stalk has been suggested by Bierich (24), who found an inordinate incidence of complicated births among children with pituitary dwarfism.

It is likely that the primary defect is hypothalmic, rather than adenohypophysial, in most cases of idiopathic pituitary dwarfism, particularly when the deficiency is limited to GH secretion. Rimoin & Schechter (221) have reported a post-mortem examination on one man with familial isolated GH deficiency. His adenohypophysis contained cells with large secretory granules similar to those of GH-secreting cells. Other evidence of hypothalamic involvement has been provided by Costom et al (42) and Foley et al (71), who reported that children with idiopathic GH and thyrotropin (TSH) deficiency responded to thyrotropin releasing hormone (TRH) with a rise in thyrotropin. In addition, patients with idiopathic hypopituitarism responded to TRH with increased prolactin secretion (70, 126). Since both thyrotropin and prolactin are responsive to TRH in idiopathic panhypopituitarism, it seems likely that the abnormality in GH secretion is also the result of a hypophysiotropic hormone deficiency.

The cardinal features of the growth response to hGH therapy in hypopituitary dwarfism were described by investigators in the early 1960s, and recent reports (1, 262, 275) of large series of children have added to our understanding. Tanner et al (275), employing careful anthropometric methods, studied 100 children treated with GH for one to seven years. Thirty-five of these cases had idiopathic GH deficiency. When GH was administered in the relatively large dose of 20 IU per week, mean growth increased from 3.1 to 9.1 cm for the first year, with a progressive decline in growth in subsequent years. Doses of 40 IU of GH per week did not produce greater growth than 20 IU/week, whereas 10 IU resulted in somewhat slower growth.

Tanner et al (275) identified a group of children with definite but low GH responses to provocative stimuli, who also appeared to benefit from GH treatment. This group, previously recognized by others (191), is difficult to distinguish from children with constitutional short stature (see below).

Treatment with GH has seldom led to worthwhile acceleration of growth except in children with complete or partial GH deficiency. Occasional responses have been encountered and full dosage ranges have not been explored, so that future progress in this area may be possible with greater experience.

GROWTH HORMONE SECRETION IN MALNUTRITION

Kwashiorkor

Since prolonged malnutrition in both animals and man is associated with poor growth and a decrease in size of endocrine tissues, it has been assumed that starvation may lead to a form of hypopituitarism. However, pituitary and adrenal hormone levels are not decreased in children with kwashiorkor, a disease of severe protein deficiency. Pimstone et al (207) reported that concentrations of plasma GH were characteristically elevated in children with untreated kwashiorkor, and Alleyne & Young (4) have demonstrated elevations in plasma steroid levels. Insulin hypoglycemia or arginine infusion did not consistently produce further elevations in GH levels (8, 90, 192), perhaps due to the high basal level of secretion. In addition, administration of glucose seldom produced the expected fall in plasma GH concentrations, and frequently there was a paradoxical rise (204). When these children were given a normal diet, GH concentrations promptly fell to near normal values (205).

Attempts have been made to determine the cause of increased GH secretion in kwashiorkor. Serum albumin levels are low in patients with kwashiorkor (11, 154, 206) but increased serum GH is probably not a simple response to albumin depletion. It has been suggested that low levels of key amino acids might stimulate GH secretion. Pimstone et al (206) found a strong inverse relationship between plasma GH levels and concentrations of leucine, isoleucine, and valine, and the best correlation with concentrations of alanine. However, Suskind et al (270) felt that the restoration of plasma alanine levels was too slow to account for the rapid fall in GH concentration observed with refeeding, and that levels of arginine, lysine, and tyrosine might be more important. While these studies are of interest, at the present time there is no direct evidence that low concentrations of amino acids stimulate GH secretion.

The possibility of resistance to GH action in kwashiorkor is suggested by the failure of administered GH to induce nitrogen retention during prolonged fasting (63). Grant et al (92) have proposed that defective SM generation may be a possible mechanism for resistance to GH action in protein-calorie malnutrition. They studied children with severe kwashiorkor and found low initial levels of SM, with a rapid rise upon institution of adequate diet.

Marasmus

While GH hypersecretion has been found consistently in children with kwashiorkor, plasma GH levels have been reported to be either low, normal, or elevated in children with marasmus (8, 9, 89, 90, 120, 192), a form of semistarvation with more severe caloric deficiency. Samuel & Deshpende (235) noted that the level of GH tended to be elevated when plasma albumin was less than 2.5 gm%.

During refeeding, marasmic children often gain weight slowly, a response that is more common in children when initial GH levels are low (89). Beas & Muzzo (9) administered GH during early dietary repletion (before weight gain was observed) and were able to increase retention of nitrogen and phosphorus. These observations suggest that there is a subset of marasmic children who have relative GH deficiency and in whom GH therapy may be beneficial.

The influence of neonatal dietary restriction on pituitary GH content has been evaluated in nursing rat pups (268). Dietary restriction was induced by placing additional pups with the lactating mother. At four weeks of age the deprived pups had less than one quarter the normal GH content measured by bioassay, and a similar depletion in pituitary GH was detected at six weeks by radioimmunoassay.

There is a danger in attempting to equate pituitary GH content with secretion of GH. Akikusa (2) studied the in vitro incorporation of ^{14}C-leucine into GH by pituitaries from rats starved for five days. Although only half as much ^{14}C-leucine was present in GH in the pituitaries of starved rats as compared to control rats, the amount of labeled GH released into the medium was unchanged.

Psychosocial Deprivation

There has been continued interest in the interrelationships among emotional disturbance, nutritional aberration, and altered endocrine function in the growth disturbance of children with psychosocial deprivation (31, 210, 211). These children have growth retardation of sufficient severity to suggest hypopituitarism. However, when removed from their homes and placed in an institutional environment with good nutrition, they have extremely rapid growth. Endocrine studies in these children have been summarized (31, 211). Many children had deficient ACTH and GH responses to provocative stimuli. In a single patient studied by Powell et al (212), nocturnal secretion of GH was also impaired despite normal sleep patterns. Krieger & Good (134) have compared endocrine function in deprivation syndromes to that in undernutrition associated with organic diseases. Cortisol secretory rates were decreased in many children with deprivation syndrome, but were normal in children with undernutrition of organic cause. Krieger & Mellinger (135) found that, although older children with psychosocial deprivation had normal fasting GH levels with little increase after provocative stimulation, infants with deprivation syndrome had elevated fasting GH levels with a normal or exaggerated response to stimulation.

Although adequate nutritional information has been difficult to obtain, there are described cases with bizarre eating patterns and excessive food intake. In addition, many children have had normal or excessive body fat despite extreme short stature, suggesting that simple caloric deficiency may not explain the lack of growth (31). However, in a series of carefully controlled dietary experiments, Whitten et al (301) and Krieger et al (133) demonstrated that provision of an adequate diet either in the hospital or in the home (without improvement of the psychosocial environment) permitted the resumption of normal weight gain. The nutritional studies of Whitten, Krieger, and associates challenge the hypothesis that growth impairment in the deprivation syndrome is a result of decreased GH secretion due to psychologic factors.

HYPOTHALAMUS

The relationship between the hypothalamus and growth continues to attract investigators. In the experiments of Bernardis & Frohman (18), bilateral lesions in the ventromedial nuclei of rats led to reduced pituitary and plasma GH levels. These animals became hyperphagic, with decreased skeletal growth, increased body fat, and hyperinsulinism. Hypertriglyceridemia and hypercholesterolemia frequently developed (20, 82). There was a good correlation between lesion size and pituitary weight, plasma GH, linear growth, and lean body mass (18). Because of the increased body fat there was no difference in body weight between lesioned and control rats. From these experiments the investigators concluded that the ventromedial nucleus is a positive control site for GH secretion and a negative control site for insulin secretion. Considerable species difference exists in the response to hypothalamic lesions. O'Brien & Bach (190) reported that paraventricular but not ventromedial lesions were required to impair growth of kittens. Bernardis (16, 17) found that lesions in the dorsal medial nuclei of weanling rats also led to impaired growth, despite normal levels of plasma GH. These animals had a reduction in both skeletal growth and weight when compared with sham operated controls (19). Since pair-fed control rats also had impaired skeletal and ponderal growth it was concluded that dorsal medial lesions caused dwarfism due to inadequate calorie intake that did not involve adenohypophysial secretions.

Measurements of SM have suggested a mechanism for the improved growth that occurs after surgical treatment in certain short children with craniopharyngiomas and other hypothalamic tumors. After surgery, a significant number of these children become hyperphagic and obese and grow at a normal or exaggerated rate despite low basal GH levels and the continued absence of GH responses to provocative stimuli (77, 112, 130). Finkelstein et al (67) reported that three such children had normal SM activity in their plasma, a finding which was subsequently confirmed by Weldon et al (298) and by Kenny et al (129). The possibility that normal generation of SM with subsequent growth could be the result of prolactin hypersecretion as a result of hypothalamic damage has been considered (130, 298). However, Kenny et al (129) found normal serum prolactins in four children with this syndrome of "growth without growth hormone." Because most of these children have a marked increase in body weight and body fat the suggestion has been made that hyperphagia with associated hyperinsulinemia might account for the resumption of skeletal growth (67, 129). It is possible that insulin may enhance SM generation in the presence of minimal amounts of GH. While there is evidence that supraphysiologic concentrations of insulin have a SM-like action in vitro (233), there is no experimental evidence that insulin is involved in SM generation.

GROWTH PROMOTION BY *SPIROMETRA MANSONOIDES*

The spargana stage of the cat tapeworm *Spirometra mansonoides* releases a growth-promoting substance of great interest. Early observations in this field by Mueller have been reviewed by Steelman et al (266). Infestation with spargana of this cestode induced obesity in mice and stimulated growth in hypothyroid rats. In addition, implantation of spargana into hypophysectomized rats caused a marked stimulation of growth, equivalent to that induced by pituitary GH.

The plerocercoid growth factor (PGF) is present in serum of infested hosts, and growth of other hypophysectomized rats can be stimulated by administration of serum from infested rats. The factor appears to have a much longer biologic half-life than GH, since injections of serum as infrequent as every 10 days have stimulated substantial growth.

Steelman and his co-workers (266) found that rats infested with *Spirometra mansonoides* have most of the metabolic changes induced by GH except that there is no evidence of lipolysis. Recently Sogani et al (254) reported that rats infested with spargana or injected with serum containing PGF had elevations in ornithine decarboxylase levels that resembled those induced by GH administration.

Garland et al (85) investigated the relationships among PGF, GH, and SM. Infested hypophysectomized rats had nearly normal SM levels despite little or no GH by radioimmunoassay. Rats long infested with spargana appeared to develop antibodies that neutralized PGF but not SM. Other evidence of the GH-like action of PGF was also provided by Garland & Daughaday (83), who showed that normal rats carrying spargana had a significant decrease in pituitary GH content. They concluded that although PGF was immunologically different from rat GH, it stimulated the production of SM in a manner similar to GH and that actual growth was the result of SM action.

Recent reports provide more direct evidence of the GH-like properties of PGF. Chang et al (36) succeeded in maintaining spargana of *Spirometra mansonoides* in cell-free media and have shown continued production of PGF by in vivo tests. Tsushima et al (283) have reported that PGF from these cultures displaced ^{125}I-hGH from a liver membrane receptor but did not crossreact in a radioimmunoassay for rat GH. By gel filtration they estimated PGF had a molecular weight of about 70,000, over three times that of rat GH.

In parallel studies, Phares et al (199) found that PGF activity was released by spargana in short-term incubations in simple buffers. Although this material had prolactin activity by pigeon crop sac assay, Tsushima et al (283) failed to find prolactin-like effects in a rabbit mammary membrane receptor assay for prolactin.

INSULIN

The relationship between insulin and growth is complex because both GH and increased nutrition may result in increased insulin secretion. Insulin can induce some growth in the absence of GH. In classic experiments, hypophysectomized rats treated with insulin had increased body weight, body length, and epiphyseal cartilage width (141, 234). Although much of the weight gain could be attributed to fat, there was also an increase in nitrogen retention. Hyperalimentation of hypophysectomized rats produced similar results (295); in pair-fed rats, addition of exogenous insulin did not further increase weight gain or nitrogen retention (295).

Insulin is required for the full anabolic effect of GH. Depancreatized cats given GH had nitrogen retention comparable to control cats only when insulin was provided (170). Growth hormone treatment of hypophysectomized rats increased islet weight and insulin content as well as insulin release in vitro (98, 158). This does not establish a direct effect of GH on insulin secretion, since islet mass is also increased by glucose and cortisone, other agents that stimulate islet secretary activity (98). Pancreatic perfusion experiments have indicated a possible specific action of GH on insulin secretion. Pancreas preparations from hypophysectomized rats showed a decrease in both the initial and the secondary phases of insulin secretion (43). Rats pretreated with cortisone had improvement in both phases of insulin secretion, but pretreatment with GH restored only the second phase of insulin secretion (43), suggesting that cortisone and GH do not act by a common mechanism.

In pituitary dwarfism the insulin secretory response to glucose and arginine is greatly diminished (41, 285). The defect is partially corrected by GH administration, but full correction requires the administration of both GH and cortisone (285).

Laron (136) recently reviewed clinical conditions where insulinopenia was associated with poor growth and hyperinsulinism with good growth. Kwashiorkor is associated with insulinopenia and retardation of growth despite elevated growth hormone levels (154). In one study, decreased insulin levels were significantly correlated with decreased serum albumin and elevated fasting growth hormone levels (154). Somatomedin levels are low in children with kwashiorkor (92), suggesting that insulin may play a permissive role in growth hormone-dependent somatomedin generation. (See GH and Malnutrition.)

Children with juvenile diabetes mellitus, a disease of primary insulin deficiency, require exogenous insulin for control of blood sugar levels. Inadequate insulin therapy is associated with retardation of growth (25, 97, 209) despite mean growth hormone levels significantly higher than those in normal children (106).

When hyperglycemia is accompanied by insulin secretion increased growth may occur in man. Infants born to diabetic mothers have hyperplasia of islet tissue, hyperinsulinism, and increased birth weight and birth length (55, 171, 197). Many diabetic children are taller than normal at the onset of their disease despite eventual retardation of growth (209). Some of these children have only relative insulin deficiency when their disease is first discovered, and it seems likely that many of these children go through a period of modest hyperglycemia with hyperinsulinism (and increased growth) before they develop complete insulin deficiency.

Increased food intake with adequate insulin secretion may also increase growth. Obese children tend to have increased height for age as well as increased weight (86). Obesity is associated with hyperinsulinism (33), and growth hormone responses to provocative stimuli are often low (40). Children with craniopharyngioma may become hyperphagic and obese after surgery, with hyperinsulinism and normal or increased growth despite low growth hormone levels (see Hypothalamus).

CORTICOSTEROIDS

Excess glucocorticoid is associated with retardation of growth in experimental animals and man (88, 249, 252). Glucocorticoid overtreatment in children with congenital adrenal hyperplasia will produce retardation of growth (217, 265); replacement with cortisone acetate in doses approximating normal cortisol production rates has been recommended (167). The claim has been made that synthetic glucocorticoids produce greater retardation of growth than natural glucocorticoids of comparable therapeutic potency (62, 138). Alternate-day therapy with longer-acting synthetic glucocorticoids may also allow improved growth (13). Substitution of ACTH for prednisone therapy has led to modest improvements in growth when initial retardation of growth was not severe (280).

Retardation of growth with excess glucocorticoid may be due to decreased secretion of growth hormone, antagonism of growth hormone action, direct effects on cartilage, or a combination of these effects.

Glucocorticoid Effects on GH Secretion

The acute administration of high doses of glucocorticoids to adult human subjects decreased growth hormone responses to hypoglycemia; with long-term administration of steroids, higher dosage was associated with greater suppression of GH responses (75). In one study, increasing duration of dexamethasone administration was associated with progressive inhibition of growth hormone responses to hypoglycemia (299). The daily administration of prednisone to normal women significantly decreased mean growth hormone production rates, but alternate-day prednisone produced a smaller decrease (277). In contrast, studies of glucocorticoid-induced growth retardation in children have often revealed normal GH responses to provocative stimuli (174, 269), suggesting either that stimulated GH responses are not representative of GH production, or that other mechanisms of growth retardation are more important.

Steroid Antagonism of GH Action

Administration of cortisone has decreased linear growth in hypopituitary children and hypophysectomized rats treated with human growth hormone (263). In another study, children treated with prednisone (5–20 mg/day) had little anabolic or growth response to the administration of large doses of hGH (173). Hypopituitary children had less retention of nitrogen and phosphorus with administration of hGH when glucocorticoids (replacement dosage) were given simultaneously rather than when separated by a period of 9–10 hr, suggesting that even very modest levels of glucocorticoids may antagonize growth hormone action (227).

Glucocorticoids may antagonize growth hormone action by interfering with somatomedin generation or somatomedin action. Moderately high levels of serum cortisol (20–110 μg%) had little effect on somatomedin action on rat, chick, or pig cartilage in vitro (201), although Clarke et al (39) claimed that higher levels of cortisol (900 μg%) inhibit somatomedin action on chick cartilage. Administration of cortisone acetate decreased the rise in serum somatomedin in hypophysectomized rats treated with marginal doses of bGH (201, 202), suggesting that glucocorticoid inhibition of growth may involve antagonism of GH-induced somatomedin generation.

Direct Effects of Steroids on Cartilage

Although normal rats exposed to high levels of glucocorticoids have epiphyseal narrowing similar to that of hypophysectomized rats or rats subjected to caloric restriction (12), changes in cartilage histology suggest additional direct action on the skeleton. Cortisone acetate induced a decrease in both number and size of proliferating chondrocytes (21). In addition, diaphysial trabeculae contained wide bands of calcified cartilage covered by a thin layer of bone (21). In another experiment, mice treated with cortisone acetate rapidly developed changes in cartilage ultrastructure, with swollen and vacuolated mitochondria, increased Golgi size, and discontinuous or vesiculated endoplasmic reticulum (248). By contrast, cartilage from hypophysectomized rats or starved rats showed much less cellular disorganization.

High concentrations of glucorticoid appear to be required for inhibition of chondromucoprotein synthesis in cartilage segments incubated in vitro. Cortisol (1.4×10^{-5} M) greatly decreased incorporation of sulfate by costal cartilage (49), but more physiological concentrations of cortisol (10^{-6} M) had no effect on incorporation of sulfate into rat or pig costal cartilage or embryonic chick pelvic rudiments (Phillips et al, unpublished).

Cultures of rapidly growing cartilage and bone cells are more sensitive to glucocorticoids than cartilage segments. As little as 10^{-7} to 10^{-8} M cortisol added to isolated bone cells produced small but significant decreases in synthesis of protein and RNA (196).

Further evidence for a direct effect of glucocorticoids on growing bone and cartilage is suggested by failure of "catch-up" growth in childhood Cushing's syndrome (176) and in rats with growth retardation due to glucocorticoid treatment (175). Since "catch-up" growth is rapid in starved children given food (213) and in hypopituitary children treated with hGH (275), poor "catch-up" growth following high doses of glucocorticoids cannot be adequately explained either by lack of growth hormone or lack of food, and a direct effect on growing cartilage seems likely.

ANDROGENS

Animal Studies

The administration of androgens to normal rats or mice increases body weight and skeletal maturation with little change in longitudinal growth. Hypophysectomized rats treated with androgens have increased weight of secondary sexual tissues (seminal vesicles and prostate), but little overall body growth (250, 267) or increase in epiphyseal cartilage width (250). However, Salmon et al (229) claimed that hypophysectomized rats treated with testosterone or testosterone propionate had increased incorporation of (^{35}S–) sulfate into their cartilage in vivo.

Hypophysectomized rats treated with androgens and large doses of growth hormone (0.1–0.25 mg/day) were found to have an increase in body weight, body length, and epiphyseal cartilage width little greater than that produced by the administration of GH alone (88, 242). However, the use of testosterone and submaximal doses of growth hormone (5–10 μg) produced synergistic increases in epiphyseal cartilage width (88) and incorporation of sulfate into cartilage (229).

Considerable effort has been expended in attempts to obtain an androgen that has anabolic (growth) potency in excess of androgenic potency. Androgens that have little virilizing potency may have substantial effects on bone maturation: in mice, dehydroepiandrosterone had 0.1–2% the virilizing effects of testosterone, but equal tendency to cause epiphysiodiaphyseal union (114). Although increase in the weight of the levator ani muscle in rats has frequently been used as a measure of anabolic potency (73), testosterone given to hypophysectomized rats increased levator ani weight as well as weight of seminal vesicles and ventral prostate (used as measures of androgenic potency) without increasing body weight (267). Different growth parameters were weighted separately in a recent bioassay which measured anabolic /androgenic activity ratios in rats treated for 60–90 days with test androgens: body weight, length, and weight of kidney and heart were used for anabolic potency; weights of pituitary, ovaries, uterus, adrenals, and thymus and clitoral length for androgenic potency (294). It has not been demonstrated that these indices will reflect anabolic/androgenic activity ratios in humans.

Human Studies

Clinical observations in man differ in some respects from results in animals. Congenital adrenal hyperplasia with overproduction of adrenal androgens produces increased growth rates, accelerated epiphyseal maturation, early puberty, and reduced ultimate stature. Growth hormone deficiency in man appears to decrease the growth response to administered androgen (309).

Androgens have frequently been used to stimulate growth in cases of "constitutional short stature" (short stature with appropriately delayed bone maturation, normal endocrine measurements, and low-normal rate of growth). Careful studies have generally shown that both growth and bone maturation are increased during androgen treatment, with slower growth despite continued bone maturation after treatment is discontinued (87, 253). The same result was obtained with normal children in a double-blind study using both fluoxymestrone and methyltestosterone (165). Bone maturation was increased more than height, which would be expected to lead to reduced ultimate stature. Bone maturation was dose-related, while linear growth was not (253). Much of the excessive bone maturation occurred early in treatment, and it has been claimed that continued treatment will not further decrease ultimate stature (113); this has not been substantiated with actual measurements of ultimate stature. Two studies suggested that treatment of younger children with lower bone maturation (<9 yr) is associated with a greater decrease in predicted ultimate height (23, 118). This is substantiated by studies showing no decrease in ultimate height when treatment was begun at more advanced bone ages (12–14 yr) (7, 72, 127).

In two studies, low-dose synthetic androgens were used as adjunctive therapy in hypopituitary patients treated with hGH (156, 216). Bone maturation increased more than height in both studies, but the increased growth was felt to justify the decrease in theoretical ultimate stature, since in these children ultimate stature is determined by the withdrawal of hGH therapy (after achieving a height of 5 ft) and not by the genetic growth potential of the cartilage.

Low-dose synthetic androgens have also been used to promote growth in children with gonadal dysgenesis (Turner's syndrome). Johanson et al (121) and Rosenbloom et al (226) have claimed that administration of androgens to children with Turner's syndrome increases growth velocity with minimal acceleration of bone maturation. However, there were no controlled studies demonstrating improvement in ultimate stature.

ESTROGENS

Animal Studies

Estrogen administration decreases growth and epiphyseal cartilage width in a number of species, including rats (54) and rabbits (22). Cartilage from mice treated with estradiol benzoate had decreased incorporation of sulfate into chondroitin sulfate (107). Neonatal gonadectomy in pair-fed female rats allowed growth of humerus and tibia comparable to that of male rats (96). Since gonadectomy in males had no effect, the shorter bone length in female controls may have been due to inhibition of growth by normal estrogen levels (96). However, very low doses of estradiol valerate have been reported to increase femur length in castrated male mice (271). Rats treated with estrogens had decreased skeletal growth despite increased serum levels of growth hormone (151).

Estrogens antagonize the effects of administered growth hormone on epiphyseal cartilage in hypophysectomized rats (124). Estrogens inhibited the GH-induced rise in serum somatomedin in hypophysectomized rats (201) and in human subjects with hypopituitarism (302). Moderately high levels of estradiol (1–100 ng/ml) added to serum did not inhibit somatomedin action on cartilage from hypophysectomized rats, normal young pigs, or embryonic chicks (201, 302). However, Herbai (108) has claimed that high concentrations of estradiol (10 μg/ml) added to cartilage in vitro decreased basal incorporation of sulfate by cartilage from normal mice, but had no effect on cartilage from hypophysectomized mice (108).

Both estrogen administration and hypophysectomy lead to epiphyseal narrowing with decrease in chondrocyte size and number, but estrogens also produce accelerated skeletal maturation with increased deposition of bone (247). In growing rodents, estrogen treatment decreased resorption of primary spongiosa, with scanty osteoclasts, increased osteoblasts, and the development of a thick network of bone (247). Endosteal proliferation is most marked in mice (247).

Human Studies

The growth-inhibiting effects of estrogens are used clinically to limit excessive stature in girls with predicted height over six feet. In older girls (bone maturation over 12 yr) the decrease in ultimate stature is usually of little clinical significane (78, 238). Prepubertal girls with bone maturation 11 yr or less may have a decrease of several inches in ultimate stature (93, 300).

PUBERTY

The endocrinology of puberty has recently been reviewed (223, 224) and is not discussed in detail here.

Although complete sexual development can take place in the absence of growth hormone (220, 243), both growth hormone and the gonadal steroids appear to be required for the pubertal growth spurt. One out of six cases in a family with isolated

GH deficiency had a pubertal growth spurt, but the remainder had no definite acceleration of growth (220).

Qualitative and quantitative changes in the secretion of GH occur at puberty. Serial measurement of GH in blood samples obtained at 20 min intervals over a 24 hr period has provided information about spontaneous GH secretion in puberty. In the studies of Finkelstein et al (68), prepubertal GH secretion occurred only during sleep, adolescent GH secretion was increased both during sleep and during wakefulness, and GH secretion in young adults was somewhat lower than adolescent levels both during sleep and during wakefulness. Thompson et al (208, 278) obtained blood with a constant withdrawal pump to determine the integrated concentration of growth hormone (ICGH) over a 24 hr period. They found no difference between prepubertal and pubertal levels in either males or females. It has been suggested that the apparent differences in these studies of GH secretion may be due to increased level of activity in the ICGH subjects (208), or to inadequate correction for changing pool size needed to estimate production rates from ICGH (66).

Growth hormone secretion following provocative stimulation may be increased by exposure to endogenous or exogenous gonadal steriods. Three boys with short stature and apparent hGH deficiency (undetectable GH responses to either arginine infusion or insulin hypoglycemia) had normal GH responsiveness following the development of spontaneous puberty (198), and a single injection of testosterone increased the GH response to insulin hypoglycemia in five children with anorchia or delayed puberty (117). In one study, GH responses to insulin hypoglycemia were higher in adolescent children than in preadolescent children (76). However, Sperling et al (264) found increased GH responsiveness to arginine infusion only in pubertal girls, with no increase in pubertal boys. Arginine infusion produced higher GH responses in adult females than in adult males; pretreatment with stilbestrol (2 or 5 mg twice a day for two days) increased GH responses in males (166).

THYROID

The importance of thyroid hormone in normal growth is well established. In hypopituitary rats, thyroid hormone acts synergistically with GH. This synergism has been reevaluated by Thorngren & Hansson (279) using a tetracycline labeling technique to measure bone growth in hypophysectomized rats. Thyroxine alone stimulated bone growth without significant increase in epiphyseal cartilage width. When thyroxine was given with GH, the combined effects on growth were more than additive, indicating synergism.

The effects of thyroid deficiency on GH secretion and storage have been restudied by Daughaday et al (51) using radioimmunoassay techniques in propylthiouracil-fed rats. A profound fall in pituitary GH content began after about 10 days, with a parallel but less striking fall in plasma GH (193). Similar changes have been observed in thyroparathyroidectomized rats (57). The effect of hypothyroidism on pituitary GH-secreting cells may be direct and not mediated by the hypothalamus, as propylthiouracil feeding of rats bearing a transplanted GH secreting tumor led to an equally impressive fall in plasma and tumor GH (193).

The marked alteration in somatotropic cell function seen in the hypothyroid rat may not occur so dramatically in other species. In human hypothyroidism there is no consistent change in basal levels of plasma GH, and the GH responses to provocative stimuli, while often decreased, may be entirely normal (128, 155, 225).

Literature Cited

1. Aceto, T. Jr. et al 1972. Collaborative study of the effects of human growth hormone in growth hormone deficiency. I. First year of therapy. *J. Clin. Endocrinol. Metab.* 35:483–96
2. Akikusa, Y. 1971. Effect of starvation on synthesis and release of growth hormone and prolactin in the rat anterior pituitary. *Endocrinol. Jap.* 18:411–16
3. Alford, F. P., Bellair, J. T., Burger, H. G., Lovett, N. 1972. A simplified assay for somatomedin. *J. Endocrinol.* 54:365–66
4. Alleyne, G. A. O., Young, V. H. 1967. Adrenocortical function in children with severe protein and calorie malnutrition. *Clin. Sci.* 33:189–200
5. Almqvist, S., Ikkos, D., Luft, R. 1961. Studies on sulfation factor (SF) activity of human serum. The variation of serum SF with age. *Acta Endocrinol.* 36:566–76
6. Arezzini, C., De Gori, V., Tarli, P., Neri, P. 1972. Weight increase of body and lymphatic tissues in dwarf mice treated with human chorionic somatomammotropin (HCS). *Proc. Soc. Exp. Biol. Med.* 141:98–100
7. Bayley, N., Gordan, G. S., Lisser, H. 1957. Long-term experiences with methyltestosterone as a growth stimulant in short immature boys. *Pediat. Clin. N. Am.* 4:819–25
8. Beas, F., Contreras, I., Maccioni, A., Arenas, S. 1971. Growth hormone in infant malnutrition: the arginine test in marasmus and kwashiorkor. *Brit. J. Nutr.* 26:169–75
9. Beas, F., Muzzo, S. 1973. Growth hormone and malnutrition: the Chilean experience. *Endocrine Aspects of Malnutrition,* ed. L. J. Gardner, P. Amacher, 1–18. Santa Ynez, Calif.: Kroc Foundation. 519 pp.
10. Beas, F., Salinas, A., Pak, N. 1969. Action of chorionic growth hormone-prolactin on growth and carcass composition of hypophysectomized rat. *Proc. Soc. Exp. Biol. Med.* 131:1171–75
11. Becker, D. J., Pimstone, B. L., Hansen, J. D. L., Hendricks, S. 1971. Serum albumin and growth hormone relationships in kwashiorkor and the nephrotic syndrome. *J. Lab. Clin. Med.* 78: 865–71
12. Becks, H., Simpson, M. E., Li, C. H., Evans, H. M. 1944. Effects of adrenocorticotrophic hormone (ACTH) on the osseous system in normal rats. *Endocrinology* 34:305–10
13. Bell, M. J., Martin, C. W., Gonzales, C. C., McEnery, P. T., West, C. D. 1972. *J. Pediat. Surg.* 7:223–29
14. Bellair, J. T. 1972. Ovine growth hormone sequence of the C-terminal 68 amino acids. *Biochem. Biophys. Res. Commun.* 46:1128–34
15. Bern, H. A., Nicoll, C. S. 1968. The comparative endocrinology of prolactin. *Recent Progr. Horm. Res.* 24:681–720
16. Bernardis, L. L. 1970. Participation of the dorsomedial hypothalamic nucleus in the "feeding center" and water intake circuitry of the weanling rat. *J. Neuro Visceral Relat.* 31:387–98
17. Bernardis, L. L. 1972. Hypophagia, hypodipsia and hypoactivity following dorsomedial hypothalamic lesions. *Physiol. Behav.* 8:1161–64
18. Bernardis, L. L., Frohman, L. A. 1970. Effect of lesion size in the ventromedial hypothalamus on growth hormone and insulin levels in weanling rats. *Neuroendocrinology* 6:319–28
19. Bernardis, L. L., Goldman, J. K. 1972. Growth with metabolic changes in weanling rats with lesions in the dorsomedial hypothalamic nuclei. *Exp. Brain Res.* 15:425–29
20. Bernardis, L. L., Schnatz, J. D. 1971. Localization in the ventromedial hypothalamus of an area affecting plasma lipid levels. *J. Neuro Visceral Relat.* 32:90–99
21. Bernick, S., Ershoff, B. H. 1963. Histochemical study of bone in cortisone-treated rats. *Endocrinology* 72:231–37
22. Berntsen, E. 1968. Epiphyseal growth zones in oestradiol-treated rabbits. *Acta Endocrinol.* 57:69–80
23. Bettman, H. K., Goldman, H. S., Abramowicz, M., Sobel, E. H. 1971. Oxandrolone treatment of short stature: Effect on predicted mature height. *J. Pediat.* 79:1018–23

24. Bierich, J. R. 1972. On the aetiology of hypopituitary dwarfism. *Growth and Growth Hormone, Proc. 2nd Int. Symp. on Growth Hormone, 1971, Milan,* ed. A. Pecile, E. E. Muller, Int. Congr. Ser. 244, 408–14. Amsterdam: Excerpta Med. 511 pp.
25. Birkbeck, J. A. 1972. Growth in juvenile diabetes mellitus. *Diabetologia* 8:221–24
26. Blizzard, R. M. et al 1966. Comparative effects of animal prolactins and human growth hormone in hypopituitary children. *J. Clin. Endocrinol. Metab.* 26: 852–58
27. Bornstein, J. 1972. A proposed mechanism of the diabetogenic action of growth hormone and its relation in the action of insulin. *Isr. J. Med. Sci.* 8:407–12
28. Bornstein, J. 1972. Relation of the structure of human growth hormone to the control of carbohydrate and fat metabolism. See Ref. 24, 68–74
29. Bornstein, J., Armstrong, J. McD., Ng, F., Paddle, B. M., Misconi, L. 1971. Structure and synthesis of biologically active peptides derived from pituitary growth hormone. *Biochem. Biophys. Res. Commun.* 42:252–58
30. Bornstein, J., Armstrong, J. McD., Taft, H. P., Ng, F. M., Gould, M. K. 1973. The mechanism of the diabetogenic effects of pituitary growth hormone. *Postgrad. Med. J.* Suppl. 49: 219–42
31. Brasel, J. A. 1973. Review of findings in patients with emotional deprivation. See Ref. 9, 115–27
32. Breuer, C. B. 1969. Stimulation of DNA synthesis in cartilage of hypophysectomized rats by native and modified placental lactogen and anabolic hormones. *Endocrinology* 85:989–99
33. Cacciari, E., Tassoni, P., Cicognani, A., Pirazzoli, P., Collina, A. 1972. Entero-insular axis and relationship between insulin and growth hormone in the normal and obese child. Effects of oral lipidic and proteic load. *Helv. Paediat. Acta* 27:405–14
34. Catt, K. J. 1970. Growth Hormone. *Lancet* 1:933–39
35. Catt, K. J., Moffat, B., Niall, H. D. 1967. Human growth hormone and placental lactogen: structural similarity. *Science* 157:321
36. Chang, T. W., Raben, M. S., Mueller, J. F., Weinstein, L. 1973. Cultivation of the sparganum of Spirometra mansonoides in vitro with prolonged production of sparganum growth factor. *Proc. Soc. Exp. Biol. Med.* 143:457–59
37. Chillemi, F., Aiello, A., Pecile, A. 1972. Synthesis of human growth hormone fragments with growth-promoting activity. *Nature* 238:243–45
38. Chillemi, F., Pecile, A. 1971. Solid phase synthesis and bioassay by tibia test of monotetracontapeptide 81–121 and of ditriacontapeptide 122–153 of human growth hormone. *Experientia* 27:385–86
39. Clarke, J. S. et al 1974. Mechanism of growth retardation in children maintained on long term cancer chemotherapy. *Clin. Res.* 12:90A (Abstr.)
40. Copinschi, G., Wegienka, L. C., Hane, S., Forsham, P. H. 1967. Effect of arginine on serum levels of insulin and growth hormone in obese subjects. *Metabolism* 16:485–91
41. Costin, G., Kogut, M. D., Frasier, S. D. 1972. Effect of low-dose human growth hormone on carbohydrate metabolism in children with hypopituitarism. *J. Pediat.* 80:796–803
42. Costom, B. H., Grumbach, M. M., Kaplan, S. L. 1971. Effect of thyrotropin-releasing factor on serum thyroid-stimulating hormone. An approach to distinguishing hypothalamic from pituitary forms of idiopathic hypopituitary dwarfism. *J. Clin. Invest.* 50:2219–25
43. Curry, D. L., Bennett, L. I. 1973. Dynamics of insulin release by perfused rat pancreases: effect of hypohysectomy, growth hormone, adrenocorticotrophic hormone and hydrocortisone. *Endocrinology* 93:602–9
44. Daughaday, W. H. 1971. Regulation of skeletal growth by sulfation factor. *Advan. Intern. Med.* 17:237–63
45. Daughaday, W. H., Garland, J. T. 1972. The sulfation factor hypothesis: recent observations. See Ref. 24, 168–79
46. Daughaday, W. H., Jacobs, L. S. 1972. Human prolactin. *Rev. Physiol.* 67: 169–94
47. Daughaday, W. H., Kipnis, D. M. 1966. The growth promoting and anti-insulin actions of growth hormone. *Recent Progr. Horm. Res.* 22:49–99
48. Daughaday, W. H., Laron, Z., Pertzelan, A., Heins, J. N. 1969. Defective sulfation factor generation: a possible etiological link in dwarfism. *Trans. Assoc. Am. Physicians* 82:129–38
49. Daughaday, W. H., Mariz, I. K. 1962. Conversion of proline-C^{14} to labeled hydroxyproline by rat cartilage in vitro: effects of hypophysectomy, growth hor-

mone and cortisol. *J. Lab. Clin. Med.* 59:741–52

50. Daughaday, W. H., Parker, M. L. 1965. Human pituitary growth hormone. *Ann. Rev. Med.* 16:47–66
51. Daughaday, W. H., Peake, G. T., Birge, C. A., Mariz, I. K. 1968. The influence of endocrine factors on the concentration of growth hormone in rat pituitary. *Growth Hormone, Proc. 1st Int. Symp. on Growth Hormone, 1967, Milan,* ed. A. Pecile, E. E. Muller, Int. Congr. Ser. 158, 238–52. Amsterdam: Excerpta Med. 455 pp.
52. Daughaday, W. H., Reeder, C. 1966. Synchronous activation of DNA synthesis in hypophysectomized rat cartilage by growth hormone. *J. Lab. Clin. Med.* 68:357–68
53. Daughaday, W. H., Salmon, W. D. Jr., Alexander, F. 1959. Sulfation factor activity of sera from patients with pituitary disorders. *J. Clin. Endocrinol. Metab.* 7:743–58
54. Day, H. G., Follis, R. H. Jr. 1941. Skeletal changes in rats receiving estradiol benzoate as indicated by histological studies and determinations of bone ash, serum calcium and phosphatase. *Endocrinology* 28:83–93
55. Driscoll, S. G. 1965. The pathology of pregnancy complicated by diabetes mellitus. *Med. Clin. N. Am.* 49:1053–67
56. Dulak, N. C., Temin, H. M. 1973. A partially purified polypeptide fraction from rat liver cell conditioned medium with multiplication-stimulating activity for embryo fibroblasts. *J. Cell. Physiol.* 81:153–60
57. Eisenberg, R. M., Sorrentino, S. Jr., Knigge, K. M. 1972. Plasma growth hormone and corticosterone levels in the hypothyroid and athyroid rat. *Neuroendocrinology* 10:58–63
58. Elders, M. J. et al 1973. Laron's dwarfism: studies on the nature of the defect. *J. Pediat.* 83:253–63
59. Elsair, J., Variel, E., Gerbaux, S., Dartois, A. M., Royer, P. 1964. Effets de l'hormone de croissance dans le nanisme hypothalamo-hypophysaire. II. Etude des actions métaboliques de nouvelles préparations d'hormone de croissance bovine partiellement hydrolysée. *Rev. Fr. Etud. Clin. Biol.* 9:614–24
60. Engel, F. L., Kostyo, J. L. 1964. Metabolic actions of pituitary hormones. *Hormones* 5:69–158
61. Eshet, R., Laron, Z., Brown, M., Arnon, R. 1973. Immunoreactive properties of the plasma hGH from patients with the syndrome of familial dwarfism and high plasma IR-hGH. *J. Clin. Endocrinol. Metab.* 37:819–21
62. Falliers, C. J., Tan, L. S., Jørgensen, J. R., Bukantz, S. C. 1963. Childhood asthma and steroid therapy as influences on growth. *Am. J. Dis. Child.* 105:41–51
63. Felig, P., Marliss, E., Cahill, G. F. Jr. 1971. Metabolic response to human growth hormone during prolonged starvation. *J. Clin. Invest.* 50:411–21
64. Fellows, R. E. 1973. In discussion of Ref. 184, 404–7
65. Fellows, R. E. 1973. In discussion of Ref. 184, 416
66. Finkelstein, J. W. 1974. In discussion of Thompson, R. G., Plotnick, C., Kowarski, A., Blizzard, R. M. The pubertal growth spurt: role of human growth hormone. See Ref. 201, 670–94
67. Finkelstein, J. W., Kream, J., Ludan, A., Hellman, L. 1972. Sulfation factor (somatomedin): an explanation for continued growth in the absence of immunoassayable growth hormone in patients with hypothalamic tumors. *J. Clin. Endocrinol. Metab.* 35:13–17
68. Finkelstein, J. W., Roffwarg, H. P., Boyar, R. M., Kream, J., Hellman, L. 1972. Age-related change in the 24-hour spontaneous secretion of growth hormone. *J. Clin. Endocrinol. Metab.* 35:665–70
69. Florini, J. R. et al 1966. Characterization and biological effects of purified placental protein (human). *Endocrinology* 79:692–708
70. Foley, T. P. Jr., Jacobs, L. S., Hoffman, W., Daughaday, W. H., Blizzard, R. M. 1972. Human prolactin and thyrotropin concentrations in the serums of normal and hypopituitary children before and after the administration of synthetic thyrotropin releasing hormone. *J. Clin. Invest.* 51:2143–50
71. Foley, T. P. Jr., Owings, J., Hayford, J. T., Blizzard, R. M. 1972. Serum thyrotropin responses to synthetic thyrotropin releasing hormone in normal children and hypopituitary patients: a new test to distinguish primary releasing hormone deficiency from primary pituitary hormone deficiency. *J. Clin. Invest.* 51:431–37
72. Foss, G. L. 1965. The influence of androgen treatment on ultimate height in males. *Arch. Dis. Childhood* 40:66–70
73. Fox, M., Minot, A. S., Liddle, G. W. 1962. Oxandrolone: a potent anabolic steroid of novel chemical configuration.

J. Clin. Endocrinol. Metab. 22:921–24
74. Frantz, A. G., Kleinberg, D. L., Noel, G. L. 1972. Studies on prolactin in man. *Recent Progr. Horm. Res.* 28:527–90
75. Frantz, A. G., Rabkin, M. T. 1964. Human growth hormone. Clinical measurement, response to hypoglycemia, and suppression by glucocorticoids. *N. Eng. J. Med.* 271:1375–81
76. Frasier, S. D., Hilburn, J. M., Smith, F. G. Jr. 1970. Effect of adolescence on the serum growth hormone response to hypoglycemia. *J. Pediat.* 77:465–67
77. Frasier, S. D., Smith, F. G. Jr. 1968. Return of normal growth following removal of a craniopharyngioma. *Am. J. Dis. Child.* 116:311–14
78. Frasier, S. D., Smith, F. G. Jr. 1968. Effect of estrogens on mature height in tall girls: a controlled study. *J. Clin. Endocrinol. Metab.* 28:416–19
79. Friesen, H. 1965. Purification of a placental factor with immunological and chemical similarity to human growth hormone. *Endocrinology* 76:369–81
80. Friesen, H. G., Suwa, S., Pare, P. 1969. Synthesis and secretion of placental lactogen and other proteins by the placenta. *Recent Progr. Horm. Res.* 25:161–205
81. Friesen, H., Tolis, G., Shiu, R., Hwang, P. 1973. Studies on human prolactin: chemistry, radioreceptor assay and clinical significance. *Human Prolactin, Proc. Int. Symp. on Human Prolactin, Brussels,* ed. J. C. Pasteels, C. Robyn, Int. Congr. Ser. 308, 11–47. Amsterdam: Excerpta Med. 340 pp.
82. Frohman, L. A., Bernardis, L. L., Schnatz, J. D., Burek, L. 1968. Effect of ventromedial hypothalamic lesions on carbohydrate and lipid metabolism in weanling rats. *Am. J. Physiol.* 216: 1496–1501
83. Garland, J. T., Daughaday, W. H. 1972. Feedback inhibition of pituitary growth hormone in rats infected with *Spirometra mansonoides*. *Proc. Soc. Exp. Biol. Med.* 139:497–99
84. Garland, J. T., Lottes, M. E., Kozak, S., Daughaday, W. H. 1972. Stimulation of DNA synthesis in isolated chondrocytes by sulfation factor. *Endocrinology* 90:1086–90
85. Garland, J. T., Ruegamer, W. R., Daughaday, W. H. 1971. Induction of sulfation factor activity by infection of hypophysectomized rats with *Spirometra mansonoides. Endocrinology* 88: 924–27
86. Garn, S. M., Haskell, J. A. 1960. Fat thickness and developmental status in childhood and adolescence. *Am. J. Dis. Child.* 99:746–51
87. Geller, J. 1968. Oxandrolone effect on growth and bone age in idiopathic growth failure. *Acta Endocrinol.* 59: 307–16
88. Geschwind, I. I., Li, C. H. 1955. The tibia test for growth hormone. *The Hypophyseal Growth Hormone, Nature and Actions,* ed. R. W. Smith Jr., O. H. Goebler, C. N. H. Long, 28–53. New York: McGraw. 576 pp.
89. Godard, C. 1973. Plasma growth hormone levels in severe infantile malnutrition in Bolivia. See Ref. 9, 19–30
90. Godard, C., Zahnd, G. R. 1971. Growth hormone and insulin in severe infantile malnutrition. I. Plasma growth hormone response to hypoglycemia. *Helv. Paediat. Acta* 26:266–75
91. Goodman, H. M. 1968. Growth hormone and the metabolism of carbohydrate and lipid in adipose tissue. *Ann. NY Acad. Sci.* 148:419–40
92. Grant, D. B., Hambley, J., Becker, D., Pimstone, B. L. 1973. Reduced sulphation factor in undernourished children. *Arch. Dis. Childhood* 48:596–600
93. Greenblatt, R. B., McDonough, P. G., Mahesh, V. B. 1968. Estrogen therapy for the inhibition of linear growth. *Clin. Endocrinol.* 2:117–31
94. Greenwood, F. C. 1972. Evidence for the separate existence of a human pituitary prolactin—a review and results. See Ref. 24, 91–97
95. Grumbach, M. M., Kaplan, S. L., Sciarra, J. J., Burr, I. M. 1968. Chorionic growth hormone-prolactin (CGP): secretion, disposition, biological activity in man and postulated function as the growth hormone of the second half of pregnancy. *Ann. NY Acad. Sci.* 148:501–31
96. Grunt, J. A. 1964. Effects of neonatal gonadectomy on skeletal growth and development in the rat. *Endocrinology* 75:805–8
97. Guest, G. M. 1953. The Mauriac syndrome. Dwarfism, hepatomegaly and obesity with juvenile diabetes mellitus. *Diabetes* 2:415–17
98. Haist, R. E. 1955. The influence of growth hormone and other factors on the islets of Langerhans and the pancreas. See Ref. 88, 437–47
99. Hall, K. 1970. Quantitative determination of the sulfation factor activity in

human serum. *Acta Endocrinol.* 63: 338–50

100. Hall, K. 1971. Effect of intravenous administration of human growth hormone on sulfation factor activity in serum of hypopituitary subjects. *Acta Endocrinol.* 66:491–97
101. Hall, K. 1972. Human somatomedin. Determination, occurrence, biologic activity and purification. *Acta Endocrinol.* 70(Suppl. 163):5–52
102. Hall, K., Bozovic, M. 1969. Stimulation of ^{35}S incorporation into embryonic chick cartilage by extract from rat muscle. *Horm. Metab. Res.* 1:235–40
103. Hall, K., Olin, P. 1972. Sulphation factor activity and growth rate during long-term treatment of patients with pituitary dwarfism with human growth hormone. *Acta Endocrinol.* 69:417–33
104. Hall, K., Uthne, K. 1971. Some biological properties of purified sulfation factor (SF) from human plasma. *Acta Med. Scand.* 190:137–43
105. Hall, K., Uthne, K. 1972. Human growth hormone and sulfation factor. See Ref. 24, 192–98
106. Hansen, Aa. P., Johansen, K. 1970. Diurnal patterns of blood glucose, serum free fatty acids, insulin, glucagon, and growth hormone in normals and juvenile diabetics. *Diabetologia* 6:27–33
107. Herbai, G. 1970. Retardation of body growth and inhibition of sulphate incorporation into costal cartilage of the mouse by various natural and synthetic oestrogens and two oestrogen antagonists. *Acta Soc. Med. Upsal.* 75:209–28
108. Herbai, G. 1971. Studies on the site and mechanism of action of the growth inhibiting effects of estrogens. *Acta Physiol. Scand.* 83:77–90
109. Hintz, R. L., Clemmons, D. R., Underwood, L. E., Van Wyk, J. J. 1972. Competitive binding of somatomedin to the insulin receptors of adipocytes, chondrocytes, and liver membranes. *Proc. Nat. Acad. Sci. USA* 69:2351–53
110. Hintz, R. L., Orsini, E. M., Van Camp, M. G. 1974. Evidence for a somatomedin binding protein in plasma. *Proc. 56th Ann. Meet. Endocrine Soc.* A-71 (Abstr.)
111. Hjalmarson, A. 1968. *Acta Endocrinol.* 57(Suppl. 126):1–60
112. Holmes, L. B., Frantz, A. G., Rabkin, M. T., Soeldner, J. S., Crawford, J. D. 1968. Normal growth with subnormal growth hormone levels. *N. Engl. J. Med.* 279:559–66
113. Hortling, H., Wahlfors, K. 1959. Long-term treatment of dwarfism with androgens and thyroid hormone. *Acta Endocrinol.* 32:563–71
114. Howard, E. 1963. Effects of steroids on epiphysiodiaphysial union in prepuberal mice. *Endocrinology* 72:11–18
115. Hoyt, W. F., Kaplan, S. L., Grumbach, M. M., Glaser, J. S. 1970. Septo-optic dysplasia and pituitary dwarfism. *Lancet* 1:893–94
116. Hwang, P., Guyda, H., Friesen, H. G. 1972. Purification of human prolactin. *J. Biol. Chem.* 247:1955–58
117. Illig, R., Prader, A. 1970. Effect of testosterone on growth hormone secretion in patients with anorchia and delayed puberty. *J. Clin. Endocrinol. Metab.* 30:615–18
118. Jackson, S. T., Rallison, M. L., Buntin, W. H., Johnson, S. B., Flynn, R. R. 1973. Use of oxandrolone for growth stimulation in children. *Am. J. Dis. Child.* 126:481–84
119. Jakob, A., Hauri, C., Froesch, E. R. 1968. Non-suppressible insulin-like activity in human serum. III. Differentiation of two distinct molecules with non-suppressible ILA. *J. Clin. Invest.* 47: 2678–88
120. Jaya Rao, K. S., Ragmuramulu, N. 1973. Growth hormone and insulin secretion in protein calorie malnutrition as seen in India. See Ref. 9, 91–98
121. Johanson, A. J., Brasel, J. A., Blizzard, R. M. 1969. Growth in patients with gonadal dysgenesis receiving fluoxymestrone. *J. Pediat.* 75:1015–21
122. Josimovich, J. B., MacLaren, J. A. 1962. Presence in the human placenta and term serum of a highly lactogenic substance immunologically related to pituitary growth hormone. *Endocrinology* 131:1171–75
123. Josimovich, J. B., Mintz, D. H. 1968. Biological and immunochemical studies on human placental lactogen. *Ann. N.Y. Acad. Sci.* 148:488–500
124. Josimovich, J. B., Mintz, D. H., Finster, J. L. 1967. Estrogenic inhibition of growth hormone-induced tibial epiphyseal growth in hypophysectomized rats. *Endocrinology* 81:1428–30
125. Kaplan, S. L., Grumbach, M. M. 1964. Studies of a human and simian placental hormone with growth hormone-like and prolactin-like activities. *J. Clin. Endocrinol. Metab.* 24:80–100
126. Kaplan, S. L., Grumbach, M. M., Friesen, H. G., Costom, B. H. 1972. Thyrotropin-releasing factor (TRF)

effect on secretion of human pituitary prolactin and thyrotropin in children and in idiopathic hypopituitary dwarfism: further evidence for hypophysiotropic hormone deficiencies. *J. Clin. Endocrinol. Metab.* 35:825–30
127. Kaplan, J. G., Moshang, T. Jr., Bernstein, R., Parks, J. S., Bongiovanni, A. M. 1973. Constitutional delay of growth and development: effects of treatment with androgens. *J. Pediat.* 82:38–44
128. Katz, H. P., Youlton, R., Kaplan, S. L., Grumbach, M. M. 1969. Growth and growth hormone. III. Growth hormone release in children with primary hypothyroidism and thyrotoxicosis. *J. Clin. Endocrinol. Metab.* 29:346–51
129. Kenny, F. M., Guyda, H. J., Wright, J. C., Friesen, H. G. 1973. Prolactin and somatomedin in hypopituitary patients with "catch-up" growth following operations for craniopharyngioma. *J. Clin. Endocrinol. Metab.* 36:378–80
130. Kenny, F. M. et al 1968. Iatrogenic hypopituitarism in craniopharyngioma: unexplained catch-up growth in three children. *J. Pediat.* 72:766–75
131. Kolli, E. A., Simitsyna, A. L., Keda, Y. M. 1969. The effect of enzymatic hydrolysis and aggregation on the biological activity of bovine growth hormone. *Protein and Polypeptide Hormones, Proc. Int. Symp., 1968, Liege,* ed. M. Margoulies, Int. Cong. Ser. 161, 239–41. Amsterdam: Excerpta Med. 939 pp.
132. Korner, A. 1965. Growth hormone control of biosynthesis of protein and ribonucleic acid. *Recent Progr. Horm. Res.* 21:205–40
133. Krieger, I., Chen, Y. C. 1969. Calorie requirements for weight gain in infants with growth failure due to maternal deprivation, undernutrition and congenital heart disease. A correlation analysis. *Pediatrics* 44:647–54
134. Krieger, I., Good, M. H. 1970. Adrenocortical and thyroid function in the deprivation syndrome. *Am. J. Dis. Child.* 120:95–102
135. Krieger, I., Mellinger, R. C. 1971. Pituitary function in the deprivation syndrome. *J. Pediat.* 79:216–25
136. Laron, Z., Karp, M., Pertzelan, A., Kauli, R. 1972. Insulin, growth and growth hormone. *Isr. J. Med. Sci.* 8:440–50
137. Laron, Z. et al 1972. The syndrome of familial dwarfism and high plasma immunoreactive human growth hormone (IR-HGH). See Ref. 24, 458–82
138. Laron, Z., Pertzelan, A. 1968. The comparative effect of 6α-fluoroprednisolone, 6α-methylprednisolone and hydrocortisone on linear growth of children with congenital adrenal virilism and Addison's diseases. *J. Pediat.* 73:774–82
139. Laron, Z., Pertzelan, A., Karp, M. Kowadlo-Silbergeld, A., Daughaday, W. H. 1971. Administration of growth hormone to patients with familial dwarfism with high plasma immunoreactive growth hormone: measurement of sulfation factor, metabolic and linear growth responses. *J. Clin. Endocrinol. Metab.* 33:332–42
140. Laron, Z., Pertzelan, A., Mannheimer, S. 1966. Genetic pituitary dwarfism with high serum concentration of growth hormone: a new inborn error of metabolism? *Isr. J. Med. Sci.* 2:152–55
141. Lawrence, R. I. B., Salter, J. M., Best, C. H. 1954. Effect of insulin on nitrogen retention in the hypophysectomized rat. *Brit. Med. J.* 2:437–39
142. Levine, L. S., Sonenberg, M., New, M. I. 1973. Metabolic effects in children of a 37 amino acid fragment of bovine growth hormone. *J. Clin. Endocrinol. Metab.* 37:607–15
143. Lewis, U. J. 1973. In discussion of Ref. 81, 37–38
144. Lewis, U. J., Singh, R. N. P., Seavey, B. K. 1971. Human prolactin: isolation and some properties. *Biochem. Biophys. Res. Commun.* 44:1169–76
145. Li, C. H. 1957. Properties of and structural investigations on growth hormones isolated from bovine, monkey and human pituitary glands. *Fed. Proc.* 16:775–83
146. Li, C. H., Dixon, J. S. 1971. Human pituitary growth hormone. XXXII. The primary structure of the hormone: revision. *Arch. Biochem. Biophys.* 146: 233–36
147. Li, C. H., Dixon, J. S., Chung, D. 1971. Primary structure of the human chorionic somatomammotropin (hCS) molecule. *Science* 173:56–58
148. Li, C. H., Dixon, J. S., Liu, W. K. 1969. Human pituitary growth hormone. XIX. The primary structure of the hormone. *Arch. Biochem. Biophys.* 133: 70–91
149. Li, C. H., Gordon, D., Knorr, J. 1973. The primary structure of sheep pituitary growth hormone. *Arch. Biochem. Biophys.* 156:493–508
150. Li, C. H., Yamashiro, D. 1970. The synthesis of a protein possessing growth-

promoting and lactogenic activities. *J. Am. Chem. Soc.* 92:7608–9
151. Lloyd, H. M., Meares, J. D., Jacobi, J., Thomas, F. J. 1971. Effects of stilboestrol in growth hormone secretion and pituitary cell proliferation in the male rat. *J. Endocrinol.* 51:473–81
152. Lostroh, A. J., Krahl, M. E., Marshall, L. B. 1973. Diabetogenic peptides of pituitary origin: preparation from sheep or from human growth hormone by pepsin digestion. *Proc. 55th Ann. Meet. Endocrine Soc.* A-242 (Abstr.)
153. Luft, R., Cerasi, E. 1968. Human growth hormone in blood glucose homeostasis. See Ref. 51, 373–81
154. Lunn, P. G., Whitehead, R. G., Hay, R. W., Baker, B. A. 1973. Progressive changes in serum cortisol, insulin and growth hormone concentrations and their relationship to the distorted amino acid pattern during the development of kwashiorkor. *Brit. J. Nutr.* 29:399–422
155. MacGillivray, M., Aceto, T. Jr., Frohman, L. 1968. Plasma growth hormone response and growth retardation of hypothyroidism. *Am. J. Dis. Child.* 115:273–76
156. MacGillivray, M., Kolotkin, M., Munschauer, R. W. 1974. Enhanced linear growth responses in hypopituitary dwarfs treated with growth hormone plus androgen versus growth hormone alone. *Pediat. Res.* 8:103–8
157. Marshall, R. N., Underwood, L. E., Voina, S. J., Van Wyk, J. J. 1974. Characterization of the insulin and somatomedin-C receptors in human placental membranes. *J. Clin. Endocrinol. Metab.* 39:283–92
158. Martin, J. M., Gagliardino, J. J. 1967. Effect of growth hormone on the isolated pancreatic islets of rat in vitro. *Nature* 213:630–31
159. McConaghey, P. 1972. The production of "sulphation factor" by rat liver. *J. Endocrinol.* 52:1–9
160. McConaghey, P., Dehnel, J. 1972. Preliminary studies of "sulphation factor" production by rat kidney. *J. Endocrinol.* 52:587–88
161. McConaghey, P., Sledge, C. B. 1970. Production of "sulphation factor" by the perfused liver. *Nature* 225:1249–50
162. Megyesi, K. et al 1974. Insulin and nonsuppressible insulin-like activity (NSILA-S): evidence for separate plasma membrane receptor sites. *Biochem. Biophys. Res. Commun.* 57: 307–15
163. Megyesi, K., Kahn, C. R., Roth, J., Gorden, P. 1974. Hypoglycemia in association with extrapancreatic tumors: demonstration of elevated plasma NSILA-S by a new radioreceptor assay. *J. Clin. Endocrinol. Metab.* 38:931–34
164. Meites, J. et al 1972. Recent studies on functions and control of prolactin secretion in rats. *Recent Progr. Horm. Res.* 28:471–526
165. Mellman, W. J., Bongiovanni, A. M., Garrison, M., Steiker, D. D. 1961. Comparison of fluoxymestrone and methyltestosterone as growth stimulants. *Pediatrics* 27:525–30
166. Merimee, T. J., Rabinowitz, D., Fineberg, S. E. 1969. Arginine-initiated release of human growth hormone. Factors modifying the response in normal man. *N. Engl. J. Med.* 280:1434–38
167. Migeon, C. J. 1968. Updating of the treatment of congenital adrenal hyperplasia. *J. Pediat.* 73:805–6
168. Mills, J. B. et al 1973. Metabolic effects of plasmin digests of human growth hormone in the rat and man. *J. Clin. Invest.* 52:2941–51
169. Mills, J. B., Wilhelmi, A. E. 1972. Studies on the primary structure of porcine growth hormone. See Ref. 24, 38–41
170. Milman, A. E., deMoor, P., Lukens, F. D. W. 1951. Relation of purified pituitary growth hormone and insulin in regulation of nitrogen balance. *Am. J. Physiol.* 166:354–64
171. Mølsted-Pedersen, L., Jørgensen, K. R. 1972. Aspects of carbohydrate metabolism in newborn infants of diabetic mothers. III. Plasma insulin during intravenous glucose tolerance test. *Acta Endocrinol.* 71:115–25
172. Morell, B., Froesch, E. R. 1973. Fibroblasts as an experimental tool in metabolic and hormone studies. *Eur. J. Clin. Invest.* 3:119–23
173. Morris, H. G., Jørgensen, J. R., Elrick, H., Goldsmith, R. E. 1968. Metabolic effects of human growth in corticosteroid-treated children. *J. Clin. Invest.* 47:436–51
174. Morris, H. G., Jørgensen, J. R., Jenkins, S. A. 1968. Plasma growth hormone concentration in corticosteriod-treated children. *J. Clin. Invest.* 47:427–35
175. Mosier, H. D. Jr. 1971. Failure of compensatory (catch-up) growth in the rat. *Pediat. Res.* 5:59–63
176. Mosier, H. D. Jr., Smith, F. G. Jr., Schultz, M. A. 1972. Failure of catch-up growth after Cushing's syndrome in

childhood. *Am. J. Dis. Child.* 124: 251–53
177. Murakawa, S., Raben, M. S. 1968. Effect of growth hormone and placental lactogen on DNA synthesis in rat costal cartilage and adipose tissue. *Endocrinology* 83:645–50
178. Nadler, A. C., Sonenberg, M., New, M. I., Free, C. A. 1967. Growth hormone activity in man with components of tryptic digests of bovine growth hormone. *Metabolism* 16:830–45
179. Neri, P., Arezzini, C., Canali, G., Cocola, F., Tarli, P. 1971. Effect of chemical modifications and tryptic digestions on biological and immunological activities of human chorionic somatomammotropin. See Ref. 24, 199–208
180. New, M. I., Schwartz, E., Parks, G. A., Landey, S., Wiedemann, E. 1972. Pseudohypopituitary dwarfism with normal plasma growth hormone and low serum sulfation factor. *J. Pediat.* 80:620–26
181. Niall, H. D. 1971. Revised primary structure for human growth hormone. *Nature New Biol.* 230:90–91
182. Niall, H. D. 1972. The chemistry of the lactogenic hormones. *Prolactin and Carcinogenesis, Proc. 4th Tenovus Inst. Workshop, Cardiff,* ed. A. R. Boyns, K. Griffiths, 13–24. Cardiff: Alpha Omega Alpha. 229 pp.
183. Niall, H. D., Hogan, M. L., Sauer, R., Rosenblum, I. Y., Greenwood, F. C. 1971. Sequences of pituitary and placental lactogenic and growth hormone: evolution from a primordial peptide by gene reduplication. *Proc. Nat. Acad. Sci. USA* 68:866–69
184. Niall, H. D. et al 1973. The chemistry of growth hormone and the lactogenic hormones. *Recent Progr. Horm. Res.* 29:387–416
185. Norman, N., Turter, A. R. 1968. Radioimmunoassay studies with human growth hormone and a pituitary lipid mobilizing factor. *Acta Endocrinol.* 58:318–38
186. Nutting, D. F. 1973. In discussion of Ref. 184, 415–16
187. Nutting, D. F., Kostyo, J. L., Goodman, H. M., Fellows, R. E. 1970. Biologically active cyanogen bromide fragments of bovine growth hormone. *Endocrinology* 86:416–19
188. Nutting, D. F., Kostyo, J. L., Mills, J. B., Wilhelmi, A. E. 1970. A cyanogen bromide fragment of reduced and S-aminoethylated porcine growth hormone with anabolic activity. *Biochim. Biophys. Acta* 200:601–4
189. Nutting, D. F., Kostyo, J. L., Mills, J. B., Wilhelmi, A. E. 1972. Dissociation of some of the biological activities of porcine and human growth hormones by cyanogen bromide cleavage. *Endocrinology* 90:1202–13
190. O'Brien, C. P. Jr., Bach, L. M. 1970. Observations concerning hypothalamic control of growth. *Am. J. Physiol.* 218:226–30
191. Parker, M. L., Daughaday, W. H. 1968. Growth retardation: correlation of plasma GH responses to insulin and arginine with subsequent metabolic and skeletal responses to GH treatment. See Ref. 51, 398–407
192. Parra, A. et al 1973. Insulin-growth hormone adaptations in marasmus and kwashiorkor as seen in Mexico. See Ref. 9, 31–43
193. Peake, G. T., Birge, C. A., Daughaday, W. H. 1973. Alterations of radioimmunoassayable growth hormone and prolactin during hypothyroidism. *Endocrinology* 92:487–93
194. Peake, G. T., Mariz, I. K., Daughaday, W. H. 1968. Radioimmunoassay of growth hormone in rats bearing somatotropin producing tumors. *Endocrinology* 83:714–20
195. Pecile, A., Muller, E. E. 1972. See Ref. 24, 1–511
196. Peck, W. A., Brandt, J., Miller, I. 1967. Hydrocortisone-induced inhibition of protein synthesis and uridine incorporation in isolated bone cells in vitro. *Proc. Nat. Acad. Sci. USA* 57:1599–1606
197. Pedersen, J. 1954. Weight and length at birth of infants of diabetic mothers. *Acta Endocrinol.* 16:330–42
198. Penny, R., Blizzard, R. M. 1972. The possible influence of puberty on the release of growth hormone in three males with apparent isolated growth hormone deficiency. *J. Clin. Endocrinol. Metab.* 34:82–84
199. Phares, C. K., Ruegamer, W. R. 1973. In vitro preparation of a growth factor from plerocercoids of the tapeworm, *Spirometra mansonoides*. *Proc. Soc. Exp. Biol. Med.* 142:374–77
200. Phillips, L. S., Herington, A. C., Daughaday, W. H. 1974. Somatomedin stimulation of sulfate incorporation in porcine costal cartilage discs. *Endocrinology* 94:856–63
201. Phillips, L. S., Herington, A. C., Daughaday, W. H. 1974. Hormone effects on somatomedin action and

somatomedin generation. *Advances in Human Growth Hormone Research, Proc. Symp. Nat. Pituitary Agency, NIAMDD, 1973, Baltimore,* ed. S. Raiti, 50–75. DHEW Pub. No. (NIH) 74–612. 961 pp.

202. Phillips, L. S., Herington, A. C., Mueller, M. C., Daughaday, W. H. 1973. Effect of cortisol on somatomedin generation in vivo and somatomedin action in vitro. *Proc. 55th Ann. Meet. Endocrine Soc.* A-122 (Abstr.)
203. Pierson, R. W. Jr., Temin, H. M. 1972. The partial purification from calf serum of a fraction with multiplication-stimulating activity for chicken fibroblasts in cell culture with non-suppressible insulin-like activity. *J. Cell. Physiol.* 79:319–30
204. Pimstone, B., Barbezat, G., Hansen, J. D. L., Murray, P. 1967. Growth hormone and protein-calorie malnutrition. Impaired suppression during induced hyperglycemia. *Lancet* 2:1333–34
205. Pimstone, B. L., Barbezat, G., Hansen, J. D. L., Murray, P. 1968. Studies on growth hormone secretion in protein-calorie malnutrition. *Am. J. Clin. Nutr.* 21:482–87
206. Pimstone, B. L., Becker, D.J., Hansen, J. D. L. 1972. Human growth hormone in protein-calorie malnutrition. See Ref. 24, 389–401
207. Pimstone, B. L., Wittmann, W., Hansen, J. D. L., Murray, P. 1966. Growth hormone and kwashiorkor. Role of protein in growth hormone homeostasis. *Lancet* 2:779–80
208. Plotnick, L. P., Thompson, R. G., Beitins, I., Blizzard, R. M. 1974. Integrated concentrations of growth hormone correlated with stage of puberty and estrogen levels in girls. *J. Clin. Endocrinol. Metab.* 38:436–39
209. Pond, H. 1970. Some aspects of growth in diabetic children. *Postgrad. Med. J. Suppl.* 46:616–23
210. Powell, G. F., Brasel, J. A., Blizzard, R. M. 1967. Emotional deprivation and growth retardation simulating idiopathic hypopituitarism. I. Clinical evaluation of the syndrome. *N. Engl. J. Med.* 276:1271–78
211. Powell, G. F., Brasel, J. A., Raiti, S., Blizzard, R. M. 1967. Emotional deprivation and growth retardation simulating idiopathic hypopituitarism. II. Endocrinologic evaluation of the syndrome. *N. Engl. J. Med.* 276:1279–83
212. Powell, G. F., Hopwood, N. J., Barrett, E. S. 1973. Growth hormone studies before and during catch-up growth in a child with emotional deprivation and short stature. *J. Clin. Endocrinol. Metab.* 37:674–79
213. Prader, A., Tanner, J. M., von Harnack, G. A. 1963. Catch-up growth following illness or starvation. *J. Pediat.* 62:646–59
214. Raben, M. S., Murakawa, S., Matute, M. 1972. Some observations concerning serum "thymidine factor". See Ref. 24, 124–31
215. Raiti, S., Blizzard, R. M. 1970. Human growth hormone: current knowledge regarding its role in normal and abnormal metabolic states. *Advan. Pediat.* 17:99–123
216. Raiti, S., Trias, E., Levitsky, L., Grossman, M. S. 1973. Oxandrolone and human growth hormone. Comparison of growth-stimulating effects in short children. *Am. J. Dis. Child.* 126:597–600
217. Rappaport, R., Bouthreuil, E., Marti-Henneberg, C., Basmaciogullari, A. 1973. Linear growth rate, bone maturation and growth hormone secretion in prepubertal children with congenital adrenal hyperplasia. *Acta Paediat. Scand.* 62:513–19
218. Renner, R., Hepp, K. D., Humbel, R. E., Froesch, E. R. 1973. Mechanism of the anti-lipolytic action of NSILA-S: inhibition of adenylate cyclase activity in lipocyte ghosts. *Horm. Metab. Res.* 5:56–57
219. Reusser, F. 1965. Enzymatic modification of bovine growth hormone by proteolytic streptomycete extracts. *Acta Endocrinol.* 49:578–88
220. Rimoin, D. L., Merimee, T. J., McKusick, V. A. 1966. Growth hormone deficiency in man: an isolated, recessively inherited defect. *Science* 152:1635–37
221. Rimoin, D. L., Schechter, J. E. 1973. Histological and ultrastructural studies in isolated growth hormone deficiency. *J. Clin. Endocrinol. Metab.* 37:725–35
222. Root, A. W. 1972. *Human Pituitary Growth Hormone.* Springfield, Ill.: Thomas. 247 pp.
223. Root, A. W. 1973. Endocrinology of puberty. I. Normal sexual maturation. *J. Pediat.* 83:1–19
224. Root, A. W. 1973. Endocrinology of puberty. II. Aberrations of sexual maturation. *J. Pediat.* 83:187–200
225. Root, A. W., Rosenfield, R. L., Bongiovanni, A. M., Eberlein, R. 1967. The plasma growth hormone response to insulin-induced hypoglycemia in children

with retardation of growth. *Pediatrics* 39:844–52
226. Rosenbloom, A. L., Frias, J. L. 1973. Oxandrolone for growth promotion in Turner's syndrome. *Am. J. Dis. Child.* 125:385–87
227. Rudman, D., Freides, D., Patterson, J. H., Gibbas, D. L. 1973. Diurnal variation in the responsiveness of human subjects to human growth hormone. *J. Clin. Invest.* 52:912–18
228. Salmon, W. D. 1972. Investigation with a partially purified preparation of serum sulfation factor: lack of specificity for cartilage sulfation. See Ref. 24, 180–91
229. Salmon, W. D. Jr., Bower, P. H., Thompson, E. Y. 1963. Effect of protein anabolic steroids on sulfate incorporation by cartilage of male rats. *J. Lab. Clin. Med.* 61:120–28
230. Salmon, W. D. Jr., Daughaday, W. H. 1957. A hormonally controlled serum factor which stimulates sulfate incorporation by cartilage in vitro. *J. Lab. Clin. Med.* 49:825–36
231. Salmon, W. D. Jr., DuVall, M. R. 1970. A serum fraction with "sulfation factor activity" stimulates in vitro incorporation of leucine and sulfate into protein-polysaccharide complexes, uridine into RNA, and thymidine into DNA of costal cartilage from hypophysectomized rats. *Endocrinology* 86:721–27
232. Salmon, W. D. Jr., DuVall, M. R. 1970. In vitro stimulation of leucine incorporation into muscle and cartilage protein by a serum fraction with sulfation factor activity: differentiation of effects from those of growth hormone and insulin. *Endocrinology* 87:1168–80
233. Salmon, W. D. Jr., DuVall, M. R., Thompson, E. Y. 1968. Stimulation by insulin in vitro in incorporation of (^{35}S)sulfate and (^{14}C)leucine into protein-polysaccharide complexes, (^{3}H)uridine into RNA, and (^{3}H)thymidine into DNA of costal cartilage from hypophysectomized rats. *Endocrinology* 82:493–99
234. Salter, J. M., Best, C. H. 1953. Insulin as a growth hormone. *Brit. Med. J.* 2:353–56
235. Samuel, A. M., Deshpande, U. R. 1972. Growth hormone levels in protein calorie malnutrition. *J. Clin. Endocrinol. Metab.* 35:863–67
236. Santomé, J. A. et al 1973. Primary structure of bovine growth hormone. *Eur. J. Biochem.* 37:164–70
237. Saxena, B. N. 1971. Protein-polypeptide hormones of the human placenta. *Vitam. Horm.* 29:95–151
238. Schoen, E. J., Solomon, I. L., Warner, O., Wingerd, D. 1973. Estrogen treatment of tall girls. *Am. J. Dis. Child.* 125:71–74
239. Schultz, R. B., Blizzard, R. M. 1966. A comparison of human placental lactogen (HPL) and human growth hormone (HGH) in hypopituitary patients. *J. Clin. Endocrinol. Metab.* 26:921–24
240. Schutt-Aine, J. C., Drash, A. L. 1972. Human placental lactogen and human growth hormone for hypopituitarism. Absence of growth potentiation. *Am. J. Dis. Child.* 123:475–79
241. Schwartz, P. L. 1972. Lack of effect of a cyanogen bromide fragment of human growth hormone on some aspects of carbohydrate metabolism in vitro. *Proc. Soc. Exp. Biol. Med.* 141:419–22
242. Scow, R. O., Hagen, S. N. 1965. Effect of testosterone propionate and growth hormone on growth and chemical composition of muscle and other tissues in hypophysectomized male rats. *Endocrinology* 77:852–58
243. Seip, M., van der Hagen, C. B., Trygstad, O. 1968. Hereditary pituitary dwarfism with spontaneous puberty. *Arch. Dis. Childhood* 43:47–52
244. Selenkow, H. A., Saxena, B. N., Dana, C. L., Emerson, K. 1969. Measurement and pathophysiologic significance of human placental lactogen. *The Foeto-Placental Unit. Proc. Int. Symp. Foeto-Placental Unit, 1968, Milan,* ed. A. Pecile, C. Finzi. Int. Congr. Ser. 183, 340–62. Amsterdam: Excerpta Med. 425 pp.
245. Sherwood, L. M., Handwerger, S., McLaurin, W. D., Lanner, M. 1971. Amino acid sequence of human placental lactogen. *Nature New Biol.* 233: 59–61
246. Sherwood, L. M., Handwerger, S., McLaurin, W. D., Pang, E. G. 1972. Comparison of the structure and function of human placental lactogen and human growth hormone. See Ref. 24, 209–23
247. Silberberg, M., Silberberg, R. 1971. Steroid hormones and bone. *The Biochemistry and Physiology of Bone,* ed. G. H. Bourne, 3: Chap. 11, 401–84. New York: Academic. 2nd ed. 3 vols. 584 pp.
248. Silberberg, M., Silberberg, R., Hasler, M. 1966. Fine structure of articular cartilage in mice receiving cortisone acetate. *Arch. Pathol.* 82:569–82
249. Simmons, D. J., Kunin, A. S. 1967. Autoradiographic and biochemical investi-

gations of the effect of cortisone on bones of the rat. *Clin. Orthop.* 55: 201–15

250. Simpson, M. E., Marx, W., Becks, H., Evans, H. M. 1944. Effect of testosterone propionate on the body weight and skeletal system of hypophysectomized rats. Synergism with pituitary growth hormone. *Endocrinology* 35:309–16
251. Singh, R. N. P., Seavey, B. K., Rice, V. P., Lindsey, T. T., Lewis, U. J. 1974. Modified forms of human growth hormone with increased biological activities. *Endocrinology* 94:883–91
252. Smith, Q. T., Allison, D. J. 1965. Skin and femur collagens and urinary hydroxyproline of cortisone-treated rats. *Endocrinology* 77:785–91
253. Sobel, E. H., Raymond, C. S., Quinn, K. V., Talbot, N. B. 1956. The use of methyltestosterone to stimulate growth: relative influence on skeletal maturation and linear growth. *J. Clin. Endocrinol. Metab.* 16:241–48
254. Sogani, R. K., Matsushita, S., Mueller, J. F., Raben, M. S. 1972. Stimulation of ornithine decarboxylase activity in rat tissues by growth hormone and by serum growth factor from rats infested with spargana of *Spirometra mansonoides*. *Biochim. Biophy. Acta* 279: 377–86
255. Solomon, S., Friesen, H. 1968. Endocrine relations between the mother and fetus. *Ann. Rev. Med.* 19:399–430
256. Sonenberg, M. 1971. Interaction of human growth hormone and human erythrocyte membranes studied by intrinsic fluorescence. *Proc. Nat. Acad. Sci. USA* 68:1051–55
257. Sonenberg, M., Dellacha, J. M. 1967. Anabolic effects in man of papain digests of bovine growth hormone. *J. Clin. Endocrinol. Metab.* 27:1035–40
258. Sonenberg, M., Dellacha, J. M., Free, C. A., Nadler, A. C. 1969. Growth hormone activity in man of chymotryptic digests of bovine growth hormone. *J. Endocrinol.* 44:255–65
259. Sonenberg, M. et al 1965. The metabolic effects in man of bovine growth hormone digested with trypsin. *Metabolism* 14:1189–1213
260. Sonenberg, M., Kikutani, M., Free, C. A., Nadler, A. C., Dellacha, J. M. 1968. Chemical and biological characterization of clinically active tryptic digests of bovine growth hormone. *Ann. NY Acad. Sci.* 148:532–58
261. Sonenberg, M. et al 1972. Studies on active fragments of bovine growth hormone. See Ref. 24, 75–90
262. Soyka, L. F., Bode, H. H., Crawford, J. D., Flynn, F. J. Jr. 1970. Effectiveness of long-term human growth hormone therapy for short stature in children with growth hormone deficiency. *J. Clin. Endocrinol. Metab.* 30:1–14
263. Soyka, L. F., Crawford, J. D. 1965. Antagonism by cortisone of the linear growth induced in hypopituitary patients and hypophysectomized rats by human growth hormone. *J. Clin. Endocrinol. Metab.* 25:469–75
264. Sperling, M. A., Kenny, F. M., Drash, A. L. 1970. Arginine-induced growth hormone responses in children: effect of age and puberty. *J. Pediat.* 77:462–65
265. Sperling, M. A., Kenny, F. M., Schutt-Aine, J. C., Drash, A. L. 1971. Linear growth and growth hormone responsiveness in treated congenital adrenal hyperplasia. *Am. J. Dis. Child.* 122: 408–13
266. Steelman, S. L., Glitzer, M. S., Ostlind, D. A., Mueller, J. F. 1971. Biological properties of the growth hormone-like factor from the plerocercoid of *Spirometra mansonoides*. *Recent Progr. Horm. Res.* 27:97–120
267. Steinetz, B. G., Giannine, T., Butler, M., Popiele, F. 1972. The role of growth hormone in the anabolic action of methandrostenolone. *Endocrinology* 90: 1396–98
268. Stephan, J. K., Chow, B., Frohman, L. A., Chow, B. F. 1971. Relationship of growth hormone to the growth retardation associated with maternal dietary restriction. *J. Nutr.* 101:1453–58
269. Strickland, A. L., Underwood, L. E., Voina, S. J., French, F. S., Van Wyk, J. J. 1972. Growth retardation in Cushing's syndrome. *Am. J. Dis. Child.* 123:207–13
270. Suskind, R., Amatayakul, K., Leitzmann, C., Olson, R. E. 1973. Interrelationships between growth hormone and amino acid metabolism in protein-calorie malnutrition. See Ref. 9, 99–114
271. Suzuki, H. K. 1958. Effects of estradiol-17-β-n-valerate in endosteal ossification and linear growth in the mouse femur. *Endocrinology* 63:743–77
272. Swislocki, N. I. 1969. In vitro metabolic effects of proteolytic digests of bovine growth hormone in adipose tissue. *Metabolism* 18:895–900
273. Swislocki, N. I., Sonenberg, M., Yamasaki, N. 1970. In vitro metabolic effects of bovine growth hormone frag-

ments in adipose tissue. *Endocrinology* 87:900–4

274. Tanner, J. M. 1972. Human growth hormone. *Nature* 237:433–39
275. Tanner, J. M., Whitehouse, R. H., Hughes, P. C. R., Vince, F. P. 1971. Effect of human growth hormone treatment for 1 to 7 years on growth of 100 children with growth hormone deficiency, low birthweight, inherited smallness, Turner's syndrome, and other complaints. *Arch. Dis. Childhood* 46:745–82
276. Tell, G. P., Cuatrecasas, P., Van Wyk, J. J., Hintz, R. L. 1972. Somatomedin: inhibition of adenylate cyclase activity in subcellular membranes of various tissues. *Science* 180:312–15
277. Thompson, R. G., Rodriguez, A., Kowarski, A., Blizzard, R. M. 1972. Growth hormone: metabolic clearance rates, integrated concentrations and production rates in normal adults and the effect of prednisone. *J. Clin. Invest.* 51:3193–99
278. Thompson, R. G., Rodriguez, A., Kowarski, A., Migeon, C. J., Blizzard, R. M. 1972. Integrated concentrations of growth hormone correlated with plasma testosterone and bone age in preadolescent and adolescent males. *J. Clin. Endocrinol. Metab.* 35:334–37
279. Thorngren, K.-G., Hansson, L. I. 1973. Effect of thyroxine and growth hormone on longitudinal bone growth in the hypophysectomized rat. *Acta Endocrinol.* 74:24–40
280. Tribe, A. E., Malone, D. N., Grant, I. W. 1973. The substitution of corticotrophin for corticosteroid in the treatment of children and adults with chronic asthma. *Aust. N.Z. J. Med.* 3:6–13
281. Trygstad, O., Foss, I. 1968. The lipid-mobilizing effect of some pituitary gland preparations. IV. Subdivision of a human growth hormone preparation into a somatotrophic and an adipokinetic-hyperglycemic agent. *Acta Endocrinol.* 58:295–317
282. Tsushima, T., Friesen, H. 1973. Radioreceptor assay (RRA) for human growth hormone (hGH). *J. Clin. Invest.* 52:85a (Abstr.)
283. Tsushima, T., Friesen, H., Chang, T. W., Raben, M. S. 1974. Studies by radioreceptor assay (RRA) of a factor with growth hormone-like activity in incubation media of spargana of Spirometra mansonoides. *Proc. 56th Ann. Meet. Endocrine Soc.* (Abstr.). In press
284. Underwood, L. E., Hintz, R. L., Voina, S. J., Van Wyk, J. J. 1972. Human somatomendin, the growth hormone-dependent sulfation factor, is antilipolytic. *J. Clin. Endocrinol. Metab.* 35:194–98
285. Underwood, L. E., Van den Brande, J. L., Antony, G. J., Voina, S. J., Van Wyk, J. J. 1973. Islet cell function and glucose homeostasis in hypopituitary dwarfism: synergism between growth hormone and cortisone. *J. Pediat.* 82:28–37
286. Uthne, K. 1973. Human somatomedins: purification and some studies on their biological actions. *Acta Endocrinol.* 73(Suppl. 175):1–35
287. Uthne, K., Uthne, T. 1972. Influence of liver resection and regeneration on somatomedin (sulphation factor) activity in sera from normal and hypophysectomized rats. *Acta Endocrinol.* 71:255–64
288. Van den Brande, J. V. L. 1973. *Plasma somatomedin. Studies on some of its characteristics and on its relationship with growth hormone.* Rotterdam: Gemeentedrukkerij. 72 pp.
289. Van den Brande, J. L., Du Caju, M. V. L. 1974. An improved technique for measuring somatomedin activity in vitro. *Acta Endocrinol.* 75:233–42
290. Van Wyk, J. J., Hall, K., Van den Brande, J. L., Weaver, R. P. 1971. Further purification and characterization of sulfation factor and thymidine factor from acromegalic plasma. *J. Clin. Endocrinol. Metab.* 32:389–403
291. Van Wyk, J. J. et al 1972. Partial purification from human plasma of a small peptide with sulfation factor and thymidine factor activities. See Ref. 24, 155–67
292. Van Wyk, J. J., Underwood, L. E., Lister, R. C., Marshall, R. N. 1973. The somatomedins: a new class of growth-regulating hormones. *Am. J. Dis. Child.* 126:705–11
293. Van Wyk, J. J. et al 1974. Somatomedin: an insulin-like peptide under growth hormone control. *Recent Progr. Horm. Res.* In press
294. Vargas, L., Abelink, J. 1972. An integrated bioassay for anabolic-androgenic activity. Its application to Stenozolal. *Steroid Lipid Res.* 3:353–62
295. Wagner, E. M., Scow, R. O. 1957. Effect of insulin on growth in force-fed hypophysectomized rats. *Endocrinology* 61:419–25

296. Wallis, M. 1973. The primary structure of bovine growth hormone. *FEBS Lett.* 35:11–14
297. Weil, R. 1965. I. The hormonal effect on the metabolism of fat and carbohydrate. *Acta Endocrinol.* Suppl. 98, 1–92
298. Weldon, V. V., Jacobs, L. S., Pagliara, A. J., Daughaday, W. H. 1972. Prolactin hypersecretion: a cause of somatomedin generation and normal growth. *Abstr. IV Int. Congr. Endocrinol., Washington DC,* Int. Congr. Ser. 256, 16. Amsterdam: Excerpta Med. 264 pp. (Abstr.)
299. Werder, K. von, Hane, S., Forsham, P. H. 1971. Suppression of the hypothalamo-pituitary-adrenal axis and growth hormone release with dexamethasone. *Horm. Metab. Res.* 3:171–74
300. Whitelaw, M. J. 1967. Experiences in treating excessive height in girls with cyclic oestradiol valerate. *Acta Endocrinol.* 54:473–84
301. Whitten, C. F., Pettit, M. G., Fischhoff, J. 1969. Evidence that growth failure from maternal deprivation is secondary to undereating. *J. Am. Med. Assoc.* 209:1675–82
302. Wiedemann, E., Schwartz, E. 1972. Suppression of growth hormone-dependent human serum sulfation factor by estrogen. *J. Clin. Endocrinol. Metab.* 34:51–58
303. Wolstenholme, G. E. W., Knight, J. 1972. *Lactogenic Hormones. Ciba Foundation Symp. 1971, London*. Edinburgh: Churchill-Livingstone. 416 pp.
304. Yadley, R. A., Chrambach, A. 1973. Isohormones of human growth hormone. II. Plasmin-catalyzed transformation and increases in prolactin biological activity. *Endocrinology* 93: 858–65
305. Yadley, R. A., Rodbard, D., Chrambach, A. 1973. Isohormones of human growth hormone. III. Isolation by preparative polyacrylamide gel electrophoresis and characterization. *Endocrinology* 93:866–73
306. Yamasaki, N., Kangawa, K., Kobayashi, S., Kikutani, M., Sonenberg, M. 1972. Amino acid sequence of a biologically active fragment of bovine growth hormone. *J. Biol. Chem.* 247:3874–80
307. Yamasaki, N., Kikutani, M., Sonenberg, M. 1970. Peptides of a biologically active tryptic digest of bovine growth hormone. *Biochemistry* 9:1107–14
308. Yde, H. 1968. A simplified technique for the determination of growth hormone dependent sulfation factor, using intact animals. *Acta Endocrinol.* 57:557–64
309. Zachmann, M., Prader, A. 1970. Anabolic and androgenic effect of testosterone in sexually immature boys and its dependency on growth hormone. *J. Clin. Endocrinol. Metab.* 30:85–95
310. Zakin, M. M., Poskus, E., Dellacha, J. M., Paladini, A. C., Santome, J. A. 1973. The amino acid sequence of equine growth hormone. *FEBS Lett.* 34:353–55
311. Zuppinger, K. A., Sutter, M., Zurbrügg, R. P., Joss, E. E., Oetliker, O. 1971. Cleft lip and choroideal coloboma associated with multiple hypothalamo-pituitary dysfunctions. *J. Clin. Endocrinol. Metab.* 33:934–39

Copyright 1975. All rights reserved

PERIPHERAL ACTIONS OF GLUCOCORTICOIDS

♦1130

Kiu Leung and Allan Munck
Department of Physiology, Dartmouth Medical School, Hanover, New Hampshire 03755

INTRODUCTION

During the past 10–15 yr glucocorticoids have come of age in the sense that they have at last acquired a set of established target tissues. Whereas prior to about 1960 it could be argued that most, if not all, physiological effects of glucorticoids in vivo were due to direct actions solely upon the liver, or solely on peripheral tissues (165), now there is no doubt that the liver is only one among many targets. In fact, it may yet turn out that the targets of glucocorticoids comprise virtually every tissue in the body.

Despite this progress, glucocorticoid physiology remains a collage in which the parts bear little discernable relation to a central theme. That theme, if survival of the organism is the fundamental criterion, is by classical accounts the protection afforded by glucocorticoids against stress (110, 207). But what purpose, if any, such effects as the glucorcorticoid-induced breakdown of lymphoid tissue serve in protecting against stress still remains a mystery (167). Peripheral tissues must certainly contribute significantly to protecting the organism, however, since infusion of glucocorticoids into eviscerated animals markedly prolongs survival (106, 109).

Peripheral tissues that by the strict criterion of physiological responsiveness in vitro are targets of the glucocorticoids include lymphoid (84, 149, 187, 210) and adipose tissue (72, 162), skin (175), bone (177, 192), fibroblasts (99, 204), polymorphonuclear leukocytes (187, 218), pituitary (26, 56, 79), diaphragm (126), embryonic mammary gland cells (195, 244), and chick neural retina (156). (We regard as peripheral, tissues lying wholly or partly outside the abdominal cavity.) Judging from experiments in vivo or from the presence of receptor-like substances for glucocorticoids it is likely that the fetal lung (14, 88, 90, 120), the brain (42, 145), the heart (16, 83), and some part of the eye involved in the regulation of intraocular pressure (21, 24), are also targets. Undoubtedly this list is incomplete.

The effects of glucocorticoids on these varied tissues have little in common. One fairly general effect is inhibition of glucose uptake. It has been observed in skin (175), adipose tissue (72, 164), lymphoid cells (149, 165, 201), polymorphonuclear leukocytes (187, 218), and fibroblasts (94), and undoubtedly underlies some of the catabolic effects that ensue (165). But inhibition of glucose uptake does not appear to be a universal glucocorticoid effect—for instance, it has not been observed in muscle or with glucose analogs in brain tissue (78, 92, 165, 166)—and it is not likely to provide a general explanation for all peripheral actions.

Glucocorticoids often appear to act in concert with cAMP (20, 232), and cAMP is frequently invoked in efforts to explain the ever-perplexing "permissive" effects. Though a persuasive case can be made for such a relationship (20, 232), its general physiological significance remains to be established. With such ubiquitously active substances there is always the danger that under experimental conditions they may display a multitude of interactions that are not all physiologically relevant.

Perhaps the only elements that the target tissues have in common are glucocorticoid receptors. Substances that by all available criteria are receptors have been detected in several peripheral tissues, and have been intensively studied in lymphoid cells and fibroblasts, among others (121). Glucocorticoid receptors receive only brief mention in this review since they have been covered in considerable detail elsewhere (121, 123, 135). In all essential respects those glucocorticoid receptors that have been identified to date are very similar to other steroid hormone receptors. They are found in what appear to be cytoplasmic and nuclear forms, the cytoplasmic form undergoing a temperature-sensitive transformation on interaction with the hormone that leads to translocation of the hormone-receptor complex to the nucleus. The available evidence suggests strongly that in the nucleus the primary role of the hormone-receptor complex is to initiate synthesis of mRNA coding for certain proteins that in turn give rise to the hormone effects (20, 123, 165, 232).

Despite the widespread acceptance of this general scheme, it is well to keep in mind that it may not apply universally. Many peripheral effects of the glucocorticoids—their anti-inflamatory effects, their controversial therapeutic effects when used in massive doses in shock (159), their ability to maintain muscle work—are not understood at all, and it remains a real possibility that at least those requiring pharmacological doses may depend on entirely different mechanisms.

Our goal in this review is to survey briefly the effects of glucocorticoids in a number of peripheral tissues that are either established or probable targets of the hormones. In order to include studies in important areas that have received relatively little attention, we omit all discussion of glucocorticoids and lymphoid tissue, a large and complex field that has been extensively surveyed in the last few years from a variety of viewpoints (44, 112, 121, 123, 165, 167). Several recent reviews touch on some of the topics we deal with and should be consulted for further details (20, 54, 123, 135, 165, 232).

ADIPOSE TISSUE

Adipose tissue is one of the most promiscuous of endocrine target tissues, responding directly to a bewildering array of hormones. Among these are the glucocorticoids. They not only exert actions on their own, but modulate the actions of other hormones, notably insulin and the catecholamines (190, 191, 203). We review here some of these actions and discuss briefly current views on underlying mechanisms.

Physiological Role of Glucocorticoids

In vivo, the most important direct effect or glucocorticoids on adipose tissue appears to be enhancement of fatty acid mobilization (203). It becomes evident with normal levels of glucocorticoids, and is generally classed as a "permissive" effect since, although glucocorticoids may have some intrinsic fatty acid-mobilizing activity of their own, their main role is apparently to permit expression of the lipolytic activity of hormones such as the catecholamines. In the absence of glucocorticoids, the activity of these other hormones is drastically curtailed (191).

At moderate to high concentrations, glucocorticoids may also inhibit lipogenesis, and certainly can reduce the sensitivity of adipose tissue to insulin. Superimposed upon these direct effects are the effects on adipose tissue of insulin, the levels of which are raised by glucocorticoids (179). Interplay of these effects and perhaps others, along with the differential sensitivities of various fat depots to each hormone, gives rise to the characteristic increase and redistribution of fat observed in Cushing's syndrome.

Hormones such as growth hormone, glucagon, and ACTH are also potentiated in their lipolytic activities by glucocorticoids (190, 203), but whether these activities are important in vivo is doubtful.

Fatty Acid Mobilization and Lipolysis

By themselves, glucocorticoids in vivo have little if any fatty acid-mobilizing activity (191, 203). Nevertheless, these hormones sometimes (72, 113), but not always (70), stimulate fatty acid release in vitro. Insulin counteracts the glucocorticoids (72). This effect of glucocorticoids, found with white adipose tissue but not with brown (68), is due to decreased reesterification rather than to increased lipolysis, since released fatty acids are not accompanied by glycerol (71, 113, 259). It may be secondary to inhibition of glucose uptake (72, 113, 164).

Lipolysis in isolated fat cells can be induced [at times inconsistently (70)] by addition of both dexamethasone and growth hormone, and is also suppressed by insulin (71). Growth hormone and dexamethasone together consistently increase sensitivity to lipolysis by norepinephrine (70). A time lag of about 2 hr precedes the glucocorticoid-stimulated effects (71, 72). Lipolysis due to glucocorticoids and growth hormone is blocked by actinomycin D and by cycloheximide, suggesting that this effect may involve RNA and protein synthesis (69).

Glucocorticoid effects may also involve cAMP, known to be a potent lipolytic agent and the probable mediator of the actions of catecholamines (36, 197), but the situation is confusing. In adipose tissue, liver, and other tissues, levels of the phosphodiesterase that inactivate cAMP are elevated in adrenalectomized rats and lowered by glucocorticoids in vivo (214). Glucocorticoids are counteracted by insulin (214), which supresses lipolysis and cAMP levels (36). An attractive hypothesis is that glucocorticoids act by elevating cAMP levels. An observation consistent with this hypothesis is that the lipolytic activity in isolated fat cells of theophylline, an inhibitor of phosphodiesterase, is somewhat enhanced by added dexamethasone (70). Under similar conditions, however, dexamethasone reduces the lipolytic activity of dibutyryl cAMP and of the combination of dibutyryl cAMP and theophylline (70), observations not explained by the hypothesis. Reduction of phosphodiesterase activity does not appear to play a role in the action of glucocorticoids on livers from diabetic rats, since stimulation of gluconeogenesis can take place without significant changes in cAMP levels (65). It has been reported that glucocorticoid treatment of adrenalectomized rats increased the response of adenyl cyclase (measured in isolated fat cell ghosts) to added ACTH, but not to epinephrine or glucagon (31).

Inhibition of Glucose Uptake

Inhibition of glucose uptake is a consistently reproducible effect of glucocorticoids added at physiological concentrations to intact tissue, as well as isolated fat cells (29, 71, 72, 113, 162, 164). It takes place in vivo following injection of glucocorticoids into adrenalectomized, alloxan-diabetic, or hypophysectomized rats (66, 163, 164, 166). Only white adipose tissue is sensitive (68).

With physiological concentrations of glucocorticoids in vitro, the effect takes 2–3 hr to develop (72, 162, 164). This time lag, and the fact that the glucocorticoid effect can be suppressed by actinomycin D present during the first 2 hr or so, suggests that the effect is mediated by RNA and protein synthesis (51).

In vivo (193) or added to isolated fat cells (52), glucocorticoids antagonize the stimulatory effects of insulin on glucose uptake. Insulin antagonism is apparently not related to any alteration in affinity or number of insulin receptors (248). These findings are consistent with the view that glucocorticoids block glucose uptake at an early stage of glucose utilization (164), quite possibly at the transport step (29, 52, 67, 259), since insulin is thought to act on the rate-limiting transport step (46).

How inhibition of glucose uptake is related to the other effects of glucocorticoids on adipose tissue remains uncertain. Undoubtedly it may be responsible for some degree of fatty acid mobilization by decreasing reesterification, and for reduced lipogenesis by decreasing substrate. But the major question is the relation to lipolysis. Even for lipolysis induced by growth hormone and dexamethasone the question remains open, since glucose is required in intact adipose tissue, whereas with free fat cells it is not (71). Which of these tissue preparations best represents the intact organism is not clear.

Receptors

Adipose tissue contains binding sites with high specificity and affinity for glucocorticoids (202). These binding sites may represent glucocorticoid receptors, but their concentration appears low compared to other glucocorticoid target tissues such as liver (202).

BONE

In this section we discuss the independent effects of glucocorticoids on bone, and not their complex interplay with calcitonin and parathyroid hormone (61, 62, 115, 231, 234). Perhaps the most striking effect of large amounts of endogenous glucocorticoids on bone can be seen in patients with Cushing's syndrome who have thinning of bones with frequent compression fractures of the vertebrae (254). Data on such patients indicate that bone formation is decreased; results on bone resorption are conflicting (116, 118 119, 194).

Bone growth in rats is inhibited following subcutaneous injection of cortisone acetate (40–50 mg kg^{-1} day^{-1}) for three weeks (81). Rabbits similarly treated with 20 mg kg^{-1} day^{-1} develop osteroporosis (1). Cortisol (10 nM–1 μM) inhibits the incorporation of proline and uridine into protein and RNA, respectively, by rat fetal bone cells in culture (177). The inhibition of uridine incorporation can be prevented by insulin (178). In bone rudiments taken from 7-day-old chick embryos, cultured for 6 days, addition of cortisol (30 nM–3 μM) on day 0 inhibited growth but increased collagen content (192). Cortisol also decreased polysaccharide synthesis (17, 192). Injection of cortisone (20 mg kg^{-1} day^{-1}) into adrenalectomized rats for 10 days decreased phosphatidylcholine in the diaphysis, phosphatidylethanolamine in both metaphysis and diaphysis, and hydroxyproline in the metaphysis, but had no effect on hexosamine level (47).

Morphological data show that high doses of cortisol (up to 50 mg kg^{-1} day^{-1} for 3–30 days) consistently supress cell division, bone formation, number of osteoblasts, bone mass, and number of osteoclasts (18, 28, 64, 116, 226, 233). Low doses of cortisol (less than 2 mg kg^{-1} day^{-1} for 8 days) result in osteoporosis by producing excessive bone resorption and drastically reducing bone formation. In addition, precursor cell proliferation increases (114, 198). Based on these data with high and low doses of cortisol, a four-compartment model has been proposed for bone remodeling under normal conditions and when exposed to cortisol (115).

BRAIN

Different effects of glucocorticoids and evidence for the presence of glucocorticoid receptors is discussed in individual subsections. We do not refer to studies on tumor cell lines, the unit firing of neurons, and behavioral effects.

Control of Glycerolphosphate Dehydrogenase

Adrenalectomy or hypophysectomy decreases glycerolphosphate dehydrogenase activity in cerebrum and brain stem of adult male rats, but not in muscle or liver. Thyroidectomy and gonadectomy have no effect on the enzyme. Administration of ACTH or cortisol to hypophysectomized rats and cortisol to adrenalectomized rats for 14 days partially restores the enzyme activity. The normal increase with age in enzyme activity of cerebrum and brain stem of 20-day-old rats is inhibited by hypophysectomy (59) and accelerated by injection of cortisol from 7 to 15 days of age (60). Glycerolphosphate dehydrogenase can be induced by cortisol in tissue culture of explants from various regions of rat embryonic brain (32, 199). All these results indicate that the enzyme is regulated by glucocorticoids.

Induction of Glutamine Synthetase

Glutamine synthetase activity in organ cultures of optic tectum derived from 12-day-old embryonic chick increased after 2 days in the presence of cortisol (1 μM) to levels found in 18-day-old embryos. Injection of cortisol (1 mg/egg) into the yolk sac of 14-day-old embryos resulted after 2 days in higher glutamine synthetase levels in optic tecta than are found in 16-day-old control embryos (215). There is a precocious increase of the activity of this enzyme when the area containing the ectostriatum from cerebral hemispheres of 15-day-old embryonic chicks is cultured with cortisol for 1–2 days (180).

Na^+-K^+ ATPase

Administration of cortisol (20 μg) in vivo to embryonic chicks on day 11 or 13 causes a significant increase over saline controls in levels of Na^+-K^+ ATPase in the cerebral hemispheres by day 15, but has no effect on Mg^{2+} ATPase. Injection of cortisol on day 11 or 13 increases potassium concentrations of cerebral hemispheres 2 days later. Sodium concentrations increase 2 days later only when cortisol is injected on day 11 (222).

Tryptophan Hydroxylase and Serotonin

In rats, intraperitoneal injection of corticosterone (6 mg/kg) or ACTH for 10 min prior to a 30 min pulse of [^{14}C]tryptophan increases cerebral [^{14}C]serotonin content (147). However, intraperitoneal injection of cortisol (5 mg/kg) decreases total brain serotonin and 5-hydroxyindoleacetic acid, both of which reach a minimum after 6–7 hr and return to control levels after 11 hr. Daily injection of cortisol for 5 days causes no decrease in brain serotonin (50). As is well known, administration of cortisol also results in an increase in hepatic tryptophan pyrrolase after about 3 hr. Allopurinol, a powerful tryptophan pyrrolase inhibitor, blocks the effects of cortisol on both hepatic pyrrolase and brain serotonin, and on 5-hydroxyindoleacetic acid (49, 95). Consequently, it has been postulated that metabolism of brain serotonin is regulated by hepatic tryptophan pyrrolase (48).

Adrenalectomy decreases total midbrain tryptophan hydroxylase activity, which can be restored partially by injection of corticosterone (about 6 mg/kg). The restoration of hydroxylase activity is inhibited by intracisternal administration of cycloheximide (10).

RNA, Protein, and Mitochondrial Metabolism

RNA polymerase activity of nuclei from the cells of the porcine hypothalamus, measured by incorporation of UTP into RNA, has been reported to be increased significantly by cytosol protein-cortisol complex, but not by cortisol or by cortisol and albumin or buffer (225).

Subcutaneous injection of a large dose of cortisol (60 mg/kg) into 6–8-day-old rats results in decreased incorporation of thymidine and L-leucine into brain DNA and protein respectively. In 20-day-old rats it causes a decrease in incorporation of thymidine into brain DNA, but an increase in incorporation of L-leucine into brain protein (229).

With pyruvate and malate as substrates, the in vitro state-3 respiration (oxygen uptake in the presence of substrate and ADP) and respiratory control ratio (the ratio of oxygen consumption in the presence of substrate and ADP to oxygen consumption in the presence of substrate alone) of cerebral mitochondria is increased by 1 hr after cortisol injection into adrenalectomized rats. With succinate as substrate, cortisol injection 1 hr prior to sacrifice decreases in vitro state-3 respiration in the presence of rotenone. Such increases and decreases are blocked by concomitant administration of actinomycin D and cycloheximide, which by themselves have no effect. Since cortisol treatment increases the rotenone-sensitive factor of the NADH dehydrogenase complex, but has no effect on mitochondrial cytochrome content, it has been suggested that the increase in mitochondrial state-3 respiration and respiratory control ratio is due to an increased level of rotenone-sensitive factor (200).

DNA and Development

Subcutaneous implantation of corticosterone pellets in mice at 2 or 3 days of age significantly reduces body weight, brain weight, DNA, RNA, water content, and free cholesterol of brain at 7 days of age (107). Similar subcutaneous implantation of corticosterone from day 2 to 14 causes a significant reduction in cerebral and cerebellar DNA up to 1 yr later (108). Treatment of rats with cortisol from 1 to 5 days after birth inhibits both cell division and the incorporation of thymidine into brain DNA. Mitotic activity is restored upon cessation of cortisol treatment (12). Recently it has been shown that a single injection of methylprednisone (0. 8 mg) into 6-day-old rats results in a significant decrease in body weight, brain weight, frequency of myelinated fibers, and mean number of myelin lamellae in the brain (101). All these data indicate that neonatal treatment with glucocorticoids can produce irreversible reduction in brain size and cell numbers and result in delayed myelination.

Receptors

Binding proteins for corticosterone have been demonstrated in rat brain cytosol (97, 98, 143, 223, 224). Cytoplasmic binding proteins, possibly the same as those found with corticosterone, have been demonstrated in rat brain with triamcinolone acetonide (43) and with dexamethasone (202). Nuclear binding of corticosterone has also been demonstrated in rat brain (142–144). In contrast to what has been found with most glucocorticoid receptors, corticosterone has a higher affinity than cortisol (145).

FIBROBLASTS

As major components of connective tissue, fibroblasts are of interest in relation to such actions of glucocorticoids as suppression of inflamation, retardation of wound-healing, and general catabolic effects (20).

Glucocorticoids at physiological concentrations inhibit growth of fibroblasts in culture (23, 99, 184, 204). In this system cortisone and other generally inactive 11-keto analogs are slightly stimulatory (23, 136). The growth inhibitory effect of glucocorticoids is accompanied by depression of the rate of DNA synthesis per surviving cell, as measured by incorporation of thymidine. This effect first becomes apparent by 3–6 hr after addition of steroid. RNA synthesis per surviving cell is depressed more slowly, and protein synthesis is unchanged or increased (184).

Uptake of hexoses (glucose, galactose, deoxyglucose) is depressed more rapidly (94). Galactose uptake is reduced by 1 to 2 hr in the absence of glucose and by ½ to 1 hr in its presence. Little effect on hexose transport is seen in fibroblasts that are resistant to the growth-inhibitory action of glucocorticoids. For several glucocorticoids, the dose-response relationships with respect to inhibition of growth and of hexose uptake are in close agreement (94). These results suggest that inhibition of DNA synthesis and growth are secondary to the prior effect on hexose metabolism. It remains unclear whether the effect on hexose metabolism is due to inhibition of transport or some other step (94).

Paradoxically, in certain strains of fibroblasts (3T3 and HF) growing under contact-inhibited conditions, glucocorticoids stimulate cell division (236). Glucocorticoids added to fibroblasts have also been reported to induce alkaline phosphatase (252) and to enhance the growth-stimulatory activity of pituitary extracts (9).

Convincing experiments have shown that fibroblasts contain glucocorticoid receptors (111, 121, 185). They also appear to have the curious ability to transport certain glucocorticoids and other steroids out of the cell (96).

HEART

In this section we describe certain actions of glucocorticoids on "beating" and metabolism of myocardial cells in culture and recent studies on glucocorticoid receptors in the heart.

Effects on Beating of Myocardial Cells

Myocardial cells from fetal mouse, embryonic chick, and newborn rat in culture are known to beat (contract) spontaneously (55, 93, 103, 137). Individual cells beat at different rates, but when they come in contact with each other, either directly, or indirectly through nonmyocardial cells, after a few minutes they beat in synchrony. In monolayer cultures, cells with the highest rate of contraction play the role of pacemakers for other cells in the sheet.

Addition of cortisol acetate to cells 24 hr after culturing results in a greater number of beating cells and prolongs beating. Cortisol acetate restores beating within 24 hr when added to control cells that have stopped beating after 7 days in culture, and maintains beating for as long as 2 months (141).

Metabolic Effects on Myocardial Cells

Lipids play an important role in maintaining the ability of myocardial cells to beat. Cells cultured in complete medium stop beating after a period of 7 to 20 days. Cells in lipid-deficient medium stop beating after 2 or 3 days, though cellular protein content increases slowly; beating is restored by adding serum lipids or certain fatty acids. With fatty acids, restoration is only temporary (104). It has been suggested that metabolism changes from lipid to carbohydrate when cells in culture age and stop beating (82). In various species, including man, the heart uses lipids as its source of energy (25, 173).

In culture, myocardial cells that are beating actively oxidize fatty acids, hydrolyze triglycerides to fatty acids and glycerol, and synthesize glycogen from glucose in the medium. When cells begin to lose their ability to beat, fatty acid oxidation, ATP concentration, and lipase activity decrease. Cortisol acetate (1 μM) not only restores beating but reverses these metabolic changes. The effects of cortisol acetate take at least 24 hr to be manifested (4).

Receptors

Receptors with high affinity for dexamethasone have been demonstrated in cytosol of adrenalectomized rat and dog hearts (16, 83), in hearts of fetal and adult rabbits, and in hearts of human fetuses (14–16). Addition of aldosterone to blood taken from adrenalectomized rats, which was used to perfuse a heart-lung preparation from an intact rat, restores the "left ventricular work index." No cardiac mineralocorticoid receptor, however, has been demonstrated as yet (208). A lack of aldosterone effect has been reported in other cardiac preparations (161).

LUNG

Surface tension-reducing lecithins (surfactants) are present in lungs of mammalian fetuses during the last trimester of pregnancy (105, 176). Surfactants are thought to prevent collapse of newborn infants' lungs after they have been expanded with air. If surfactants are present in insufficient amounts, as frequently occurs in premature infants, the respiratory distress syndrome (RDS) may develop. RDS, a developmental disease, is a frequent cause of death in premature infants and is due primarily to lung immaturity.

It was observed some years ago that infusion of cortisol into fetal lambs resulted not only in premature parturition as early as 115 days of gestation (term 147 days), but also in an unusually high survival rate (131). This observation led to the postulation of a role for glucocorticoids in lung maturation. Accelerated maturation of the lung by glucocorticoids administered just before the normal period of differentiation has been shown unequivocally in sheep, monkeys, rabbits, and rats (57, 58, 74, 128, 183), and indirectly in man (134, 221). Selected studies on these species are discussed below, followed by a brief section on evidence for glucocorticoid receptors in lung.

Sheep

Two studies have been carried out with twin lambs in utero. Infusion of cortisol hemisuccinate into one twin at various times between 100 and 130 days of gestation (the other twin being infused with saline and acting as control) accelerated maturation of lungs by at least a week and increased the content of surfactants (58). Treatment with dexamethasone for 2 days, beginning from day 126 or from day 132, elevated the concentration of surfactant in the tracheal fluid to nearly 5 times that in the control (183). Normally surfactants are first detectable in tracheal fluid by 120–122 days. With 2 to 4 days of dexamethasone treatment, surfactants become detectable as early as day 108, but not earlier, indicating that surfactants can be induced by glucocorticoids only during a critical period of fetal development. As is described in the following sections, this also holds true in other species.

Monkey

In monkey fetuses, three injections of glucocorticoids made over 7 days at various times from day 80 to 101 (term 168 days) resulted in pulmonary surface tensions that were lower than those in saline-treated controls 2 weeks after the first injection. No difference in the pulmonary surface tension was seen with fetuses delivered before day 100 (57).

Rats

Increased incorporation of choline into lecithin by lung slices of intact fetal rat followed 24 hr after the sudden increase in fetal plasma cortisol that peaked on day 20 (74). Decapitation in utero of fetuses on day 16 (term 22 days) resulted in low plasma cortisol throughout gestation, retarded differentiation of lungs, impairment of surfactant synthesis (as measured by reduced number of osmiophilic inclusion bodies), failure of minces of lungs to reduce surface tension, and reduced choline phosphotransferase (27, 74). Choline phosphotransferase level in decapitated fetuses was restored by dexamethasone to 96% of control level (74).

Rabbit

Direct injection of glucocorticoids into fetuses and amniotic sacs on day 24 (term 31 days) resulted in more viable fetuses, accelerated lung maturation (as shown by distensibility, presence of surfactant, increased formation of osmiophilic bodies in type II alveolar cells, and abundant osmiophilic material in alveolar space), and a lower lung weight-body weight ratio when fetuses were delivered on day 26 or 27 (37, 120, 128, 129, 158, 251). Cortisol injected into fetuses on day 26 resulted in longer survival time of newborns delivered 2 days later (230). However, when cortisol was injected into pregnant rabbits on day 27 and fetuses were delivered 3 days later, accelerated lung maturation was not observed (158).

The most direct evidence on induction of surfactants by glucocorticoids comes from a study in which fetuses were injected with glucocorticoids on day 23 or 24 and were delivered 3 days later. Lungs of steroid-treated fetuses had higher lecithin concentration, choline phosphotransferase activity, and choline incorporation into lecithin than controls. Incorporation of methionine into lecithin by lung slices in both groups of fetuses was similar, indicating that glucocorticoids probably increase lecithin synthesis through the choline incorporation pathway (75).

Studies with lungs of newborn rabbits with mild RDS revealed that cortisol injected at birth did not affect choline phosphotransferase activity and lecithin synthesis over a postnatal period of 3 to 12 hr (73).

Man

A number of situations that are "stressful" to human fetuses are associated with low incidence of RDS or death. Infants 36 weeks and older with infections contracted in utero had lower incidence of RDS than uninfected infants (171). Infants with rupture of membranes more than 16–24 hr prior to delivery had lower incidence of RDS than infants with rupture of membranes less than 16 hr before delivery (19, 258). The number of deaths in infants with RDS was reduced 15-fold when they were delivered by cesarean section after, rather than before, the onset of labor (76).

A recent report shows that plasma levels of cortisol in newborn infants that eventually develop RDS are one third of those in normal infants (169). This report suggests that immaturity of lungs in infants with RDS is probably due to less surfactant present as a result of low cortisol levels. Only after the onset of RDS (a form of stress in itself) are adrenals of such infants stimulated to synthesize more cortisol (19).

Indirect evidence on induction of maturation of lungs by glucocorticoids comes from two observations. In the first, intramuscular injection of betamethasone into pregnant women with premature labor resulted in 5-fold reduction of neonatal deaths and in lower incidence of RDS (134). In the second observation, oral glucocorticoid therapy given to women between 28 and 32 weeks of gestation resulted in a higher lecithin-sphingomyelin ratio in amniotic fluid than that in control women or in women given oral estrogen (221). An increase in lecithin-sphingomyelin ratio is considered a reflection of pulmonary surfactant production (91, 220, 238, 253).

In contrast, postnatal cortisol treatment of newborn infants with RDS failed to yield any benefit (11). Similar data have also been obtained in newborn rabbits (73). These observations strengthen the argument that induction of lung maturation takes place only during a critical period of fetal development. Once the damage is done, it cannot be corrected neonatally.

Receptors

High affinity glucocorticoid binding sites have been found in fetal lungs of sheep, lungs of adult rats and rabbits, and lungs of fetal and newborn rats (239). With dexamethasone, the presence of such sites has been demonstrated in cytoplasmic extracts from fetal lungs of rats, guinea pigs, rabbits, man, and lungs of normal human neonates, but not in lungs of premature neonates with idiopathic RDS (14–16, 88–90). Nuclear binding sites are present in the lungs of fetal rats (74).

MAMMARY GLAND

In this section we discuss effects of glucocorticoids on the differentiation and milk yield of mammary glands in rat, mouse, and rabbit. The role played by insulin and prolactin is mentioned briefly in relation to the action of glucocorticoids.

Rat

Daily injection of corticosterone from days 7 to 19 of lactation increases milk yield as measured by increases in litter weight (102). Hypophysectomy decreases the weight of lactating mammary glands and the activity of the following enzymes: fatty acid synthetase, phosphoglucomutase, 6-phosphogluconic dehydrogenase, citrate cleavage enzyme, UDP-glucose pyrophosphorylase, and glucose-6-phosphate dehydrogenase. Treatment of the hypophysectomized rats with either cortisol or prolactin alone increases mammary gland weight and enzyme activities slightly; treatment with cortisol and prolactin together restores weight and enzyme activities completely (124).

An increase in the total RNA in the mammary gland is observed following subcutaneous daily injections of cortisol acetate from days 16 to 20 of gestation (77). Similarly, increases in both DNA and RNA relative to body weight are seen following injection of corticosterone from days 1 to 19 of gestation (130). As shown by polyacrylamide gel electrophoresis, adrenalectomy changes the pattern of RNA synthesis in isolated nuclei from lactating mammary glands. Cortisol administration restores the normal pattern (13). Adrenalectomy also causes a decrease in lactating mammary gland DNA, lactose, citrate cleavage enzyme, UDP-glucose pyrophosphorylase, glucose-6-phosphate dehydrogenase, succinic dehydrogenase, malic enzyme, UDP-glucose 4-epimerase, 6-phosphogluconic dehydrogenase, and hexokinase, all of which can be restored to normal levels in intact rats by cortisol administration (125).

Mouse

Differentiation of mammary gland tissue in culture, as measured by histological appearance and casein synthesis, requires the presence of insulin (5 μg/ml), prolactin (5 μg/ml), and cortisol (0.3 μM) (244). After 3 days in culture with these hormones, activities of glucose 6-phosphate dehydrogenase and 6-phosphogluconic dehydrogenase double. If only one or two of the hormones is included, the increase in enzyme activity is much smaller. With no hormones, activities decrease. The hormone-induced increase in dehydrogenases can be completely blocked by the addition to the culture medium of cycloheximide or actinomycin D together with the hormones. Cycloheximide added 44 hr later has no effect, whereas actinomycin D inhibits by 50% (196). For the increase in dehydrogenase activity, the three hormones are required only during the first 2 days in culture (195). The three hormones are also required for increased incorporation of thymidine into DNA (140). There have been a number of reports on gene activation, but these findings are not discussed here since the concentrations of cortisol (10 μM) used were above physiological (242, 243, 245, 246).

Rabbit

Lipid synthesis increases in mammary glands of pseudopregnant animals cultured with insulin (5 μg/ml), prolactin (1 μg/ml), and corticosterone (1 μM) (30, 227). Triglycerides enriched with caprylic acid and capric acid (characteristic of rabbit milk) are predominant (227). Maximal rates of fatty acid synthesis under these conditions are similar to those in the lactating mammary gland.

Possible Role of Glucocorticoids

Epithelial cells of the mammary gland must divide before they can differentiate into secretory alveolar cells. Insulin induces epithelial cells to undergo cell division. It has been suggested that glucocorticoids must act on the daughter cells before they can respond to prolactin to synthesize milk proteins (242, 243, 245, 246).

Receptors

High affinity binding of glucocorticoids to putative glucocorticoid receptors has been demonstrated in cytoplasmic and nuclear fractions of bovine mammary gland in culture (241), in cytoplasm from lactating mouse (217), and in rat mammary glands (85).

PARTURITION

The role of glucocorticoids in initiation of parturition in a number of species, particularly sheep, is discussed in this section. For the role of other hormones in labor (oxytocin, vasopressin, prostaglandin, progesterone, and estrogen) readers should refer to various recent publications (22, 80, 122, 219). Corticosteroid-induced parturition in domestic animals has also been reviewed (117). To date, it has not been possible to induce parturition with glucocorticoids in swine, horse, dog, and rat.

Control of Parturition

The mechanism of parturition has been studied in greater detail in the sheep than in any other species (132, 133). An intact fetal pituitary and adrenal cortex appear to be essential for parturition at term, as fetal hypophysectomy or stalk section, or fetal bilateral adrenalectomy (but not ablation of the adrenal medulla) prolong gestation. Fetal plasma concentrations of total cortisol and unbound cortisol increase 10-fold on the day of parturition (132, 133).

Prolonged pregnancy in man is often associated with fetal anencephaly and adrenal hyperplasia (5, 146, 174, 247), and in cattle with adenohypophyseal aplasia (117). Angora goats abort habitually owing to fetal adrenal hyperplasia (117). Fetal plasma levels of cortisol increase with gestation and peak on the last day of gestation in man (168, 170), cattle (45, 117), goats (235), and rabbits (160).

Induction of Parturition

Glucocorticoids can induce precocious or premature parturition. (*Precocious parturition* is defined as parturition 2 to 3 weeks earlier than term, when the newborn needs no special care. *Premature parturition* means parturition in the last trimester of pregnancy, when the newborn requires special care for survival.) Intramuscular injection of dexamethasone or flumethasone into pregnant ewes induces precocious parturition after 2 to 3 days. Premature parturition can be induced only by infusion of cortisol (25–50 mg/24 hr) or dexamethasone (0.06–1 mg/24 hr) into the fetus. Parturition occurs about 56 hr after the beginning of the infusion. Premature lambs delivered after glucocorticoid infusion are more viable than other lambs of the same gestation age owing to the accelerated maturation of lungs induced by glucocorticoids (see section on lung) (117, 132, 133).

Precocious and premature parturition can be induced by glucocorticoids in cattle (45, 117) and goats (117). In the rabbit, intravenous infusion of cortisol into the pregnant animal on day 21 results in parturition 3 days later (172). Evidence for glucocorticoid-induced parturition in man is inconclusive (6, 138).

Discussion

From previous subsections, it is clear that in some species glucocorticoids in the fetal compartment may play an important role in initiating labor. We discuss briefly a current hypothesis (132) on the relationship of glucocorticoids to estrogen, progesterone, prostaglandin $F_{2\alpha}$, and oxytocin in the sheep (Figure 1).

It is postulated that as term approaches, the fetal hypothalamus receives a signal, perhaps from fetal thermoreceptors, that stimulates the anterior pituitary to release ACTH. ACTH then stimulates fetal adrenals to synthesize cortisol, giving rise to the sharp peak of cortisol observed in the fetal circulation just before onset of labor. The cortisol signal is postulated to act on the placenta to bring about the observed decrease of progesterone and increase of unconjugated estradiol in maternal plasma, and the increase of prostaglandin $F_{2\alpha}$ in maternal placenta and uterine vein blood.

The increase in prostaglandin $F_{2\alpha}$ in the maternal placenta is thought to reach the myometrium and trigger the onset of myometrial contraction. Infusion of prostaglandin $F_{2\alpha}$ into the pregnant ewe is known to reduce the threshold of the myometrium to oxytocin. The descending fetus dilates the cervix and the vagina and probably stimulates the maternal posterior pituitary to release oxytocin. Concerted contraction of the uterus (maintained by oxytocin) and the abdomen then expel the fetus.

Receptors

Recent reports of glucocorticoid receptors in calf uterus, cytosol of rabbit uterus, and mouse placenta further strengthen evidence for glucocorticoid involvement in

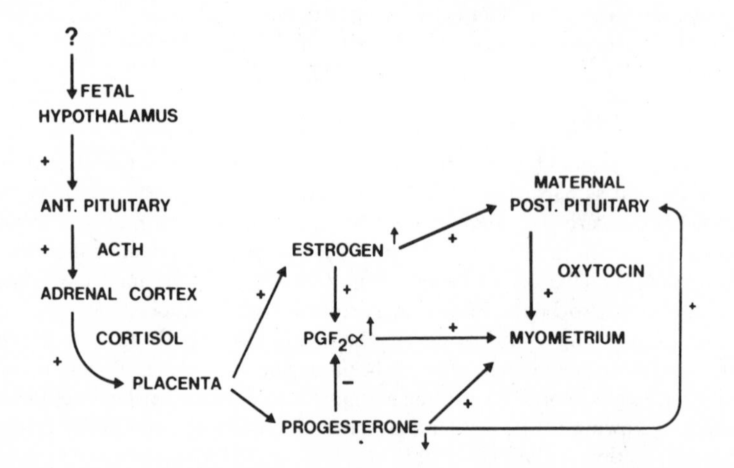

Figure 1 Current model of the mechanism controlling the initiation of parturition in the ewe. Plus and minus signs represent positive and negative effects. Reproduced by permission from Liggins et al (132).

parturition (87, 250, 255). If these reports can be confirmed in the sheep and in other species, glucocorticoids may ultimately be shown to act directly on the uterus and the placenta in a wide variety of mammals.

RETINA

The retina of the embryonic chick has been studied extensively as a model for glucocorticoid action during development. Most reports describe effects on glutamine synthetase (GS) acvtivity, but the function of this enzyme in the retina remains unknown.

Normal Development of GS

GS activity in the retina is very low in chick embryos up to 16 days old, but rises sharply thereafter, reaching a plateau about 4 days after hatching. (Hatching takes place on day 21.) This level is maintained throughout adult life. The more than 100-fold increase in enzyme activity is not due to cell growth because by day 12 total cellular protein and cell numbers have reached the maximal level (152).

Induction of GS

GS is induced prematurely by addition of cortisol (1–100 nM) to organ cultures of retinas from 12-day-old embryos or by injection of cortisol into embryonic chicks 14 days of age. The enzyme level 2 days later is typical of that in 19–20-day-old embryos (155). There is a 2 hr lag period before the induced enzyme is detectable (154). Continuous presence of cortisol is required, since removal of cortisol after 4 hr of induction terminates the rise in GS (153). The ability of steroids to induce GS correlates well with glucocorticoid activity (156, 188). Inducibility of GS in vitro is highest in intact retina, lower in aggregates of dissociated cells, and lowest in cells in monolayer (150, 151).

Occurrence of GS in Retina of Different Species

In addition to embryonic and adult chickens, GS is present in normal retina of human neonate and adult man and in a retinoblastoma derived from a 3-yr-old boy and cultured for 2 yr. GS of this retinoblastoma increased 8-fold when cultured for 14 days in the presence of cortisol (189). GS is very low in retina of fetal and neonatal rats but increases sharply at 12 days of age. By day 17, GS has increased 25-fold to about adult levels (38). It is interesting to note that eye opening in rats occurs normally at 14–15 days of age when the increase in GS is sharpest, suggesting a possible relation between these events.

Participation of Nucleic Acid and Protein Synthesis in Induction of GS

DNA SYNTHESIS Rapid and complete inhibition of incorporation of thymidine into DNA can be obtained with cytosine arabinoside (10 μM) in retinas of all embryonic ages. Retinas from 9-day-old chick embryos cultured with cytosine arabinoside (10 μM) for 24 hr respond normally to added cortisol as judged by levels of GS measured 24 hr later (152). It appears, therefore, that DNA synthesis is not required for GS induction.

RNA SYNTHESIS Unless otherwise stated, all studies described below on induction of GS measured the enzyme after 24 hr incubation with cortisol and/or inhibitors of RNA and protein synthesis. Incubation of retina from 12-day-old embryonic chick with cortisol and actinomycin D (10 μg/ml) added together inhibited induction of GS. When actinomycin D (10 μg/ml) was added 3 or 4 hr after cortisol, the level of induced GS was within the usual range of induction with cortisol alone (154). According to one study (3), this effect is peculiarly dependent on dose: a smaller dose (0.05 μg/ml) added 4 hr after cortisol yields GS levels about one third those with cortisol alone. The increase in GS following the addition of 10 μg/ml of actinomycin D 4 hr after cortisol takes place whether or not cortisol is left in after 4 hr (157). Based upon these paradoxical effects of actinomycin D, a 3-gene model for regulation of GS has been proposed (157).

In similar experiments conducted by another group, both high (10 μg/ml) and low (0.05 μg/ml) doses of actinomycin D gave identical levels of GS, about half that in control retinas with cortisol alone (212). Both doses of actinomycin D lowered not only rates of incorporation of uridine into RNA and polysome content, but also oxygen consumption and ATP concentrations, the effects of the higher dose being more pronounced. The high dose also caused derangements in cell structure (212). The discrepancies between this and the previous study are hard to explain, but it appears that actinomycin D acts not only as an inhibitor of RNA synthesis but also as a more general metabolic poison.

More direct evidence for the involvement of RNA in induction of GS comes from studies on cultured retinas pulsed for 15 min with uridine. When rapidly labeled RNA was separated on sucrose gradients and further characterized on caesium chloride gradients, 99% appeared as a single polyribosomal peak. Dual-labeled RNA, obtained by pooling cortisol-treated retinas incubated with [^{3}H]uridine with control retinas incubated with [^{14}C]uridine, was fractionated on polyacrylamide gel electrophoresis and exhibited a distinct increase in the [^{3}H]/[^{14}C] ratio after 3 hr incubation with cortisol, but not after 2 hr. Polysomal profiles of control and cortisol-treated retinas were identical. This RNA has been suggested to be the glucocorticoid-induced mRNA (for GS) for the following reasons: 1. It is found only in polyribosomes from cortisol-treated retinas. 2. Its appearance coincides in time with that of GS. 3. Newly synthesized protein that can be precipitated with anti-GS antibody is located in same fraction of polyribosomes. 4. The size of RNA is appropriate to code for the subunit of GS (211).

PROTEIN SYNTHESIS Cycloheximide added together with cortisol to retina cultures derived from 12-day-old embryonic chicks completely blocks cortisol induction of GS. Cycloheximide added 4 or 6 hr after cortisol blocks further increase in GS. The block is reversible because if retinas cultured with cortisol and cycloheximide for 6 hr were transferred to identical medium without cycloheximide, near normal induction of GS occurs (154).

The GS activity induced by cortisol has been measured by immunoprecipitation and is due to synthesis of new enzyme. The incorporation of labeled amino acid into the enzyme supports the immunoprecipitation measurement (2). Using immunoprecipitation with anti-GS gammaglobulin, it has been shown that polysomes prepared from induced retinas have nascent enzyme at 3 times higher level than control polysomes (206). Furthermore, the increase in GS concentration induced by cortisol is correlated with elevated incorporation of aspartic acid (an abundant amino acid in GS) into protein, and of uridine into RNA. Both labeled precursors were observed as peaks of radioactivity in the same polysomal region (205). Total protein and RNA did not change after the addition of cortisol to retinal cultures (205, 211).

Receptors

Retinas of embryonic chicks contain saturable glucocorticoid binding sites that may well be associated with receptors (41). A binding macromolecule for cortisol has been demonstrated by gel filtration (39, 40).

SKELETAL MUSCLE

Glucocorticoids at high levels in vivo are known to cause extensive myopathies characterized by weakness and loss of muscle mass (34, 53, 63, 237). The changes are seen in skeletal but not heart muscle (34, 63), and are reported to be accompanied or preceded by: (*a*) changes in water, electrolyte, glycogen, and lipid content (53, 237); (*b*) striking alterations—e.g. enlargement with formation of bizzarre shapes, proliferation, collapse—in mitochondrial structure (33, 34, 53, 237), with some loss of mitochondrial function (34, 249); (*c*) changes in myofibril structure (237) and diminished membrane excitability in type II fibrils (100); (*d*) decreased ability to incorporate amino acids, glucose, and other precursors into protein (256, 257); (*e*) increased sensitivity of phosphorylase to activation by epinephrine and cAMP (209); (*f*) loss of isozymes of lactic dehydrogenase (240); and (*g*) defective ribosomal function (33, 34).

Neither the interrelationships between these effects nor a primary cause for all of them has been identified. It has been pointed out, though, that some of the structural alterations are common to myopathies of varied origins (237). After a single injection of hormone in rabbits, defects in ribosomal function appear more rapidly than changes in mitochondria, and for this and other reasons the ribosomal effects are thought to be closer to the initiating events (33, 34). The earliest effect that has been observed is inhibition of amino acid transport, which develops in diaphragm muscle of rats 1–2 hr after injection of dexamethasone phosphate (126). This inhibition is apparently the only significant effect that has also been elicited in isolated muscle by addition of glucocorticoids in vitro at physiological concentrations (126). However, it is doubtful that amino acid transport limits the rate of protein synthesis (216, 256, 257), and the role this effect plays in relation to other changes is not clear (127).

Many of the glucocorticoid-induced changes in muscle could be indirect consequences of primary effects on other tissues. For example, slow inhibitory effects on glucose uptake [such as have been shown in heart muscle (148)] and various structural changes could be a result of changes in plasma fatty acids concentrations arising from stimulation by glucocorticoids of lipolysis in adipose tissue (53, 86, 186).

Glucocorticoid binding substances that may be receptors have been detected in skeletal muscle of rats and rabbits (16, 202). They are present at relatively low concentrations compared to liver.

SKIN

High concentrations of glucocorticoids such as occur in Cushing's syndrome result in marked thinning of skin. In mouse epidermis, glucocorticoids in vivo decrease the rate of mitosis (35), an effect that presumably contributes to thinning. A quite different influence is observed with embryonic skin in culture, where glucocorticoids accelerate keratinization (228).

Mitotic rate in the epidermis is apparently regulated by the supply of glucose, an observation that led to the suggestion that hormones influence mitosis through their effects on glucose metabolism (35). Experiments with isolated skin have demonstrated a direct inhibitory effect of glucocorticoids at physiological concentrations on glucose uptake (175) and oxidation (181). This inhibition is counteracted by insulin (181). As in adipose and lymphoid tissue (165), it probably results from slowing of glucose transport, since cortisol inhibits metabolism of various sugars and other substrates to CO_2, fatty acids, glycogen (139, 182), and 2-deoxyglucose transport and phosphorylation (8). None of these metabolic studies establish which cells in skin—epidermal cells, fibroblasts, or other cells—are the glucocorticoid targets. As discussed elsewhere in this review, fibroblasts in culture show somewhat similar responses.

Glucocorticoids also decrease amino acid incorporation into protein (7). Whereas the inhibition of glucose metabolism takes about 1 hr to develop, that of protein metabolism takes about 3 hr, and furthermore requires substrate in the form of glucose (7). Pyruvate is less effective. As in the case of lymphoid tissue, the inhibition of protein metabolism appears to be secondary to effects on glucose metabolism (7). A separate inhibitory effect of glucocorticoids is exerted on amino acid transport, but this effect does not require substrate (7). In a different context, inhibition of glucose metabolism has been invoked as a possible explanation for the inhibition by dexamethasone in vivo of promotion of mouse skin tumors (213).

Glucocorticoid binding substances that may be receptors are present in human fetal skin, but at concentrations much lower than in other tissues such as lung or liver (15).

Acknowledgments

The authors wish to express their gratitude to Mrs. Rosemary Foley for skillful assistance in the preparation of this review.

Literature Cited

1. Adams, P., Jowsey, J. 1967. Effect of calcium on cortisone-induced osteoporosis: a preliminary communication. *Endocrinology* 81:152–54
2. Alescio, T., Moscona, A. A. 1969. Immunochemical evidence for enzyme synthesis in the hormonal induction of glutamine synthetase in embryonic retina in culture. *Biochem. Biophys. Res. Commun.* 34:176–82
3. Alescio, T., Moscona, M., Moscona, A. A. 1970. Induction of glutamine synthetase in embryonic retina: Effects of partial and complete inhibition of RNA synthesis on enzyme accumulation. *Exp. Cell Res.* 61:342–46
4. Anastasia, J. V., McCarl, R. L. 1973. Effects of cortisol on cultured rat heart cells: Lipase activity, fatty acid oxidation, glycogen metabolism, and ATP levels as related to the beating phenomenon. *J. Cell Biol.* 57:109–16
5. Anderson, A. B. M., Laurence, K. M., Turnbull, A. C. 1969. The relationship in anencephaly between the size of the adrenal cortex and length of pregnancy. *J. Obstet. Gynecol. Brit. Commonw.* 76:196–99
6. Anderson, A. B. M., Turnbull, A. C. 1973. Comparative aspects of factors involved in the onset of labour in ovine and human pregnancy. See Ref. 122, 149–51
7. Ariyoshi, Y., Plager, J. E. 1970. Relationships between the influence of cortisol on tissue amino acid accumulation and amino acid incorporation into protein, and the cortisol inhibition of substrate metabolism. *Endocrinology* 86:996–1003
8. Ariyoshi, Y., Plager, J., Matsui, N. 1973. The influence of cortisol on 2-deoxyglucose penetration and phosphorylation by the mouse ear strip preparation. *Acta Endocrinol.* 74:723–31
9. Armelin, H. A. 1973. Pituitary extracts and steroid hormones in the control of 3T3 cell growth. *Proc. Nat. Acad. Sci. USA* 70:2702–6
10. Azmitia, E. C. Jr., McEwen, B. S. 1969. Corticosterone regulation of tryptophan hydroxylase in midbrain of the rat. *Science* 166:1274–76
11. Baden, M. et al 1972. A controlled trial of hydrocortisone therapy in infants with respiratory distress syndrome. *Pediatrics* 50:526–34
12. Balazs, R. 1972. Effects of hormones and nutrition on brain development. In *Human Development and the Thyroid Gland,* ed. J. B. Stanbury, R. L. Kroc, 385–415. New York: Plenum
13. Baldwin, R. L., Korsrud, G. O., Martin, R. J., Cheng, W., Schober, N. A. 1969. Effects of endocrinectomy and hormone replacement therapies upon RNA synthesis in isolated lactating rat mammary gland nuclei. *Biol. Reprod.* 1:31–40
14. Ballard, P. L., Ballard, R. A. 1972. Glucocorticoid receptors and the role of glucocorticoids in fetal lung development. *Proc. Nat. Acad. Sci. USA* 69:2668–72
15. Ballard, P. L., Ballard, R. A. 1974. Cytoplasmic receptor for glucocorticoids in lung of the human fetus and neonate. *J. Clin. Invest.* 53:477–86
16. Ballard, P. L., Baxter, J. D., Higgins, S. J., Rousseau, G. G., Tomkins, G. M. 1974. General presence of glucocorticoid receptors in mammalian tissues. *Endocrinology* 94:998–1002
17. Barrett, A. J., Sledge, C. B., Dingle, J. T. 1966. Effect of cortisol on the synthesis of chondroitin sulphate by embryonic cartilage. *Nature* 211:83–84
18. Bartley, M. H. Jr. 1968. *Structural activities of the anti-inflammatory steroids and their relationship to osseous tissue.* Thesis, Univ. Utah, Salt Lake City
19. Bauer, C. R., Stern, L., Colle, E. 1974. Prolonged rupture of membranes associated with a decreased incidence of respiratory distress syndrome. *Pediatrics* 53:7–12
20. Baxter, J. D., Forsham, P. H. 1972. Tissue effects of glucocorticoids. *Am. J. Med.* 53:573–89
21. Becker, B. 1965. Intraocular pressure response to topical corticosteroids. *Invest. Ophthalmol.* 4:198–205
22. Bergström, S., Ed. 1973. International Conference on Prostaglandins. *Advan. Biosci.* 9:1–887
23. Berliner, D. L., Ruhmann, A. G. 1966. Comparison of the growth of fibroblasts under the unfluence of 11β-hydroxy and 11-keto corticosteroids. *Endocrinology* 78:373–82
24. Bigger, J. F., Palmberg, P. F., Becker, B. 1972. Increased cellular sensitivity to glucocorticoids in primary open-angle glaucoma. *Invest. Ophthalmol.* 11:832–37
25. Bing, R. J., Siegel, A., Ungar, I., Gilbert, M. 1954. Metabolism of the human heart. II. Studies on fat, ketone and

amino acid metabolism. *Am. J. Med.* 16:504–15

26. Birge, C. A., Peake, G. T., Mariz, I. K., Daughaday, W. H. 1967. Effects of cortisol and diethylstilbestrol on growth hormone release by rat pituitary in vitro. *Proc. Soc. Exp. Biol. Med.* 126:342–45
27. Blackburn, W. R., Travers, H., Potter, D. M. 1972. The role of the pituitary-adrenal-thyroid axes in lung differentiation. I. Studies of the cytology and physical properties of anencephalic fetal rat lung. *Lab. Invest.* 26:306–18
28. Blackwood, E. L. 1969. *The effects of cortisol on the bones and teeth of young and adult rabbits.* Thesis, Univ. Utah, Salt Lake City
29. Blecher, M. 1965. Phospholipase C and mechanisms of action of insulin and cortisol on glucose entry into free adipose cells. *Biochem. Biophys. Res. Commun.* 21:202–9
30. Bolton, C. E. 1971. Effect of prolactin and corticosterone on lipid synthesis by rabbit mammary gland explants. *J. Endocrinol.* 51:xxxi–xxxii
31. Braun, T., Hechter, O. 1970. Glucocorticoid regulation of ACTH sensitivity of adenyl cyclase in rat fat cell membranes. *Proc. Nat. Acad. Sci. USA* 66:995–1001
32. Breen, G., DeVellis, J., Cole, R. 1973. Induction of glycerolphosphate dehydrogenase by hydrocortisone in primary rat brain culture. *Trans. 3rd Meet. Soc. Neurosci., San Diego*
33. Bullock, G. R., Christian, R. A., Peters, R. F., White, A. M. 1971. Rapid mitochondrial enlargement in muscle as a response to triamcinolone acetonide and its relationship to the ribosomal defect. *Biochem. Pharmacol.* 20:943–53
34. Bullock, G. R. et al 1972. Relative changes in the function of muscle ribosomes and mitochondria during the early phase of steroid-induced catabolism. *Biochem. J.* 127:881–92
35. Bullough, W. S. 1955. Hormones and mitotic activity. *Vitam. Horm.* 13:261–92
36. Butcher, R. W., Sneyd, J. G. T., Park, C. R., Sutherland, E. W. Jr. 1966. Effect of insulin on adenosine 3',5'-monophosphate in the rat epididymal fat pad. *J. Biol. Chem.* 241:1652–53
37. Carson, S. H., Taeusch, H. W. Jr., Avery, M. E. 1973. Inhibition of lung cell division after hydrocortisone injection into fetal rabbits. *J. Appl. Physiol.* 34:660–63
38. Chader, G. J. 1971. Hormonal effects on the neural retina. I. Glutamine synthetase development in the retina and liver of the normal and triiodothyonine-treated rat. *Arch. Biochem. Biophys.* 144:657–62
39. Chader, G. J. 1973. Some factors affecting the uptake, binding and retention of [^{3}H]cortisol by the chick embryo retina as related to enzyme induction. *J. Neurochem.* 21:1525–32
40. Chader, G. J., Meltzer, R., Silver, J. 1972. A soluble receptor for corticoids in the neural retina of the chick embryo. *Biochem. Biophys. Res. Commun.* 46:2026–33
41. Chader, G. J., Reif-Lehrer, L. 1972. Hormonal effects on the neural retina: corticoid uptake, specific binding and structural requirements for the induction of glutamine synthetase. *Biochim. Biophys. Acta* 264:186–96
42. Chowers, I., Conforti, N., Feldman, S. 1968. Local effect of cortisol in the preoptic area on temperature regulation. *Am. J. Physiol.* 214:538–42
43. Chytil, F., Toft, D. 1972. Corticoid binding component in rat brain. *J. Neurochem.* 19:2877–80
44. Claman, H. N. 1972. Corticosteroids and lymphoid cells. *N. Engl. J. Med.* 287:388–97
45. Comline, R. S., Silver, M., Nathanielsz, P. W., Hall, L. W. 1973. Parturition in the larger herbivores. See Ref. 80, 606–12
46. Crofford, O. B., Renold, A. E. 1965. Glucose uptake by incubated rat epididymal adipose tissue. Rate-limiting steps and site of insulin action. *J. Biol. Chem.* 240:14–21
47. Cruess, R. L., Sakai, T. 1972. Effect of cortisone upon synthesis rates of some components of rat bone matrix. *Clin. Orthop.* 86:253–59
48. Curzon, G. 1969. Tryptophan pyrrolase —a biochemical factor in depressive illness? *Brit. J. Psychiat.* 115:1367–74
49. Curzon, G. 1971. Effects of adrenal hormones and stress on brain serotonin. *Am. J. Clin. Nutr.* 24:830–34
50. Curzon, G., Green, A. R. 1968. Effect of hydrocortisone on rat brain 5-hydroxytryptamine. *Life Sci.* 7(I):657–63
51. Czech, M. P., Fain, J. N. 1971. Dactinomycin inhibition of dexamethasone action on glucose metabolism in white fat cells. *Biochim. Biophys. Acta* 230:185–93

52. Czech, M. P., Fain, J. N. 1972. Antagonism of insulin action on glucose metabolism in white fat cells by dexamethasone. *Endocrinology* 91:518–22
53. D'Agostino, A. N., Chiga, M. 1966. Cortisone myopathy in rabbits. *Neurology* 16:257–63
54. David, D. S., Grieco, M. H., Cushman, P. 1970. Adrenal glucocorticoids after twenty years. A review of their clinically relevant consequence. *J. Chronic Dis.* 22:637–711
55. DeHaan, R. L., Hirakow, R. 1972. Synchronization of pulsation rates in isolated cardiac myocytes. *Exp. Cell Res.* 70:214–20
56. DeKloet, E. R., van der Vies, J., de Wied, D. 1974. The site of the suppressive action of dexamethasone on pituitary-adrenal activity. *Endocrinology* 94:61–73
57. DeLemos, R. A., McLaughlin, G. W. 1973. Induction of the pulmonary surfactant in the fetal primate by the intrauterine administration of corticosteroids. *Pediat. Res.* 7:425/197 (Abstr.)
58. DeLemos, R. A., Shermeta, D. W., Knelson, J. H., Kotas, R., Avery, M. E. 1970. Acceleration of appearance of pulmonary surfactant in the fetal lamb by administration of corticosteroids. *Am. Rev. Resp. Dis.* 102:459–61
59. DeVellis, J., Inglish, D. 1968. Hormonal control of glycerolphosphate dehydrogenase in the rat brain. *J. Neurochem.* 15:1061–70
60. DeVellis, J., Inglish, D. 1969. Effect of cortisol and epinephrine in the biochemical differentiation of clonal glial cells in culture and of the developing rat brain. *Trans. 2nd Int. Meet. Soc. Neurochem., Milan,* 151–52
61. Eliel, L. P., Palmieri, G. M. A., Thompson, J. S., Bird, P. C., Hawryiko, J. 1971. The relationships between adrenal cortical steroids, parathyroid extract, and calcitonin. *Pediatrics* 47:229–38
62. Eliel, L. P., Thomsen, C., Chanes, R. 1965. Antagonism between parathyroid extract and adrenal cortical steroids in man. *J. Clin. Endocrinol. Metab.* 25:457–64
63. Ellis, J. T. 1956. Necrosis and regeneration of skeletal muscles in cortisone-treated rabbits. *Am. J. Pathol.* 32:993–1013
64. Epker, B. N. 1970. Studies on bone turnover and balance in the rabbit. I. Effects of hydrocortisone. *Clin. Orthop.* 72:315–26
65. Exton, J. H., Harper, S. C., Tucker, A. L., Flagg, J. L., Park, C. R. 1973. Effects of adrenalectomy and glucocorticoid replacement on gluconeogenesis in perfused livers from diabetic rats. *Biochim. Biophys. Acta* 329:41–57
66. Fain, J. N. 1962. Effects of dexamethasone and growth hormone on fatty acid mobilization and glucose utilization in adrenalectomized rats. *Endocrinology* 71:633–35
67. Fain, J. N. 1964. Effects of dexamethasone and 2-deoxy-D-glucose on fructose and glucose metabolism by incubated adipose tissue. *J. Biol. Chem.* 239:958–62
68. Fain, J. N. 1965. Comparison of glucocorticoid effects on brown and white adipose tissue of the rat. *Endocrinology* 76:549–52
69. Fain, J. N. 1967. Studies on the role of RNA and protein synthesis in the lipolytic action of growth hormone in isolated fat cells. *Advan. Enzyme Res.* 5:39–51
70. Fain, J. N. 1968. Effect of dibutyryl-3', 5'-AMP, theophylline and norepinephrine on lipolytic action of growth hormone and glucocorticoid in white fat cells. *Endocrinology* 82:825–30
71. Fain, J. N., Kovacev, V. P., Scow, R. O. 1965. Effect of growth hormone and dexamethasone on lipolysis and metabolism in isolated fat cells of the rat. *J. Biol. Chem.* 240:3522–29
72. Fain, J. N., Scow, R. O., Chernick, S. S. 1963. Effects of glucocorticoids on metabolism of adipose tissue in vitro. *J. Biol. Chem.* 238:54–58
73. Farrell, P. M. 1973. Choline phosphotransferase (CPT) and lecithin synthesis in newborn rabbits treated with corticosteroids. *Pediat. Res.* 7:311/83 (Abstr.)
74. Farrell, P. M., Blackburn, W. R. 1973. Cortisol and lung choline phosphotransferase (CPT) activity in the fetal rat after in utero decapitation. *Pediat. Res.* 7:308/80 (Abstr.)
75. Farrell, P. M., Zachman, R. D. 1973. Induction of choline phosphotransferase and lecithin synthesis in the fetal lung by corticosteroids. *Science* 179:297–98
76. Fedrick, J., Butler, N. R. 1972. Hyaline-membrane disease. *Lancet* 2:768–69
77. Ferreri, L. F., Griffith, D. R. 1969. Effect of hydrocortisone acetate on mammary gland nucleic content of pregnant rats. *Proc. Soc. Exp. Biol. Med.* 130:1216–18

78. Fishman, R. A., Reiner, M. 1972. Failure of hydrocortisone to alter the transport of hexoses into rat brain and other tissues. *J. Neurochem.* 19:2221–24
79. Fleischer, N., Vale, W. 1968. Inhibition of vasopressin-induced ACTH release from the pituitary by glucocorticoids in vitro. *Endocrinology* 83:1232–36
80. Foetal and Neonatal Physiology. 1973. *Proceedings of the Sir Joseph Barcroft Centenary Symposium.* London: Cambridge Univ. Press. 641 pp.
81. Follis, R. H. Jr. 1951. Effect of cortisone on growing bones of the rat. *Proc. Soc. Exp. Biol. Med.* 76:722–24
82. Fujimoto, A., Harary, I. 1964. Studies in vitro on single beating rat heart cells. IV. The shift from fat to carbohydrate metabolism in culture. *Biochim. Biophys. Acta* 86:74–80
83. Funder, J. W., Duval, D., Meyer, P. 1973. Cardiac glucocorticoid receptors: The binding of tritiated dexamethasone in rat and dog heart. *Endocrinology* 93:1300–8
84. Gabourel, J. D., Aronow, L. 1962. Growth inhibitory effects of hydrocortisone on mouse lymphoma ML-388 in vitro. *J. Pharmacol. Exp. Ther.* 136:213–21
85. Gardner, D. G., Wittliff, J. L. 1973. Characterization of a distinct glucocorticoid-binding protein in the lactating mammary gland of the rat. *Biochim. Biophys. Acta* 320:617–27
86. Garland, P. B., Randle, P. J. 1964. Regulation of glucose uptake by muscle, 10. *Biochem. J.* 93:678–87
87. Giannopoulos, G. 1973. A specific glucocorticoid binding macromolecule of rabbit uterine cytosol. *Biochem. Biophys. Res. Commun.* 54:600–6
88. Giannopoulos, G. 1973. Glucocorticoid receptors in lung. I. Specific binding of glucocorticoids to cytoplasmic components of rabbit fetal lung. *J. Biol. Chem.* 248:3876–83
89. Giannopoulos, G. 1974. Variations in the levels of cytoplasmic glucocorticoid receptors in lungs of various species at different developmental stages. *Endocrinology* 94:450–58
90. Giannopoulos, G., Mulay, S., Solomon, S. 1973. Glucocorticoid receptors in lung. II. Specific binding of glucocorticoids to nuclear components of rabbit fetal lung. *J. Biol. Chem.* 248:5016–23
91. Gluck, L., Kulovich, M. V. 1973. Lecithin/sphingomyelin ratios in amniotic fluid in normal and abnormal pregnancy. *Am. J. Obstet. Gynecol.* 115:539–46
92. Goldman, J. K., Frohman, L. A. 1974. Effects of glucocorticoid administration to rats on in vitro intermediary metabolism. *J. Pharmacol. Exp. Ther.* 188:310–17
93. Goshima, K., Tonomura, Y. 1969. Synchronized beating of embryonic mouse myocardial cells mediated by FL cells in monolayer culture. *Exp. Cell Res.* 56:387–92
94. Gray, J. G., Pratt, W. B., Aronow, L. 1971. Effect of glucocorticoids on hexose uptake by mouse fibroblasts in vitro. *Biochemistry* 10:277–84
95. Green, A. R., Curzon, G. 1968. Decrease of 5-hyroxytryptamine in the brain provoked by hydrocortisone and its prevention by allopurinol. *Nature* 220:1095–97
96. Gross, S. R., Aronow, L., Pratt, W. B. 1970. The outward transport of cortisol by mammalian cells in vitro. *J. Cell Biol.* 44:103–14
97. Grosser, B. I., Stevens, W., Bruenger, F. W., Reed, D. J. 1971. Corticosterone binding by rat brain cytosol. *J. Neurochem.* 18:1725–32
98. Grosser, B. I., Stevens, W., Reed, D. J. 1973. Properties of corticosterone-binding macromolecules from rat brain cytosol. *Brain Res.* 57:387–95
99. Grosser, B. I., Swim, H. E. 1957. Inhibitory effects of steroids on the growth of uterine fibroblasts: the isolation of steroid-resistant variants. *J. Lab. Clin. Med.* 50:820–21
100. Gruener, R., Stern, L. Z. 1972. Corticosteroids: Effects on muscle membrane excitability. *Arch. Neurol.* 26:181–85
101. Gumbinas, M., Oda, M., Huttenlocher, P. 1973. The effects of corticosteroids on myelination of the developing rat brain. *Biol. Neonate* 22:355–66
102. Hahn, D. W., Turner, C. W. 1966. Effect of corticosterone and aldosterone upon milk yield in the rat. *Proc. Soc. Exp. Biol. Med.* 121:1056–58
103. Harary, I., Farley, B. 1963. In vitro studies on single beating rat heart cells. I. Growth and organization. *Exp. Cell Res.* 29:451–65
104. Harary, I., McCarl, R., Farley, B. 1966. Studies in vitro on single beating rat heart cells. IX. The restoration of beating by serum lipids and fatty acids. *Biochim. Biophys. Acta* 115:15–22
105. Harlan, W. R. Jr., Margraf, J. H., Said, S. I. 1966. Pulmonary lipid composition

of species with and without surfactant. *Am. J. Physiol.* 211:855–61
106. Hofert, J. F., White, A. 1965. Inhibition of the lymphocytolytic activity of cortisol by total hepatectomy. *Endocrinology* 77:574–81
107. Howard E. 1965. Effects of corticosterone and food restriction on growth and on DNA, RNA and cholesterol contents of the brain and liver in infant mice. *J. Neurochem.* 12:181–91
108. Howard, E. 1968. Reductions in size and total DNA of cerebrum and cerebellum in adult mice after corticosterone treatment in infancy. *Exp. Neurol.* 22:191–208
109. Ingle, D. J. 1938. Effect of cortin on survival and work capacity of rats after removal of intra-abdominal organs. *Proc. Soc. Exp. Biol. Med.* 39:151–53
110. Ingle, D. J. 1952. The role of the adrenal cortex in homeostasis. *J. Endocrinol.* 8:xxiii–xxxvii
111. Ishii, D. N., Pratt, W. B., Aronow, L. 1972. Steady-state level of the specific glucocorticoid binding component in mouse fibroblasts. *Biochemistry* 11:3896–3904
112. Jasani, M. K. 1972. Possible modes of action of ACTH and glucocorticoids in allergic diseases. *Clin. Allergy* 2:1–41
113. Jeanrenaud, B., Renold, A. E. 1966. The effects of glucocorticoids upon adipose tissue in vitro. *Excerpta Med. Int. Congr.* 132:769–78
114. Jee, W. S. S., Park, H. Z., Roberts, W. E., Kenner, G. H. 1970. Corticosteroid and bone. *Am. J. Anat.* 129:477–80
115. Jee, W. S. S., Roberts, W. E., Park, H. Z., Julian, G., Kramer, M. 1972. Interrelated effects of glucocorticoid and parathyroid hormone upon bone remodeling. *Excerpta Med. Int. Congr.* 243:430–39
116. Jett, S., Wu, K., Duncan, H., Frost, H. M. 1970. Adrenalcorticosteroid and salicylate actions on human and canine haversian bone formation and resorption. *Clin. Orthop.* 68:301–15
117. Jöchle, W. 1973. Corticosteroid-induced parturition in domestic animals. *Ann. Rev. Pharmacol.* 13:33–55
118. Jowsey, J. et al 1965. Quantitative microradiographic studies of normal and osteoporotic bone. *J. Bone Joint Surg. Am. Vol.* 47:785–806
119. Jowsey, J., Riggs, B. L. 1970. Bone formation in hypercortisonism. *Acta Endocrinol.* 63:21–28
120. Kikkawa, Y., Kiabara, M., Motoyama, E. K., Orzalesi, M. M., Cook, C. D. 1971. Morphologic development of fetal rabbit lung and its acceleration with cortisol. *Am. J. Pathol.* 64:423–34
121. King, R. J., Mainwaring, W. I. P. 1974. *Steroid-Cell Interactions.* Baltimore: Univ. Park Press. 440 pp.
122. Klopper, A., Gardner, J., Eds. 1973. Endocrine factors in labour. *Memoirs of the Society for Endocrinology No. 20.* London: Cambridge Univ. Press. 193 pp.
123. Kornel, L. 1973. On the effects and the mechanism of action of corticosteroids in normal and neoplastic target tissues: findings and hypotheses. *Acta Endocrinol.* 74:Suppl. 178
124. Korsrud, G. O., Baldwin, R. L. 1969. Effects of endocrinectomy and hormone replacement therapies upon enzyme activities in lactating rat mammary glands. *Biol. Reprod.* 1:21–30
125. Korsrud, G. O., Baldwin, R. L. 1972. Effects of adrenalectomy, adrenalectomy-ovariectomy, and cortisol and estrogen therapies upon enzyme activities in lactating rat mammary glands. *Can. J. Biochem.* 50:366–76
126. Kostyo, J. L. 1965. In vitro effects of adrenal steroid hormones on amino acid transport in muscle. *Endocrinology* 76:604–13
127. Kostyo, J. L., Redmond, A. F. 1966. Role of protein synthesis in the inhibitory action of adrenal steroid hormones on amino acid transport by muscle. *Endocrinology* 79:531–40
128. Kotas, R. V., Avery, M. E. 1971. Accelerated appearance of pulmonary surfactant in the fetal rabbit. *J. Appl. Physiol.* 30:358–61
129. Kotas, R. V., Fletcher, B. D., Torday, J., Avery, M. E. 1971. Evidence for independent regulators of organ maturation in fetal rabbits. *Pediatrics* 47:57–64
130. Kumaresan, P., Anderson, R. R., Turner, C. W. 1967. Effect of corticosterone upon mammary gland growth of pregnant rats. *Endocrinology* 81:658–61
131. Liggins, G. C. 1968. Premature parturition after infusion of corticotrophin or cortisol into foetal lambs. *J. Endocrinol.* 42:323–29
132. Liggins, G. C., Fairclough, R. J., Grieves, S. A., Kendall, J. Z., Knox, B. S. 1973. The mechanism of initiation of parturition in the ewe. *Recent Progr. Horm. Res.* 29:111–59
133. Liggins, G. C., Grieves, S. A., Kendall, J. Z., Knox, B. S. 1972. The physiological roles of progesterone, oestradiol-17β and prostaglandin $F_{2\alpha}$ in the con-

trol of ovine parturition. *J. Reprod. Fert. Suppl.* 16:85–103
134. Liggins, G. C., Howie, R. N. 1972. A controlled trial of antepartum glucocorticoid treatment for prevention of the respiratory distress syndrome in premature infants. *Pediatrics* 50:515–25
135. Litwack, G., Singer, S. 1972. Subcellular actions of glucocorticoids. In *Biochemical Actions of Hormones,* ed. G. Litwack, 2:113–63. New York: Academic. 542 pp.
136. Macieira-Coelho, A. 1966. Action of cortisone on human fibroblasts in vitro. *Experientia* 22:390–91
137. Mark, G. E., Strasser, F. F. 1966. Pacemaker activity and mitosis in cultures of newborn rat heart ventricle cells. *Exp. Cell Res.* 44:217–33
138. Mati, J. K. G., Horrobin, D. F., Bramley, P. S. 1973. Induction of labour in sheep and in humans by single doses of corticosteroids. *Brit. Med. J.* 2:149–51
139. Matsui, N., Plager, J. E. 1969. "Anti-insulin" action of cortisol. 1. Influence of cortisol on the metabolism of specifically labeled glucose, pyruvate and Glucose-6-phosphate. *Endocrinology* 84:1439–49
140. Mayne, R., Barry, J. M. 1970. Biochemical changes during development of mouse mammary tissue in organ culture. *J. Endocrinol.* 46:61–70
141. McCarl, R. L., Szuhaj, B. F., Houlihan, R. T. 1965. Steroid stimulation of beating of cultured rat-heart cells. *Science* 150:1611–13
142. McEwen, B. S. 1973. Glucocorticoid binding sites in rat brain: subcellular and anatomical localizations. *Progr. Brain Res.* 39:87–97
143. McEwen, B. S., Magnus, C., Wallach, G. 1972. Soluble corticosterone-binding macromolecules extracted from rat brain. *Endocrinology* 90:217–26
144. McEwen, B. S., Plapinger, L. 1970. Association of [3H]corticosterone-1,2 with macromolecules extracted from brain cell nuclei. *Nature* 226:263–65
145. McEwen, B. S., Wallach, G. 1973. Corticosterone binding to hippocampus: nuclear and cytosol binding in vitro. *Brain Res.* 57:373–86
146. Milie, A. B., Adamson, K. G. 1969. The relationship between anencephaly and prolonged pregnancy. *J. Obstet. Gynecol. Brit. Commonw.* 76:102–11
147. Millard, S. A., Costa, E., Gal, E. M. 1972. On the control of brain serotonin turnover rate by end product inhibition. *Brain Res.* 40:545–51
148. Morgan, H. E., Regen, D. M., Henderson, M. J., Sawyer, T. K., Park, C. R. 1961. Regulation of glucose uptake in muscle, VI. *J. Biol. Chem.* 236:2162–68
149. Morita, Y., Munck, A. 1964. Effect of glucocorticoids in vivo and in vitro on net glucose uptake and amino acid incorporation by rat thymus cells. *Biochim. Biophys. Acta* 93:150–57
150. Morris, J. E., Moscona, A. A. 1970. Induction of glutamine synthetase in embryonic retina: its dependency on cell interactions. *Science* 167:1736–38
151. Morris, J. E., Moscona, A. A. 1971. The induction of glutamine synthetase in cell aggregates of embryonic neural retina: correlations with differentiation and multicellular organization. *Develop. Biol.* 25:420–44
152. Moscona, A. A. 1972. Induction of glutamine synthetase in embryonic neural retina: a model for the regulation of specific gene expression in embryonic cells. *FEBS Symp.* 24:1–23
153. Moscona, A. A., Moscona, M., Jones, R. E. 1970. Induction of glutamine synthetase in embryonic neural retina in vitro by inhibitors of macromolecular synthesis. *Biochem. Biophys. Res. Commun.* 39:943–49
154. Moscona, A. A., Moscona, M. H., Saenz, N. 1968. Enzyme induction in embryonic retina: the role of transcription and translation. *Proc. Nat. Acad. Sci. USA* 61:160–67
155. Moscona, A. A., Piddington, R. 1966. Stimulation by hydrocortisone of premature changes in the developmental pattern of glutamine synthetase in embryonic retina. *Biochim. Biophys. Acta* 121:409–11
156. Moscona, A. A., Piddington, R. 1967. Enzyme induction by corticosteroids in embryonic cells: steroid structure and inductive effect. *Science* 158:496–97
157. Moscona, M., Frenkel, N., Moscona, A. A. 1972. Regulatory mechanisms in the induction of glutamine synthetase in the embryonic retina: immonochemical studies. *Develop. Biol.* 28:229–41
158. Motoyama, E. K. et al 1971. Effect of cortisol on the maturation of fetal lungs. *Pediatrics* 48:547–55
159. Motsay, G. J., Alho, A., Jaeger, T., Dietzman, R. H., Lillehei, R. C. 1970. Effects of corticosteroids on the circulation in shock: experimental and clinical results. *Fed. Proc.* 29:1861–73
160. Mulay, S., Giannopoulos, G., Solomon, S. 1973. Corticosteroid levels in the

mother and fetus of the rabbit during gestation. *Endocrinology* 93:1342–48
161. Mulrow, P. J. 1967. *The Adrenal Cortex by 26 Authors,* ed. A. B. Eisenstein, 301-2. Boston: Little, Brown. 685 pp.
162. Munck, A. 1961. The effect in vitro of glucocorticoids on net glucose uptake by rat epididymal adipose tissue. *Biochim. Biophys. Acta* 48:618–20
163. Munck, A. 1961. The effect of cortisol on glucose uptake by rat epididymal fat pads. *Endocrinology* 68:178–80
164. Munck, A. 1962. Studies on the mode of action of glucocorticoids in rats. II. The effects in vivo and in vitro on net glucose uptake by isolated adipose tissue. *Biochim. Biophys. Acta* 57:318–26
165. Munck, A. 1971. Glucocorticoid inhibition of glucose uptake by peripheral tissues: old and new evidence, molecular mechanisms, and physiological significance. *Perspect. Biol. Med.* 14:265–89
166. Munck, A., Koritz, S. B. 1962. Studies on the mode of action of glucocorticoids in rats. I. Early effects of cortisol on blood glucose and on glucose entry into muscle, liver and adipose tissue. *Biochem. Biophys. Acta* 57:310–17
167. Munck, A., Young, D. A. 1974. Corticosteroids and lymphoid tissue. *Handb. Physiol.* In press
168. Murphy, B. E. P. 1973. Does the human fetal adrenal play a role in parturition? *Am. J. Obstet. Gynecol.* 115:521–25
169. Murphy, B. E. P. 1974. Evidence of cortisol deficiency at birth in infants with the respiratory distress syndrome. *J. Clin. Endocrinol. Metab.* 38:158
170. Murphy, B. E. P., Diez d'Aux, R. C. 1972. Steroid levels in the human fetus: cortisol and cortisone. *J. Clin. Endocrinol. Metab.* 35:678–83
171. Naeye, R. L., Harcke, H. T., Blanc, W. A. 1971. Adrenal gland structure and the development of hyaline membrane disease. *Pediatrics* 47:650–57
172. Nathanielsz, P. W., Abel, M., Smith, G. W. 1973. Hormonal factors in parturition in the rabbit. See Ref. 80, 594–602
173. Neely, J. R., Morgan, H. E. 1974. Relationship between carbohydrate and lipid metabolism and the energy balance of heart muscle. *Ann. Rev. Physiol.* 36:413–59
174. O'Donohue, N. W., Holland, P. D. J. 1968. Familial congenital adrenal hypoplasia. *Arch. Dis. Childhood* 43:717–23
175. Overell, B. G., Condon, S. E., Petrow, V. 1960. The effect of hormones and their analogues upon the uptake of glucose by mouse skin in vitro. *J. Pharm. Pharmacol.* 12:150–53
176. Pattle, R. E. 1965. Surface lining of lung alveoli. *Physiol. Rev.* 45:48–79
177. Peck, W. A., Brandt, J., Miller, I. 1967. Hydrocortisone-induced inhibition of protein synthesis and uridine incorporation in isolated bone cells in vitro. *Proc. Nat. Acad. Sci. USA* 57:1599–1606
178. Peck, W. A., Messinger, K. 1970. Nucleoside and ribonucleic acid metabolism in isolated bone cells. *J. Biol. Chem.* 245:2722–29
179. Perley, M., Kipnis, D. M. 1966. Effect of glucocorticoids on plasma insulin. *N. Engl. J. Med.* 274:1237–41
180. Piddington, R. 1971. Distribution and development of glutamine synthetase in the embryonic cerebral hemisphere. *J. Exp. Zool.* 177:219–28
181. Plager, J. E., Matsui, N. 1966. An in vitro demonstration of the anti-insulin action of cortisol on glucose metabolism. *Endocrinology* 78:1154–58
182. Plager, J. E., Matsui, N., Ariyoshi, Y. 1969. "Anti-insulin" action of cortisol. 2. Comparison of the influence of cortisol on the metabolism of glucose, fructose, mannose, and galactose. *Endocrinology* 84:1450–55
183. Platzker, A. C. G., Kitterman, J. A., Clements, J. A., Tooley, W. H. 1972. Surfactant appearance and secretion in fetal lamb lung in response to dexamethasone. *Pediat. Res.* 6:406/146 (Abstr.)
184. Pratt, W. B., Aronow, L. 1966. The effect of glucocorticoids on protein and nucleic acid synthesis in mouse fibroblasts growing in vitro *J. Biol. Chem.* 241:5244–50
185. Pratt, W. B., Ishii, D. N. 1972. Specific binding of glucocorticoids in vitro in the soluble fraction of mouse fibroblasts. *Biochemistry* 11:1401–10
186. Randle, P. J., Hales, C. N., Garland, P. B., Newsholme, E. A. 1963. The glucose fatty-acid cycle: its role in insulin sensitivity and the metabolic disturbances of diabetes mellitus. *Lancet* 1:785–89
187. Rauch, H. C., Loomis, M. E., Johnson, M. E., Favour, C. B. 1961. *In vitro* suppression of polymorphonuclear leukocyte and lymphocyte glycolysis by cortisol. *Endocrinology* 68:375–85
188. Reif-Lehrer, L. 1968. Induction of glutamine synthetase in chick embryo retina: effects of serum and of steroid structure. *Biochim. Biophys. Acta* 170:263–70

189. Reif-Lehrer, L. 1971. Glutamine synthetase activity in human retinal tissue. *Arch. Ophthalmol.* 86:72–76
190. Renold, A. E., Cahill, G. F. Jr., Eds. 1965. *Handb. Physiol. Adipose Tissue, Sect. 5.* 824 pp.
191. Reshef, L., Shapiro, B. 1960. Effect of epinephrine, cortisone, and growth hormone on release of unesterified fatty acids by adipose tissue in vitro. *Metabolism* 9:551–55
192. Reynolds, J. J. 1966. The effect of hydrocortisone on the growth of chick bone rudiments in chemically defined medium. *Exp. Cell Res.* 41:174–89
193. Correa, P. R., Magalhaes, E., Krahl, M. E. 1960. Response of epididymal adipose tissue to small concentrations of insulin: effect of cortisone. *Proc. Soc. Exp. Biol. Med.* 103:704–6
194. Riggs, B. L., Jowsey, J., Kelly, P. 1966. Quantitative microradiographic study of bone remodeling in Cushing's syndrome. *Metabolism* 15:773–80
195. Rivera, E. M. 1972. Influence of hormones on enzyme activity in mouse mammary gland in vitro. *J. Diary Sci.* 55:1308–16
196. Rivera, E. M., Cummins, E. P. 1971. Hormonal induction of dehydrogenase enzymes in mammary gland in vitro. *Gen. Comp. Endocrinol.* 17:319–26
197. Rizack, M. A. 1964. Activation of an epinephrine-sensitive lipolytic activity from adipose tissue by adenosine 3', 5'-phosphate. *J. Biol. Chem.* 239:392–95
198. Roberts, W. E. 1969. *The effects of cortisol on the cellular kinetics and cell population dynamics of periodontal ligament bone cells.* Thesis, Univ. Utah, Salt Lake City
199. Rockstein, M., Ed. 1973. *Development and Aging in the Nervous System,* 172–98. New York: Academic. 218 pp.
200. Roosevelt, T. S., Ruhmann-Wennhold, A., Nelson, D. H. 1973. Adrenal corticosteroid effects upon rat brain mitochondrial metabolism. *Endocrinology* 93:619–25
201. Rosen, J. M., Fina, J. J., Milholland, R. J., Rosen, F. 1970. Inhibition of glucose uptake in lymphosarcoma P1798 by cortisol and its relationship to the biosynthesis of deoxyribonucleic acid. *J. Biol. Chem.* 245:2074–80
202. Roth, G. S. 1974. Age-related changes in specific glucocorticoid binding by steroid-responsive tissues of rats. *Endocrinology* 94:82–90
203. Rudman, D., DiGirolamo, M. 1971. Effect of adrenal cortical steroids on lipid metabolism. In *The Human Adrenal Cortex,* ed. N. P. Christy, 241–55. New York: Harper and Row
204. Ruhmann, A. G., Berliner, D. L. 1965. Effect of steroids on growth of mouse fibroblasts in vitro. *Endocrinology* 76:916–27
205. Sarkar, P. K., Moscona, A. A. 1971. Changes in macromolecular synthesis associated with the induction of glutamine synthetase in embryonic retina. *Proc. Nat. Acad. Sci. USA* 68:2308–11
206. Sarkar, P. K., Moscona, A. A. 1973. Glutamine synthetase induction in embryonic neural retina: immunochemical identification of polysomes involved in enzyme synthesis. *Proc. Nat. Acad. Sci. USA* 70:1667–71
207. Sayers, G. 1950. The adrenal cortex and homeostasis. *Physiol. Rev.* 30:241–320
208. Sayers, G., Solomon, N. 1960. Work performance of a rat heart-lung preparation: Standardization and influence of corticosteroids. *Endocrinology* 66: 719–30
209. Schaeffer, L. D., Chenoweth, M., Dunn, A. 1969. Adrenal cortocosteroid involvement in the control of phosphorylase in muscle. *Biochim. Biophys. Acta* 192:304–9
210. Schrek, R. 1949. Cytotoxic action of hormones of the adrenal cortex according to the method of unstained cell counts. *Endocrinology* 45:317–34
211. Schwartz, R. J. 1972. Steroid control of genomic expression in embryonic chick retina. *Nature New Biol.* 237:121–25
212. Schwartz, R. J. 1973. Control of glutamine synthetase synthesis in the embryonic chick neural retina. *J. Biol. Chem.* 248:6426–35
213. Scribner, J. D., Slaga, T. J. 1973. Multiple effects of dexamethasone on protein synthesis and hyperplasia caused by a tumor promoter. *Cancer Res.* 33:542–46
214. Senft, G., Schultz, G., Munske, K., Hoffmann, M. 1968. Effects of glucocorticoids and insulin on 3',5'-AMP phosphodiesterase activity in adrenalectomized rats. *Diabetologia* 4:330–35
215. Shimada, Y., Piddington, R., Moscona, A. A. 1967. Experimentally induced increases in glutamine synthetase in the optic tectum in the embryo and in culture. *Exp. Cell Res.* 48:240–43
216. Shimizu, C. S. N., Kaplan, S. A. 1964. Effects of cortisone on in vitro incorporation of glycine into protein of rat diaphragm. *Endocrinology* 74:709–13

217. Shyamala, G. 1973. Specific cytoplasmic glucocorticoid hormone receptors in lactating mammary glands. *Biochemistry* 12:3085–90
218. Simonsson, B. 1972. Depression of ^{3}H-glucose uptake into rabbit polymorphonuclear leukocytes by glucocorticoids in concentrations partly saturating the specific glucocorticoid uptake. Evidence for a glucocorticoid receptor. *Acta Physiol. Scand.* 86:398–409
219. Southern, E. M., Ed. 1972. *The prostaglandins—Clinical Applications in Human Reproduction.* New York: Futura. 545 pp.
220. Spellacy, W. N., Buhi, W. C. 1972. Amniotic fluid lecithin/sphingomyelin ratio as an index of fetal maturity. *Obstet. Gynecol.* 39:852–60
221. Spellacy, W. N., Buhi, W. C., Riggall, F. C., Holsinger, K. L. 1973. Human amniotic fluid lecithin/sphingomyelin ratio changes with estrogen or glucocorticoid treatment. *Am. J. Obstet. Gynecol.* 115:216–18
222. Stastny, F. 1971. Hydrocortisone as a possible inductor of Na^+-K^+-ATPase in the chick embryo cerebral hemispheres. *Brain Res.* 25:397–410
223. Stevens, W., Grosser, B. I., Reed, D. J. 1971. Corticosterone-binding molecules in rat brain cytosols: regional distribution. *Brain Res.* 35:602–7
224. Stevens, W., Reed, D. J., Erickson, S., Grosser, B. I. 1973. The binding of corticosterone to brain proteins: diurnal variation. *Endocrinology* 93:1152–56
225. Stith, R. D., Bottoms, G. D. 1972. Intracellular binding of [^{3}H] cortisol and its effect on RNA polymerase activity in hypothalamus of the pig. *Brain Res.* 41:423–34
226. Storey, E. 1963. The influence of adrenal cortical hormones on bone formation and resorption. *Clin. Orthop.* 30:197–217
227. Strong, C. R., Forsyth, I., Dils, R. 1972. The effects of hormones on milk-fat synthesis in mammary explants from pseudopregnant rabbits. *Biochem. J.* 128:509–19
228. Sugimoto, M., Endo, H. 1969. Effect of hydrocortisone on the keratinization of chick embryonic skin cultured in a chemically defined medium. *Nature* 222:1270–72
229. Szijan, I., Burdman, J. A. 1973. The relationship between DNA synthesis and the synthesis of nuclear proteins in rat brain. *Biochim. Biophys. Acta* 299:344–53
230. Taeusch, H. W. Jr., Heitner, M., Avery, M. E. 1972. Accelerated lung maturation and increased survival in premature rabbits treated with hydrocortisone. *Am. Rev. Resp. Dis.* 105:971–73
231. Talmage, R. V., Park, H. Z., Jee, W. 1970. Parathyroid hormone and thyrocalcitonin function in cortisol-treated rats. *Endocrinology* 86:1080–84
232. Thompson, E. B., Lippman, M. E. 1974. Mechanism of action of glucocorticoids. *Metabolism* 23:159–202
233. Thompson, J., Urist, M. R. 1970. Influence of cortisone and calcitonin on bone morphogenesis. *Clin. Orthop.* 71: 253–70
234. Thompson, J. S., Palmieri, G. M. A., Crawford, R. L. 1972. The effect of porcine calcitonin on osteoporosis induced by adrenal cortical steroids. *J. Bone Joint Surg. Am. Vol.* 54:1490–1500
235. Thorburn, G. D., Nicol, D. H., Bassett, J. M., Shutt, D. A., Cox, R. I. 1972. Parturition in the goat and sheep: changes in corticosteroids, progesterone, oestrogens and prostaglandin F. *J. Reprod. Fert. Suppl.* 16:61–84
236. Thrash, C. R., Cunningham, D. D. 1973. Stimulation of division of density inhibited fibroblasts by glucocorticoids. *Nature* 242:399–401
237. Tice, L. W., Engel, A. G. 1967. The effects of glucocorticoids on red and white muscles in the rat. *Am. J. Pathol.* 50:311–33
238. Tierney, D. F. 1974. Lung metabolism and biochemistry. *Ann. Rev. Physiol.* 36:209–31
239. Toft, D., Chytil, F. 1973. Receptors for glucocorticoids in lung tissue. *Arch. Biochem. Biophys.* 157:464–69
240. Tsapko, L. I., Usatenko, M. S. 1973. Effect of hydrocortisone on activity and isoenzyme composition of rabbit muscle and liver lactate dehydrogenase. *Biokhimiya* 38:158–60
241. Tucker, H. A., Larson, B. L., Gorski, J. 1971. Cortisol binding in cultured bovine mammary cells. *Endocrinology* 89:152–60
242. Turkington, R. W. 1972. *Biochemical Actions of Hormones,* ed. G. Litwack, 2:55–80. New York/London: Academic. 542 pp.
243. Turkington, R. W. 1972. *Lactogenic Hormones. A Ciba Foundation Symposium in memory of Professor S. J. Folley,* ed. G. E. W. Wolstenholme, J. Knight, 111–35. Edinburgh/London: Churchill-Livingstone. 404 pp.

244. Turkington, R. W., Juergens, W. G., Topper, Y. J. 1967. Steroid structural requirements for mammary gland differentiation in vitro. *Endocrinology* 80:1139–42
245. Turkington, R. W., Kadohama, N. 1972. *Gene Transcription in Reproductive Tissue. Karolinska Symposia No. 5,* ed. E. Diczfalusy, 346–68. Stockholm: Karolinska Institutet. 453 pp.
246. Turkington, R. W., Majumder, G. C., Kadohama, N., MacIndoe, J. H., Frantz, W. 1973. Hormonal regulation of gene expression in mammary cells. *Recent Progr. Horm. Res.* 29:417–55
247. Turnbull, A. C., Anderson, A. B. M. 1969. *Progesterone—Its regulatory Effect on the Myometrium,* ed. G. E. W. Wolstenholme, J. Knight, 106–19. London: Churchill. 193 pp.
248. Vann Bennett, G., Cuatrecasas, P. 1972. Insulin recepter of fat cells in insulin-resistant metabolic states. *Science* 176:805–6
249. Vignos, P. J., Greene, R. 1973. Oxidative respiration of skeletal muscle in experimental corticosteroid myopathy. *J. Lab. Clin. Med.* 81:365–78
250. Wagner, R. K., Görlich, L., Jungblut, P. W. 1972. Multiple steroid hormone receptors in calf uterus. Binding specificities and distributions. *Z. Physiol. Chem.* 353:1654–56
251. Wang, N. S., Kotas, R. V., Avery, M. E., Thurlbeck, W. M. 1971. Accelerated appearance of osmiophilic bodies in fetal lungs following steroid injection. *J. Appl. Physiol.* 30:362–65
252. Waters, M. D., Summer, G. K. 1970. Regulation of alkaline phosphatase in human skin fibroblasts. *Proc. Soc. Exp. Biol. Med.* 133:925–30
253. Whitfield, C. R., Sproule, W. B. 1972. Prediction of neonatal respiratory disgress. *Lancet* 1:382
254. Williams, R. H., Ed. 1968. *Texbook of Endocrinology.* Philadelphia: Saunders. 1259 pp. 4th ed.
255. Wong, M. D., Burton, A. F. 1974. Studies on corticosterone-receptor complexes from mouse placenta. *Can. J. Biochem.* 52:190–195
256. Wool, I. G., Weinshelbaum, E. I. 1959. Incorporation of C^{14}-amino acids into protein of isolated diaphragms: role of the adrenal steroids. *Am. J. Physiol.* 197:1089–92
257. Wool, I. G., Weinshelbaum, E. I. 1960. Adrenal cortical hormone and incorporation of C14 from amino acid precursors into muscle protein. *Am. J. Physiol.* 198:360–62
258. Yoon, J. J., Harper, R. G. 1973. Observations on the relationship between duration of rupture of the membranes and the development of idiopathic respiratory distress syndrome. *Pediatrics* 52:161–68
259. Yorke, R. E. 1967. The influence of dexamethasone on adipose tissue metabolism in vitro. *J. Endocrinol.* 39:329–43

Copyright 1975. All rights reserved

HORMONAL REGULATION OF THE REPRODUCTIVE TRACT IN FEMALE MAMMALS[1,2]

❖1131

Robert M. Brenner and Neal B. West
Department of Reproductive Physiology, Oregon Regional Primate Research Center, Beaverton, Oregon 97005

INTRODUCTION

This review covers only a small part of what has recently become an enormous literature on hormonal regulation of the female reproductive tract. We used the following guidelines in selecting papers for review: 1. The reproductive tract is exposed to varying levels of sex steroids during the menstrual and estrous cycles. With the advent of radioimmunoassay techniques, these patterns are now known more precisely than at any previous time. 2. The steroids are concentrated in the target cells of the tract by mechanisms that, because of recent findings in steroid-receptor interactions, are more fully understood than ever before. Here we pay particular attention to reports of fluctuations in receptor levels during reproductive cycles and pregnancy and to the correlation between such changes and the fluctuating levels of steroids in plasma. 3. Within the target cells, the steroids interact with the cell machinery to produce multiple effects. This is the frontier of the modern research effort on hormone actions; the potential for future success here is enormous. So far, however, species and organ differences have thwarted attempts to define any universal principles of hormone action, although evidence is accumulating in favor of the idea that one of the key endpoints of steroid hormone action is the production of specific RNA molecules.

As to our method of selecting reports to review, we have chosen those that illustrate the interactions between estrogens and progestins in regulating the growth and function of the tract, that point to the complexity of these interactions, and that serve as guidelines for future study. No attempt was made to be comprehensive. Some emphasis has been placed on the reproductive tract of primates because of our special interests.

[1]Publication No. 752 of the Oregon Regional Primate Research Center.
[2]Supported by NIH Grant No. FR-00163 and No. HD-05969.

Additional information is available in a recently published series of definitive reviews concerned with various aspects of endocrine control of the female reproductive system (66). These include the effects of steroid hormones on uterine metabolism (205); endocrine control of implantation (153); the overall role of hormones in pregnancy (76, 161); various aspects of the biosynthesis, metabolism, and uterine binding of estrogens (42, 61, 178, 185); the biosynthesis, metabolism, and physiological role of progesterone (35, 59, 104, 145); the effects of hormones on the anatomy and physiology of the cervix (63, 128); and the biological effects of oral contraceptive steroids (168).

STEROID LEVELS DURING REPRODUCTIVE CYCLES

Menstrual Cycles

ESTROGENS The cyclic pattern of estrogen secretion in nonhuman primates has been investigated in the rhesus monkey (11–14, 78, 85, 86, 100, 157, 207), cynomolgus monkeys (163), bonnet macaques (120), baboons (186), and chimpanzees (65). It is generally agreed that in the rhesus monkey the level of estradiol (E_2) in peripheral plasma during the early follicular phase (days 1–8) is ∼50 pg/ml, and that about 4 days before the luteinizing hormone (LH) peak there is a steady rise to ∼150 pg/ml; on the day of the LH peak there is a surge to a peak of 350 pg/ml, then 2 days after the LH peak a rapid fall to ∼25 pg/ml and a rise for the duration of the luteal phase back to ∼50 pg/ml. The pattern then is an essentially constant level of estradiol secretion throughout the menstrual cycle except for a relatively brief midcycle surge. Variations in plasma estrone (E_1) levels correspond to those of estradiol, but the baseline (∼5 pg/ml) and peak surge (∼40 pg/ml) levels are approximately nine times less (78). In one study (11), estrone levels rose above baseline in the late luteal phase.

When samples of peripheral blood were drawn every 3 hr over the 72 hr period that encompassed the midcycle LH surge (206), the peak of estradiol preceded that of LH by 9–15 hr. Total plasma estrogens in cynomolgus monkeys (163) show a secretory pattern similar to that of the rhesus monkey, though the levels reported are considerably higher (early follicular, ∼183 pg/ml; midcycle peak, 680–850 pg/ml; luteal phase, ∼183 pg/ml, except for a decline on day 17).

In the chimpanzee (65), variations in urinary estrogens (estrone, estradiol-17β) during the cycle correspond to those in human rather than in other nonhuman primates because the typical midcycle peak of estrogens is followed by a second peak in the luteal phase. Measurements of urinary estrogens in the baboon reveal a gradual increase during the follicular phase and a sharp midcycle surge. No second peak of urinary estrogens is seen during the luteal phase (186).

The pattern of estrogen secretion in human females has been studied in several laboratories (1, 4, 37, 84, 129, 171). These authors agree that the early follicular phase has levels of ∼50 pg/ml and that there is a midcycle surge to a peak of 200–300 pg/ml on the day of the LH peak, a rapid post-peak drop to 80–100 pg/ml, and a second rise during the midluteal phase to ~100 pg/ml. The only significant difference between this pattern and that of most nonhuman primates is the second rise of estrogen in the luteal phase. Urinary estrogens (129) reflect the pattern seen in plasma: early follicular phase ~17.6 $\mu g\ hr^{-1}$, midcycle peak ~34.2 $\mu g\ hr^{-1}$, and luteal phase ~24.9 $\mu g\ hr^{-1}$. The pattern of estrone secretion (37) differs slightly from that of estradiol: early follicular ~50 pg/ml, midcycle peak ~92 pg/ml, luteal phase ~50 pg/ml. Estrone secretion does not reach as high a peak as estradiol, nor does it increase during the luteal phase. The lowest levels of estradiol are found in castrate (~36 pg/ml) and postmenopausal (~19 pg/ml) women (4).

PROGESTINS Cyclic changes in progesterone (P_4) levels have been studied in rhesus monkeys (11–14, 78, 99, 137, 138, 157), baboons (186), chimpanzees (65), cynomolgus monkeys (183), bonnet macaques (182), stump-tailed macaques (113), and women (1, 37, 84, 129, 171).

The pattern of secretion is remarkably alike in the different species. During the follicular phase, progesterone levels range from 0.5–1.0 ng/ml. A small but significant rise in peripheral progesterone levels coincides with the LH surge (1, 99, 100, 129). After the LH peak, by day 15 in most primates (rhesus monkeys, cynomolgus monkeys, stump-tailed macaques, bonnet macaques, baboons), progesterone levels rise to maximal values of 3–7 ng/ml. In women and chimpanzees the luteal peak of progesterone is three- to fourfold higher. Three days before the onset of menstruation, the level of progesterone falls sharply to the low values typical of the early follicular phase.

The cyclic secretion pattern of a few other progestins has been studied. In the rhesus monkey, 20α-hydroxypregn-4-ene-3-one is secreted in a pattern similar to that of progesterone, and the peak luteal value is ~3 ng/ml (157). The secretion pattern of 17α-hydroxypregn-4-ene-3,20-dione (17α-hydroxyprogesterone) in women (1, 84) is similar to that of estradiol rather than of progesterone, with a sharp preovulatory peak of ~2 ng/ml followed by a fall to ~0.67 ng/ml and a second luteal rise to ~2 ng/ml.

Estrous Cycles

SHORT CYCLES

Rats In adult cycling female rats (38, 133), peripheral blood levels of estradiol and estrone range from 2–4 pg/ml through most of the cycle with a gradual rise during late diestrus to a peak of 20–50 pg/ml on the day of proestrus. Much higher levels are present in ovarian venous blood; techniques for cannulating these small vessels have been developed (43). The concentrations of estradiol and estrone in ovarian venous plasma are low in diestrus-2 ($E_1 \approx 70$ pg/ml; $E_2 \approx 500$ pg/ml), reach peak levels on proestrus before the LH peak ($E_1 \approx 400$ pg/ml; $E_2 \approx 2200$ pg/ml), fall to their lowest levels during estrus ($E_1 \approx 26$ pg/ml; $E_2 \approx 161$ pg/ml), and show a slight rise during diestrus-1 ($E_1 \approx 128$ pg/ml; $E_2 \approx 400$ pg/ml) (172).

The secretion rate of progesterone in ovarian venous blood is low during estrus (~1.0 $\mu g\ hr^{-1}\ ovary^{-1}$), rises slightly in diestrus-1 (metestrus) (~2.0 $\mu g\ hr^{-1}$

ovary^{-1}), is low in diestrus-2 (~1.0 μg hr^{-1} ovary^{-1}), and surges during proestrus (~4.4 μg hr^{-1} ovary^{-1}) after the LH peak (212).

Hamsters The hamster has considerable quantities of estradiol in the peripheral circulation and in this respect is more like the primate than other rodents. Estradiol levels are low during estrus (~25 pg/ml) and metestrus (~35 pg/ml), rise during diestrus (~90 pg/ml), and fall somewhat and then peak during proestrus (115–186 pg/ml). Estrone levels in peripheral plasma fluctuate very little during the cycle (40–50 pg/ml) (5). Concentrations of these two steroids in ovarian venous blood follow the same pattern as in the peripheral blood, except for a proestrus peak of estrone secretion (173).

The pattern of progesterone secretion differs from that of the rat; levels are low in estrus (~0.8 μg/ml), fall steadily during metestrus and diestrus to a low of ~0.03 μg/ml, and rise to a peak of ~1.7 μg/ml during late proestrus after the LH peak (173).

Rabbits Rabbits do not show estrous cycles, but the response of the ovary to mating or human chorionic gonadotropin (HCG) stimulation has been studied. Ovarian venous samples were taken at hourly intervals for 12 hr after mating and then at daily intervals for 10 days throughout the periods of tubal transport and blastocyst implantation (79). Secretion rates of estradiol increased from an average of about 17 ng ovary^{-1} hr^{-1} in estrous rabbits to ~62 ng ovary^{-1} hr^{-1} by 4 hr after coitus. These rates then decreased to undetectable values by 9 hr after coitus and remained low throughout the 3-day period of tubal transport. Modest increases occurred on days 4–6 (~13 ng ovary^{-1} hr^{-1}; blastocysts free in utero) and days 8–10 (~20 ng ovary^{-1} hr^{-1}; blastocysts implanted).

In another study of the response of the rabbit ovary, a similar postcoital, preovulatory surge of estradiol secretion was observed by Shaikh & Harper (174). They found substantial differences in concentrations of steroids between the two ovarian veins of individual estrous animals. However, Hilliard et al (80) have shown that one member of a pair of ovaries does not act predominantly as the steroid-secreting ovary.

Progesterone and 20α-hydroxyprogesterone also rise to maximal levels by 4 hr after coitus and before ovulation ($P_4 \approx 20$ μg ovary^{-1} hr^{-1}; 20α-hydroxyprogesterone ≈ 300 μg ovary^{-1} hr^{-1}), then fall to undetectable levels. These progestins are undetectable during the period of tubal transport (days 1, 2, 3), and then show modest increases during the period of implantation ($P_4 \approx$ 13–23 μg ovary^{-1} hr^{-1}; 20α-hydroxyprogesterone ≈ 24–29 μg ovary^{-1} hr^{-1}) (79).

LONG CYCLES Guinea pig ovaries secrete far less estradiol than those of rats, hamsters, and rabbits. Levels in ovarian venous blood are low in the early part of the cycle (~23 pg/ml; ~50 pg ovary^{-1} hr^{-1}) and rise to a proestrous peak of ~187 pg/ml or ~500 pg ovary^{-1} hr^{-1} (94). Progesterone levels in ovarian venous blood peak during the luteal phase at ~100 ng/ml (days 11–13) and are low (~40 pg/ml) throughout the rest of the cycle (94) except for a brief preovulatory rise (48) that becomes maximal when sexual receptivity is highest.

A recent review compares the hormonal patterns found during estrous cycles (∼20 days) in the cow, ewe, and sow (73). In the cow and the ewe, plasma estrogens peak three times. The first surge triggers LH release and begins the cycle; the second occurs on days 1–4 of the cycle. These two peaks are due to simultaneous surges of both estradiol and estrone. A third peak of estrone occurs on days 13–16 in the cow; in the ewe, the third surge of plasma estrogen occurs on days 7–10 and presumably is also due to estrone. In sows, one peak of plasma estrogen occurs just before estrus and the LH peak.

Plasma progesterone follows a uniform pattern in these three species. In the cow and the ewe, progesterone levels are low during the first few days of the cycle, rise rapidly as the corpus luteum becomes functional (days 3–12), and then declines precipitously 3 or 4 days before the next estrus. In the sow, progesterone levels rise earlier and reach higher levels during the cycle than in cows and ewes. Progesterone secretion in the mare follows a similar pattern during the ∼22-day cycle. During estrus, levels are less than 1 ng/ml, rise during diestrus to a peak of ∼8 ng/ml, and decline sharply to undetectable levels on days 13–17 (176).

The blue fox has an ∼60-day cycle with an ∼10-day proestrus, 3- to 5-day estrus, and ∼45-day diestrus. Progesterone levels are undetectable in proestrus, rise significantly in estrus to 20–40 ng/ml, peak in diestrus at 100–120 ng/ml, and decline to undetectable levels after approximately day 25 (130).

Female dogs have similarly long cycles, with 5- to 12-day proestrus, 5- to 12-day estrus, and 30- to 90-day diestrus or pseudopregnancy, the latter characterized by lactation and nest-building behavior. In beagle bitches, progesterone levels are undetectable in proestrus, rise in estrus, and peak at 20–30 ng/ml ∼10 days after the LH peak (179). After 20–30 days, these levels slowly decline to undetectable values. A sharp proestrous rise in estradiol levels to 20–40 pg/ml before the LH peak and a subsequent decline to low levels (∼10 pg/ml) for the remainder of the cycle have been observed in beagles (93).

Additional information on ovarian secretion of estrogens and progestins is available in several recent reviews (42, 185, 189, 212).

HORMONAL INFLUENCES ON STEROID-RECEPTOR PROTEINS

Steroid hormones are preferentially concentrated in target tissues by soluble proteins called receptors. Many lines of evidence suggest that hormonal regulation of the female reproductive tract is mediated at the receptor level. Changes in the quantity, compartmentalization, and form of receptors have been correlated with changes in the target tissues during menstrual and estrous cycles. Recent reviews have extensively covered the steroid-hormone-receptor interactions more generally (90, 143, 192, 193). Here we emphasize that steroid hormone receptors are themselves influenced by the fluctuating levels of estradiol and progesterone during the estrous and menstrual cycles.

To begin with, there is considerable evidence that estrogens stimulate the synthesis of the estrogen, progestin, and androgen receptors within the tissues of the reproductive tract and that progesterone antagonizes these effects. For example, in the immature rat uterus, an initial depletion of cytoplasmic estradiol receptor 4 hr after estradiol injection, which is caused by binding and transfer to the nuclear site of action, is followed by a general increase in protein synthesis and 1 or 2 days later by the recovery of the cytoplasmic estradiol receptor to higher levels than before (91, 164). If, however, cycloheximide or actinomycin D is administered between 30 min before and 2 hr after the estradiol injection, protein synthesis and the subsequent rise in cytoplasmic receptor are blocked (91, 164). Diethylstilbestrol injection into immature chicks increases the content of both progesterone (144, 177, 194) and androgen receptors (74). Estradiol injected into immature rats causes a threefold increase in the in vitro uptake of progesterone by the uterus 1 and 2 days later (162).

Three days of estradiol treatment triples the protein content and doubles the estradiol binding capacity of the uteri of ovariectomized adult rats (40, 49). Estrogen injected into spayed rats (50, 125), rabbits (46, 154, 155, 211), mice (50), hamsters (105–107, 156, 158), and guinea pigs (28, 47, 55, 56, 123, 204) causes an eventual increase in detectable uterine progesterone receptor and tissue uptake of progesterone. Estrogen priming increases progesterone receptor as well as tissue uptake of progesterone in the vaginas of spayed hamsters (105, 158), guinea pigs (2, 3), and mice (152) and in the cervix of guinea pigs (2). After estrogen withdrawal in guinea pigs, there is a gradual decrease of uterine progesterone-binding activity with a half-life of about 3–5 days (56, 126). Administration of progesterone to spayed guinea pigs either 20 hr (126) or 48 hr (56) after estrogen priming causes an even more rapid decrease in the uterine content of progesterone receptors. Binding by endogenous progesterone or a shift to the nucleus has been ruled out as the cause of the fall in cytoplasmic progesterone receptor in the uterus of progesterone-treated guinea pigs (56, 126).

During pseudopregnancy in the rabbit, there is a fall in the uterine content of estrogen receptor that can be reversed by lutectomy (89). Progesterone administration at the time of lutectomy keeps the uterine estrogen receptor suppressed. The content of estradiol receptor in the oviducts of spayed rhesus monkeys treated with estrogen is decreased by progesterone treatment under conditions of continuous estradiol administration (17). Ovariectomy is eventually followed (2 weeks or later) by a decrease in estradiol receptors in rat (40, 121) and hamster (98) uteri and in the oviducts of rhesus monkeys (17), and in progesterone receptors in mouse, rat (50), and hamster (107) uteri. These various reports support the conclusion that estrogen treatment increases the amount of not only the estrogen receptor but also of progesterone and possibly androgen receptors as well. On the other hand, ovariectomy (long term) and progesterone treatment seem to decrease the quantity of estrogen and progesterone receptors in various tissues of the female reproductive tract.

Considerable attention has been paid to the behavior of the uterine estrogen receptor in the rat during the early postnatal period. The ontogeny of estrogen receptor in the cytoplasm of the rat uterus during the first 3 weeks of life does not appear to depend on the pups' ovarian estrogen (26). The peak number of binding sites was reached at day 10 despite ovariectomy on day 2. Receptor synthesis may be thus an autonomous property of the uterine cells in the immature rat (26) or may be stimulated by small quantities of nonovarian estrogen. A decline in the concentration of estradiol receptor in uterine cytoplasm from days 10 to 20 (49) coincides with the start of ovarian steroid secretion (26) and reaches a plateau around day 30 (49, 109). Another sharp decline occurs at the time of pubescence (109).

Maximal uterine responsiveness to estrogen may be gradually acquired during postnatal development. Kaye, Sheratsky & Lindner (96) have reported that only rats at least 20 days old show maximal responses in uterine wet weight, DNA, RNA, and protein synthesis 24 hr after the injection of estradiol. Sömjen, Kaye & Lindner (180) showed that no increases occurred in the same parameters in 5- or 10-day-old rats, whereas an increase in wet weight, RNA, and protein occurred in 15- and 20-day-old rats and an increase in DNA additionally only in 30-day-old rats. The nuclear binding properties of estradiol-17β as well as induced protein synthesis have also been investigated during postnatal development (181). Uterine nuclear binding capacity was present at birth, increased at 5 days, was maximal at 10, and declined somewhat at 15 and 20 days of age. Induced protein synthesis was absent at 5 days but had developed at 10 days and older. This group has suggested that the sequence of events—cytoplasmic receptor $\longrightarrow$ nuclear receptor $\longrightarrow$ induced protein synthesis $\longrightarrow$ (wet weight increase) $\longrightarrow$ RNA synthesis $\longrightarrow$ protein synthesis $\longrightarrow$ DNA synthesis, which occurs in estrogen action in a fully competent and mature uterine system—is only gradually acquired during a day-by-day postnatal development (181).

Luck, Gschwendt & Hamilton (112) demonstrated that the uterine nuclear receptor complex is formed from the cytoplasmic complex in 7-, 13-, and 20-day-old rats given estrogen in vivo 1 hr before. However, the transfer of the receptor complex and the stimulation of wet weight, RNA, protein, and DNA synthesis occurred in the uteri of rats in all these age groups 24 hr after estradiol treatment. The apparent discrepancy between the findings of these laboratories remains to be dissolved.

The variations in estrogen receptor content in uterine cytoplasm during the estrous cycle of the rat have been studied by different workers with conflicting results (192). Feherty et al (49) reported a low concentration of available cytoplasmic receptor sites during estrus and early diestrus (metestrus), followed by a rise in mid-diestrus and a maximum on proestrus, paralleling the pattern of ovarian estradiol secretion. However, Lee & Jacobson (109) reported that uterine receptor concentrations were higher during estrus and diestrus than during proestrus and metestrus. Shain & Barnea (175) also found that the cytoplasmic receptor content was highest during estrus but progressively less during diestrus, proestrus, and metestrus. Various reports concur on the cyclic changes in the quantity of nuclear estrogen receptor complex in the rat uterus (25, 87). The concentration of nuclear complex is highest during proestrus, lowest during estrus and metestrus, and rises during diestrus. This follows the pattern of ovarian estrogen secretion. The relative rate of induced protein (IP) synthesis, one of the earliest responses to estradiol, is also highest during proestrus in cycling rat uterus (87). Thus the concentration of the nuclear receptor complex correlates with a biological action. These findings support the possibility that progesterone suppresses the estrogen receptor because progesterone levels in blood are higher during proestrus and metestrus than at other times in the estrous cycle of the rat. In addition, the proestrous estradiol surge may deplete spare cytoplasmic receptor by translocation of the steroid-receptor complex to the nucleus.

The ability of rat uteri to concentrate ^{3}H-estradiol from plasma after injections or infusions at various stages of the estrous cycle has been examined in several laboratories (33, 103, 121, 175, 207). Most reports agree that there is maximal uptake of ^{3}H-estradiol during diestrus, but there is considerable discrepancy about the uptake at other times in the cycles.

Corroborative studies are needed before the estrogen receptor quantities, intracellular distributions, and patterns of uptake of labeled hormone during short estrous cycles can be confidently described. At present, one can tentatively conclude that a complex system, probably governed by estrogen secretion rates and quantities and possibly modulated by progesterone levels, seems to determine receptor content in the uterus of rodents.

Kimball & Hansel reported that the estrogen receptor concentration in the endometrial cytoplasm of bovines was low on days 2, 5, and 10 of the estrous cycle and increased to significantly higher levels on days 15 and 21 (97). This increase in receptor content is highly correlated with the estrone surge on day 10, elevated estradiol levels, and decreasing progesterone levels. In contrast, no significant change was detected by Jackson & Chalkley (88) in the same receptor. However, they did report a variation in nuclear estradiol receptor sites during the estrous cycle (88). During estrus and early metestrus (days 1–7), when plasma estrogens were high, the number of high affinity nuclear binding sites was high. During late metestrus (days 7–15), as circulating estrogens declined and progesterone increased, nuclear receptor content was low. After the declining progesterone and the estrone plasma peak at days 13–16, a diestrous (days 15–19) increase in nuclear receptor was detected. During proestrus (days 19–22), the nuclear receptor content was low, perhaps because the sites were saturated by rapidly rising levels of endogenous estrogen (88).

The quantity as well as the sedimentation coefficient of the progesterone receptor in uterine cytoplasm varies during the estrous cycle. Maximum receptor amounts during proestrus have been reported in the rat (39, 50), mouse (50), hamster (106, 107, 158), and guinea pig (124). The proestrous receptor in the guinea pig and hamster is also predominantly a heavier form (6.7 *s* on sucrose gradient ultracentrifugation) than that found at diestrus (4.5 *s*) (107, 124). The rapid rise of progesterone receptor in the guinea pig uterus during proestrus may be promoted by the maximum estradiol secretion in the ovary (127). The rapid fall in receptor throughout estrus, metestrus, and diestrus may be due to progesterone secretion that leads to decreasing rates of synthesis and/or inactivation of the progesterone receptor (107, 127). Indeed, treatment of cycling hamsters at proestrus with exogenous progesterone causes a rapid, premature decline in the progesterone receptor (107). Thus the cyclically fluctuating hormone levels during the estrous cycle may regulate the flux in receptor content (109).

There are several studies of the changes in receptor content during pregnancy and pseudopregnancy. For example, Feherty et al (49) reported that the in vitro estradiol binding capacity of rat uterus during pseudopregnancy rose gradually to a peak on days 10–11, then fell rapidly as estrus began again. During pregnancy, the uterine binding capacity was consistently low except in implantation areas. After day 10, the various regions of the implanted fetus were assayed and the maternal placenta was found to be the source of the high estradiol binding capacity. The placenta receptor fell somewhat by day 13 and was undetectable at day 18 (49).

Wiest (208) induced deciduomas in one uterine horn of pseudopregnant rats by traumatization. At intervals up to 5 days post-trauma, the rats were eviscerated and then killed 1 hr after injection with progesterone-4-^{14}C (208). The ^{14}C/mg dry tissue was significantly greater in traumatized than in control horns, an indication that progesterone or metabolites are concentrated within decidual tissue (208, 210). Pseudopregnancy induced by cervical stimulation at estrus provoked a high uterine progesterone content 3 days later, whereas nonstimulated animals had low uterine progesterone. Induction of decidual cell reaction in one horn of the pseudopregnant rat resulted in significantly higher progesterone content after trauma than in the contralateral horn of the control (210).

Davies & Ryan (30) found high concentrations of ^{3}H-progesterone in uterine myometrium 4 hr after injection into 11-day pregnant rats and undetectable amounts after injection of 21-day pregnant animals. They also detected a receptor peak by sucrose density gradient analysis of cytosols incubated in vitro with ^{3}H-progesterone from 11-day but not 21-day pregnant animals. In a later study (31), they used equilibrium dialysis to quantify the concentration of cytoplasmic progesterone-receptor sites throughout pregnancy. The number of receptor sites reaches a maximum around day 9 ($\sim$20 pmol/mg protein), declines by day 12 ($\sim$14 pmol/mg protein), and is low from days 15 to 22 ($\sim$5 pmol/mg protein) (31).

The concentrations of endogenous progesterone in the myometrium and plasma of similar animals were measured by Wiest (209). Plasma progesterone was elevated until the day before parturition (day 21), when the level fell sharply. The concentration of progesterone in myomentrium ($\sim$16 μg/100 g) was initially much higher than in plasma ($\sim$7 μg/100 ml). Later in pregnancy, shortly after the progesterone receptor had declined but before any substantial change in plasma level had occurred, the concentration of progesterone in myometrium declined and eventually reached levels equivalent to that found in plasma. These data suggest that the concentration of progesterone receptor plays a much more important regulatory role in myometrium than the concentration of progesterone in blood. This finding may apply to other steroid hormone receptors as well (31).

Nearly all reports concur on the cyclic changes in the level of estrogen receptor as well as in the tissue uptake of labeled estradiol in the uteri of women. Higher levels of estrogen binding have usually been found during the proliferative rather than the luteal phase (22, 44, 45, 77, 159, 160, 196, 197). For example, Brush et al (22) obtained tissue from 18 nonpregnant women injected with ^{3}H-estradiol 2 hr before hysterectomy. Endometrial uptake was higher in the follicular than in the luteal phase. After tissue fractionation of endometrium, proprotionally more radioactivity was found in the nuclear pellet of follicular than of luteal endometrium. Robertson et al (159) determined the concentration of estradiol receptors in endometrial samples from 40 cycling women. The average concentration of binding sites was higher during the late proliferative and early secretory phase and lower during the late secretory phase (22–28 days) in both endometrial curettings and biopsy samples.

In two uteri sampled throughout the length, the concentration of receptor decreased from fundus to cervix (159). Trams et al (196) demonstrated that the in vitro uptake of ^{3}H-estradiol into tissue slices was significantly higher in human follicular endometrium and myometrium than during the midcycle or luteal phase. Spare cytoplasmic receptor was also assayed in several hysterectomy samples (with agar gel electrophoresis) and the amount correlated with the day of the cycle and plasma estradiol concentration. Follicular estrogen receptor was significantly higher than luteal. Plasma estradiol in cycling females did not correlate with receptor content. The uteri of pregnant patients at term and of patients being treated with estrogens had the highest plasma estradiol levels (350–2000 pg/ml) and lowest receptor content (196).

Tseng & Gurpide (197) measured ^{3}H-estradiol bound in nuclei isolated from slices of human endometrium superfused 2 hr with ^{3}H-estradiol. Estradiol receptor concentrations are significantly higher in proliferative than in secretory endometria. There is one discordant report; no statistically significant difference was found in the amount of available estrogen receptor in endometrial biopsies taken from five women on days 8 and 21 of the ovulatory menstrual cycles (110). The data from most of the reports, however, suggest that despite a rise in the luteal levels of estradiol, the high level of progesterone characteristic of the luteal phase suppresses the estradiol binding capacity of uterine tissues in women.

Brenner et al (18) measured the residual estradiol binding capacity (receptors) of the oviducts obtained from 20 adult female cynomolgus monkeys autopsied at random stages of their menstrual cycles. Estradiol receptor content was significantly higher in the follicular than in the luteal phase tissue and varied inversely with plasma progesterone levels (18).

There are only a few analogous studies of the cyclic changes in the progesterone receptor in the endometrium of women. Grundsell et al (68) examined the progesterone concentration in endometrium obtained by curettage from 29 subjects during the secretory phase. The middle secretory phase (days 18–23) had significantly more progesterone per milligram than the early and late secretory phases, a pattern that correlated positively with the rise and fall of plasma progesterone. Haukkamaa, Karjalainen & Luukkainen (75) demonstrated greater in vitro binding of ^{3}H-progesterone in endometrium from the late proliferative and secretory phase than from the early proliferative phase. Thus in women, as in other species, progesterone receptor content appears to be increased by the action of estrogen during the proliferative phase.

THE ROLE OF RNA IN STEROID HORMONE ACTION

The pathway through which the steroid-receptor complex presumably exerts its effects on target tissue includes stimulation of specific RNA synthesis. Estrogenic stimulation increases DNA-dependent RNA polymerase activity (139). Measured by the rate of incorporation of precursors into RNA, overall RNA synthesis is enhanced by estrogen (62). Within 2 min after estradiol administration, the rate of nuclear RNA synthesis in rat uterus is increased (122). The RNAs synthesized by uterine nuclei from estrogen-treated rats differ in nucleotide sequence from those from unstimulated rats (195). The response of the rat uterus to estradiol treatment is prevented by local or systemic administration of actinomycin D, which inhibits DNA-dependent RNA synthesis (71, 190, 199). Estradiol stimulation of vaginal cornification in ovariectomized rats is blocked by topical actinomycin D application (167).

The possibility that steroid hormones stimulate the synthesis of new messenger RNAs, which in turn alter new protein synthesis, has been tested directly. RNA extracted from various steroid-treated tissues has been tested for biological activity by local application to appropriate unstimulated tissues (167). RNA extracted from the uteri of ovariectomized rats stimulated for 4 hr with estradiol was applied to one horn of ovariectomized rats through indwelling uterine catheters. Saline or other control solutions were applied to the other uterine horn. The RNA extract initiated morphological changes in the endometrium that were characteristic of estradiol stimulation. Saline, vagina, or liver RNA prepared from estradiol-stimulated rats, uterine RNA prepared from nonstimulated rats, and RNase-treated uterine RNA (prepared from estradiol-stimulated rats) failed to cause the estrogen effect in the control horn of the same rat (169). The stimulatory uterine RNA extracts were not contaminated with enough estradiol to account for the effect. Actinomycin D treatment does not block the cellular hypertrophy induced by active RNA extracts (169).

Unhjem, Attramadal & Sölna (200) verified the work of Segal, Davidson & Wada (169) with the rat uterus and demonstrated that the active factor is concentrated in the macromolecular fraction after gel filtration with Sephadex G-100. Mansour & Niu (116) demonstrated that when RNA prepared from the uteri of mature cycling mice was administered by intrauterine injection to spayed mice, the biosynthesis of alkaline phosphatase was increased and the normal adult appearance of the endometrium was restored. The ability of RNAs from bovine ovary and uterus to stimulate the local response and to increase mouse uterine β-glucuronidase activity was reported in a later study (114). The possibility that contaminating estradiol is the basis for the RNA effect was considerably lessened when RNA prepared from bacteria, which possess an alkaline phosphatase and no known estrogenic activity, and injected into the ovariectomized mouse uterus stimulated alkaline phosphatase activity (115).

Fencl & Villee (51) studied the increased incorporation of amino acids into protein of immature rat uterus after the application of RNA prepared from uteri and various other tissues of estradiol-stimulated rats. Uterus and liver RNAs produced an estradiol-like increase in the rate of protein synthesis by uteri not demonstrable with RNA prepared from kidney, adrenals, lungs, skeletal muscle, or thymus. The effect of hepatic RNA may be related to the role of liver in estrogen metabolism (51).

Zinca & Cîrlan extracted RNA from the vaginas of estrogenized spayed rats and applied it intravaginally to ovariectomized rats (214). This RNA stimulated keratinization and exfoliation in the vaginal mucosa, typical of estradiol-induced development (214).

Blastocyst implantation in postcoitally ovariectomized rats is an estrogen-dependent physiological process. RNA extracted from the uteri of estrogen-treated rats was effective in causing implantation when injected parametrially (167).

Treatment of diethylstilbestrol-primed chicks with progesterone increases oviductal RNA and avidin synthesis. RNA extracted from the oviduct but not the shell gland or liver of chicks treated with a combination of diethylstilbestrol and progesterone induced the synthesis of avidin when instilled into the lumens of diethylstilbestrol-primed chicks' oviducts (198). The same oviductal RNA induced a slight synthesis of avidin when instilled into the lumens of shell glands of diethylstilbestrol-primed chicks. Shell glands do not normally produce avidin (198). Segal et al also (170) demonstrated the heterospecific transfer of avidin stimulation by RNA. Intraoviductal instillation of oviductal RNA from diethylstilbestrol-progesterone-treated chicks into diethylstilbestrol-primed pigeons and from similarly treated pigeons into diethylstilbestrol-primed chicks resulted in the stimulation of avidin synthesis (170). Total RNA was purified by nitrocellulose chromatography that preferentially concentrates messenger RNAs. The greatly increased biological activity of RNA so prepared suggests that messenger RNA is an intermediate in steroid hormone action (170).

The hormone receptor complex apparently stimulates the production of specific RNAs that carry the information necessary for new specific protein synthesis and thus promote physiological change.

HORMONAL EFFECTS ON THE OVIDUCT

The burgeoning literature on the various functions of the oviducts and their hormonal regulation includes several recent reviews of the field (6, 16, 69, 70, 72, 92). Here we discuss some recent examples that clearly demonstrate the role of hormones in regulating growth and differentiation, fluid secretion, and muscular contractility of the fallopian tube in various species. The oviduct of the rhesus monkey (16) as well as that of the cynomolgus monkey (18) undergoes a dramatic waxing and waning of the epithelium during natural menstrual cycles that is characterized by hypertrophy, hyperplasia, and cell differentiation during the early follicular phase and atrophy and dedifferentiation during the late luteal phase. For example, the ciliated cells in the epithelium cyclically shed (luteal phase) and regenerate (early follicular phase) their cilia. Except for a midcycle surge, estradiol levels in these species are mostly constant throughout the menstrual cycle; progesterone dominates the luteal phase (see "Steroid Levels During Reproductive Cycles"). We and others had previously shown that the proliferative response of the oviduct could be produced in spayed monkeys by the administration of estradiol benzoate (16). Therefore, progesterone appears to antagonize estrogen-driven growth and differentiation in the oviduct of these species during the natural menstrual cycle even though the ovary continues to secrete adequate amounts of estradiol during the luteal phase.

To further document these effects, we produced two consecutive artificial menstrual cycles in spayed rhesus monkeys by sequential administration of estradiol and progesterone (17). Estradiol levels averaged 200–300 pg/ml in blood throughout the study; during the artificial luteal phases, progesterone averaged 5–7 ng/ml. The epithelium of the oviduct hypertrophied and differentiated during the first artificial follicular phase, and then atrophied and dedifferentiated during the artificial luteal phase. This cycle recurred during the second artificial follicular and luteal phases. Therefore the cyclic changes that occur in the oviduct during the natural menstrual cycle are probably caused by periodic antagonism by progesterone of the effects of estradiol. The dramatic surge of growth and differentiation in the oviduct during the early follicular phase cannot be due to a rise in plasma estradiol (since none occurs), but rather is due to a release from the antagonism imposed by progesterone in the previous luteal phase.

Apparently progesterone has direct, reversible effects that lead to suppression of the estradiol response. We measured the changes in the amount of spare cytoplasmic estradiol receptors (residual binding capacity) in these same oviducts during the artificial cycles and found that a marked depression in residual cytoplasmic binding capacity for estradiol occurred during progesterone treatment. This depression was reversed when progesterone treatment ceased. We suggested that such a depression in the cytoplasmic binding capacity of oviductal tissues for estradiol could lead to an estrogen withdrawal syndrome even in the presence of an adequate reservoir of estradiol in plasma. The mechanism by which progesterone antagonizes estradiol in the oviduct of rhesus monkeys may, of course, be far more complex.

The human oviduct also undergoes periodic growth and atrophy during the menstrual cycle (140). The degree of atrophy and dedifferentiation that occurs, however, is not as dramatic as in the rhesus monkey. Considerable numbers of ciliated cells apparently persist throughout the luteal phase (148). However, there are some reports of extensive luteal deciliation in the human oviduct (52). Some workers report that contraceptive gestagens lead to deciliation in the human oviduct (54, 141), but others report no loss of cilia with similar gestagens (148). The human menstrual cycle, unlike that of the rhesus monkey, is characterized by a luteal rise in plasma estradiol (see "Steroid Levels During Reproductive Cycles"). This second estradiol peak may tend to offset the antagonistic effects of progesterone on the oviduct. Variations in the progesterone:estradiol ratio during the luteal phase in the human menstrual cycle may well account for these varied reports in the literature on the degree of oviductal dedifferentiation.

There are several other examples of the growth-promoting effects of estradiol and/or the antagonistic effect of progesterone on the oviduct. DNA synthesis is at a maximum in the epithelium of the human oviduct when estradiol levels surge during days 9–12 of the cycle (32). Ciliogenesis has also been noted in this phase of the cycle in women (148).

During the estrous cycle of the dog, the oviduct hypertrophies and becomes ciliated and secretory in proestrus and estrus, the periods of estrogen domination. Atrophy and dedifferentiation, which includes deciliation, occur during metestrus when progesterone levels are high (201). In prepubertal dogs, the oviductal epithelium is low, nonciliated, and nonsecretory; estrogen treatment stimulates the development of a fully differentiated epithelium (202).

After ovariectomy the oviduct of the cat atrophies and becomes deciliated. Estradiol treatment of spayed cats promotes the development and maintenance of a fully differentiated oviductal epithelium. In this species, progesterone also antagonizes the effects of estradiol on oviductal differentiation. When spayed cats are treated with a combination of estradiol and progesterone for 1 week, the oviduct develops in almost normal fashion except that cell height and degree of ciliation are less than in controls treated only with estradiol. During the second week of combined treatment, the oviduct atrophies and becomes extensively deciliated. Apparently, a period of estradiol-induced differentiation must occur before progesterone can completely antagonize the effects of estradiol on the oviduct of the cat (203).

In laboratory rodents the oviduct is much less responsive to the hormonal changes during the estrous cycle. There is no dramatic cycle of hypertrophy and atrophy, perhaps because the cycle is so short. One report cites fluctuations in ^{3}H-thymidine uptake in the oviductal epithelium of mice during the estrous cycle (34), but another reports no changes in whole-organ DNA concentrations during the cycle (19). Fluctuations in whole-organ RNA concentrations in the oviducts of mice correlate positively with estrogen levels. However, progesterone does not antagonize this estrogen effect in the mouse oviduct (20).

Some preliminary reports suggest that ovariectomy leads to complete atrophy and deciliation in the oviduct of the pig, and that estrogen treatment stimulates complete regeneration of a fully ciliated and secretory epithelium (135, 136). These same reports suggest that treating spayed gilts with progesterone alone causes some reciliation. According to another preliminary report from the same group, the rat oviduct atrophies and deciliates after ovariectomy, and testosterone treatment stimulates complete restoration of oviductal epithelium (134). However, another report suggests that the development and maintenance of a fully differentiated oviductal epithelium in rats is completely independent of hormonal control (36).

Hormonal regulation of the fluid secreted by the oviduct has been recently reviewed (72, 119, 151). There is general agreement that the volume of fluid secreted increases under the influence of estrogens and that progestins antagonize this effect. For example, when spayed rhesus monkeys were treated with estradiol for 10 days, the volume of oviductal fluid increased substantially over initial levels. Continued treatment with a combination of progesterone and estradiol for an additional 10 days led to a marked reduction in the output of oviductal fluid. A third 10 days of treatment with estradiol alone elicited renewed secretion (213). Similar cyclic changes in the volume of oviductal fluid have been observed during the natural menstrual cycles of rhesus monkeys (119) and women (111) and during the estrous cycles of various species (72).

Oviductal fluid is a combination of a secretion and a transudate and contains specific proteins different from any observed in serum (15). Hormonal influences on fluid composition vary with the species. For example, in the rat, lactic dehydrogenase levels are increased by progesterone treatment (149), whereas estradiol appears to stimulate the production of the same enzyme in the oviducts of rhesus monkeys (213). Recently, inhibitors of acrosomal proteinase have been observed in the oviductal fluid of rhesus monkeys. The concentrations of these inhibitors were elevated before ovulation, depressed during induced superovulation, and elevated after ovulation (184). The roles played by estradiol and progesterone in regulating the concentration of these inhibitors deserve intensive study.

An interesting, if obscure, effect of progesterone on the ability of the oviduct of the rat to concentrate radioiodide has been noted. The oviducts of intact and spayed rats treated with progesterone, as well as of pregnant rats, concentrate [^{125}I]iodide well above the level found in plasma (21).

Oviductal cilia play an extremely important role in egg transport. In several species, the fimbriated end is essential for ovum pickup, and the ovum in cumulus is transported over the fimbrial surface and into the ostium by means of ciliary action (6). Very little is known about the influence of hormones on the rate of ciliary beat (6) except for a recent report that ciliary activity is greatest at midcycle in human and macaque oviducts (58).

In long-term (4–6 months) spayed rabbits, the epithelium is atrophied and has fewer ciliated cells (45–65%) than that of ovulatory controls (66–76%). When eggs in cumulus were placed on the fimbriae of spayed rabbits, transport was generally much slower than in ovulatory controls. Treatment with estradiol benzoate for 10 days causes some deciliation over the first 4–5 days (to as low as 22%), which is followed by reciliation (~61%) during the remainder of the treatment. The rate of egg transport increases as the number of ciliated cells increases during the later phase of estrogen treatment. Fimbriae with less than 44% ciliated cells fail to transport eggs; those with 61% or higher transport eggs at almost normal rates (142).

Cilia are important in ovum pickup, but in most species, once the egg enters the ostium, contraction of the muscular coats of the oviduct provides the major force that propels the cumulus mass towards the uterus (6). However, in primates and cats very little muscular activity is evident during egg transport, and ciliary activity may provide the more important propulsive force in these species (6).

Interesting new hypotheses have recently been introduced about the hormonal regulation of muscular contractions in the ampullary and isthmic regions. Studies of the rate of egg transport through the ampulla of the rabbit oviduct show that estrogen withdrawal from estrogen-primed tissues leads to a greatly accelerated rate of transport. For example, transport time in castrate rabbits is ~15 min. In castrate rabbits treated with estradiol-17β and sampled 1–3 hr after the last injection, the transport time is ~12 min; if sampled 30–32 hr after the last injection, the transport time is only ~2.5 min (9). In normal estrous rabbits, the mean transport time is ~9 min. This time is decreased to ~3–4 min by all of the following: ovariectomy, injection of 20α-hydroxyprogesterone, progesterone, and an estrogen antagonist

(CN-55, 945–27) (10). Transport times are much shorter in estrous does examined ~12 hr after treatment with estradiol and 20α-hydroxyprogesterone than in those treated with estradiol alone (8). These authors suggest that the normal increase in the rate of tubal transport a few days after mating in the rabbit is due to the preovulatory rise and fall of estradiol, a hormonal shift that would lead to estrogen withdrawal from the estrogen-primed oviductal musculature. The concurrent preovulatory rise and fall of 20α-hydroxyprogesterone (see "Steroid Levels During Reproductive Cycles") may favor the withdrawal of estradiol from the oviductal musculature.

After their rapid transit through the ampulla, ova remain at the ampullary-isthmic junction, the site of fertilization, for several hours. Passage through the isthmus is very slow, usually 2–3 days (6). According to some suggestions, the sphincter action of the ampullary-isthmic junction and the contractions of the isthmus are regulated by shifts in the population of α- and β-adrenergic receptors within the smooth muscle; the isthmus is quiet when α-receptors dominate and active when β-receptors dominate. Recent evidence suggests that when estrogen is dominant in estrous does, α-receptors are prevalent in the isthmus. 72 hr after ovulation (induced by HCG), the β-receptor activity of the isthmic musculature increases significantly (83).

A recent review compares the role of hormones in the regulation of tubal motility in rabbits and women (27). In women, the tubes show maximal sensitivity to oxytocin, epinephrine, and norepinephrine during menstruation, a period when endogenous estrogens and progestins are both declining from midluteal levels. In spayed rabbits treated with combinations of estradiol and progesterone, withdrawal of both hormones is followed by an increase in tubal motility (27).

To further document these effects, the changes in estradiol concentration within the oviductal musculature during the period of estrogen withdrawal and progestin antagonism should be measured.

HORMONAL EFFECTS ON THE UTERUS, CERVIX, AND VAGINA

One of the most significant papers in recent years on the regulation of the primate endometrium is that of Good & Moyer (60), who studied the effects of varying estradiol:progesterone ratios on the development of secretory endometrium in spayed rhesus monkeys. This work is an extension of Hisaw's classic work (81) on the influence of these hormones on the primate uterus. Artificial menstrual cycles were produced with a sequential regimen of estradiol on days 1–10 and estradiol plus progesterone on days 11–22. Endometrial biopsies were made through a uterocutaneous fistula on luteal days 6 and 12. Normal secretory endometria were produced in 4–5.5 kg monkeys by 20–40 μg of estradiol in combination with 1–2 mg of progesterone. When the estradiol dose was varied and the progesterone kept constant, the degree of glandular maturation was proportional to the dose of estradiol. Stromal maturation was favored by an excess of progesterone over estradiol. When the estradiol dose was held constant and the progesterone varied, the degree of stromal maturation varied directly with the dose of progesterone. Glandular maturation was antagonized by high doses of progesterone.

When the ratio between estradiol and progesterone was held constant and the dose of each was doubled, the effects of progesterone on stromal maturation and glandular regression became dominant. These elegant experiments revealed that primate endometria contain two target populations, the glandular epithelium and the stromal tissues. Maturation of the stroma is promoted by progesterone and is antagonized by excessive estradiol; maturation of the glands is promoted by estradiol and is antagonized by excessive progesterone. Development of a mature secretory endometrium depends on the sequential action of estradiol followed by a combination of estradiol plus progesterone in the appropriate amounts.

The older research on the menstrual cycle of the chimpanzee has also been recently extended (64). A careful analysis of endometrial changes during normal cycles reveals that the proliferative-secretory patterns are similar to those of women. Artificial cycles were induced in spayed chimpanzees by administering an estrogen (mestranol) for 12–14 days, and then a combination of mestranol and a progestin (chlormadinone) for 5 days. Histological evaluation revealed normal proliferative and secretory changes during the artificial follicular and luteal phases.

In women, cyclic treatment with a sequential contraceptive produces endometrial cycles which closely resemble normal ones. Twenty-eight women were treated for 15 months with mestranol (7 days) followed by mestranol plus lynestrol (15 days). Proliferative activity, including DNA synthesis, was abundant in the glandular epithelium and stroma during mestranol treatment. Secretory activity, cessation of mitotic activity in the glands, and persistence of DNA synthesis in the stroma were prevalent during combined mestranol-lynestrol treatment (95).

There is considerable evidence that the amount of estrogen receptor in the endometrium declines during the luteal phase (see "Hormonal Influences on Steroid-Receptor Proteins"). A recent report shows that concomitant with this decline in the human endometrium is a rise in the activity of estradiol-17β dehydrogenase, an enzyme that favors the conversion of estradiol to estrone and thereby decreases the intracellular levels of estradiol. Thus at least two factors may operate during the luteal phase to diminish the effect of circulating estradiol on the endometrium, namely, a decrease in the estrogen receptor content and an increase in the activity of estradiol-17β dehydrogenase (197).

The nucleolar channel system is a specific morphological entity found to date only in the endometrial glandular cells of women. The function of this unique organelle is obscure, but its presence apparently varies with the stage of the menstrual cycle. The organelle consists of a spherical stack of interdigitating membrane-bound tubules within the nucleus and is found most commonly between the 17th and 20th day of the menstrual cycle. Later in the luteal phase the channel system becomes disrupted and disappears (131).

Ciliated cells are present in the glandular and surface epithelia of the human endometrium and their number varies during the cycle. In the glands, ciliogenesis occurs in the early proliferative phase under the influence of estradiol; the ciliated cells may disappear completely during the luteal phase. On the surface, ciliated cells are present in the epithelium throughout the cycle, but some ciliogenesis occurs during postmenstrual repair (53).

The interactions between estradiol and progesterone in regulating uterine growth have been extensively studied in rodents. In spayed mice, estradiol treatment stimulates the lumenal epithelium of the uterus to two rounds of cell division in quick succession. The glandular epithelium also shows a mitotic burst that takes longer to appear. Progesterone suppresses these epithelial mitoses if applied before or with but not after estrogen. Apparently, progesterone must be present early in the G1 phase of the cell cycle to block the mitogenic effect of estradiol on the epithelium (29, 117). If progesterone treatment of spayed mice is begun several days before estradiol, the mitogenic action of the estradiol is redirected to the stromal cells (118). A similar progesterone-induced redirection of the mitogenic effects of estradiol occurs in the uterus of the spayed rat (23, 24, 188). Treatment of spayed rats with progesterone 12 hr before giving estradiol abolishes the mitotic activity, nucleolar enlargement, ^{3}H-uridine uptake, and ^{3}H-estradiol uptake usually seen in the lumenal epithelium after treatment with estradiol alone. Mitotic activity is also blocked in the glandular epithelium by progesterone pretreatment, although ^{3}H-uridine and ^{3}H-estradiol uptake are not suppressed. When progesterone pretreatment is extended to 36 hr, epithelial mitoses are blocked and the subepithelial stromal cells show a burst of mitosis and nucleolar enlargement plus ^{3}H-uptake, effects that do not occur in the stromal cells of mice treated with estradiol alone. How progesterone "redirects" the effect of estradiol on the rodent uterus is obscure. Autoradiograms show that the lumenal epithelium does not take up exogenous estradiol after pretreatment with progesterone; this may explain the failure of estradiol to act on these cells. However, the glandular epithelium takes up estradiol yet fails to undergo mitosis. Stromal cells also take up estradiol at all times yet fail to mitose unless progesterone has acted first for 36 hr (188).

In the uterus of the spayed rabbit, progesterone does not appear to have effects similar to those seen in rodents. For example, low doses of progesterone stimulate epithelial mitoses after estrogen priming (108) and high doses of progesterone stimulate epithelial mitoses without any estrogen priming (101).

Another good example of species differences in the actions of estrogen and progesterone is the behavior of carbonic anhydrase in the uterus of the rabbit and guinea pig. In the rabbit, estrogen priming followed by administration of progesterone leads to a marked increase in activity by the third day after progesterone. In the guinea pig, however, estrogen treatment alone stimulates the enzyme markedly and subsequent progesterone treatment has no further stimulatory effect (82).

In the spayed rat (150) and rabbit (41), estrogen treatment causes an increase in uterine glycogen that can be prevented by treatment with progesterone. In the spayed guinea pig, uterine glycogen is unaffected by estrogen, either with or without progesterone (67).

Some of the effects of progesterone are identical with estrogen withdrawal. A good example is the suppression by progesterone of the activity of glucose-6-phosphate dehydrogenase in the uterus of the rat. Estradiol treatment of spayed rats causes an eightfold increase in the level of this enzyme within 3 days. When progesterone is administered 3 days after estradiol treatment has begun and the estradiol is continued, the enzyme levels decline at a rate nearly equivalent to that after estrogen withdrawal. However, if progesterone and estradiol are administered together from the start, the enzyme levels increase for the first 36 hr at a rate like that with estradiol alone. The enzyme levels decline only after 36 hr of combined treatment. This suggests that progesterone does not act as an antagonist until estradiol has stimulated some early changes in the uterine tissues, one of the most important of which may be the synthesis of the progesterone receptor (132; see "Hormonal Influences on Steroid-Receptor Proteins").

In the uterus of the rat, the eosinophil population has been identified as a possible reactive system involved in the very early effects of estrogen. Radioautographic studies show that uterine eosinophils can selectively bind ^{3}H-estradiol-17β, both in vivo and in vitro, and that this binding is blocked in vitro by unlabeled estradiol-17β, estrone, and estriol but not by progesterone, testosterone, or corticosterone (191). The suggestion has been made that the eosinophil binding system is different from that of other uterine cells and functions to promote the imbibition of water and release of histamine, which are among the earliest responses of the rodent uterus to estrogen treatment (191).

In an attempt to explain some of the very early effects of estrogens, Szego (187) proposed that the steroid interacts first with proteins localized in various cell membranes, especially those of primary lysosomes, that this interaction leads to the release of histamines and cyclic AMP, and that the lysosomes bearing the steroid penetrate the nucleus and set off nuclear changes via a discharge of lysosomal enzymes. This novel hypothesis awaits further documentation.

The literature on the biology of the cervix and its endocrine control has been admirably brought up to date in a recent compendium (7). Considerable attention has been paid to the biophysical and biochemical properties of cervical mucus because of the obvious importance of this potential barrier to sperm migration. An ingenious, relatively simple, microdiffusion technique has been devised for study of the soluble proteins in cervical mucus (165).

This technique has been used in a study of the endocrine regulation of these proteins during both ovulatory and contraceptive-regulated cycles in women. Nine serum proteins, as well as lactoflavin, lysozyme, α-amylase, alkaline phosphatase, ribonuclease A, nonspecific protease, and plasminogen activator, were decreased during the follicular and increased during the luteal phase. Three protease inhibitors found in cervical mucus—α_1-antitrypsin, α_{1x}-chymotrypsin inhibitor, and inter-α-trypsin inhibitor—were also decreased by estrogen and increased by progestin (166). A good review of the effects of oral contraceptives on the ultrastructure of the secretory cells in the cervix is also included in the above volume (57).

An excellent review of the literature on the hormonal regulation of the vagina is included in a report by Parakkal & Gregoire (147). These authors studied the ultrastructure of the vagina of the rhesus monkey under various hormonal conditions. In juvenile, spayed, or progesterone-treated spayed animals, the vaginal epithelium was only 3–4 cell layers thick and the superficial epithelial cells were cuboidal and contained numerous mucous granules. In spayed animals treated with estrogen or in intact animals during the follicular phase, the vagina was lined by a thick (40–50 layers) stratified squamous epithelium consisting, from within outwards, of basal, spinous, granular, and partially cornified layers. Membrane-coating and keratohyalin granules, the hallmarks of keratinization in other stratified squamous epithelia, were well developed. In pregnant animals, those in the luteal phase of the normal cycle, or spayed animals treated with a combination of estradiol benzoate (30 μg/day) and progesterone (25 mg/day), keratinization was greatly suppressed, membrane-coating and keratohyalin granules were absent, and the superficial cells were filled with mucous granules of various sizes. The vaginal epithelium in primates, as in rodents, exhibited natural cycles of mucification and keratinization. Mucification predominated either when estrogen was lacking, as in spayed or juvenile animals, or when progesterone dominated, as during pregnancy, the luteal phase, or in spayed animals treated with a combination of estradiol and progesterone. Keratinization occurred only when estrogen dominated, as during the follicular phase or in spayed animals treated with estradiol alone. Parakkal (146) also used scanning electron microscopy to examine the surface characteristics of the vagina of the rat under different hormonal conditions. The surface configurations during estrus or after estrogen treatment were typical of keratinizing epithelia with a characteristic microridge pattern. The surface of the vaginas of progestin-treated [3 mg Provera (medroxy progesterone acetate) for 3 days], estrogen plus progestin-treated, and diestrous animals was typical of nonkeratinized, mucified epithelia and similar to that of spayed animals.

The responses of the vagina of the rhesus monkey bear a close resemblance to those of the oviduct in the same species (153). Progesterone dominance leads to a basal state in the oviduct (nonsecretory and nonciliated) similar to that seen in spayed animals. Only when estrogen dominates, as during the follicular phase, does the oviduct develop its full complement of ciliated and secretory cells (153). In the rhesus monkey, progesterone dominance (even in the presence of estrogen) leads to an effective estrogen withdrawal syndrome within the tissues of both the vagina and the oviduct.

However, as we stated in the introduction, species and organ differences make it extraordinarily difficult to make general, universally applicable statements concerning the interaction between estradiol and progesterone in the regulation of the tissues of the reproductive tract. For example, ovariectomized rats were treated for 3 days with either estradiol alone or estradiol in combination with either 1, 5, 10, or 15 mg of progesterone, and the level of DNA synthesis in the cervix and vagina was examined by autoradiographic methods (102). In the cervix, 1 mg of progesterone did not suppress the estrogen-induced DNA synthesis in the epithelium, but 5, 10, or 15 mg did. In the vagina, however, 1 mg of progesterone enhanced the level of estrogen-induced DNA synthesis, whereas 5, 10, or 15 mg had no effect (102). These authors suggest that the stratified squamous epithelium of the cervix responds (to these doses of progesterone) more like the simple columnar lumenal epithelium of the uterus than like the stratified squamous epithelium of the vagina (102).

CONCLUSIONS

It would be foolhardy to attempt to summarize the above material. Rather we present a few thoughts that have occurred to us repeatedly as we sifted through it. Very few investigators use multiple techniques in their experiments. Rarely does one find a report that correlates the morphological or physiological response of a tissue with the levels of steroid in blood during the course of the response. In these days of radioimmunoassay, it seems inappropriate to refer simply to the amount of steroid administered and not the amount found in plasma. Whether an administered dose is physiological or not can now be easily determined by consulting the numerous reports on the levels of ovarian steroids in plasma during the cycles of various species. Even fewer investigators have made concurrent measurements of steroid-receptor levels, plasma steroid levels, and tissue steroid levels during the course of a physiological or morphological response. The technology is available and the rewards should be great for those who pursue this admittedly difficult course. As for new physiological principles that can be derived from the above reports, we think one is emerging, especially from the studies in primates. The proliferative phase of the menstrual cycle is characterized by increases in mitotic activity and cellular differentiation in the uterus, the vagina, and (at least in the rhesus and cynomolgus monkeys) the fallopian tubes, increases known to be estrogen dependent. But there is no corresponding increase in the level of estradiol in plasma. Indeed, in women, the level of estradiol is lower in the early follicular phase than in the previous luteal phase.

There is, however, a precipitous decline in the levels of progesterone in blood with the demise of the corpus luteum of the previous cycle. In primates, progesterone clearly antagonizes the proliferative effects of estradiol on the epithelium of the reproductive tract. Therefore, the burst of growth and differentiation during the early follicular phase is probably due to a release of the antagonism imposed by progesterone on the effects of estradiol during the previous luteal phase.

A reasonable body of evidence suggests that progesterone suppresses the level of estradiol receptor protein in the reproductive tract, and that such a suppression may lead to an effective estrogen withdrawal from the tissues. Cyclic synthesis and decay of the estradiol receptor, controlled somehow by cyclic changes in the level of plasma progesterone, may well be an important component of the mechanism by which the reproductive tract tissues of primates respond cyclically to the essentially constant plasma levels of estradiol. That such a simplistic explanation will be adequate for very long seems unlikely. Indeed, it may not apply at all to the estrous cycle because much more rapid shifts occur in the level of circulating estradiol.

But this viewpoint is somewhat refreshing because it brings together in a coherent way data gathered by the techniques of radioimmunoassay and receptor protein analysis and focuses attention on the importance of the regulatory mechanisms that must operate within the cells of the reproductive tract.

ACKNOWLEDGMENTS

The authors wish to thank Ms. Bernie Humburg and Ms. Nancy Martin for their invaluable assistance during the preparation of this manuscript.

Literature Cited

1. Abraham, G. E., Odell, W. D., Swerdloff, R. S., Hopper, K. 1972. Simultaneous radioimmunoassay of plasma FSH, LH, progesterone, 17-hydroxyprogesterone, and estradiol-17β during the menstrual cycle. *J. Clin. Endocrinol.* 34:312–18
2. Atger, M., Baulieu, E.-E., Milgrom, E. 1974. An investigation of progesterone receptors in guinea pig vagina, uterine cervix, mammary glands, pituitary and hypothalamus. *Endocrinology* 94: 161–67
3. Attramadal, A. 1973. *Acta Endocrinol. Suppl.* 177:248 (Abstr.)
4. Baird, D. T., Guevara, A. 1969. Concentration of unconjugated estrone and estradiol in peripheral plasma in nonpregnant women throughout the menstrual cycle, castrate and postmenopausal women and in men. *J. Clin. Endocrinol. Metab.* 29:149–56
5. Baranczuk, R., Greenwald, G. S. 1973. Peripheral levels of estrogen in the cyclic hamster. *Endocrinology* 92:805–12
6. Blandau, R. J. 1973. Gamete transport in the female mammal. *Handb. Physiol. Sect. 7.* 2(2):153–63
7. Blandau, R. J., Moghissi, K., Eds. 1973. *The Biology of the Cervix.* Chicago, Ill.: Univ. Chicago Press. 450 pp.
8. Boling, J. L. 1973. *Anat. Rec.* 175:275 (Abstr.)
9. Boling, J. L., Blandau, R. J. 1971. The role of estrogens in egg transport through the ampullae of oviducts of castrate rabbits. *Fert. Steril.* 22:544–51
10. Boling, J. L., Blandau, R. J. 1971. Egg transport through the ampullae of the oviducts of rabbits under various experimental conditions. *Biol. Reprod.* 4: 174–84
11. Bosu, W. T. K., Holmdahl, T. H., Johansson, E. D. B., Gemzell, C. 1972. Peripheral plasma levels of oestrogens, progesterone and 17α-hydroxyprogesterone during the menstrual cycle of the rhesus monkey. *Acta Endocrinol.* 71:755–64
12. Bosu, W. T. K., Johansson, E. D. B. 1974. Effects of postovulatory norethindrone and estrogens on the plasma levels of estrogen and progesterone in rhesus monkeys. *Contraception* 9: 357–67
13. Bosu, W. T. K., Johansson, E. D. B., Gemzell, C. 1973. Ovarian steroid patterns in peripheral plasma during the menstrual cycle in the rhesus monkey. *Folia Primatol.* 19:218–34
14. Bosu, W. T. K., Johansson, E. D. B., Gemzell, C. 1973. Peripheral plasma levels of oestrone, oestradiol-17β and progesterone during ovulatory menstrual cycles in the rhesus monkey with special reference to the onset of menstruation. *Acta Endocrinol.* 74:732–42
15. Brackett, B. G., Mastroianni, L. Jr. 1974. Composition of oviductal fluid. In *The Oviduct and Its Functions,* ed. A. D. Johnson, C. W. Foley, 133–60. New York: Academic. 369 pp.
16. Brenner, R. M., Anderson, R. G. W. 1973. Endocrine control of ciliogenesis in the primate oviduct. *Handb. Physiol. Sect. 7.* 2(2):123–40
17. Brenner, R. M., Resko, J. A., West, N. B. 1974. Cyclic changes in oviductal morphology and residual cytoplasmic estradiol binding capacity induced by sequential estradiol-progesterone treatment of spayed rhesus monkeys. *Endocrinology* 95:1094–1104
18. Brenner, R. M., West, N. B., Hoskins, N. L., Beamer, N. B. 1973. *Biol. Reprod.* 9:70–71 (Abstr.)
19. Bronson, F. H., Hamilton, T. H. 1972. RNA synthesis in the mouse oviduct and uterus: variations before, during and after zygote transport. *J. Endocrinol.* 54:15–24
20. Bronson, F. H., Hamilton, T. H. 1972. A comparison of nucleic acid synthesis in the mouse oviduct and uterus: interactions between estradiol and progesterone. *Biol. Reprod.* 6:160–67
21. Brown-Grant, K., Rogers, A. W. 1972. The sites of iodide concentration in the oviduct and the uterus of the rat. *J. Endocrinol.* 53:355–62
22. Brush, M. G., Taylor, R. W., King, R. J. B. 1967. The uptake of [6,7,-^{3}H] oestradiol by the normal human female reproductive tract. *J. Endocrinol.* 39:599–607

23. Clark, B. F. 1971. The effects of oestrogen and progesterone on uterine cell division and epithelial morphology in spayed, adrenalectomized rats. *J. Endocrinol.* 50:527–28
24. Clark, B. F. 1973. The effect of oestrogen and progesterone on uterine cell division and epithelial morphology in spayed-hypophysectomized rats. *J. Endocrinol.* 56:341–42
25. Clark, J. H., Anderson, J., Peck, E. J. 1972. Receptor-estrogen complex in the nuclear fraction of rat uterine cells during the estrous cycle. *Science* 176: 528–30
26. Clark, J. H., Gorski, J. 1970. Ontogeny of the estrogen receptor during early uterine development. *Science* 169: 76–78
27. Coutinho, E. M. 1973. Hormonal control of tubal musculature. In *The Regulation of Mammalian Reproduction,* ed. S. J. Segal, R. Crozier, P. A. Corfman, P. G. Condliffe, 385–99. Springfield, Ill.: Thomas. 586 pp.
28. Corvol, P., Falk, R., Freifeld, M., Bardin, C. W. 1972. In vitro studies of progesterone binding proteins in guinea pig uterus. *Endocrinology* 90:1464–69
29. Das, R. M., Martin, L. 1973. Progesterone inhibition of mouse uterine epithelial proliferation. *J. Endocrinol.* 59:205–6
30. Davies, I. J., Ryan, K. J. 1972. Uptake of progesterone by the uterus of the pregnant rat in vivo and its relationship to cytoplasmic progesterone-binding protein. *Endocrinology* 90:507–15
31. Davies, I. J., Ryan, K. J. 1973. The modulation of progesterone concentration in the myometrium of the pregnant rat by changes in cytoplasmic "receptor" protein activity. *Endocrinology* 92:394–401
32. Dedes, M., Krauer, F. 1974. Cyclusobhängige veranderungen in der zellteilungshäufigkeit im menschlichen eileiterepithel. *Arch. Gynäkol.* 216: 133–44
33. De Hertogh, R., Ekka, E., Vanderheyden, I., Hoet, J. J. 1971. In vivo observation on cyclic variations of estradiol-17β 6,7-H^3 uptake by the uterus of the adult rat. *Endocrinology* 88:175–79
34. Devoe, L., Freese, U. E., Paulos, G. 1973. Autoradiographic studies of the mouse fallopian tube. *Am. J. Obstet. Gynecol.* 117:490–96
35. Dorfman, R. I. 1973. Biosynthesis of progesterone. *Handb. Physiol. Sect. 7.* 2(2):537–46
36. Dubuisson, L., Duluc, A. J., Bousquet, J., Zaray, M. 1972. Role des hormones ovariennes dans le processus de ciliation de l'oviducte de ratte. *C.R. Soc. Biol.* 166:574–77
37. Dupon, C., Hosseinian, A., Kim, M. H. 1973. Simultaneous determination of plasma estrogens, androgens, and progesterone during the human menstrual cycle. *Steroids* 22:47–61
38. Dupon, C., Kim, M. H. 1973. Peripheral plasma levels of testosterone, androstenedione, and estradiol during the rat oestrous cycle. *J. Endocrinol.* 59:653–54
39. Eaton, L. W. Jr., Feil, P., Strott, C. A., Glasser, S. R., Toft, D. O. 1971. *Endocrinol. Suppl.* 88:A-187 (Abstr.)
40. Eisenfeld, A. J., Axelrod, J. 1966. Effect of steroid hormones, ovariectomy, estrogen pretreatment, sex and immaturity on the distribution of ^{3}H-estradiol. *Endocrinology* 79:38–42
41. Endo, M., Yosizawa, Z. 1973. Hormonal effect on glycoproteins and glycosaminoglycans in rabbit uteri. *Arch. Biochem. Biophys.* 156:397–403
42. Engel, L. L. 1973. The biosynthesis of estrogens. *Handb. Physiol. Sect. 7.* 2(1): 467–84
43. Eto, T., Masuda, M., Suzuki, Y., Mosi, T. 1962. Progesterone and pregn-20α-ol-3-one in rat ovarian blood at different stages in reproductive cycle. *Jap. J. Anim. Reprod.* 8:34–40
44. Evans, L. H., Hähnel, R. 1971. Oestrogen receptors in human uterine tissue. *J. Endocrinol.* 50:209–29
45. Evans, L. H., Martin, J. D., Hähnel, R. 1974. Estrogen receptor concentration in normal and pathological human uterine tissues. *J. Clin. Endocrinol. Metab.* 38:23–32
46. Faber, L. E., Sandmann, M. L., Stavely, H. E. 1973. Progesterone and corticosterone binding in rabbit uterine cytosols. *Endocrinology* 93:74–80
47. Falk, R. J., Bardin, C. W. 1970. Uptake of tritiated progesterone by the uterus of the ovariectomized guinea pig. *Endocrinology* 86:1059–63
48. Feder, H. H., Resko, J. A., Goy, R. W. 1968. Progesterone concentrations in the arterial plasma of guinea pigs during the oestrous cycle. *J. Endocrinol.* 40:505–13
49. Feherty, P., Robertson, D. M., Waynforth, H. B., Kellie, A. E. 1970. Changes in the concentration of high-affinity oestradiol receptors in rat uterine supernatant preparations during the

oestrous cycle, pseudopregnancy, pregnancy, maturation and after ovariectomy. *Biochem. J.* 120:837–44

50. Feil, P. D., Glasser, S. R., Toft, D. O., O'Malley, B. W. 1972. Progesterone binding in the mouse and rat uterus. *Endocrinology* 91:738–46
51. Fencl, M. M., Villee, C. A. 1971. Effect of RNA from estradiol-treated immature rats on protein synthesis in immature uteri. *Endocrinology* 88:279–85
52. Ferenczy, A., Richart, R. M., Agate, F. J. Jr., Purkerson, M. L., Dempsey, E. W. 1972. Scanning electron microscopy of the human fallopian tube. *Science* 175:783–84
53. Ferenczy, A., Richart, R. M., Agate, F. J. Jr., Purkerson, M. L., Dempsey, E. W. 1972. Scanning electron microscopy of the human endometrial surface epithelium. *Fert. Steril.* 23:515–21
54. Fredricsson, B., Björkman, N. 1973. Morphologic alterations in the human oviduct epithelium induced by contraceptive methods. *Fert. Steril.* 24:19–30
55. Freifeld, M., Bardin, C. W. 1972. *Kinetics of Progesterone Receptor Activity in Guinea Pig (GP) Uterus.* Presented at IVth Int. Congr. Endocrinol., Washington. (Abstr.)
56. Freifeld, M. L., Feil, P. D., Bardin, C. W. 1974. The in vivo regulation of the progesterone receptor in guinea pig uterus: dependence on estrogen and progesterone. *Steroids* 23:93–104
57. Friedrich, E. R. 1973. The effects of oral contraceptives on the cytology of the secretory cells of the cervix. See Ref. 7, 367–84
58. Gaddum-Rosse, P., Blandau, R. J., Thiersch, J. B. 1973. Ciliary activity in the human and *Macaca nemestrina* oviduct. *Am. J. Anat.* 138:269–75
59. Goldman, B. D., Zarrow, M. X. 1973. The physiology of progestins. *Handb. Physiol. Sect. 7.* 2(1):547–72
60. Good, R. G., Moyer, D. L. 1968. Estrogen-progesterone relationships in the development of secretory endometrium. *Fert. Steril.* 19:37–49
61. Gorski, J. 1973. Estrogen binding and control of gene expression in the uterus. *Handb. Physiol. Sect. 7.* 2(1):525–36
62. Gorski, J., Nicolette, J. A. 1963. Early estrogen effects on newly synthesized RNA and phospholipid in subcellular fractions of rat uteri. *Arch. Biochem. Biophys.* 103:418–23
63. Graham, C. E. 1973. Functional microanatomy of the primate uterine cervix. *Handb. Physiol. Sect. 7.* 2(2):1–24
64. Graham, C. E. 1973. Chimpanzee endometrium and sexual swelling during menstrual cycle or hormone administration. *Folia Primatol.* 19:458–68
65. Graham, C. E., Collins, D. C., Robinson, H., Preedy, J. R. K. 1972. Urinary levels of estrogens and pregnanediol and plasma levels of progesterone during the menstrual cycle of the chimpanzee: relationship to the sexual swelling. *Endocrinology* 91:13–24
66. Greep, R. O., Astwood, E. B., Eds. 1973. *Handb. Physiol. Sect. 7.* Vol. 2
67. Gregoire, A. T., Goldfoot, D., Goy, R. W. 1972. The effect of estrogen and progesterone on genital tract weight and glycogen content in ovariectomized guinea pigs. *Proc. Soc. Exp. Biol. Med.* 139:176–78
68. Grundsell, H., Nilsson, I., Nordqvist, S. 1973. Progesterone concentration in human endometrium. *Lancet* 1:888
69. Hafez, E. S. E. 1973. Endocrine control of the structure and function of the mammalian oviduct. *Handb. Physiol. Sect. 7.* 2(2):97–122
70. Hafez, E. S. E., Blandau, R. J., Eds. 1969. *The Mammalian Oviduct.* Chicago, Ill.: Univ. Chicago Press. 546 pp.
71. Hamilton, T. H. 1964. Sequences of RNA and protein synthesis during early estrogen action. *Proc. Nat. Acad. Sci. USA* 51:83–89
72. Hamner, C. E. 1973. Oviductal fluid—composition and physiology. *Handb. Physiol. Sect. 7.* 2(2):141–52
73. Hansel, W., Concannon, P. W., Lukaszewska, J. H. 1973. Corpora lutea of the large domestic animals. *Biol. Reprod.* 8:222–45
74. Harrison, R. W., Toft, D. O. 1973. Testosterone binding in the chick oviduct. *Biochem. Biophys. Res. Commun.* 55:857–63
75. Haukkamaa, M., Karjalainen, O., Luukkainen, T. 1971. In vitro binding of progesterone by the human endometrium during the menstrual cycle and by hyperplastic, atrophic, and carcinomatous endometrium. *Am. J. Obstet. Gynecol.* 111:205–10
76. Heap, R. B., Perry, J. S., Challis, J. R. G. 1973. The hormonal maintenance of pregnancy. *Handb. Physiol. Sect. 7.* 2(2): 217–60
77. Henderson, S. R., Schalch, D. S. 1972. Estrogen receptors in the human uterus. *Am. J. Obstet. Gynecol.* 112:762–71

78. Hess, D. L., Resko, J. A. 1973. The effects of progesterone on the patterns of testosterone and estradiol concentrations in the systemic plasma of the female rhesus monkey during the intermenstrual period. *Endocrinology* 92:446–53
79. Hilliard, J., Eaton, L. W. Jr. 1971. Estradiol-17β, progesterone and 20α-hydroxypregn-4-en-3-one in rabbit ovarian venous plasma. II. From mating through implantation. *Endocrinology* 89:522–27
80. Hilliard, J., Pang, C.-N., Scaramuzzi, R. J., Penardi, R., Sawyer, C. H. 1974. Secretion rates of estradiol, testosterone, and progesterone from right and left rabbit ovaries cannulated concurrently or successively. *Biol. Reprod.* 10:364–69
81. Hisaw, F. L., Hisaw, F. L. Jr. 1961. Action of estrogen and progesterone on the reproductive tract of lower primates. In *Sex and Internal Secretions,* ed. W.C. Young, 1:556–89. Baltimore: Williams & Wilkins. 3rd ed. 704 pp.
82. Hodgen, G. D., Falk, R. J. 1971. Estrogen and progesterone regulation of carbonic anhydrase isoenzymes in guinea pig and rabbit uterus. *Endocrinology* 89:859–64
83. Hodgson, B. J., Pauerstein, C. J. 1974. The effect of ovulation on the response of the rabbit oviduct to adrenergic agonists in vitro. *Biol. Reprod.* 10:346–53
84. Holmdahl, T. H., Johansson, E. D. B. 1972. Peripheral plasma levels of 17α-hydroxyprogesterone, progesterone and oestradiol during normal menstrual cycles in women. *Acta Endocrinol.* 71:743–54
85. Hopper, B., Tullner, W. W. 1970. Urinary estrone and plasma progesterone levels during the menstrual cycle of the rhesus monkey. *Endocrinology* 86:1225–30
86. Hotchkiss, J., Atkinson, L. E., Knobil, E. 1971. Time-course of serum estrogen and luteinizing hormone (LH) concentrations during the menstrual cycle of the rhesus monkey. *Endocrinology* 89:177–83
87. Iacobelli, S. 1973. Oestrous cycle-induced protein synthesis and oestradiol binding to the nuclei in the rat uterus. *Nature New Biol.* 245:154–55
88. Jackson, V., Chalkley, R. 1974. The binding of estradiol-17β to the bovine endometrial nuclear membrane. *J. Biol. Chem.* 249:1615–26
89. Jacobson, H. I., Keyes, P. L., Bullock, D. W. 1972. *Biol. Reprod.* 7:108 (Abstr.)
90. Jensen, E. V., DeSombre, E. R. 1973. Estrogen-receptor interaction. *Science* 182:126–34
91. Jensen, E. V., Suzuki, T., Numata, M., Smith, S., DeSombre, E. R. 1969. Estrogen-binding substances of target tissues. *Steriods* 13:417–27
92. Johnson, A. D., Foley, C. W., Eds. 1974. *The Oviduct and Its Functions.* New York: Academic. 369 pp.
93. Jones, G. E. et al 1973. Plasma oestradiol, luteinizing hormone and progesterone during the oestrous cycle in the beagle bitch. *J. Endocrinol.* 57:331–32
94. Joshi, H. S., Watson, D. J., Labhsetwar, A. P. 1973. Ovarian secretion of oestradiol, oestrone, 20-dihydroprogesterone and progesterone during the oestrous cycle of the guinea pig. *J. Reprod. Fert.* 35:177–81
95. Kaltenbach, F. J., Fettig, O., Welter, J. 1973. Histologische und autoradiographische untersuchungen am menschlichen endomentrium unter der 2-phasen-therapie mit mestranol-lynestrenol. *Arch. Gynäkol.* 215:3–20
96. Kaye, A. M., Sheratsky, D., Lindner, H. R. 1972. Kinetics of DNA synthesis in immature rat uterus: age dependence and estradiol stimulation. *Biochim. Biophys. Acta* 261:475–86
97. Kimball, F. A., Hansel, W. 1973. *Physiologist* 16:363 (Abstr.)
98. King, R. J. B., Gordon, J., Marx, J., Streggles, A. W. 1971. Localization and nature of sex steroid receptors within the cell. In *Basic Actions of Sex Steroids on Target Organs,* eds. P. O. Hubinont, F. Leroy, P. Galand, 21–43. Basel: Karger. 296 pp.
99. Kirton, K. T., Niswender, G. G., Midgley, A. R. Jr., Jaffe, R. B., Forbes, A. D. 1970. Serum luteinizing hormone and progesterone concentration during the menstrual cycle of the rhesus monkey. *J. Clin. Endocrinol.* 30:105–10
100. Knobil, E. 1972. Hormonal control of the menstrual cycle and ovulation in the rhesus monkey. *Acta Endocrinol. Suppl.* 166:137–44
101. Koseki, Y., Fujimoto, G. I. 1974. Progesterone effects contrasted with 17β-estradiol on DNA synthesis and epithelial nuclear proliferation in the castrate rabbit uterus. *Biol. Reprod.* 10:596–604

102. Krueger, W. A., Bo, W. J., Garrison, B. M. 1974. DNA replication in the epithelium of rat vagina and lower cervix following estrogen-progesterone treatment. *Am. J. Anat.* 139:123–28
103. Labhsetwar, A. P., Perser, N. 1972. Uterine uptake of [6,7-^{3}H] oestradiol in the presence of intrauterine contraceptive device in cyclic and pregnant rats. *Acta Endocrinol.* 69:583–88
104. Landau, R. L. 1973. The metabolic influence of progesterone. *Handb. Physiol. Sect. 7.* 2(1):573–90
105. Leavitt, W. W., Blaha, G. C. 1972. Estrogen-stimulated, progesterone-binding system in the hamster uterus and vagina. *Steroids* 19:263–74
106. Leavitt, W. W., Strott, C. A. 1973. Presented at the 55th Ann. Meet. Endocrine Soc. A-186 (Abstr.)
107. Leavitt, W. W., Toft, D. O., Strott, C. A., O'Malley, B. W. 1974. A specific progesterone receptor in the hamster uterus: physiologic properties and regulation during the estrous cycle. *Endocrinology* 94:1041–53
108. Lee, A. E., Dukelow, W. R. 1972. Synthesis of DNA and mitosis in rabbit uteri after oestrogen and progesterone injections, and during early pregnancy. *J. Reprod. Fert.* 31:473–76
109. Lee, C., Jacobson, H. I. 1971. Uterine estrogen receptor in rats during pubescence and the estrous cycle. *Endocrinolgy* 88:596–601
110. Limpaphayom, K., Lee, C., Jacobson, H. I., King, T. M. 1971. Estrogen receptor in human endometrium during the menstrual cycle and early pregnancy. *Am. J. Obstet. Gynecol.* 111:1064–68
111. Lippes, J., Enders, R. G., Pragay, D. A., Bartholomew, W. R. 1972. The collection and analysis of human fallopian tubal fluid. *Contraception* 5:85–103
112. Luck, I. N., Gschwendt, M., Hamilton, T. H. 1973. Oestrogenic stimulation of macromolecular synthesis is correlated with nuclear hormone-receptor complex in neonatal rat uterus. *Nature New Biol.* 245:24–25
113. Macdonald, G. J., Demers, L. M., Greep, R. O. 1973. Peripheral serum progesterone and correlated endometrial glycogen levels during the menstrual cycle of *Macaca arctoides. Fert. Steril.* 24:98–103
114. Mansour, A. M. 1967. Further studies on RNA and protein biosynthesis in the ovariectomized mouse uterus. *Acta Endocrinol.* 54:541–56
115. Mansour, A. M. 1968. The effect of exogenous ribonucleic acid on alkaline phosphatase acitivty in the ovariectomized mouse uterus. *Acta Endocrinol.* 57:465–72
116. Mansour, A. M., Niu, M. C. 1965. Functional studies with uterine RNA. *Proc. Nat. Acad. Sci. USA* 53:764–70
117. Martin, L., Das, R. M., Finn, C. A. 1973. The inhibition by progesterone of uterine epithelial proliferation in the mouse. *J. Endocrinol.* 57:549–54
118. Martin, L., Finn, C. A., Trinder, G. 1973. DNA synthesis in the endometrium of progesterone-treated mice. *J. Endocrinol.* 56:303–7
119. Mastroianni, L. Jr., Urzua, M., Stambaugh, R. 1973. The internal environmental fluids of the oviduct. See Ref. 27, 376–84
120. McArthur, J. W., Ovadia, J., Smith, O. W., Bashir-Farahmand, J. 1972. The menstrual cycle of the bonnet monkey (*Macaca radiata*). Changes in cervical mucus secretion, vaginal cytology, sex skin and urinary estrogen excretion. *Folia Primatol.* 17:107–21
121. McGuire, J. L., Lisk, R. D. 1968. Estrogen receptors in the intact rat. *Proc. Nat. Acad. Sci. USA* 61:497–503
122. Means, A. R., Hamilton, T. H. 1966. Early estrogen action: concomitant stimulations within two minutes of nuclear RNA synthesis and uptake of RNA precursor by the uterus. *Proc. Nat. Acad. Sci. USA* 56:1594–98
123. Milgrom, E., Atger, M., Baulieu, E.-E. 1970. Progesterone in uterus and plasma. IV. Progesterone receptor(s) in guinea pig uterus cytosol. *Steroids* 16:741–54
124. Milgrom, E., Atger, M., Perrot, M., Baulieu, E.-E. 1972. Progesterone in uterus and plasma. VI. Uterine progesterone receptors during the estrous cycle and implantation in the guinea pig. *Endocrinology* 90:1071–78
125. Milgrom, E., Baulieu, E.-E. 1970. Progesterone in uterus and plasma. I. Binding in rat uterus 105,000 *g* supernatant. *Endocrinology* 87:276–87
126. Milgrom, E., Thi, L., Atger, M., Baulieu, E.-E. 1973. Mechanisms regulating the concentration and the conformation of progesterone receptors in the uterus. *J. Biol. Chem.* 248:6366–74
127. Milgrom, E., Thi, M. L., Baulieu, E.-E. 1973. *Karolinska Symp. on Res. Methods in Reprod. Endocrinol., 6th Symp. Protein Synthesis in Reprod. Tissue,* 380–403

128. Moghissi, K. S. 1973. Composition and function of cervical secretion. *Handb. Physiol. Sect. 7.* 2(2):25–48
129. Moghissi, K. S., Syner, F. N., Evans, T. N. 1972. A composite picture of the menstrual cycle. *Am. J. Obstet. Gynecol.* 114:405–18
130. Møller, O. M. 1973. Progesterone concentrations in the peripheral plasma of the blue fox (*Alopex lagopus*) during pregnancy and the estrous cycle. *J. Endocrinol.* 59:429–38
131. More, I. A. R., Armstrong, E. M., McSeveney, D., Chatfield, W. R. 1974. The morphogenesis and fate of the nucleolar channel system in the human endometrial glandular cell. *J. Ultrastruct. Res.* 47:74–85
132. Moulton, B. C., Barker, K. L. 1973. A delayed antagonistic effect of progesterone on estradiol-induced increases in uterine glucose-6-phosphate dehydrogenase. *Endocrinology* 92:636–38
133. Naftolin, F., Brown-Grant, K., Corker, C. S. 1972. Plasma and pituitary luteinizing hormone and peripheral plasma oestradiol concentrations in the normal oestrous cycle of the rat and after experimental manipulation of the cycle. *J. Endocrinol.* 53:17–30
134. Nayak, R. K., Osland, R. B., Ellington, E. F. 1972. *Biol. Reprod.* 19:1161 (Abstr.)
135. Nayak, R. K., Zimmerman, D. R. 1972. *Biol. Reprod.* 19:1161 (Abstr.)
136. Nayak, R. K., Zimmerman, D. R. 1973. *Biol. Reprod.* 22:322 (Abstr.)
137. Neill, J. D., Johansson, E. D. B., Knobil, E. 1967. Levels of progesterone in peripheral plasma during the menstrual cycle of the rhesus monkey. *Endocrinology* 81:1161–64
138. Neill, J. D., Johansson, E. D. B., Knobil, E. 1969. Patterns of circulating progesterone concentrations during the fertile menstrual cycle and the remainder of gestation in the rhesus monkey. *Endocrinology* 84:45–48
139. Noteboom, W. D., Gorski, J. 1963. *Fed. Proc.* 22:329 (Abstr.)
140. Novak, E., Everett, H. S. 1928. Cyclical and other variations in the tubal epithelium. *Am. J. Obstet. Gynecol.* 16:499–530
141. Oberti, C., Dabancens, A., Garcia-Huidobro, M., Rodriguez-Bravo, R., Zanartu, J. 1974. Low-dosage oral progesterone to control fertility. II. Morphologic modifications in the gonad and oviduct. *Obstet. Gynecol.* 43:285–94
142. Odor, D. L., Blandau, R. J. 1973. Egg transport over the fimbrial surface of the rabbit oviduct under experimental conditions. *Fert. Steril.* 24:292–300
143. O'Malley, B. W., Means, A. R. 1974. Female steroid hormones and target cell nuclei. *Science* 183:610–20
144. O'Malley, B. W., Sherman, M. R., Toft, D. O. 1970. Progesterone "receptors" in the cytoplasm and nucleus of chick oviduct target tissue. *Proc. Nat. Acad. Sci. USA* 67:501–8
145. O'Malley, B. W., Strott, C. A. 1973. The mechanism of action of progesterone. *Handb. Physiol. Sect. 7.* 2(1):591–602
146. Parakkal, P. F. 1974. Cyclical changes in the vaginal epithelium of the rat seen by scanning electron microscopy. *Anat. Rec.* 178:529–38
147. Parakkal, P. F., Gregoire, A. T. 1972. Differentiation of vaginal epithelium in the normal and hormone-treated rhesus monkey. *Biol. Reprod.* 6:117–30
148. Patek, E. 1974. The epithelium of the human fallopian tube. *Acta Obstet. Gynecol. Scand.* 53:Suppl. 31
149. Patterson, C., Masters, C. J. 1970. The influence of progesterone on the lactate dehydrogenase isoenzymes of the rat reproductive tract. *FEBS Lett.* 12:69–71
150. Paul, P. K., Duttagupta, P. N. 1973. Inhibition of oestrogen-induced increase in hepatic and uterine glycogen by progesterone in the rat. *Acta Endocrinol.* 72:762–70
151. Perkins, J. L. 1974. Fluid flow of the oviduct. See Ref. 15, 19–32
152. Podratz, K. C., Katzman, P. A. 1968. *Fed. Proc.* 27:497 (Abstr.)
153. Psychoyos, A. 1973. Endocrine control of egg implantation. *Handb. Physiol. Sect. 7.* 2(2):187–216
154. Rao, B. R., Wiest, W. G. 1971. *Fed. Proc.* 30:1213 (Abstr.)
155. Rao, B. R., Wiest, W. G., Allen, W. M. 1973. Progesterone "receptor" in rabbit uterus. I. Characterization and estradiol-17β augmentation. *Endocrinology* 92:1229–40
156. Reel, J. R., Shih, Y. 1973. Presented at the 55th Ann. Meet. Endocrine Soc. A-186 (Abstr.)
157. Resko, J. A., Norman, R. L., Niswender, G. D., Spies, H. G. 1974. The relationship between progestins and gonadotropins during the late luteal phase of the menstrual cycle in rhesus monkeys. *Endocrinology* 94:128–35
158. Reuter, L. A., Ciaccio, L. A., Lisk, R. D. 1970. *Fed. Proc.* 29:250 (Abstr.)

159. Robertson, D. M., Mester, J., Beilby, J., Steele, S. J., Kellie, A. E. 1971. The measurement of high-affinity oestradiol receptors in human uterine endometrium and myometrium. *Acta Endocrinol.* 68:534–42
160. Rosner, J. M., Martinez, I. M., Mendizabal, A. F., Spaltro, N. A. 1971. The in vivo and in vitro uptake of labeled estradiol by different segments of the human uterus. *Steroidologia* 2:283–88
161. Ryan, K. J. 1973. Steroid hormones in mammalian pregnancy. *Handb. Physiol. Sect. 7.* 2(2):285–94
162. Saffran, J., Bostleman, B. K., Haas, B. M., Stavely, H. E. 1971. *Biol. Reprod.* 5:83–84 (Abstr.)
163. Saldarini, R. J., Spieler, J. M., Coppola, J. A. 1972. Plasma estrogens, progestins and spinnbarkeit characteristics during selected portions of the menstrual cycle of the cynomolgus monkey (*Macaca fascicularis*). *Biol. Reprod.* 7:347–55
164. Sarff, M., Gorski, J. 1971. Control of estrogen binding protein concentration under basal conditions and after estrogen administration. *Biochemistry* 10:2557–62
165. Schill, W., Schumacher, G. F. B. 1973. Micro radial diffusion in gel methods for the quantitative assessment of soluble proteins in genital secretions. See Ref. 7, 173–200
166. Schumacher, G. F. B. 1973. Soluble proteins in cervical mucus. See Ref. 7, 201–34
167. Segal, S. J. 1967. Regulatory action of estrogenic hormones. *Develop. Biol. Suppl.* 1:264–80
168. Segal, S. J., Atkinson, L. E. 1973. Biological effects of oral contraceptive steroids. *Handb. Physiol. Sect. 7.* 2(2): 349–58
169. Segal, S. J., Davidson, O. W., Wada, K. 1965. Role of RNA in the regulatory action of estrogen. *Proc. Nat. Acad. Sci. USA* 54:782–87
170. Segal, S. J., Ige, R. O., Tuohimaa, P., Burgos, M. H. 1973. Progesterone-dependent messenger RNA: heterospecific activity in vivo. *Science* 181:569–70
171. Shaaban, M. M., Klopper, A. 1973. Plasma oestradiol and progesterone concentration in the normal menstrual cycle. *J. Obstet. Gynaecol. Brit. Commonw.* 80:776–82
172. Shaikh, A. A. 1971. Estrone and estradiol levels in the ovarian venous blood from rats during the estrous cycle and pregnancy. *Biol. Reprod.* 5:297–307
173. Shaikh, A. A. 1972. Estrone, estradiol, progesterone and 17α-hydroxyprogesterone in the ovarian venous plasma during the estrous cycle of the hamster. *Endocrinology* 91:1136–40
174. Shaikh, A. A., Harper, M. J. K. 1972. Ovarian steroid secretion in estrous, mated and HCG-treated rabbits, determined by concurrent cannulation of both ovarian veins. *Biol. Reprod.* 7:387–97
175. Shain, S. A., Barnea, A. 1971. Some characteristics of the estradiol binding protein of the mature, intact rat uterus. *Endocrinology* 89:1270–79
176. Sharp, D. C., Black, D. L. 1973. Changes in peripheral plasma progesterone throughout the oestrous cycle of the pony mare. *J. Reprod. Fert.* 33:535–38
177. Sherman, M. R., Corvol, P. L., O'Malley, B. W. 1970. Progesterone-binding components of chick oviduct. I. Preliminary characterization of cytoplasmic components. *J. Biol. Chem.* 245: 6085–96
178. Slaunwhite, W. R. Jr., Kirdani, R. Y., Sandberg, A. A. 1973. Metabolic aspects of estrogens in man. *Handb. Physiol. Sect. 7.* 2(1):485–524
179. Smith, M. S., McDonald, L. E. 1974. Serum levels of luteinizing hormone and progesterone during the estrous cycle, pseudopregnancy and pregnancy in the dog. *Endocrinology* 94:404–12
180. Sömjen, D., Kaye, A. M., Lindner, H. R. 1973. Postnatal development of uterine response to estradiol-17β in the rat. *Develop. Biol.* 31:409–12
181. Sömjen, D., Sömjen, G., King, R. J. B., Kaye, A. M., Lindner, H. R. 1973. Nuclear binding of oestradiol-17β and induction of protein synthesis in the rat uterus during postnatal development. *Boichem. J.* 136:25–33
182. Stabenfeldt, G. H., Hendrickx, A. G. 1972. Progesterone levels in the bonnet monkey (*Macaca radiata*) during the menstrual cycle and pregnancy. *Endocrinology* 91:614–19
183. Stabenfeldt, G. H., Hendrickx, A. G. 1973. Progesterone studies in the *Macaca fascicularis. Endocrinology* 92:1296–1300
184. Stambaugh, R., Seitz, H. M. Jr., Mastroianni, L. Jr. 1974. Acrosomal proteinase inhibitors in rhesus monkey (*M. mulatta*) oviduct fluid. *Fert. Steril.* 25:352–57

185. Steinetz, B. G. 1973. Secretion and function of ovarian estrogens. *Handb. Physiol. Sect. 7.* 2(1):439–66
186. Stevens, V. C., Sparks, S. J., Powell, J. E. 1970. Levels of estrogens, progestogens and luteinizing hormone during the menstrual cycle of the baboon. *Endocrinology* 87:658–66
187. Szego, C. 1971. The lysosomal membrane complex as a proximate target for steroid hormone action. In *The Sex Steroids: Molecular Mechanisms,* ed. K. W. McKerns, 1:1–52. New York: Appleton. 454 pp.
188. Tachi, C., Tachi, S., Lindner, H. R. 1972. Modification by progesterone of oestradiol-induced cell proliferation, RNA synthesis and oestradiol distribution in the rat uterus. *J. Reprod. Fert.* 31:59–76
189. Tagatz, G. E., Gurpide, E. 1973. Hormone secretion by the normal human ovary. *Handb. Physiol. Sect. 7.* 2(1): 603–14
190. Talwar, G. P., Segal, S. J. 1963. Prevention of hormone action by local application of actinomycin D. *Proc. Nat. Acad. Sci. USA* 50:226–30
191. Tchernitchin, A. 1972. Radioautographic study of the effect of estradiol-17β, estrone, estriol, progesterone, testosterone and corticosterone on the in vitro uptake of 2, 4, 6, 7-^{3}H estradiol-17β by uterine eosinophils of the rat. *Steroids* 19:575–86
192. Thomas, P. J. 1973. Steroid hormones and their receptors. *J. Endocrinol.* 57:333–59
193. Toft, D. 1973. Steroid hormone receptors in reproductive tissues. *Obstet. Gynecol. Ann.* 2:405–30
194. Toft, D. O., O'Malley, B. W. 1972. Target tissue receptors for progesterone: the influence of estrogen treatment. *Endocrinology* 90:1041–45
195. Trachewsky, D., Segal, S. J. 1967. Selective stimulation of ribonucleic acid synthesis in uterine nuclei by estradiol-17β. *Biochem. Biophys. Res. Commun.* 27:588–94
196. Trams, G., Engel, B., Lehmann, F., Maass, H. 1973. Specific binding of oestradiol in human uterine tissue. *Acta Endocrinol.* 72:351–60
197. Tseng, L., Gurpide, E. 1974. Estradiol and 20α-dihydroprogesterone dehydrogenase activities in human endometrium during the menstrual cycle. *Endocrinology* 94:419–23
198. Tuohimaa, P., Segal, S. J., Koide, S. S. 1972. Induction of avidin synthesis by RNA obtained from chick oviduct. *Proc. Nat. Acad. Sci. USA* 69:2814–17
199. Ui, H., Mueller, G. C. 1963. The role of RNA synthesis in early estrogen action. *Proc. Nat. Acad. Sci. USA* 50:256–60
200. Unhjem, O., Attramadal, A., Sölna, J. 1968. Changes in uterine RNA following stimulation with 17β-oestradiol. *Acta Endocrinol.* 58:227–34
201. Verhage, H. G., Abel, J. H. Jr., Tietz, W. J. Jr., Barrau, M. D. 1973. Development and maintenance of the oviductal epithelium during the estrous cycle in the bitch. *Biol. Reprod.* 9:460–74
202. Verhage, H. G., Abel, J. H. Jr., Tietz, W. J. Jr., Barrau, M. D. 1973. Estrogen-induced differentiation of the oviductal epithelium in prepubertal dogs. *Biol. Reprod.* 9:475–88
203. Verhage, H. G., West, N. B., Brenner, R. M. 1974. Progesterone antagonism of estrogen-driven ciliogenesis in the oviduct of the cat. *Biol. Reprod.* (Abstr.). In press
204. Wade, G. N., Feder, H. H. 1972. [1,2-^{3}H] Progesterone uptake by guinea pig brain and uterus: differential localization, time-course of uptake and metabolism and effects of age, sex, estrogen-priming and competing steroids. *Brain Res.* 45:525–43
205. Warren, J. C., Crist, R. D. 1973. Effects of ovarian steroids on uterine metabolism. *Handb. Physiol. Sect. 7.* 2(2): 49–68
206. Weick, R. F., Dierschke, D. J., Karsch, F. J., Hotchkiss, J., Knobil, E. 1973. 55th Ann. Meet. Endocrine Soc. A-112 (Abstr.)
207. Whalen, R. E., Maurer, R. A. 1969. Estrogen "receptors" in brain: an unsolved problem. *Proc. Nat. Acad. Sci. USA* 63:681–85
208. Wiest, W. G. 1963. Extrahepatic metabolism of progesterone in pseudopregnant rats. Identification of reduction products. *J. Biol. Chem.* 238:94–99
209. Wiest, W. G. 1970. Progesterone and 20 α-hydroxypregn-4-en-3-one in plasma, ovaries and uteri during pregnancy in the rat. *Endocrinology* 87:43–48
210. Wiest, W. G. 1973. 55th Ann. Meet. Endocrine Soc. A-65 (Abstr.)
211. Wiest, W. G., Rao, B. R. 1971. Progesterone binding proteins in rabbit uterus and human endometrium. *Advan. Biosci.* 7:251–64
212. Yoshinaga, K. 1973. Gonadotrophin-induced hormone secretion and structural changes in the ovary during the

nonpregnant reproductive cycle. *Handb. Physiol. Sect. 7.* 2(1):363–88

213. Yoshinaga, K., Demers, L. M. 1971. *Biol. Reprod.* 5:105 (Abstr.)

214. Zinca, V., Cîrlan, M. 1969. The reproduction of hormonal effects by macromolecular RNA. *Acta Cytol.* 13: 679–84

Copyright 1975. All rights reserved

REGULATION OF RESPIRATION IN MAN[1]

◆1132

A. Guz
Department of Medicine, Charing Cross Hospital Medical School,
London, United Kingdom

The last review on respiratory regulation published by the *Annual Review of Physiology* appeared in 1970 (74a). I have therefore reviewed work published between June 1969 and March 1974. Although I have tried to confine myself to studies in man, I have not hesitated to quote references on relevant animal models. I have also taken examples from the clinical literature, if relevant to the elucidation of a physiological mechanism. The subjects chosen are those in which I have a particular interest.

The most serious difficulty in this field is that it is rarely possible to do definitive physiological studies in man because of ethical considerations. Much of the conceptual framework in which studies are done derives from animal physiology; analogy is freely used. Many authors seem remarkably free of concern about the problem of species differences.

A particular problem in conscious man concerns the effect of the use of traditional mouthpieces and noseclips on ventilatory variables measured. This has recently been highlighted (42) by the use on the chest and abdomen of magnetometers calibrated to record breathing. The application of a mouthpiece and noseclip caused V_T to increase by 29 ± 21% and f to decrease by 25 ± 16%. The need to distract conscious subjects (particularly resting subjects) during a respiratory study has been known for many years.

[1]Abbreviations used:

V_T	tidal volume	P_{ACO_2},P_{AO_2}	alveolar CO_2 and O_2 tensions
f	respiratory frequency	$\dot{V}_E$	minute ventilation
FRC	functional residual capacity	T_I	inspiratory time
RV	residual volume	T_E	expiratory time
Pa_{CO_2},Pa_{O_2}	arterial CO_2 and O_2 tensions		

PULMONARY VAGAL REFLEX REGULATION

The Hering-Breuer Centenary Symposium (81) provides an excellent review. Noteworthy publications in this symposium are English translations, with commentary, or the original papers by Hering and Breuer (97). A more recent symposium on "Neural Control of Breathing" (59) also deals extensively with lung reflexes. Pulmonary vagal afferents are reviewed by Paintal (75); the characteristics and possible regulatory roles of stretch, "irritant" airway and juxtapulmonary capillary (Type J) receptors are fully discussed.

There is still no explanation for the remarkable absence of an effect on any aspect of ventilation when cervical vagi are blocked with local anesthetic in anesthetized and conscious man with normal lungs (45). This is certainly compatible with the fact that under general anesthesia, lungs need to be inflated up to 1–1½ liters above the FRC before an apnoeic response to inflation dependent on intact vagi (inflation reflex) can be seen. Pulmonary stretch receptor activity is recorded in human cervical vagi; both qualitatively and quantitatively the presence of a tonic discharge at FRC and the increase in discharge that accompanies a eupnoeic tidal volume resemble closely the findings in dog and cat (48, 63). The absence of an effect of this discharge on ventilation suggests that a high central threshold exists at medullary level, perhaps due to descending inhibitory input. No studies have yet reported whether the sensitivity of the inflation reflex increases in patients with diffuse cortical lesions in whom there may be a reduction in such descending inhibitory input (78) There are also no studies on any effect of neuropharmacological agents on the sensitivity of the reflex.

The opportunity presented by the occurrence of spontaneous pneumothorax has been used to look for the Hering-Breuer deflation reflex in man (46). With a tube in the pleural cavity, it has been possible to allow one lung to deflate below its RV; this has resulted in an increased f, a reduction in Pa_{CO_2}, and an activation of external intercostals. This resembles the classical deflation reflex, but as yet has not been proven to be vagally mediated (as has the inflation reflex). Reductions in lung volume down to RV do not have this effect. If this is indeed the deflation reflex, then it has the same high threshold outside the eupnoeic range as has the inflation reflex.

Evidence is slowly accumulating of the presence in man of receptors in or close to the pulmonary circulation that can be activated to modify ventilation by chemical substances such as lobeline (8, 54). It is assumed that these are vagal receptors. The occurrence of an apnoea or ventilatory depression within 1–2 sec of injecting lobeline into the main pulmonary artery closely resembles a similar vagally mediated effect in the cat using lobeline (or phenyldiguanide), almost certainly resulting from Type J receptor stimulation. These precede the increases in ventilation brought about by the stimulating effect of lobeline on the arterial chemoreceptors. Striking species differences exist for activation of Type J receptors in cat, dog, and rabbit both with respect to the substances that will activate and the ventilatory effect of activating. The analogy of the human and cat experiments may therefore be somewhat farfetched!

The cough reflex is probably the most significant vagal reflex from the clinical viewpoint. In the 1950s (10, 11) it was shown that a citric acid aerosol could be safely used to produce cough. Recently 2–15% citric acid aerosols have been used to study cough in a quantitative and reproducible manner (7). Ethanol (plasma levels 80–100 mg%) has been shown to strikingly depress this crucial defence reflex; this may contribute to the susceptibility of the alcoholic to pneumonia.

There is a need for more studies on pulmonary vagal reflex control in normal conscious man both at rest and during exercise, but nerve block at the base of the skull with local anesthetic is a difficult technique; the associated inevitable block of the glossopharyngeal nerve makes interpretation difficult. It should be remembered, particularly in relation to the next section of this review, that our information on the lack of effect of vagal block in resting conscious man comes from studies on three subjects, of whom two were respiratory physiologists! There is hope that a local anesthetic aerosol that blocks at least airway reflexes may prove adequate and safe for use in man (55).

Pulmonary Vagal Reflex Control in Cardiopulmonary Disease

Results of vagal block at the base of the skull in 12 patients with a wide variety of cardiopulmonary disease have been presented (44). Breathing has slowed and dyspnoea has been reduced in resting patients with lung infiltrations, left ventricular failure, and pulmonary vascular obstruction; no effect was seen in patients with a rigid chest wall or chronic bronchitis with emphysema. The changes seen were not thought to be due to the associated glossopharyngeal block because the patients were not hypoxic or hypercapnoeic. As the anesthetic wore off, both ventilation and dyspnoea returned to the control situation. By contrast with what was found in the 3 normal subjects, it would seem, therefore, that an abnormal vagal "drive to breathe" exists in patients with certain cardiopulmonary abnormalities. A further striking case report has appeared (6) in which a patient with a neoplastic obstruction of the right main pulmonary artery and who was intensely dyspnoeic, hypoxic ($Pa_{O_2} < 60$ mm Hg), and hypocapnoeic was given a unilateral vagus and glossopharyngeal nerve block on the side ipsilateral to the lesion at the base of the skull on 9 separate occasions with striking elimination of dyspnoea, reduction in V_T, and elevation of Pa_{CO_2} to normal levels on each occasion. The type of anesthetic used was varied and the duration of effect entirely depended on the known duration of action of the anesthetic. Regrettably the authors did not eliminate the hypoxia and the results found may be due to a unilateral carotid body block.

The tachypnoea and dyspnoea of asthma has excited considerable attention since it has been realized that hypocapnoea is more common than hypercapnoea even with severe obstruction (87); this is not due to the associated hypoxia. The asthmatic breathes faster the more the degree of airway constriction, and in doing so the respiratory work done also increases (51). A remarkable study has appeared in which both a bilateral vagal nerve block at the base of the skull (1 subject) or an anesthetic aerosol block of the airways was performed in patients with allergic asthma (77). Both procedures were done after the systemic administration of atropine to block parasympathetic efferent pathways; this drug had no effect on ventilation or dyspnoea, and lung resistance remained moderately elevated with alveolar hyperventilation. Under these conditions both anesthetic procedures caused a fall in f and a rise in Pa_{CO_2} to the normal range. An inhalation of an aerosol of histamine caused bronchoconstriction in these patients with tachypnoea, alveolar hyperventilation, and dyspnoea. After either type of anesthetic block the degree of bronchoconstriction following the inhalation of histamine was of the same magnitude, but now there were no changes in ventilation. Dyspnoea was absent, but a sense of excessive resistance to breathing remained. This is the first good evidence that the typical ventilatory reactions of an asthmatic are mediated by vagal afferents; the trigger may be somewhere on the surface of the airways and here it can be blocked by an anesthetic aerosol. This provocative paper badly needs confirmation. It is clearly important to ensure the maximum parasympathetic efferent block possible before administration of an anesthetic block; this was unfortunately not done in a subsequent study (32). The activation of superficial irritant airway receptors (74) may well be the mechanism underlying this vagal "drive to breathe" in asthma, but the gross abnormality in stretch receptor discharge during an asthmatic paroxysm may also contribute. Vagal reflex hyperpnoea during anaphylactic reactions in the rabbit has been studied and irritant airway receptors have been implicated (58); the appropriateness of this animal model to human asthma is unknown.

Lung inflammation has been induced unilaterally in the rabbit and cat by the instillation of a 1% solution of carageenin (96). The evolution of the alveolar lesion resembles that found in pneumonia in man, with the notable exceptions of an absence of pleurisy and of fibrin deposition within the alveoli. The animals are tachypnoeic and there is alveolar hyperventilation that can hardly be accounted for by a mild degree of hypoxia. The hyperpnoea depends on the integrity of the vagus nerve ipsilateral to the side of the lesion. The evidence from differential blocking studies (anodal hyperpolarization) suggests that the fibers mediating this vagal "drive to breathe" are nonmyelinated, presumably associated with the Type J receptors in the alveolar walls. The appropriateness of this model to human pneumonia may well be questioned. Hyperpnoea, tachypnoea, and dyspnoea are prominent in clinical pneumonia even when the lesion is unilateral at an early stage and hyperoxia is maintained.

Pulmonary microembolism has been produced in rabbits by the intravenous injection of 50 μm inert microspheres (49). A vagally mediated tachypnoea and alveolar hyperventilation results, while hyperoxia can be maintained. This ventilatory reaction has also been shown to depend on the integrity of nonmyelinated vagal fibers. Clinical pulmonary microembolism involves release of chemicals from platelets in clots; this is quite different from the experimental model that has been studied. Nevertheless in the clinical situation tachypnoea, alveolar hyperventilation, and dyspnoea are prominent features.

Animal models for human disease are acceptable only if they do not leave the investigator satisfied that the human problems are solved! There is no substitute for direct experiments in man, but the paucity and poverty of methods applicable to man are holding back this branch of medicine and physiology.

CHEMICAL REGULATION OF BREATHING

This subject continues to be the "hot" favorite with investigators. Much of the stimulus continues to come from the attempt at understanding mechanisms of acclimatization to altitude, but a new and wholly welcome clinical orientation to the subject has appeared.

Regulation by CO_2

The last few years have seen an explosion of interest in the assessment of the ventilatory response to inhaled CO_2 using the non-steady-state rebreathing method of Read (83). The subject rebreathes from a bag containing 6–7% CO_2 in O_2; the average rate of rise of PA_{CO_2} is 4–6 mm Hg/min, and the presence of hyperoxia throughout the test probably diminishes or even nullifies the contribution of the arterial chemoreceptors to the response. The method has become popular because it is both simpler and quicker to perform than the classical steady state method. A shift to the right of the linear response curve relating PA_{CO_2} to $\dot{V}_E$ is inherent in the method, but the slope of the response curve is very similar to that obtained in the same subjects with the classical method. Linton et al (68) have recently confirmed this, but give an important warning: normal subjects were made acidotic with the administration of ammonium chloride and alkalotic with sodium bicarbonate. Entirely opposite effects on the slope of the response curve and intercept on the PA_{CO_2} axis were found, depending on which method was used! Some authors have found good reproducibility of the rebreathing method in the same subjects (85, 86, 95), but others have not been so fortunate (1, 53).

The enormous differences between different subjects in their ventilatory response to inhaled CO_2 was documented by Schaeffer (89). More recently (86), the range of normal responses using the rebreathing method has been extended from a low point of 0.57 liter min^{-1} mm Hg^{-1} to a high point of 8.17 liter min^{-1} mm Hg^{-1}. A long distance runner was found to have the lowest sensitivity, whereas a sprinter was found to have high sensitivity; no claim was made that this would be generally true for long distance runners or sprinters. Others have claimed (19) that athletes have low sensitivities to inhaled CO_2.

The factors responsible for this enormous variability in sensitivity to CO_2 are not understood, but some fascinating correlations have been suggested. The most striking correlation has been a positive one with vital capacity (72); the same authors did not find any correlation with age or sex. The sensitivity has been found to be less among 12 Enga tribesmen of New Guinea than among 27 Caucasians living in New Guinea and reasonably well matched (5); the claim for a racial variation in sensitivity was made, but this would seem to require validation in many more subjects. The existence of genetic differences in the ventilatory response to inhaled CO_2 has been elegantly examined by Arkinstall et al (1). These authors compared the response to 3 different levels of CO_2 inhalation in mono- and dizygotic twins. No difference was found for the response in f but the intrapair variance for V_T was much greater for dizygotic than for monozygotic twins, suggesting the operation of a genetic factor.

An extraordinary development in this field has been that respiratory physiologists have ventured into the psychological arena! Clark & Cochrane (22) examined a group of patients with chronic airway obstruction; some had a much lower mixed venous CO_2 than would have been predicted from their measured degree of airway obstruction. This subgroup presumably maintained a high ventilatory sensitivity to CO_2. A personality assessment of the entire group of patients using an Eysenk Personality Inventory showed that those patients with a high score for extraversion were generally the ones who kept high sensitivity to CO_2. This has been confirmed (88) for women, but not for men, in normal subjects whose ventilatory sensitivity to CO_2 was measured with the rebreathing technique. It is of interest that the correlation was with the extraversion score and not with the neuroticism score. A third group (1) has again confirmed this relationship of CO_2 sensitivity with extraversion index, but thought that it applied equally to men and women. These papers may well herald a new discipline of psychorespiratory physiology.

The clinical problem of why some patients with chronic obstructive airway disease develop CO_2 retention with low sensitivity to CO_2 and others maintain a high sensitivity to CO_2 with normal or near normal values for Pa_{CO_2} underlies much of this interest in variability of CO_2 response. This clinical question has never been answered, and the studies cited raise the question of whether normal individuals with a low sensitivity to CO_2 are the ones who will develop CO_2 retention when they develop airway obstruction. The question will only be answered with the techniques of the epidemiologist using longitudinal studies over many years in a large, initially healthy population.

In a small group of 11 laboratory normals, the sensitivity to inhaled CO_2 correlated highly and very significantly with the exercise ventilation expressed per unit CO_2 output or per unit O_2 uptake (84). This very important paper needs confirmation on larger numbers of individuals. It has a direct bearing on the quantitative role of chemical stimuli in ventilation on exercise. Another interesting relationship has emerged in hyperthyroidism (33). With each patient acting as his own control after treatment, the slope of CO_2 response curve has been shown to be increased with hyperthyroidism due to increased respiratory frequency.

The classical steady state CO_2 response curve recently had one significant provocative comment (39). An exponential relationship between $\dot{V}_E$ and PA_{CO_2} has been found to fit the observed data much better than a linear relationship.

The Role of Cerebrospinal Fluid (CSF) pH

The view that extracellular pH of the brain is a most important determinant of $\dot{V}_E$ in man has not been questioned in the last few years. Two excellent reviews have appeared (70, 91) on the acid-base status of CSF. Both concluded that homeostasis of CSF pH is only present during peturbations of a metabolic nature and not of a respiratory nature. The reasons for this are entirely speculative. It has taken many years to reach this conclusion partly because of the great difficulties in measuring pH accurately in a relatively buffer-free fluid as CSF, and also because of the belated realization that there are significant differences in pH and P_{CO_2} of lumbar and cisternal fluid (79, 98). The fullest definition of this problem in man, acutely ill but in a metabolically steady state, has recently appeared (80). Lumbar CSF was more acid by 0.039 ± 0.344 pH units than cisternal CSF; the HCO_3^- concentrations were similar and the P_{CO_2} in the cisternal fluid was 3.8 ± 5.2 mm Hg higher than in lumbar CSF.

The problem of the mechanism of acclimatization to altitude has involved a great deal of controversy about how HCO_3^- in the CSF falls to compensate for the alkaline change consequent upon acute hypoxic hypocapnoea with removal from sea level to altitude (see 74a). Sφrensen & Milledge (93) studied high altitude natives at 4300 m with minimal or absent hypoxic drive (see below). They were hyperventilating with a mean Pa_{CO_2} of 33 mm Hg, and lumbar spinal fluid was found to have a mean pH of 7.295; this was 0.02 units less than the mean of sea level natives. The previously current view that CSF pH regulation was perfect under these altitude conditions was thus reversed. The CSF lactate was found to be on average 1 mM higher than at sea level and the HCO_3^- was 4–5 mM lower. The authors concluded that increased cerebral anaerobiosis had brought the pH down and that this was responsible for the maintained hyperventilation in the absence of a hypoxic drive. The explanation given for the lack of stoichiometric relationship between the rise of lactate and fall of HCO_3^- is, in my view, unconvincing.

Different results have been presented subsequently (15) in high altitude natives at 3800 m. Cisternal CSF was sampled, and a mean level of 7.36 pH units found. The authors did not compare these measurements with those obtained from sea level natives. The patients were chronically hyperventilating and the CSF HCO_3^- was reduced; CSF lactate was 1.85 mM and serum lactate was 1.14 mM on average. The authors concluded that HCO_3^- decrease in the CSF under these conditions occurs without any evidence of brain anaerobiosis.

Very recently (29) a study was made of the spinal fluid during ventilatory acclimatization to moderate hypoxia of sea level natives at 3100 m with a Pa_{O_2} of 50–60 mm Hg. At 8 hr after being brought to altitude, Pa_{CO_2} had fallen, but after 3–4 weeks hyperventilation was much greater, Pa_{CO_2} lower, and Pa_{O_2} higher than at 8 hr. Lumbar CSF became alkaline. Thus all known chemical factors in breathing would act to depress ventilation and yet ventilation gradually increased. There was no evidence of any precise CSF HCO_3^- regulation. Chronic exposure to mild hypoxia had caused an "extra" input into the regulatory system for ventilation! This enigmatic conclusion in 1974 means that this subject remains wide open for further investigation.

Respiratory Response to Metabolic Acid-Base Changes

The ventilatory response to chronic metabolic acid-base changes has been quantitated in elegant studies that have used the opportunities provided by patients on maintenance haemodialysis (99, 100). The degree of uraemic acidosis could be varied easily at each dialysis; a degree of alkalosis with elevation of HCO_3^- concentration could be obtained by increasing acetate concentration in the dialysate. The advantages of this type of study were that stable HCO_3^- levels were achieved that could not be altered by the patients' own kidneys; furthermore, alkalosis and acidosis were obtained with a net negative or positive H^+ balance. Pa_{CO_2} was found to be a linear function of HCO_3^- in both acidosis and alkalosis. The slope of the relationship was the same in each subject; 1 mM fall in HCO_3^- resulted in a 1.2 mm Hg fall in Pa_{CO_2}, whereas a 1 mM rise in HCO_3^- resulted in an 0.9 mm Hg rise in Pa_{CO_2}. Each subject's slope had its own intercept so that at a HCO_3^- level of 17.2 mM, Pa_{CO_2} ranged from 28.3 to 35.2 mm Hg, whereas at a HCO_3^- level of 26.6 mM, Pa_{CO_2} ranged from 36.6 to 42.6 mm Hg. At the highest HCO_3^- level of 37.5 mM, Pa_{CO_2} could reach 50 mm Hg. Lest it be thought that these results are only applicable to uremia, a similar study has recently been done (40) in patients with diabetic ketoacidosis; very similar equations relating Pa_{CO_2} to HCO_3^- were obtained, and the degree of acidosis studied was taken as far down as an arterial pH of 6.8 without change in the linearity of the relationship.

It would be fascinating to know if the individual differences in sensitivity of ventilation to metabolic acid-base change, expressed by the differences in intercept, correlate in any way with the individual's sensitivity to the inhalation of CO_2.

Arterial Chemoreceptor Function

There is still general agreement that hypoxia stimulates breathing in man primarily by an action on the arterial chemoreceptors. There is also a modicum of agreement that a certain fraction of the ventilatory stimulation by CO_2 arises from these same chemoreceptors, but this depends on the prevailing Pa_{O_2}; hypoxia exaggerates the response.

Two informative reviews (90, 92) have been published, and the subject has been discussed as part of a symposium (82). Since the ventilatory response to hypoxia is not a linear function of the degree of hypoxia, there has been considerable argument about how best to quantitate a response that also interacts strikingly with the degree of CO_2 stimulation. The subject badly needs agreement among workers in this field. Some authors continue to use a steady state CO_2 response curve at high and low levels of Pa_{O_2} (69); the change in slope and position of the response curve is used as a measure of sensitivity to hypoxia. More recently Weil et al (103) discussed the problems with this method, and described a non-steady-state method. This consists of breathing from a bag containing enough oxygen to result in PA_{O_2} values of approximately 120 mm Hg. N_2 is then slowly added to the bag so that PA_{O_2} slowly falls down to levels just below 40 mm Hg. Any fall of PA_{CO_2} due to hyperventilation was prevented by the addition of CO_2 to the inspired gas. The use of the non-steady state is justified primarily because of the finding that the phase lag between a sudden change in PA_{O_2} and the ventilatory response is of the order of 25 sec. A curvilinear hyperbolic relationship between PA_{O_2} and $\dot{V}_E$ was found, with $\dot{V}_E$ becoming infinite at an asymptotic PA_{O_2} of 32 mm Hg; each curve was derived from 100–150 data points. A simple shape parameter A derived from the equation for a hyperbola was used to quantitate hypoxic sensitivity; the closeness of fit to the data of this sort of equation was excellent. The reproducibility in an individual was good and response interaction with a ±5 mm Hg change in PA_{CO_2} could be easily demonstrated. The authors suggested that $\dot{V}_E$ appeared to be a linear function of the oxygen content of hemoglobin. The problem of methodology in testing for hypoxic sensitivity has been further studied by Kronenberg et al (61), who compared different methods and introduced the idea that ventilatory response to hypoxia may be a logarithmic function of the stimulus.

Transients of hyperoxia and hypoxia achieved by the inhalation of 1 or 2 breaths of O_2 or N_2, as pioneered by Dejours (27), continue to be used in the assessment of chemoreceptor function.

The physiology of the carotid body has received a great deal of attention in the last few years, and an excellent review has been published (12). Not everyone would agree with the author's conclusion that these bodies have little relevance to sea level breathing. Two studies have recently appeared on the ventilatory effects of carotid body removal in man. Wade et al (101) reported on 7 patients studied before and 3–38 days after bilateral carotid endarterectomy involving the area of the bifurcation of the common carotid artery. Hypoxic sensitivity was tested with the steady state CO_2 response curve at high and low P_{AO_2} tensions. Sensitivity to hypoxia present in all subjects before surgery was abolished after surgery; in some patients hypoxia after surgery depressed the ventilatory response. The average resting P_{ACO_2} breathing air rose from 38.9 mm Hg before to 44.7 mm Hg after surgery. The authors concluded (*a*) that aortic bodies did not seem to play a significant role in the ventilatory response to hypoxia, and (*b*) that the carotid bodies were responsible for approximately 13% of the "drive to breathe" at rest.

The only difficulties of interpretation with this study arise from the certain removal of carotid baroreceptor function and also the possible increase in total cerebral blood flow consequent upon the corrective surgery. Lugliani et al (71) studied 7 patients with asthma who had had a selective destruction of both carotid bodies (with preservation of baroreceptor function) some 2 weeks to 8 years previously. At the time of study these patients had only minimal evidence of airway obstruction. Their sensitivity to hypoxia was studied in the steady state, breathing air or 12% O_2, both at rest and at exercise mild enough (not greater than 306 kg m • min^{-1}) to insure the absence of any metabolic acidosis. P_{ACO_2} was allowed to fall if ventilation increased. The ventilatory responses to hypoxia, and also to the inhalation of 5% CO_2, were compared with those obtained in control groups of comparable asthmatics and normals. The ventilatory response to hypoxia down to a Pa_{O_2} of 36 mm Hg was abolished both at rest and during exercise by the surgical procedure. There was no difference between the patient and the control group in the average Pa_{CO_2} while breathing air at rest and during exercise. The inhalation of 5% CO_2 in air resulted in a ventilatory response approximately 70% of that found in the control groups. The authors concluded that though 30% of the ventilatory response to the elevation of Pa_{CO_2} with normoxia originated from carotid body stimulation, there was little evidence that these structures contributed to ventilatory drive at rest or during mild exercise while breathing air. The importance of this study lies in the fact that the change in function studied is confined to the carotid bodies. The difficulties of interpretation lie in the absence of data before and after the surgical procedure in each subject. Individual variability of the ventilatory response to CO_2 and hypoxia is of sufficient magnitude to cause doubts about the significance of group studies.

The blunted ventilatory response to hypoxia in high altitude natives and in patients with cyanotic congenital heart disease continues to excite great interest. Edelman et al (31) used an unconventional form of the transient hypoxia test by plotting change in arterial O_2 saturation obtained by an ear oximeter against the associated maximum change in ventilation. Remarkably linear plots were obtained, and patients with cyanotic congenital heart disease clearly had a blunted response. The greatest interest of this paper lies in studies before and after corrective surgery in 2 of the subjects. After relief of cyanosis, these 2 subjects had a normal response to hypoxia. The authors give an excellent discussion justifying their unconventional methodology in a clinical setting. Their results differ from an earlier opinion (94) that respiratory insensitivity to hypoxia remains in such subjects even after adequate surgery; 5 such subjects were studied only after surgery, with steady state CO_2 response curves at low and high PA_{O_2}.

A question at issue is whether this blunted sensitivity requires hypoxia in early life or whether it results from severe prolonged hypoxia. Previous workers have even suggested the possibility of a genetic abnormality in sensitivity to hypoxia present in closely inbred high altitude natives. Two important recent contributions suggest that the crucial factor is time spent in a hypoxic environment. The response of children aged 9–10 yr, native to high altitude, was studied by measuring parameter *A* in the non-steady-state test (18). The response was found to be entirely normal as compared to that obtained in children of the same age living in a nonhypoxic environment. Individuals who moved to high altitude in adult life have been studied by the same technique after 5, 10, and 20 yr residence in the hypoxic environment (102). A decrease in sensitivity to hypoxia was related to length of exposure to high altitude conditions, being just measurable at 5 yr, partial at 10 yr, and complete at 20 yr. These results were obtained at rest, but on submaximal exercise no depression of sensitivity could be found. The authors concluded that either the arterial chemoreceptors are irrelevant to hypoxia during exercise or depressed chemoreceptor function can be activated by exercise. It would seem likely that a metabolic acidosis was present during submaximal exercise at high altitude, and if so then the interpretation of the augmenting effect of exercise becomes difficult. Lahiri et al (62) have confirmed that exercise enhances the blunted ventilatory response to hypoxia of Sherpa high altitude natives.

It has been known for some time (27) that a potentiation of chemoreceptor hypoxic drive occurs with mild exercise; this can be demonstrated with the transient hyperoxic test. Bhattacharya et al (9) examined this problem using steady state CO_2 conditions. When PA_{CO_2} was near the CO_2 threshold, light exercise on a bicycle ergometer strikingly increased ventilation when mild hypoxia was present; there was no metabolic acidosis. This effect of exercise was more difficult to demonstrate when PA_{CO_2} was higher. Further support for this augmentation of peripheral chemosensitivity during mild exercise has come from the non-steady-state hypoxia technique at constant PA_{CO_2} with measurement of parameter *A* (104). Subjects were exercised up to an approximate O_2 uptake of 1 liter/min. Parameter *A* increased dramatically, documenting the fact that the response curves were both steeper and displaced upwards. The authors critically discussed their use of parameter *A* in these experiments; the O_2 asymptote of 32 mm Hg was only true for resting conditions and changed with exercise. If the asymptote of 32 was changed to fit the facts then parameter *A* ceased to be a descriptive shape factor. The excellent fit of the equations justifies the use of a constant O_2 asymptote. The results suggest that exercise is a variable gain controller; the startling conclusion may be that a PA_{O_2} as high as 100 mm Hg may provide a "hypoxic" drive during exercise that results in O_2 uptake of 1 liter/min and may be responsible for 59% of the ventilation! If this is confirmed and accepted, then search for chemical regulators to account for exercise hyperpnoea may be over. Before this happy day it will be necessary to study the exercise response of many more subjects with denervated arterial chemoreceptors.

With removal (71) or acquired attentuation (102) of chemoreceptor function there does seem to be a reduction in the ventilatory sensitivity to inhaled CO_2 at least under normoxic or hypoxic conditions. In the latter study (102) the sensitivity to a slowly increasing Pa_{CO_2} under the isoxic condition of a PA_{O_2} of 70 mm Hg was halved with the loss of hypoxic sensitivity after 20 yr residence at high altitude. This confirms the findings by Chiodi (20) in the original description of the blunted hypoxic and hypercapnoeic responses in long term high altitude dwellers. Even at sea level a high degree of correlation has been described between the ventilatory responses to hypoxia and hypercapnoea (85). The non-steady-state method for hypoxic stimulation with estimation of parameter *A* was used, as was the hyperoxic CO_2 rebreathing method. Parameter *A* ranged between 48 and 270 liters mm Hg P_{O_2}/min, and the slope of CO_2 sensitivity ranged from 1.17 to 3.11 liters min^{-1} mm Hg^{-1}. A linear fit was found to best relate these data from 11 normal subjects, and a correlation coefficient of 0.76 was obtained, which was significant at the 0.01 level. In addition, an inverse trend was found between the mixed venous P_{CO_2} and hypoxic and hypercapoeic sensitivity. The significance of this relationship is not clear. The hyperoxia present during the CO_2 response will have diminished the contribution of arterial chemoreceptors. If investigators are looking for individual differences in arterial chemoreceptor sensitivity, then it would seem essential to document CO_2 sensitivity under mildly hypoxic isoxic conditions. It is of interest that this has been done in athletes (19), where strikingly low sensitivities to both hypoxia (parameter *A*) and hypercapnoea have been found. The authors suggested that their athletes had reduced arterial chemoreceptor function. It is to be hoped that these athletes did not include sprinters (86)!

The effect of CO_2 transients, particularly in relation to arterial chemoreceptor function, has been as intensively studied in the 1970s as O_2 transients had been studied in the 1960s. All studies in man on the effect of the inhalation of 1 or 2 breaths of a high concentration of CO_2 in air are based on the study by Bouverot et al (16) in the conscious dog; the inhalation of 1–2 breaths of 7% CO_2 in air caused a transient hyperventilation after 10–15 sec; this did not occur when the animal was either surgically chemodenervated or hyperoxic. It has not proved easy to do this experiment in man. A 2-breath 20% CO_2 test has been described (65–67). The sensitivity of the transient ventilatory response is greater at a low PA_{O_2} and less, but significantly present, at high PA_{O_2}. A recent study (64) has claimed that it is possible to describe curvilinear chemoreflex ventilatory response curves to CO_2. 2–3 breaths of varying concentrations of CO_2 in either air or O_2 are taken, and the early ventilatory response within 15–20 sec can then be related to the PA_{CO_2}. The response with CO_2 in O_2 is grossly diminished, and this fact, together with the time of occurrence of the response, has led the authors to the view that they are recording a true arterial chemoreflex ventilatory response. It is of interest that native highlanders with chronic mountain sickness and insensitivity to hypoxia also had virtually no CO_2 chemoreflex response.

Another group (30) also studied ventilatory responses to transient hypoxia and hypercapnoea. The magnitude of the peripheral chemoreflex response to CO_2 was about 30% of the steady state response to CO_2; this agrees exactly with the results of Lugliani et al (71). However, the authors found little enhancement of the transient hypercapnoeic response by hypoxia, although there was major enhancement of the steady state response to CO_2. These data force the authors to conclude that the interaction between hypoxia and hypercapnoea is central. Do neural impulses from arterial chemoreceptors increase the general activity of medullary respiratory neurones? This fascinating question requires examination in surgically chemodenervated man. Some support for this concept comes from the study of Gelford & Lambertsen (41), who abruptly added and removed 6% CO_2 from the inspired gas in one intensively studied subject. Breath by breath analysis showed reproducible dynamic response characteristics. An early response was documented of 6 sec onset lag and 5 sec time constant of development; this was about 12% of the total ventilatory response, and the magnitude was considerably reduced by raising PA_{O_2}. Two further components of the response were then identified of 20 sec onset lag with time constants of 10 and 89 sec; both were of equal magnitude, 44%, and the component with the more rapid time constant was substantially reduced in magnitude by raising PA_{O_2}. The authors thought that the early component of the response arose from arterial chemoreceptors, and the effect of O_2 breathing supported this. The delayed components were thought to be of central origin; the effect of O_2 breathing on one of these components was surprising, but suggested that O_2 can suppress central nervous system receptors. This provocative work requires physiological dissection in an animal that shows the same phenomenon.

Arterial chemoreceptor function in man has recently been studied with considerable elegance by changing the magnitude and time profile of breath to breath oscillations of PA_{CO_2} and hence Pa_{CO_2}. The human studies follow upon the basic paper of Black & Torrance (14). These workers injected pulses of saline equilibrated with hypoxic or hypercapnoeic gas mixtures close to the carotid body in the cat; they monitored induced afferent activity in the sinus nerve and the evoked respiratory activity from single phrenic efferents. The afferent response to a hypoxic stimulus was slow and did not adapt, whereas, by contrast, the response to a hypercapnoeic stimulus was fast. The efferent response entirely depended on the phase of breathing at which the burst of afferent impulses was set up. During inspiration, excitation augmented that same breath, whereas excitation in early expiration delayed the next inspiration; by contrast, excitation in late expiration brought the next inspiration on earlier than expected. The authors presented a detailed argument suggesting that the amplitude and phase relationships of respiratory oscillations of Pa_{CO_2} are not likely to vary with body size, and hence their results could well be relevant to man. They also pointed out that in exercise a change in phase of these oscillations of Pa_{CO_2} (maximum Pa_{CO_2} earlier in inspiration) with respect to breathing must occur in addition to an increase in magnitude of the oscillations. Here there may be a significant chemical factor in the causation of exercise hyperpnoea. A further paper from the same group critically discussed the evidence that oscillations of CO_2 rather than O_2 are the responsible factors (13).

Ingenious experiments recently have been performed to test the applicability of this animal work to man. Goode et al (43) showed that breathing through a wide tube of dead space 1.4 liters under hypoxic conditions increased ventilation more than would be expected from the prevailing alveolar gas tensions; this was not found with normoxia or hyperoxia. The authors proposed that the effect observed may depend on the abnormal time profile of PA_{CO_2} and hence Pa_{CO_2} presented to arterial chemoreceptors; there was no evidence of any difference in the amplitude of PA_{CO_2} oscillations. Subsequently, the effect of imposing alternate breath oscillations of PA_{CO_2} has been studied (73). CO_2-free and CO_2-rich gas alternated so that PA_{CO_2} changed by 10 mm Hg with each breath; the studies were done with PA_{O_2} held constant at either 55–65 mm Hg or 550 mm Hg. The increase in amplitude of Pa_{CO_2} oscillations produced a breath by breath response only with sensitization by hypoxia. Alternate larger and smaller breaths cancelled out to produce no net effect on $\dot{V}_E$. The experiment had changed the amplitude of Pa_{CO_2} oscillations without a change of phase with respect to the breathing cycle.

A further most elegant study of changing the phase relationship alone has again utilized tube breathing (23). The addition of a loop to the tube distorted the time profile of PA_{CO_2} and little else. Removal of the loop increased ventilation at any PA_{CO_2}, but this occurred only in the presence of hypoxia. The tube and loop situation was simulated with a programmed series of electromagnetically operated lightweight valves. It was shown that inspiring CO_2-free gas late in inspiration resulted in $\dot{V}_E$ that was on average 20% greater than that resulting from inspiring CO_2-free gas early in inspiration. This could only be clearly demonstrated on a background of hypoxia. The simulation experiments were repeated so that O_2 could be varied in the same way, but no effect on $\dot{V}_E$ was seen. This tour de force of an experiment has clearly demonstrated that the respiratory system of man can discriminate between small differences in time patterns of PA_{CO_2}, but not of PA_{O_2}, in the presence of mild hypoxia. A review paper in this field has been published (24).

THE NEUROGENIC COMPONENT OF EXERCISE HYPERPNOEA

A neurogenic nonchemical component of breathing regulation during exercise has been invoked to account for the fast transitions in ventilation from rest to exercise and again on return to rest; the nature of this neurogenic component has been discussed at length (28). In the last few years this concept has been both attacked and defended. Beaver & Wasserman (3) found inconsistent abrupt changes in $\dot{V}_E$ at the onset and cessation of exercise. Subsequently (4) these authors repeated these studies using time averaging for 2 min and 0.5 min exercise periods. The subjects were blindfolded and instructed by verbal command; the ergometer flywheel was kept at 60 rpm before exercise commenced so that no extra work on the part of the subject was involved at the onset of work. V_T and f often changed reciprocally and differently at the onset and cessation of work. An individual's responses were, however, consistent for both exercise periods. The authors concluded that the so-called neurogenic component of the ventilatory response of exercise was due to learned responses and was not a fundamental part of the control mechanism.

The debate has continued along various lines. Jensen et al (56) tried to analyze whether conditioned or learned responses existed by studying the effect of 4 different (visual, audible, and audiovisual) combinations to start exercise. The ventilation of the first respiratory cycle was measured as the response, and this invariably increased irrespective of the type of command. In a subsequent paper the same authors (57) used a visual signal to start a variable delay triggered by a respiratory cycle to then give the command to work. This procedure enabled these workers to record the ventilatory response to work initiated at various times of the respiratory cycle. An onset of work during the first half of inspiration or expiration increased the mean flow rate in that phase of the cycle. The response in the breath that overlapped the onset of work diminished progressively the later the start of the work. The ventilation of the first complete breath after the onset of work was always increased. The total response time was, therefore, less than the duration of half a breath. These authors feel that the concept of the neural component has been defended. They are strongly supported by D'Angelo & Torelli (26), who used treadmill exercise on the level or with an uphill gradient. They documented sudden transients of $\dot{V}_E$ at the onset and cessation of work and found that the magnitude of this response was related to the intensity of the exercise; PA_{CO_2} fell by 3–4 mm Hg at the onset of work. The magnitude of the response was found to be independent of the basal PA_{CO_2} before the start of work; this was deliberately varied by breathing CO_2 mixtures. The authors concluded that at low intensity of work on the level, nearly all the ventilatory response is neurogenic, whereas with more intense uphill work, 60–70% may be neurogenic. Farber & Bedell (35) also found a neurogenic component, starting and stopping their subjects with a verbal command. These authors could find no correlation between the magnitude of this component and the individual subject's ventilatory sensitivity to CO_2.

Wigertz and his colleagues (17, 105, 106) adopted a systems analysis approach to this problem. The work load on a bicycle ergometer has been forced through sine wave, step, and ramp functions from zero work load through to a maximum of 1300 kg m • min^{-1}. Harmonic analysis of the ventilatory response showed a clear preponderance of the fundamental, over the second and third harmonics, and the system was therefore thought to be approximately linear. The mean ventilatory response to sinusoidal work was a first order transfer function with a time constant of 70 $\pm$ 6 sec. The mean ventilatory response to a step function from 300 to 950 kg m • min^{-1} was a monoexponential with a similar time constant. Under these experimental conditions, therefore, no abrupt components were seen. The authors did find abrupt components with step functions from the motionless resting state; they tended to view these as conditioned reflexes.

Fujihara et al (37, 38) have come to a different conclusion using a very similar approach. Impulse, step, and ramp functions were applied above a basal load of 200 kg m • min^{-1}. The linearity of the system was again tested (with superposition) and found to apply within limits. To an impulse function, an abrupt component of the ventilatory response was found amounting to 16% of the total response; the remaining major part of the response was delayed by an average of 20 sec. The authors characterized the transfer function between $\dot{V}_E$ and work load as two low-pass filters: one amounting to 16% of the response and having a time constant of less than 2–3 sec, and the major component having a time constant of 17 sec. The first and second component may merge during a step function so that the smoothly rising response described by Beaver & Wasserman (4) could result. The significant conclusion, however, is that in most subjects 85% of the response arises after a lag sufficiently long to permit muscle metabolites to arrive at arterial chemoreceptors or the medulla. A further contribution to this endless controversy, which clearly depends so much on the precise experimental situation, has been provided in a thoughtful paper by Asmussen (2). His subjects were told to start exercising from rest, but no commands were given and they could commence to work when they wished. An abrupt response was documented. Its magnitude was proportional to the intensity of work; movement of the legs was necessary and the amplitude of the abrupt component depended on the frequency of this movement; there was no abrupt component with isometric work. P_{ACO_2} usually fell 2–3 mm Hg during the abrupt response. If work began while the subject inhaled 5% CO_2 in air or 11% O_2 in nitrogen, then the amplitude of the abrupt component was greater. Previous voluntary hyperventilation with pure O_2 abolished the abrupt component in 4 subjects. All these facts about the abrupt component that occurs in less than 15–20 sec suggested to the author that what is being called the abrupt neurogenic component is essentially a sensitizing effect to the prevailing chemical stimulus at arterial chemoreceptors.

It does not seem as though this question of the existence and meaning of a neurogenic component can be solved with present methods.

RESPIRATORY FREQUENCY AND DEPTH OF BREATHING

The breaking up of $\dot{V}_E$ into its two components, f and V_T, is a belated recent innovation. Fencl (36) made a plea for the separate examination of the behavior of these components. He proposed that at any instant, the central regulator can only determine the depth of the next breath and how soon it should come. This plea is wholly welcome because, with many papers on the control of breathing, it is quite impossible for the reader to analyze the problem in these terms, since the relevant facts are not given even though they must almost certainly have been recorded.

Interest in this subject has gradually increased over the last 8 yr, particularly in Europe. Hey et al (52) pointed out that the relationship between $\dot{V}_E$ and V_T was essentially linear up to a V_T equal to about half the vital capacity; with further increases in $\dot{V}_E$, V_T remained constant. The relationship was unaltered by wide variations in PA_{CO_2}, PA_{O_2}, metabolic acidaemia, and moderate muscular exercise. A rise in body temperature, however, increased f for any given $\dot{V}_E$; this has recently been confirmed (107). The same relationship has been further analyzed by Pearson & Cunningham (76), who pointed out that the relationship only applies to the mean values obtained during a steady state; on and off transients of chemical stimulation change V_T at constant f, and moment to moment V_T and f may vary reciprocally. Kelman & Watson (60) have not found this unique relationship between $\dot{V}_E$ and V_T in recent studies during submaximal steady state exercise when conditions were changed by altering the amount of dead space.

At the time of the original paper by Hey et al (52), it was shown (47) that bilateral block of the vagus and glossopharyngeal nerves in man diminish the ventilatory response to CO_2; this is due to a failure of f to rise as PA_{CO_2} rises. Abolition of vagal conduction was thought to be responsible primarily because similar results could be obtained in other species with vagal section alone. This data in man was subsequently put into the form of a $\dot{V}_E/V_T$ relationship (50); it became clear that with vagal block, f was less and V_T more at any given level of $\dot{V}_E$. A likely explanation for this seemed to be that pulmonary stretch receptors were responsible for the adjustment of the pattern of breathing in man during hyperpnoea.

von Euler and his colleagues (21, 34) have used a new type of analysis of V_T and f to analyze neural control mechanisms, and they have also shown how the $\dot{V}_E/V_T$ relationship described above (52) can be used for the same purpose. A basic paper (34) in the anesthetized cat first showed that with intact vagi, the $\dot{V}_E/V_T$ relationship was similar to that found in man in response to CO_2, and that after vagotomy the relationship moved to an isofrequency line. The slope of the $\dot{V}_E/V_T$ relationship increased with an increase of body temperature irrespective of whether the vagi were cut or intact, and this suggested two f controllers, a bulbopontine mechanism (stimulated by body temperature rise), and a vagal mechanism in response to CO_2.

A much more controversial paper from the same group (21) has attempted to define the relationship between the depth of a breath and the duration of the inspiratory and expiratory phases during CO_2 breathing, both in cat and man. Inflation pulses of 200–400 msec duration with a rounded wave shape were superimposed on a normal breath in the cat; the volume needed to terminate inspiration decreased with the time at which the pulse was put in during the inspiratory phase, and this was called the Hering-Breuer "threshold." The inspiratory duration (T_I) decreased as V_T increased, and the relationship was hyperbolic in nature. A similar relationship was found between V_T and T_I during a hyperoxic CO_2 response curve, though with some differences in the constants of the hyperbola. After vagotomy, T_I remained constant with changes of V_T induced either by pulses or by elevating CO_2. The authors concluded that as the rate of inspiration increases with elevation of CO_2, the breath will reach the Hering-Breuer threshold curve earlier in inspiration and therefore will terminate that inspiration earlier. It was also found that expiratory time (T_E) was linearly related to T_I. These facts then provided some insight into why an increase in respiratory frequency necessarily accomplished an increase in V_T, but it should be noted that the explanation critically depends on the existence of a Hering-Breuer "threshold" during inspiration in the cat, and also the decrease of this threshold with time.

Do volume pulses test stretch receptors or other receptors as well? The very existence of a threshold is the subject of intense investigation. The derivation of the von Euler V_T/T_I relationship in the cat has been quoted in depth because authors in the same paper proceed to look at man when V_T is changed during a hyperoxic CO_2 response curve. They instructed their subjects to hyperventilate prior to each test to reduce respiratory drive and allow the test to begin at low V_T. They found that T_I was constant up to 1.5–2 times eupnoeic values (1.2–2.2 liters), and then fell as a hyperbolic function of V_T. In some studies, at V_T levels above 2.8 liters, an inspiratory augmenting effect was seen, with V_T and T_I both increasing. The authors consider that the V_T at which the hyperbolic relationship with T_I begins is comparable to that volume above the functional residual capacity at which a Hering-Breuer inflation reflex can be demonstrated. Below this volume man appears to be "vagotomized." This would certainly fit with the studies described in the first section of this review. A pertinent criticism of the human studies is that although 30 rebreathing experiments were done in 7 adult males, the paper only gives two typical examples in the results. No information is given about reproducibility of results. The authors concluded that the differences between cat and man are quantitative rather than qualitative.

Cunningham & Gardner (25) found that T_I remains constant, whereas T_E shortens during steady state CO_2 inhalation with and without mild hypoxia; V_T did not exceed 1.5 liters.

It would seem that use of the $\dot{V}_E/V_T$ or V_T/T_I plots may be of value in defining problems in the regulation of breathing and may even help in their experimental solution. It should not be forgotten that the exciting stimulus, Pa_{CO_2}, Pa_{O_2}, work load, etc, does not appear in these plots, and a recent tendency to present results only in this form is to be deplored.

Literature Cited

1. Arkinstall, W. W., Nirmel, K., Klissouras, V., Milic-Emili, J. 1974. Genetic differences in the ventilatory response to inhaled CO_2. *J. Appl. Physiol.* 36:6–11
2. Asmussen, E. 1973. Ventilation at transition from rest to exercise. *Acta Physiol. Scand.* 89:68–78
3. Beaver, W. L., Wasserman, K. 1968. Transients in ventilation at start and end of exercise. *J. Appl. Physiol.* 25:390–99
4. Beaver, W. L., Wasserman, K. 1970. Tidal volume and respiratory rate changes at start and end of exercise. *J. Appl. Physiol.* 29:872–76
5. Beral, V., Read, D. J. C. 1971. Insensitivity of the respiratory centre to carbon dioxide in Enga people of New Guinea. *Lancet* 2:1290–94
6. Berglund, E., Furhoff, A. K., Löfström, B., Öquist, C. 1971. Effects of unilateral vagus nerve block in a dyspnoeic patient with "unilateral lung disease." *Scand. J. Resp. Dis.* 52:34–38
7. Berkowitz, H., Reichel, J., Shim, C. 1973. The effect of ethanol on the cough reflex. *Clin. Sci. Mol. Med.* 45:527–31
8. Bevan, J. A., Murray, J. F. 1963. Evidence for a ventilation modifying reflex from the pulmonary circulation in man. *Proc. Soc. Exp. Biol. Med.* 114:393–96

9. Bhattacharya, N. K., Cunningham, D. J. C., Goode, R. C., Howson, M. G., Lloyd, B. B. 1970. Hypoxia, ventilation, P_{CO_2}, and exercise. *Resp. Physiol.* 9:329–47
10. Bickerman, H. A., Barach, A. K. 1954. The experimental production of cough in human subjects by citric acid aerosols —Part I. *Am. J. Med. Sci.* 228:156–65
11. Bickerman, H. A., Cohen, B. M., German, E. 1956. The cough response of healthy human subjects induced by citric acid aerosols—Part II. *Am. J. Med. Sci.* 232:57–66
12. Biscoe, T. J. 1971. Carotid body: structure and function. *Physiol. Rev.* 51: 437–95
13. Black, A. M. S., Goodman, N. W., Nail, B. S., Rao, P. S., Torrance, R. W. 1973. The significance of the timing of chemoreceptor impulses for their effect upon respiration. *Acta Neurobiol. Exp.* 33:139–47
14. Black, A. M. S., Torrance, R. W. 1971. Respiratory oscillations in chemoreceptor discharge in the control of breathing. *Resp. Physiol.* 13:221–37
15. Blayo, M. C., Marc-Vergnes, J. P., Pocidalo, J. J. 1973. pH, P_{CO_2}, and P_{O_2} of cisternal cerebrospinal fluid in high altitude natives. *Resp. Physiol.* 19:298–311
16. Bouverot, P., Flandrois, R., Puccinelli, R., Dejours, P. 1965. Etude du rôle des chemorécepteurs artériels dans la régulation de la respiration pulmonaire chez le chien éveillé. *Arch. Int. Pharmacodyn.* 157:253–71
17. Broman, S., Wigertz, O. 1971. Transient dynamics of ventilation and heart rate with step changes in work load from different load levels. *Acta Physiol. Scand.* 81:54–74
18. Byrne-Quinn, E., Sodal, I., Weil, J. V. 1972. Hypoxic and hypercapnic ventilatory drives in children native to high altitude. *J. Appl. Physiol.* 32:44–46
19. Byrne-Quinn, E., Weil, J. V., Sodal, I. E., Filley, G. F., Grover, R. F. 1971. Ventilatory control in the athlete. *J. Appl. Physiol.* 30:91–98
20. Chiodi, H. 1957. Respiratory adaptations to chronic high altitude hypoxia. *J. Clin. Invest.* 10:81–87
21. Clark, F. J., Euler, C. von 1972. On the regulation of depth and rate of breathing. *J. Physiol.* 222:267–95
22. Clark, T. J. H., Cochrane, G. M. 1970. Effect of personality on alveolar ventilation in patients with chronic airways obstruction. *Brit. Med. J.* 1:273–75
23. Cunningham, D. J. C., Howson, M. G., Pearson, S. B. 1973. The respiratory effects in man of altering the time profile of alveolar carbon dioxide and oxygen within each respiratory cycle. *J. Physiol.* 234:1–28
24. Cunningham, D. J. C., Pearson, S. B., Marsh, R. H. K., Kellogg, R. H. 1973. The effects of various time patterns of alveolar CO_2 and O_2 on breathing in man. *Acta Neurobiol. Exp.* 33:123–38
25. Cunningham, D. J. C., Gardner, W. N. 1973. The relation between tidal volume and inspiratory and expiratory times during steady-state CO_2 inhalation in man. *J. Physiol.* 227:50–51P
26. D'Angelo, E., Torelli, G. 1971. Neural stimuli increasing respiration during types of exercise. *J. Appl. Physiol.* 30:116–21
27. Dejours, P. 1962. Chemoreflexes in breathing. *Physiol. Rev.* 42:335–58
28. Dejours, P. 1964. Control of respiration in muscular exercise. *Handb. Physiol.* 1(3):631–48
29. Dempsey, J. A., Forster, H. V., do Pico, G. A. 1974. Ventilatory acclimatization to moderate hypoxemia in man. The role of spinal fluid. *J. Clin. Invest.* 53:1091–1100
30. Edelman, N. H., Epstein, P. E., Lahiri, S., Cherniack, N. S. 1973. Ventilatory responses to transient hypoxia and hypercapnia in man. *Resp. Physiol.* 17:302–14
31. Edelman, N. H., Lahiri, S., Braudo, L., Cherniack, N. S., Fishman, A. P. 1970. The blunted ventilatory response to hypoxia in cyanotic congenital heart disease. *N. Engl. J. Med.* 282:405–11
32. Eisele, J. H., Jain, S. K. 1971. Circulatory and respiratory changes during unilateral and bilateral cranial nerve IX and X block in two asthmatics. *Clin. Sci.* 40:117–25
33. Engel, L. A., Ritchie, B. 1971. Ventilatory response to inhaled carbon dioxide in hyperthyroidism. *J. Appl. Physiol.* 30:173–77
34. Euler, C. von, Herrero, F., Wexler, I. 1970. Control mechanisms determining rate and depth of respiratory movements. *Resp. Physiol.* 10:93–108
35. Farber, J. P., Bedell, G. N. 1973. Responsiveness of breathing control centres to CO_2 and neurogenic stimuli. *Resp. Physiol.* 19:88–95
36. Fencl, V. 1973. Notes on the centrogenic drive in respiration. *Physiologist* 16:589–92

37. Fujihara, Y., Hildebrandt, J., Hildebrandt, J. R. 1973. Cardiorespiratory transients in exercising man. I. Tests of superposition. *J. Appl. Physiol.* 35:58–67
38. Fujihara, Y., Hildebrandt, J., Hildebrandt, J. R. 1973. Cardiorespiratory transients in exercising man. II. Linear models. *J. Appl. Physiol.* 35:68–76
39. Folgering, H. Th., Bernards, J. A., Biesta, J. H., Smolders, F. 1974. Mathematical analysis of the response of lung ventilation to CO_2 in normoxia and hyperoxia. *Pfluegers Arch.* 347:341–50
40. Fulop, M., Dryer, N., Tannenbaum, H. 1974. The ventilatory response in diabetic ketoacidosis. *Clin. Sci. Mol. Med.* 46:539–49
41. Gelford, R., Lambertsen, C. J. 1973. Dynamic respiratory response to abrupt change of inspired CO_2 at normal and high P_{O_2}. *J. Appl. Physiol.* 35:903–13
42. Gilbert, R., Auchincloss, J. H. Jr., Brodsky, J., Boden, W. 1972. Changes in tidal volume, frequency, and ventilation induced by their measurement. *J. Appl. Physiol.* 33:252–54
43. Goode, R. C., Brown, E. B. Jr., Howson, M. G., Cunningham, D. J. C. 1969. Respiratory effects of breathing down a tube. *Resp. Physiol.* 6:343–59
44. Guz, A., Noble, M. I. M., Eisele, J. H., Trenchard, D. W. 1970. Experimental results of vagal block in cardiopulmonary disease. See Ref. 81, 315–28
45. Guz, A., Noble, M. I. M., Eisele, J. H., Trenchard, D. W. 1970. The role of vagal inflation reflexes in man and other animals. See Ref. 81, 17–40
46. Guz, A., Noble, M. I. M., Eisele, J. H., Trenchard, D. W. 1971. The effect of lung deflation on breathing in man. *Clin. Sci.* 40:451–61
47. Guz, A., Noble, M. I. M., Widdicombe, J. G., Trenchard, D. W., Mushin, W. W. 1966. The effect of bilateral block of vagus and glossopharyngeal nerves on the ventilatory response to CO_2 of conscious man. *Resp. Physiol.* 1:206–10
48. Guz, A., Trenchard, D. W. 1971. Pulmonary stretch receptor activity in man: a comparison with dog and cat. *J. Physiol.* 213:329–43
49. Guz, A., Trenchard, D. W. 1971. The role of nonmyelinated vagal afferent fibres from the lungs in the genesis of tachypnoea in the rabbit. *J. Physiol.* 213:345–71
50. Guz, A., Widdicombe, J. G. 1970. Pattern of breathing during hypercapnoea before and after vagal blockade in man. See Ref. 81, 41–44
51. Hedstrand, U. 1971. The optimal frequency of breathing in bronchial asthma. *Scand. J. Resp. Dis.* 52:217–21
52. Hey, E. N., Lloyd, B. B., Cunningham, D. J. C., Jukes, M. G. M., Bolton, D. P. G. 1966. Effects of various respiratory stimuli on the depth and frequency of breathing in man. *Resp. Physiol.* 1:193–205
53. Honda, Y., Miyamura, M. 1972. Increased ventilatory response to CO_2 by rebreathing in consecutive daily trials. *Jap. J. Physiol.* 22:13–23
54. Jain, S. K., Subramanian, S., Julka, D. B., Guz, A. 1972. Search for evidence of lung chemoreflexes in man: study of respiratory and circulatory effects of phenyldiguanide and lobeline. *Clin. Sci.* 42:163–77
55. Jain, S. K., Trenchard, D. W., Reynolds, F., Noble, M. I. M., Guz, A. 1973. The effect of local anaesthesia of the airway on respiratory reflexes in the rabbit. *Clin. Sci.* 44:519–38
56. Jensen, J. I., Vejby-Christensen, H., Peterson, E. S. 1971. Ventilation in man at onset of work employing different standardized starting orders. *Resp. Physiol.* 13:209–20
57. Jensen, J. I., Vejby-Christensen, H., Peterson, E. S. 1972. Ventilatory response to work initiated at various times during the respiratory cycle. *J. Appl. Physiol.* 33:744–50
58. Karczewski, W., Widdicombe, J. G. 1969. The role of the vagus nerves in the respiratory and circulatory reactions to anaphylaxis in rabbits. *J. Physiol.* 201:293–304
59. Karczewski, W. A., Widdicombe, J. G., Eds. 1973. Neural Control of Breathing. *Acta Neurobiol. Exp.* 33
60. Kelman, G. R., Watson, A. W. S. 1973. Effect of added dead space on pulmonary ventilation during submaximal, steady-state exercise. *Quart. J. Exp. Physiol.* 58:305–13
61. Kronenberg, R. et al 1972. Comparison of three methods for quantitating respiratory response to hypoxia in man. *Resp. Physiol.* 16:109–25
62. Lahiri, S., Milledge, J. S., Sφrensen, S. C. 1972. Ventilation in man during exercise at high altitude. *J. Appl. Physiol.* 32:766–69
63. Langrehr, D. 1964. Receptor-Afferenzen in Halsvagus des Menschen. *Klin. Woch.* 42:239–44

64. Lefrançois, R. et al 1972. Chemoreflex ventilatory response to CO_2 in man at low and high altitudes. *Resp. Physiol.* 14:296–306
65. Leigh, J. 1972. Evaluation of a two-breath CO_2 test as a measure of arterial chemoreflex sensitivity to CO_2 in man. *J. Physiol.* 224:28–29P
66. Leigh, J. 1972. Dependence of peripheral chemoreflex response to CO_2 in man on Po_2. *J. Physiol.* 225:63–65P
67. Leigh, J. 1972. *Factors affecting transient respiratory responses to two breaths of 20% CO_2 in man.* PhD thesis. Sydney Univ., Australia
68. Linton, R. A. F., Poole-Wilson, P. A., Davies, R. J., Cameron, I. R. 1973. A comparison of the ventilatory response to carbon dioxide by steady-state and rebreathing methods during metabolic acidosis and alkalosis. *Clin. Sci. Mol. Med.* 45:239–49
69. Lloyd, B. B., Jukes, M. G. M., Cunningham, D. J. C. 1958. The relation between alveolar oxygen pressure and the respiratory response to carbon dioxide in man. *Quart. J. Exp. Physiol.* 43:214–27
70. Loeschcke, H. H. 1972. Der Säure-Basenstatus des Liquor cerebrospinalis und seine Regulation durch die Lungen ventilation. *Klin. Woch.* 50:581–93
71. Lugliani, R., Whipp, B. J., Seard, C., Wasserman, K. 1971. Effect of bilateral carotid body resection on ventilatory control at rest and during exercise in man. *N. Engl. J. Med.* 285:1105–11
72. Lyall, J. R. W., Cameron, I. R. 1974. The relation between vital capacity and the respiratory response to inhaled carbon dioxide. *Proc. Eur. Soc. Clin. Invest., 8th Meeting,* 80 (Abstr.)
73. Marsh, R. H. K., Lyen, K. R., McPherson, G. A. D., Pearson, S. B., Cunningham, D. J. C. 1973. Breath by breath effects of imposed alternate breath oscillations of alveolar CO_2. *Resp. Physiol.* 18:80–91
74. Mills, J. E., Sellick, H., Widdicombe, J. G. 1970. Epithelial irritant receptors in the lungs. See Ref. 81, 77–92
74a. Mitchell, R. A. 1970. Respiration. *Ann. Rev. Physiol.* 32:415–38
75. Paintal, A. S. 1973. Vagal sensory receptors and their reflex effects. *Physiol. Rev.* 53:159–227
76. Pearson, S. B., Cunningham, D. J. C. 1973. Some observations on the relation between ventilation, tidal volume, and frequency in man in various steady and transient states. *Acta Neurobiol. Exp.* 33:177–88
77. Petit, J. M., Delhez, L. 1970. Quelques données expérimentales récentes concernant l'origine de la dyspnée et la régulation ventilatoire chez le malade asthmatique. *Acta Tuberc. Pneumol. Belg.* 61:169–86
78. Plum, F. 1970. Neurological integration of behavioural and metabolic control of breathing. See Ref. 81, 159–75
79. Plum, F., Posner, J. B. 1968. Inhomogeneity of cisternal and lumbar CSF acid-base balance during acute metabolic alterations in CBF and CSF. *Scand. J. Clin. Lab. Invest.* 102: Suppl. 1B
80. Plum, F., Price, R. W. 1973. Acid-base balance of cisternal and lumbar cerebrospinal fluid in hospital patients. *N. Engl. J. Med.* 289:1346–51
81. Porter, R., Ed. 1970. *Breathing: Hering-Breuer Centenary Symposium. Ciba Found. Symp.* London: Churchill. 402 pp.
82. Porter, R., Knight, J., Eds. 1971. High altitude physiology: cardiac and respiratory aspects. *Ciba Found. Symp.* London: Churchill
83. Read, D. J. C. 1967. A clinical method for assessing the ventilatory response to carbon dioxide. *Australas. Ann. Med.* 16:20–32
84. Rebuck, A. S., Jones, N. L., Campbell, E. J. M. 1972. Ventilatory response to exercise and to CO_2 rebreathing in normal subjects. *Clin. Sci.* 43:861–67
85. Rebuck, A. S., Kangalee, M., Pengelly, L. D., Campbell, E. J. M. 1973. Correlation of ventilatory responses to hypoxia and hypercapnia. *J. Appl. Physiol.* 35:173–77
86. Rebuck, A. S., Read, J. 1971. Patterns of ventilatory response to carbon dioxide during recovery from severe asthma. *Clin. Sci.* 41:13–21
87. Rebuck, A. S., Read, J. 1971. Assessment and management of severe asthma. *Am. J. Med.* 51:788–98
88. Saunders, N. A., Heilpern, S., Rebuck, A. S. 1972. Relation between personality and ventilatory response to carbon dioxide in normal subjects: a role in asthma? *Brit. Med. J.* 1:719–21
89. Schaefer, K. E. 1958. Respiratory pattern and respiratory response to CO_2. *J. Appl. Physiol.* 13:1–14
90. Severinghaus, J. W. 1972. Hypoxic respiratory drive and its loss during chronic hypoxia. *Clin. Physiol.* 2:57–79

91. Siesjö, B. K. 1972. The regulation of cerebrospinal fluid pH. *Kidney Int.* 1:360–74
92. Sϕrensen, S. C. 1971. The chemical control of ventilation. *Acta Physiol. Scand.* 361 (Suppl.)
93. Sϕrensen, S. C., Milledge, J. S. 1971. Cerebrospinal fluid acid-base composition at high altitude. *J. Appl. Physiol.* 31:28–30
94. Sϕrensen, S. C., Severinghaus, J. W. 1968. Respiratory insensitivity to acute hypoxia persisting after correction of telralogy of Fallot. *J. Appl. Physiol.* 25:221–23
95. Strachova, Z., Plum, F. 1973. Reproducibility of the rebreathing carbon dioxide response test using an improved method. *Am. Rev. Resp. Dis.* 107: 866–69
96. Trenchard, D., Gardner, D., Guz, A. 1972. Role of pulmonary vagal afferent nerve fibres in the development of rapid shallow breathing in lung inflammation. *Clin. Sci.* 42:251–63
97. Ullmann, E. 1970. The two original papers by Hering and Breuer submitted by Hering to the K. K. Akademie der Wissenschaften zu Wien in 1868. See Ref. 81, 357–94
98. Van Heijst, A. N. P., Maas, A. H. J., Visser, B. F. 1966. Comparison of the acid-base balance in cisternal and lumbar cerebrospinal fluid. *Pfluegers Arch.* 287:242–46
99. Van Ypersele de Strihou, C., Frans, A. 1970. The pattern of respiratory compensation in chronic uraemic acidosis. *Nephron* 7:37–50
100. Van Ypersele de Strihou, C., Frans, A. 1973. The respiratory response to chronic metabolic alkalosis and acidosis in disease. *Clin. Sci. Mol. Med.* 45: 429–48
101. Wade, J. G., Larson, C. P. Jr., Hickey, R. F., Ehrenfeld, W. K., Severinghaus, J. W. 1970. Effect of carotid endarterectomy on carotid chemoreceptor and baroreceptor function in man. *N. Engl. J. Med.* 282:823–29
102. Weil, J. V., Byrne-Quinn, E., Sodal, I. E., Filley, G. F., Grover, R. F. 1971. Acquired attenuation of chemoreceptor function in chronically hypoxic man at high altitude. *J. Clin. Invest.* 50: 186–95
103. Weil, J. V. et al 1970. Hypoxic ventilatory drive in normal man. *J. Clin. Invest.* 49:1061–72
104. Weil, J. V. et al 1972. Augmentation of chemosensitivity during mild exercise in normal man. *J. Appl. Physiol.* 33:813–19
105. Wigertz, O. 1970. Dynamics of ventilation and heart rate in response to sinusoidal work load in man. *J. Appl. Physiol.* 29:208–18
106. Wigertz, O. 1971. Dynamics of respiratory and circulatory adaptation to muscular exercise in man. *Acta Physiol. Scand.* 363:(Suppl.)
107. Vejby-Christensen, H., Petersen, E. S. 1973. Effect of body temperature and hypoxia on the ventilatory CO_2 response in man. *Resp. Physiol.* 19: 322–32

Copyright 1975. All rights reserved

DEFENSE MECHANISMS OF THE LUNGS[1]

❖1133

A. B. Cohen[2] *and W. M. Gold*
Department of Medicine and Cardiovascular Research Institute, University of California San Francisco, San Francisco, California 94143

ATMOSPHERIC AEROSOL

Nonantigenic Particles

Nonviable particles enter the atmosphere from forest fires, wind action on dessicated soil, entrainment of sea spray, volcanic debris, and gas phase reactions. Man-made sources account for approximately 185–415 $\times$ 10^6 metric tons per year out of an estimated total of 985–2615 $\times$ 10^6 metric tons per year and are generated from less than 1% of the earth's surface (61, 83, 195).

The size of the particle is the single most important feature of an aerosol because it determines the stability of the aerosol. The largest size, highest concentration, and greatest diversity in source and composition of particles occurs in the troposphere immediately above the surface of the earth. Although size and concentration of particles tend to decrease with altitude (and distance from urban centers), gas phase reactions activated by sunlight generate large numbers of new particles between 1000–3000 ft in the troposphere and 60,000–65,000 ft in the stratosphere (61). These reactions involve hydrocarbons and oxides of nitrogen from man-made pollution over cities, yielding complex mixtures of nitrogen dioxide, ozone, formaldehyde, ketones, peroxyacyl nitrates, carbon monoxide, etc (4). Although only 35% of the total weight of the particles in this urban aerosol is in the submicronic range, this size range contains the largest number of particles with the largest surface area. Such small size assures deep penetration into the lung, but also favors adsorption of gas by the particle, thus enhancing its capacity to potentiate reactions to irritant gases by causing a high local concentration (44). Although aerosols inside urban buildings are predominantly smaller in size than aerosols outside buildings and so increase the risk for the occupants, most urban aerosols are monitored only outside buildings

[1]Supported in part by Grant HL-14201 from the National Heart and Lung Institute, Specialized Center for Research in Pulmonary Disease and Grants 808R2 and 954 from the Council for Tobacco Research, USA, Inc.

[2]Dr. Cohen was a recipient of a grant from the National Heart and Lung Institute, Research Career Development Award HL-70701.

(110). Quantitatively more important photochemical reactions occur away from cities and involve naturally-occurring hydrocarbons (terpenes from pine forests) and oxides of nitrogen (from lightning strikes) yielding similar mixtures of toxic materials.

Antigenic Particles

Antigenic particles are important components of the atmospheric aerosol because of their complex biological effects. Spores have been recovered up to 20,000 ft and pollens up to 40,000 ft above the earth; ocean air has 4–5 bacteria per cubic meter (95). Concentrations of spores and pollens tend to have a seasonal variation. Because of their large size (10–50 μm) most whole pollens and spores have a restricted mobility and effect, even though their local concentration may be in the range of several thousand particles per cubic meter near the point of release close to the ground. Other potent allergenic particles may be airborne in a circumscribed locale such as a home or factory: animal dander, insect parts, house dust, industrial dusts (e.g. cotton seed oil, castor bean allergen), simple chemicals (platinum salts, tannic acid), as well as microorganisms (198, 224).

DEPOSITION OF PARTICLES IN THE LUNGS

Effect of Particle Size

A bibliography of mathematical models describing the variables determining the site of deposition of inhaled particles has been presented elsewhere (194). Particles 10–20 μm in diameter settle largely in the nasopharyngeal region, while less than one tenth of the inhaled mass of particles settle in the tracheobronchial region (except for particles less than 0.1 μm). Particles 1.6–3.2 μm show maximal deposition, while particles 0.2–0.5 μm show minimal deposition in the pulmonary region of the respiratory system (194). Because their small size induces stability in aerosols, however, the number of inhaled particles in the 0.2–0.5 μm range may be so great that their total mass deposited may exceed that of much larger particles (5 μm). In general, deposition in central airways tends to be by impaction, while sedimentation and diffusion predominate more peripherally (194).

Effect of Shape and Hygroscopic Properties

Irregularly shaped particles such as quartz, clay, and coal have aerodynamic diameters of spherical particles one half to three quarters of their actual diameter (213). Asbestos fibers greater that 50 μm long can penetrate deeply into the lungs of experimental animals (207), almost reaching the alveoli. There is good correlation between the shape, the site of deposition, and pathological changes produced by different types of asbestos fibers (206).

Particles discharged into the ambient air from the respiratory tract lose moisture and shrink; when inhaled, they absorb water from the saturated air in the lungs and regain their original dimensions (228). Thus the site of deposition of an hygroscopic particle depends on its growth in size as it absorbs water from the respiratory tract (228).

Many particles have a mixed composition with an inner insoluble core and an outer soluble shell. The outer shell provides an absorbing liquid phase for gases when atmospheric humidity is increased, which may account for the synergistic effects attributed to inhalation of irritant gases mixed with particles (43).

Deposition of Inhaled Pollen and Pollen Fragments

Aerodynamic calculations (see above) indicate that many pollens cannot penetrate deeply into the lungs. There is a finite probability that even large pollen grains will occasionally penetrate deeply. Hobday & Townley found by direct observation of guinea pigs exposed to whole ragweed pollen that inhaled pollen grains penetrated as far as intrapulmonary bronchi (86).

Other workers, using radiolabeled whole pollen grains of *Poa praetensis* (25 μm), found no deposition below the oropharynx in man (210). Conversely, at least 10% of inhaled radioactive pollen extract reached the lungs, although the oropharynx was still the major site of deposition (226). The same laboratory showed that inhalation of pollen extract by sensitive subjects was followed by bronchospasm in a few minutes (151), but inhalation of whole pollen grains was not associated with asthma until several hours later (227). Other workers reported that although whole pollen grains deposited in the nose caused no reaction, pollen grains deposited on the posterior one third of the tongue or inhaled through the mouth did cause cough and airway obstruction (87). Thus asthmatic patients breathing through the nose may not develop symptoms, while patients breathing through the mouth might, if the air contains whole pollen grains. Furthermore, Busse, Reed & Hoehne found that the largest fraction of antigenic determinants of pollen suspended in the atmosphere was in small fragments of pollen (1–5 μm) that could easily penetrate deeply in the lungs, rather than in whole grains (23). If a combination of whole pollen and pollen fragments is inhaled, then immediate and delayed reactions may occur due to the same immunologic mechanism.

Effect of Preexisting Respiratory Disease

Deposition of inhaled particles will also be affected by preexisting respiratory disorders, often leading to a worsening of the disease itself (71). Chronic airway obstruction alters the distribution of inspired air so that flow is diverted to unobstructed airways. Lateral diffusion gradients may enrich the central core of the airstream, permitting fine particles to penetrate more deeply into the lung than previously estimated and even across collateral channels, bypassing obstructed passages (122). This may result in increasing exposure to irritant gases and toxic particles, thereby increasing injury to the least damaged airways and alveoli.

Diseases such as pulmonary fibrosis and sarcoidosis are associated with increased airflow velocities and increased deposition of large particles in central airways; this occurs because inertial impaction increases and sedimentation decreases with increased flow rates for particles with aerodynamic diameters larger than 0.5 μm (71).

If disease causes increased turbulent airflow, then deposition in the trachea and central airways will also increase. Turbulence is increased by increased airflow rates, by irregularities in the walls due to mucus, inflammation, or contraction of airway smooth muscle, and by alterations in airway caliber, flow profile, and evaporative inhibition of deposition by use of endotracheal tubes in treatment of patients with advanced respiratory disease (153).

Increased tidal volume and respiratory rate are also associated with increased deposition of inhaled particles (14, 53). Finally, the check-valve behavior that occurs in many airway diseases may lead to increased particle deposition by sedimentation and Brownian diffusion as transit time increases; however, this effect may be mitigated by the effect of increased size of airspaces, which tends to decrease the rate of exponential decay of suspended particles 0.1–1.0 μm in diameter (71).

DEFENSE MECHANISMS OF THE NOSE

Clearance of Particles

Proctor (161, 162) and Massing (130) recently reviewed nasal physiology related to defenses against inhaled particles. The distribution of flow rates, sharp bends, and anterior nasal hairs augments particle impaction in the nose. In addition, the nose brings the inspired gas to body temperature and saturates the gas with water vapor before it reaches the subglottic area (91). This hydration may have a significant effect on the aerodynamic diameter of hygroscopic particles of droplet nuclei, causing them to settle in the nose even though they start out at sizes that would penetrate to a deeper level in the lungs.

Mucus flows from the main nasal passage posteriorly toward the nasopharynx (84). Once in the nasopharynx some of the mucus is sequestered in the adenoid crypts and the rest is moved into the stomach by swallowing. Proctor estimates that the mucus covering the main passages is cleared every 10–15 min (162). Slow clearance or stasis does occur in some normal subjects and is unaffected by the humidity of inspired air; however, the average rate of movement of a particle on the nasal mucous blanket is 4.8 mm/min (5).

Physiological Responses

As indicated in a recent review by Widdicombe (219), irritation of the nose causes potent physiological responses involving respiratory, airway, and cardiovascular reflexes. Sneezing is an effective means of clearing the nose of irritating material. Nasal irritation is reported to cause apnea (rapid shallow breathing) or sneezing; bronchoconstriction or bronchodilation; bradycardia or tachycardia; and hypotension or hypertension. Mechanical or chemical stimulation of the nasal mucosa of cats (204, 219) causes bronchodilation that appears to be primarily due to inhibition of vagal tone. The effect of nasal stimuli in man is uncertain. No detectable changes were observed in response to sulfur dioxide (188), histamine (87), or pollen grains (87). Kaufman & Wright (98) reported an increased airway resistance to silica particles; however, the particles may have reached the larynx and trachea stimulating cough or irritant receptors. Tomori & Widdicombe (203, 204) also described an aspiration reflex in cats due to mechanical irritation of the mucosa of the nasopharynx resulting in sniffing, reflex hypertension, and bronchodilation. This reflex, like the nasal reflex, was associated with decreased activity in vagal efferents in the trachea and increased activity in cervical sympathetic efferents (149, 203, 204, 219). Systematic studies are required to understand the pattern of nasal responses to different stimuli in different species with and without anesthetics.

Immune and Antimicrobial Defenses

Related antimicrobial and immune defense mechanisms are reviewed in this section. A more general treatment of immune responses is presented in the section on airway defenses.

DEFENSES AGAINST PARTICLES CONTAINING VIRUSES Virus-containing particles that land in the nose are probably handled similarly to virus-containing particles that land in the large airways. The dose of aerosolized influenza virus necessary to produce disease has been estimated at three infectious particles; the dose by nasal administration is larger but still relatively small (2). After deposition, a neuraminidase on the virus particle probably contributes to penetration of the mucus barrier. Gottschalk (73) showed that the neuraminidase activity of influenza viruses rapidly lowers the viscosity of mucus and may thereby bare the epithelial cellular receptors (49). Influenza viruses then undergo the pattern of replication seen in many viruses, although with some substantial variations (104).

Within a day after controlled exposure of people to Coxsackie virus A21, upper respiratory symptoms developed and interferon (antiviral proteins) could be located in the nasal wash solutions (29). The interferon peaked at about the second day and the symptoms peaked shortly thereafter. These data led Cate (31) to suggest that one of the major factors limiting disease after an acute viral exposure in the unimmunized host may be interferon. Interferons have been reviewed recently by Grossberg (77), Rodgers & Merigan (168), and Cate (27). When a nasal spray of interferon was administered to one group of subjects one day before and three days after rhinovirus was administered to treated and control groups, the interferon-treated group was protected against both virus shedding and illness. In addition, leukocyte interferon given early to symptomatic patients with influenza controlled fever and headache immediately, whereas local respiratory complaints were slower to resolve, but did disappear more rapidly than in control subjects (186). Cate's studies of interferon in subjects infected with rhinovirus showed that if the subjects were immediately reinfected the interferon levels were lower than during the first infection, suggesting that factors other than interferon might prevent immediate reinfection (29).

Many other changes occur in the nasal secretions during viral infections. During acute infections with viruses there is a transudation of fluid from the vascular tree and a suppression of immunoglobulin G (IgG) secreted locally (24). Immunoglobulin A (IgA) concentrations, however, increased progressively in relation to other proteins and the IgA remained elevated while the transudate proteins disappeared after the acute illness. These changes in IgA were not associated with similar changes in neutralizing antibody to the infecting virus. In two separate studies, volunteers with high control levels of IgA in nasal secretions were better able to resist infection (125, 173), but the mechanism of protection is unknown.

Virus-neutralizing antibody appears in the nasal secretions two to three weeks after the start of viral infection and following the termination of the symptoms (31,

169). This virus-neutralizing activity was mostly by secretory IgA. Secretory IgA has been the subject of several reviews (171, 174, 201). It is a dimeric form of circulating IgA, and is formed in plasma cells in the interstitial spaces of exocrine glands such as the parotid, submaxillary, and lacrimal glands (90, 200, 205). Some people with an impaired ability to make IgA are not overly susceptible to the common respiratory viruses or to vaccination with vaccinia virus (99). Although the role of secretory IgA in limiting natural infection is suspect, the antibody does offer protection in the previously immunized host (185).

In recent work a role has been suggested for cell-mediated immunity in the defense against virus infections. Studies by Cate and his co-workers have suggested that human peripheral lymphocytes are involved in the host response to acute influenza (28), and that these cells retain the ability to recognize influenza antigens for several months following infection or vaccination (30). In addition, immunologically specific protection can be provided in mice with influenza pneumonia by intravenous transfer of lymph node and spleen cells from immunized mice of the same inbred strain; this protection occurs in the absence of hemagglutination-inhibiting antibody to influenza (27).

While nonimmunologic humoral and cell-mediated immunologic defense mechanisms seem to work in concert to limit virus infections of the upper respiratory tract, occasionally they seem to work to the detriment of the host. When a cell-mediated immune response has been initiated with respiratory syncytial virus or rubeola in infants who have received a vaccine to the virus, the infant is sicker when infected by wild virus than are unvaccinated children (33). This reaction has been correlated with the presence of Arthus-type skin reactivity to viral antigen resulting from virus-antibody complex formation in small arteries.

DEFENSES AGAINST PARTICLES CONTAINING BACTERIA Normal nasal bacterial flora commonly includes *Staphylococci, Streptococcus viridans, Corynebacteria,* and *Hemophilic bacilli,* and less commonly includes *Pneumococci, Neisseriae,* and *Mycobacteria* (50). Although the nose is not sterile, it does resist the introduction of new bacteria with mechanisms that suggest an immune reaction. Ehrenkranz (57) has shown that the disappearance of a specific phage type of *S. aureus* from the nose was type-specific and accelerated on subsequent exposure, characteristic of an immunologic reaction. In addition, immunization with pneumococcal type-specific polysaccharides lowers the carrier rates for *pneumococci* of the corresponding types (51).

Many of the antibacterial functions of antibodies are related to their interactions with the components of the complement system (94, 187). However, current evidence suggests that respiratory secretions do not contain enough of the components of complement to result in complement-mediated responses in the absence of inflammation (24, 170, 172, 175). While some reports suggest that in the presence of sufficient complement, IgA may have some bactericidal properties (1, 214), opsonization and other antibacterial functions of some classes of antibodies may be denied to IgA (229). Williams & Gibbons (225) have suggested that limitation of adherence of bacteria to epithelial surfaces by IgA may also prevent colonization. Nasal secretions also contain nonspecific antibacterial substances. These include a lysozyme that contributes to lysis of some gram negative organisms and lactoferrin that inhibits the growth of bacteria dependent on iron by chelating soluble iron salts (172).

Bacterial infection in the nose is often preceded by a viral infection that disrupts antibacterial defenses (51, 58).

DEFENSE MECHANISMS OF THE AIRWAYS

Clearance of Particles

LYMPHATICS Lymphatic drainage of the lung has recently been reviewed by several investigators (136, 148). Two regions of the lymphatic system of the lung may have special importance to its defense mechanisms. There are a large number of collections of lymphoid cells in the submucosal areas of the bronchi, especially at branch points (148), that seem to lack the structure of lymph nodes but that have potential importance as sites of antigen processing or antibody production. In addition, Macklem (120) described areas that he called "sumps" at terminal bronchioles through which particles that had not been phagocytosed might gain entrance directly to the lung lymphatic system. Recently, a possible anatomic correlate has been described in an ultramicroscopic study of this area (32). Addition of tracer materials to the mucosa can be detected later in the perivascular and peribronchial lymphatics (56, 88) and the peribronchial lymph nodes. Thus these regions may permit large particles to bypass the tight junctions of the remaining portion of the airway mucosa and gain access to the deeper structures beneath the epithelium (166).

MUCOCILIARY CLEARANCE The mucous layer consists of a more fluid underlayer in which the cilia move and a more viscous gel layer that is pushed cephalad by ciliary action (116, 136). Constituent proteins have been reviewed elsewhere (180). The gel structure of mucoid sputum is probably dependent primarily on long glycoprotein chains. Barton et al (11) have shown that addition of propylene glycol or glycerin reduces viscoelastic properties of sputum but does not eliminate the ability of the mucus to be drawn out in a liquid thread (*spinnbarkeit*) and show elastic recoil. Reduction of disulfide bonds with dithiothreitol or acetylcysteine liquifies the sputum. They suggest, therefore, that both hydrogen and disulfide bonding between molecules of mucus control the viscoelastic properties (10).

In the inflammatory reaction that accompanies infection, many phagocytic cells disintegrate, and in so doing they liberate bundles of deoxyribose nucleoprotein fibrils. These fibrils become part of the gel structure and may contribute to the tenacious consistency sometimes seen in mucopurulent sputum (160, 216). Other subcellular particles are merely suspended in the gel. After mucopurulent sputum had been extracted, first with propylene glycol, and then with acetylcysteine, a residue of the fibrous gel remained; this residue resisted dispersal by concentrated salt solutions and detergents and, therefore, may have undergone some covalent crosslinking after secretion, perhaps in a manner analogous to the final stages of blood clotting (131). This crosslinking of fibrin is carried out by a plasma gamma-glutamyl transpeptidase (factor XIII), and a gamma-glutamyl transpeptidase has been demonstrated in mucopurulent sputum (9). Purulent sputum appears to contain leukocytic enzymes that can hydrolyze proteins in sputum only after the protein has been liberated from DNA by DNase or by high salt concentrations (115); these enzymes are inhibited by alpha-1-antitrypsin (115).

Either a dramatic increase or decrease in mucus viscosity will alter bronchial clearance (10). Recent studies by Proctor on mucus induced by methacholine showed that despite increased total volume, protein, and mucin secretion, which diluted nonprotein materials, mucociliary transport of tracer particles decreased, possibly due to increased depth of periciliary fluid (164). Marin and colleagues have used a short-circuit current technique (similar to that used to study electrolytes and water transport across frog skin) to evaluate electrolyte and water transfer across the epithelium of the posterior membranous portion of the canine trachea (128). They found a significant potential difference and short-circuit current largely due to active transport of chloride ion from serosa to mucosa. Since the chloride ion flux exceeded the possible net sodium ion flux, an osmotic force was available for water movement into the tracheal lumen. These experimental preparations may provide insights into normal control mechanisms and abnormalities caused by diseases, such as asthma and chronic bronchitis, that affect this critical component of the defense mechanisms of the lungs.

Ciliary function has not been studied in man in a manner that isolates its contributions to airway clearance from its effects on airway mucus. The process of ciliary action includes the beating of single cilia and the metachronic beating of one after another, so as to cause the least interference between cilia and produce the overall effect of a wave motion that passes along the cilia (163). Pacemakers and humoral transmitters of ciliary control have not been found in mammals (21, 163). Movement of cilia seems to depend on ATP or ADP but not on other phosphorylated compounds (21). To date our knowledge of ciliary function in man has been confined to a few measurements of rates of clearance of certain kinds of particles. However, the direct study of mucociliary clearance with the fiberbronchoscope (85) and the radiological study of clearance of tantalum powder (64) have demonstrated differences in clearance rates from different regions of the lung. Clearance shows an orderly progression from large to small airways except for distal bronchioles, which show no clearance initially and up to 24–48 hr. The trachea clears within 20 hr, but terminal units (structures distal to terminal bronchioles) show no significant clearance for up to 15 months (64).

Physiological Responses

ANATOMIC RELATIONSHIPS The biological response to inhaled particles depends on the nature of the particle (inorganic or organic, viable or nonviable, antigenic or nonantigenic, soluble or insoluble, etc) and on the location of deposition. Differences in physiological responses reflect differences in structure, blood supply, innervation, and immune responses in different regions of the respiratory tract (12, 121, 138, 140). Regardless of the nature of the particle itself, the physiological response to a particle deposited in central, flow-resistive airways is qualitatively different from the physiological response when a particle is deposited in small, peripheral airways less than 2 mm in diameter.

The central airways have a small total cross-sectional area with dense cholinergic and less dense sympathetic innervation (80, 107, 127); they are perfused by the bronchial artery (52). The peripheral airways have a large total cross-sectional area (121) and minimal vagosympathetic innervation (127); their blood supply comes through the pulmonary artery (138). There are considerable differences in local immune responses as well (see below). Deposition of large particles in central airways (52, 141, 152, 154, 184, 223) causes constriction of large, central, flow-resistive airways resulting in increased airflow resistance and decreased airway volume, usually associated with hyperinflation, but with no change in pulmonary compliance. A similar physiologic response occurs when broncho-active substances like histamine are added to the bronchial circulation (52, 141, 152, 154, 223).

When particles are deposited in peripheral airways (approximately 2 mm in diameter in man) terminal airways constrict, resulting in decreased static pulmonary compliance with relatively little change in airflow resistance, and a decrease in FRC (144). A similar response occurs when broncho-active substances are added to the pulmonary circulation (35, 40, 41, 142, 144).

Intermediate or mixed responses may be caused by recirculation of chemicals, variable penetration of the vagus nerves into the periphery of the lung (230), variable spectrum of size of particles inhaled (194), variable response of different species to specific chemicals (40, 62), initiation of mixed immune responses (67, 158), or the particular size of airways in which the particles settle (121).

REFLEX CONTROL Depending on the site in the respiratory tract, "irritant" stimuli initiate a variety of reflex bronchomotor responses (59, 60, 140, 154, 223). Activation of receptors in the nose (219) or epipharynx (203, 204), or slowly adapting receptors in the lungs, causes bronchodilation (154, 223) (see above). Activation of, for example, "cough" (22) or "irritant" (140, 146, 154, 223) receptors causes bronchoconstriction. Slowly adapting (stretch) and rapidly adapting (irritant) receptors may play opposing roles in the normal control of respiration since they have reciprocal actions on airway smooth muscle (139, 146). Nadel (139) suggested that the output of the slowly adapting receptors may determine the output of the irritant receptors and adjust the pattern of breathing by a negative feedback loop between the two receptor systems.

Electrical stimulation of sympathetic nerves to the airways partially inhibits vagal bronchoconstriction; however, sympathetic inhibition of vagal tone is never complete (25). The relative importance of these two systems in determining airway caliber, and the role of sympathetic reflexes in determining respiratory responses, remains to be determined. The remainder of this review focuses on the responses to inhaled irritants.

Larynx Stimulation of the mucosa of the larynx by dust particles, mechanical irritation, or chemicals like ammonia, but not sulfur dioxide, carbon dioxide, or histamine, causes cough, reflex hypertension, and bronchoconstriction (19, 146,

204). This reflex depends on cough receptors in the laryngeal epithelium that respond to mechanical stimulation and inhalation of ammonia with rapidly adapting irregular discharge (19, 218, 220), but, unlike irritant receptors in the lungs, do not respond to histamine or sulfur dioxide. The afferent pathway of the reflex is in the superior laryngeal nerves and the efferent pathway is in the vagus nerves (18, 146, 218).

Airways Cough and irritant receptors in the epithelium of the airways have been characterized by recording action potentials in their afferent fibers. These receptors are distinguished from slowly adapting stretch receptors and J receptors by their irregular, rapidly adapting discharge (133–135, 181, 182, 217, 222). Nerve terminals ramify beneath and between epithelial cells in the airways (59, 60, 80, 127). Irritation of the mucosa around these receptors activates both afferent vagal fibers to the central nervous system (19, 59, 60, 133, 146, 217, 220, 221) and efferent vagal fibers to the airways, thus resulting in bronchoconstriction (218, 220). Although, histologically, cough and irritant receptors appear identical (59), they may be distinguished physiologically (140). The reflexes triggered by stimulation of cough or irritant receptors are critically important in production of an adequate cough. The high airflow velocities achieved during this reflex response ensure expulsion of mucus and debris from the airway epithelium, thus providing an important defense of the airways and alveoli.

REFLEX STIMULI

Dusts Inhalation of chemically inert dust activates irritant receptors (182), irregular firing in cough receptors (221), and an increased airflow resistance in animals (100, 221) that is abolished by vagotomy (221) or by atropine sulfate (100). Inhalation of particles from the atmosphere also causes increased airflow resistance in normal humans (47, 55, 221) that is prevented by isoproterenol (47, 55) and by atropine sulfate (47, 221). Similar reflexes have been documented in response to cigarette smoke (19, 143, 182, 190), water droplets from ultrasonic nebulizers (159), or other particles. The mechanism of activation of the receptors by particles is unclear, and different patterns of activation have been observed (221). Activation may be coincident with the inhalation of dust or may not start until after inhalation of the dust ceases. Activation may then persist for a variable time or may start with inhalation of the dust but persist for up to 1 hr (55). In contrast, bronchoconstriction due to mechanical irritation ceases promptly after stimulation stops (146).

Since dust particles of different sizes tend to settle in airways of different sizes, small particles of cigarette smoke stimulate the pulmonary irritant receptors markedly, whereas the tracheal and laryngeal receptors are less affected (59). Very small particles of zinc sulfate penetrate deeply into the lung so that only local bronchoconstriction occurs. It can be abolished by isoproterenol but not by atropine or vagotomy (144). On the other hand, relatively large particles deposited in the upper airways stimulate cough receptors, but apparently not the irritant receptors (48).

No single substance is responsible for the documented chronic adverse health effects of pollution. However, epidemiological studies indicate that the most important constituent is dust, which either injures the lung itself or is an index of something that does (6). The pathogenetic relationship between the acute reflex changes and the long-term morbidity and mortality associated with dust remains to be determined (12, 42).

Chemicals Chemical irritants also activate superficial epithelial receptors in the airways. There is variation in the responsiveness of different species (18, 220), but a large number of chemicals cause vagally-mediated reflex bronchoconstriction in animals and in healthy man. Many of these chemicals, including sulfur dioxide (3, 63, 145), sulfuric acid (183), ammonia (8), ozone (72, 137), acetic acid (3), formaldehyde (3), and nitrogen dioxide (137), have been detected in the atmospheric aerosol previously described. Their biological effects may be potentiated by adsorption to small particles.

Although not normally found in the atmospheric aerosol, histamine is biologically important in defense mechanisms because it is released in pulmonary tissues during inflammatory and immune reactions (20, 178, 179) and has complex local and reflex actions (52, 184) (see above). Further studies are essential to determine the effect on irritant receptors of other broncho-active agents released during inflammatory and allergic reactions; these agents include serotonin, bradykinin, slow reactive substance of anaphylaxis, eosinophil chemotactic factor of anaphylaxis, and prostaglandins.

Antigens Since specific antigens release histamine and other chemicals from isolated lung tissues as well as from leukocytes of sensitized animals and asthmatic patients (20, 114, 178, 179), it has been assumed that antigen-antibody interaction on target cells in airways releases histamine that causes direct local contraction of airway smooth muscle. The main action of histamine in vivo, however, appears to be mediated by vagal reflexes. Thus it has been postulated that vagally-mediated bronchomotor reflexes are also critically important in anaphylaxis and asthma (68, 69, 97, 139).

Antigen administered intravenously causes increased pulmonary resistance in sensitized rabbits (97) and guinea pigs (135). Vagotomy inhibits the airway responses in both species, suggesting that a vagally-mediated reflex is involved (97, 135). Recordings of action potentials from vagal efferent nerve fibers during bronchoconstriction induced by anaphylaxis indicated that these pathways are involved (96). Bronchoconstriction during anaphylaxis can be reversed by cooling the vagus nerves to 8–10°C (leaving efferent pathways intact), suggesting that afferent vagal pathways are involved (97). Since irritant receptors are stimulated during anaphylaxis (133) it seems probable that these receptors are responsible for vagally-mediated reflex bronchoconstriction following intravenous administration of antigen.

However, anaphylaxis is associated with hypotension, pulmonary vasoconstriction, systemic release of chemical mediators, and abnormal patterns of respiration; these abnormalities are known to cause secondary reflex bronchoconstriction (97, 147, 182).

To avoid this secondary effect, studies have been done by inhalation of specific antigens in allergic dogs (70). These experimental animals have a naturally occurring pollenosis sometimes associated with asthma (155), and dogs sensitive to ragweed or nematode antigen have reagenic antibodies similar to immunoglobulin E (IgE) antibody in asthmatic patients (101). Inhalation of specific antigen by allergic dogs causes increased airflow resistance (69, 70) and contraction of airways (101) without hypotension. The airway reaction is abolished by vagotomy or by atropine administered either intravenously or by aerosol (69). After atropine, isoproterenol resulted in only small additional dilation, suggesting that direct local contraction of airway smooth muscle played a minor role relative to the vagally-mediated reflex (100).

The distribution and severity of the airway narrowing observed in tantalum bronchograms after inhalation of antigen is similar to that observed during electrical stimulation of the vagus nerves in the same dogs (100). These data provide additional evidence that vagal efferent pathways were involved in the reaction. Since histamine is released from the lungs during antigen-induced bronchoconstriction, the cervical vagus nerves were cooled to 5–7°C. At this temperature, conduction of action potentials from the irritant receptors is blocked, but efferent pathways remain intact (indicated by the preservation of a bronchoconstrictor response to asphyxia). This cold block abolished the reflex bronchoconstriction caused by aerosols of histamine, but also abolished antigen-induced bronchoconstriction, indicating that irritant receptors were responsible for the airway response to antigen (69). In other dogs, antigen aerosol was delivered to one lung, but airflow resistance increased in both lungs. Similarly, blocking conduction in the cervical vagus innervating the lung that received the antigen abolished the bronchoconstriction in both lungs. These results prove that a vagally-mediated reflex is of critical importance in antigen-induced bronchoconstriction in allergic dogs, and that the responsible receptors of the reflex are intrapulmonary.

Early in an asthmatic attack, vagally-mediated acute bronchoconstriction appears to be a predominant mechanism of airflow obstruction. In chronic asthma, acute contraction of airway smooth muscle is complicated by inflammation of the bronchial wall and retention of viscid sputum. The role of vagal reflexes in chronic asthma is less clear, but similar reflexes may be triggered by a number of stimuli, such as release of histamine, emotion or suggestion, hyperventilation, or hypoxemia, operant in the chronic phase (68).

Immune and Antimicrobial Defenses

There has been little work to suggest that airways have antimicrobial functions that differ substantially from nasal defense mechanisms discussed earlier. This section focuses on the immune responses of the upper respiratory tract including the nose and airway. The immune system in the lung appears to be organized anatomically, in parallel with the organization of physiological responses. There is local compartmentalization of the immune response in the lungs that is different from the systemic response. The immune response in the upper respiratory tract appears to involve IgA, IgE, and chemical mediators of low molecular weight. The physiological response to IgE-mediated reactions is characterized by airflow obstruction. The immune response in the lower respiratory tract probably involves cellular mechanisms and chemical mediators of high molecular weight elaborated by sensitized lymphocytes, IgM, and IgG, but probably not IgA or IgE. The physiological response to these precipitating antibody-antigen reactions is characterized by pulmonary restriction and pulmonary vascular obstruction. Cellular immune mechanisms may be recruited into both upper and lower compartments, but thymus-dependent cells are not ordinarily present on the air side of the respiratory epithelium.

IMMUNE RESPONSE CELLS Most antibody production requires the cooperation of thymus-derived lymphocytes and bone marrow-derived cells that produce antibody. A glass-adhering cell population augments the reaction (34). Cell-mediated immunity is a function of the thymus-derived cell. The immune cells provide memory of previous exposure to antigens and magnify responses on subsequent exposures. This augmentation results from proliferation of sensitized cells (34).

GENETIC CONTROL The genetic control of these cells and their responses is complex and involves many structural and regulatory genes. Experiments in guinea pigs and mice indicate that many, but not all, of these immune response genes are closely linked to genes that control histocompatability in these animals (15, 126). Documentation of an immune response gene in man was shown by demonstrating a genetic locus closely linked to the histocompatability system controlling IgE antibody response to antigen E and by permitting development of clinical ragweed hayfever and asthma (112). The gene controls two antibody classes (IgE and IgG), is antigen specific, and appears similar to histocompatability-linked immune response genes in mice (112). The presence of this gene is necessary, but not sufficient, for the development of intense IgE immune responses to antigen E and clinical asthma. The trait controlled by the gene is inherited as a Mendelian dominant, but its expression requires other environmental and genetic factors (76, 111, 177). The basal level of specific IgE is probably controlled by a separate gene (13). Both content of chemical mediators released during the immune response (192) and the ease of inducing release of mediators (215) appear to be controlled by autosomal dominant and different genetic loci. These observations suggest the immune reaction is associated with polymorphic genetic control mechanisms. Genetic factors of various kinds may control different molecular events in the total immune response and the different genetic factors may have to coexist in a given individual for a particular allergic response to occur.

LOCAL IMMUNE RESPONSE Since the respiratory tract is continually bombarded by infectious organisms, allergens, and carcinogens in its daily exposure to the atmospheric aerosol, and since immune responses are of fundamental importance in the defense of the host, it is not surprising that the respiratory system is specialized and not simply a passive component of the general immune system. Local respiratory immune mechanisms play an important role in enhancement of protection of the host; conversely, local hypersensitivity may contribute to certain respiratory disorders, including allergic bronchial asthma, Goodpasture's syndrome, allergic alveolitis, and certain granulomatous disorders affecting the lung (123, 124).

Nose and Airways Ishizaka demonstrated that plasma cells that synthesize IgE and others that synthesize IgA are distributed together in the tonsils, adenoids, peribronchial and hilar lymph nodes, and in the lamina propria of the airways themselves, but are not found in the pulmonary parenchyma (197). Local synthesis of IgA, IgM, and IgE in respiratory secretions of the upper respiratory tract has also been demonstrated by Tomasi and others (201).

There is a marked difference in the distribution of immunoglobulins and antibodies in internal and external fluids. IgE, IgM, and IgA are present in external secretions in concentrations greater than can be explained by transudation alone. The concentrations of IgE in saliva are significantly lower than those of other immunoglobulins, but the ratio of IgE in saliva to IgE in serum is greater than that of any other immunoglobulin. Furthermore, there is no correlation between the concentration of IgE in saliva and that in serum (92, 176, 209). Analysis of IgE concentrations in fluid from nasal polyps removed from allergic patients also shows concentrations of IgE greater than that attributable to transudation from plasma (54).

Tissue-fixed IgE appears to be involved in hypersensitivity conditions affecting airways. Tada was unable to demonstrate IgE on mast cells in a wide range of human tissues even when IgE-forming plasma cells were present in the same tissues (197). Gerber confirmed this observation, although IgE was localized in epithelium, basement membrane, and bronchial glands in airways of asthmatic patients (65). Recently, Richardson (166) reported that guinea pigs sensitized with horseradish peroxidase (HRP) developed increased airflow resistance after inhalation of aerosols of HRP. Anatomic studies showed HRP tracer in goblet cells, on glands, on cilia, and on other epithelial cells, but none was present as deep as the basement membrane or in association with mast cells. This provocative experiment requires confirmation because of a lack of proper controls for both the physiologic and anatomic studies.

On the other hand, radioautographic studies by Tomioka showed IgE to be fixed to mast cells in the airways of monkeys (93, 202). Furthermore, Patterson obtained living mast cells by brush biopsy from the airways of monkeys and humans. These mast cells become degranulated in response to specific immunologic challenge (156, 157). This confirms other studies in animals and man that IgE binds selectively to mast cells and closely related basophils in blood, skin, gastrointestinal tract, and respiratory tract (79, 93, 196).

Biochemical Mechanisms Current concepts of the biochemical mechanisms initiated by antigen-IgE interaction in the lung have been recently reviewed by several authors (7, 17, 113). In brief, the sequence of biochemical events leading to release of histamine, slow reactive substance of anaphylaxis, and eosinophil chemotactic factor of anaphylaxis from the human lung involves antigen interaction with IgE antibody fixed to tissues (probably mast cells). Secretion of the chemicals requires divalent cations, activation of a diisopropylfluorophosphate-sensitive esterase, and energy derived from glycolysis. The process appears to be bidirectionally controlled since secretion appears to vary with intracellular concentrations of cAMP and cGMP. Cyclic nucleotide levels, in turn, may be responsive to native hormones, pharmacologic agents, and autonomic nervous system stimulation.

Results obtained from these in vitro studies, however, are difficult to apply to the whole organism for the following reasons: 1. isolated tissues containing mixed cell populations were used; 2. preparative procedures may have exposed receptors in cell membranes not normally accessible in vivo to the pharmacologic agonists; 3. studies of lung tissue contained parenchyma but few airways; and 4. the tissues were stripped of normal parasympathetic and sympathetic innervation. The precise relationship between the cyclic nucleotides, release of mediators, hormone action, the autonomic nervous system and airway smooth muscle contraction in vivo remains to be defined in allergic diseases. It may then be possible to test the provocative hypothesis of Bourne and his associates that certain hormones and mediators of inflammation regulate the character and intensity of inflammatory and immune responses in vivo by the general inhibitory action of cAMP on leukocyte function (17).

DEFENSE MECHANISMS OF THE ALVEOLI

Clearance of Particles

It is evident from many studies of pneumoconiosis and some pulmonary infections of man that some particles gain access to pulmonary parenchyma and lymphoid tissues of the lungs (136). Godwin & Jagatic (66) regularly found fibers and fragments of asbestos bodies in the hilar and mediastinal lymph nodes of humans at autopsy. Many studies of parenchymal clearance of deposited particles showed that a slow clearance of particles from the lungs to the lymph nodes occurred over the duration of studies that lasted up to 7 yr (109, 132, 199). Controversy exists regarding clearance of particles from alveoli (136). It is not clear, however, whether particles within the alveolar interstitium or lymphatics is evidence of a cytotoxic reaction, or whether particles can penetrate cells by endocytosis (26, 103, 193).

Physiological Responses

Although sensory nerve endings have been described in the pulmonary parenchyma (89), their role in mediating physiological responses to inhaled particles remains to be determined. Small nonmyelinated vagal fibers are said to subserve J receptors possibly located in the alveolar septa (154, 223). They are stimulated by pulmonary congestion and edema, microembolism, and inhalation of some irritants. Since their reflex response causes rapid shallow breathing as well as hypotension and bradycardia, they may play a role in the ventilatory abnormalities occurring in diseases affecting this region of the lung. These receptors appear to have no role in regulation of airway caliber or in normal physiological conditions. They could be part of a general "nociceptive" sensory system in the lungs (223), particularly when inflammatory or immune responses cause decreased lung volumes and distensibility with or without pulmonary vascular obstruction (16, 102, 124).

Immune and Antimicrobial Responses

LOCAL IMMUNE MECHANSIMS The segregation of the immune system of the respiratory tract from that of the rest of the organism has been alluded to in the discussion of nasal and airway immune systems. The lower respiratory tract also reacts as a sequestered system to some extent, and under proper experimental conditions, immune responses can be demonstrated with lymphocytes washed from lungs after immunization by the respiratory but not by the systemic route (82, 211, 212). Although lymphocytes lavaged from lungs of animals sensitized via the airways can function as *B* cells (antibody production) or *T* cells (macrophage migration inhibition), lymphocytes that reside in lungs of nonimmunized animals appear to have only *B* cell functions. Therefore, the *T* cells must be recruited from the blood.

Immune mechanisms in the lung may contribute to hypersensitivity states that result in lung diseases. These possible mechanisms have recently been reviewed by McCombs (124). They will not be reviewed here except to note that when antigen particles are deposited in the lower respiratory tract, the immune response initiated involves IgG antibody and cellular or delayed hypersensitivity mechanisms. The physiological responses, in general, include decreased lung volumes and diffusing capacity associated with increased lung elastic recoil (102, 124).

ANTIMICROBIAL DEFENSES Even though the lung is the route of entry used by many intracellular organisms that are clinically important, the lungs are less resistant than liver and spleen to intravenously administered tubercle bacilli (165). Mackaness recently reviewed cell-mediated immunity and its relevance to defense of the lung against intracellular microorganisms and to hypersensitivity pneumonitis (82, 118, 119). Current concepts suggest that when thymus-derived lymphocytes (*T* cells) are sensitized by antigens and subsequently stimulated by antigenic challenge they undergo a proliferative or blastogenic response. The stimulated *T* lymphocytes elaborate chemical mediators of many biologic phenomena. These factors cause the sequestration of monocytes in areas containing the stimulated lymphocytes and antigens such as tubercle bacilli. The macrophages change metabolically and increase their ability to kill intracellular microorganisms. The macrophages responsible for limiting infections in the lungs are recruited from the blood stream and are not the resident alveolar macrophages (208). Other evidence suggests that the alveolar macrophage population is heterogeneous (37) and that it is different from the cell usually found to be involved in cellular immune reactions. Heise & Weiser (81) showed that alveolar macrophages undergo inhibition of migration in the presence of antigen and lymphocytes, but that the reaction was mediated by a cell-associated immunoglobulin rather than by the migration-inhibiting factor (MIF) as found in other macrophages. Leu and his co-workers found that guinea pig alveolar macrophages lack the MIF receptor on their surface (165). These and a great deal of other data suggest that the alveolar macrophage is functionally different from other macrophages in the body.

The rapid disappearance of bacteria from lungs of animals after aerosolization of the microorganisms is well documented (108, 167, 191). However, it was not until Green & Kass (75) devised their classic experiments to investigate this phenomenon that alveolar macrophages were identified as the major defense of the lung against inhaled bacteria. Radioisotope-labeled bacteria were aerosolized into the lungs of mice and at varied periods the animals were killed and their lungs homogenized.

Quantitative bacterial cultures and radioactive counts were done on the homogenates. These experiments showed that, although bacterial colony counts declined to negligible numbers by four hours, the radioactive counts in the lung tissue remained at the initial postaerosol levels. These data showed that the bacteria were killed in the lung, rather than being cleared from the lung. The investigators then stained lung sections with fluorescein-labeled antisera against the microorganisms. They found fluorescence in phagocytic cells on the surface of alveoli and respiratory bronchioles. After an initial lag period, during which time bronchial cultures were negative, small numbers of *P. mirabilis* organisms were cultured from macrophages obtained from the bronchi. This observation suggests that the macrophages are ultimately cleared (at least partially) through the trachea via the mucociliary coat. This bacterial clearing mechanism of the lungs mimics clinical phenomena such as the increased susceptibility of lungs to infections in the presence of viruses, alcohol, cold, and hypoxia (74). In addition to the apparent bactericidal action of the alveolar macrophage, aerosolization of bacteria (78) or inert particles (105) causes an increased number of macrophages retrieved with lung washes.

Alveolar macrophages contain lysozyme and proteolytic enzymes that may contribute to bactericidal activity (39); however, cationic proteins that can be extracted from neutrophils and that are bactericidal in vitro have not been demonstrated in alveolar macrophages (39). The digestion of intracellular pathogens by phagocytes has been followed through the use of isotopically-labeled organisms. Stähelin et al (189) showed that ^{14}C-labeled live tubercle bacilli sustained some oxidation to carbon dioxide. After both ^{14}C and ^{32}P labeling of organisms, extensive degradation of bacterial macro-molecules occurred with the formation of acid-soluble products. This was preceded by a period during which the organism lost its pool of small molecular weight intermediates, suggesting an initial defect in the bacterial plasma membrane (38). The majority of degraded material was subsequently liberated into the medium.

Nakashima (150) did not observe intracellular multiplication of virulent tubercle bacilli inside normal alveolar macrophages when the macrophages were innoculated with relatively small doses of virulent tubercle bacilli. However, when more than 30 bacilli were ingested, the alveolar macrophages were killed. This limited dose of bacilli was similar in macrophages from BCG-sensitized animals. In addition, Cornforth and co-workers (45) showed that animals treated with the surface-active agent WR-1339 were more resistant to challenge with tubercle bacilli. Mackaness (117) found increased resistance of moncytes from treated animals, and D'Arcy Hart (46) found both anti- and protuberculous surfactants that affected lysosomal enzyme activity in infected macrophages. These surface-active compounds were probably stored in cell lysosomes and interacted with various membranes to affect permeability. In light of the ability of alveolar and other phagocytes to produce and/or ingest surface-active materials (33, 129), the possibility could be raised that endogenously produced surfactant may also affect microbial killing. Recently, LaForce and his colleagues demonstrated that the acellular material from lung washes, including surface-active material, could augment the ability of alveolar macrophages to ingest and kill *S. aureus* (106).

Comparative studies of the ability of human alveolar macrophages, neutrophils, and monocyte-derived macrophages to kill *L. monocytogenes* and *K. pneumoniae* showed that alveolar macrophages resembled macrophages derived from monocytes in their ability to kill bacteria (36).

Therefore, cellular and humoral immune mechanisms combine with an effective antibacterial phagocytic system to render the alveolar regions microbiologically sterile in normal animals. These systems have been little studied in vivo in man, but techniques for such studies are currently becoming available.

CONCLUSION

The defense of the respiratory system against inhaled particles involves the integration of many complex biochemical, physiological, and immunological processes that interact with the properties of the inhaled particles. While many of the defense mechanisms have counterparts elsewhere in the body, these mechanisms have been uniquely adapted to suit the defense of their own environment. The integration of various defense mechanisms is determined by the limitations imposed by the structural anatomy of their immediate environment. We believe it is likely that in coming years the integral dependence of defense mechanisms on the precise anatomic and physiologic environment will become even more apparent and a full understanding of the system will be accomplished by scientists who cross the lines of recognized academic disciplines and appreciate the specific contributions of anatomic, physiologic, biochemical, and immunologic phenomena.

Literature Cited

1. Adinofli, M., Glynn, A. A., Lindsay, M., Milne, C. M. 1966. Serological properties of γA antibodies to *Escherichia coli* present in human colostrum. *Immunology* 10:517–26
2. Alford, R. H., Kasel, J. A., Gerone, J. P., Knight, V. 1966. Human influenza resulting from aerosol inhalation. *Proc. Soc. Exp. Biol. Med.* 122:800–4
3. Amdur, M. O. 1966. Respiratory absorption data and SO_2 dose-response curves. *Arch. Environ. Health* 12: 729–32
4. American Chemical Society. 1969. *Clearing our Environment: The Chemical Basis for Action.* Washington DC: Am. Chem. Soc.
5. Andersen, I., Lundqvist, G. R., Proctor, D. F. 1971. Human nasal mucosal function in a controlled climate. *Arch. Environ. Health* 23:408–20
6. Anderson, D. O. 1967. The effects of air contamination on health. *Can. Med. Assoc. J.* 97:(I) 528–36, (II) 585–93, (III) 802–6
7. Austen, K. F. 1973. A review of immunological, biochemical, and pharmacological factors in the release of chemical mediators from human lung. In *Asthma: Physiology, Immunopharmacology and Treatment,* ed. K. F. Austen, L. M. Lichtenstein, 109–22. New York: Academic. 314 pp.
8. Banister, J., Fegler, G., Hebb, C. 1949. Initial respiratory responses to intratracheal inhalation of phosgene or ammonia. *Quart. J. Exp. Physiol.* 35: 233–50
9. Barton, A. D., Lourenco, R. V. 1971. γ-Glutamyl transpeptidase and possible cross-linking in bronchial secretions. *Fed. Proc.* 30(3):1146 (Abstr.)
10. Barton, A. D., Lourenco, R. V. 1973. Bronchial secretions and mucociliary clearance: biochemical characteristics. *Arch. Intern. Med.* 131:140–44
11. Barton, A. D., Powers, J. L., Lourenco, R. V. 1972. Chemical bonding in sputum gels. *J. Clin. Invest.* 51:9a (Abstr.)
12. Bates, D. V. 1972. Air pollutants and the human lung. *Am. Rev. Resp. Dis.* 105:1–13
13. Bazarel, M., Orgal, H. A., Hamburger, R. M. 1971. IgE levels in normal infants

and mothers and an inheritance hypothesis. *J. Immunol.* 107:794–801

14. Beeckmans, J. M. 1972. Deposition of ellipsoidal particles in the human respiratory tract. *Assessment of Airborne Particles,* ed. T. T. Mercer, P. E. Morrow, W. Stöber, 361–70. Springfield, Ill.: Thomas. 540 pp.
15. Benacerraf, B., McDevitt, H. O. 1972. Histocompatibility-linked immune response genes. *Science* 175:273–79
16. Bouhuys, A., Peters, J. M. 1970. Control of environmental lung disease. *N. Engl. J. Med.* 283:573–82
17. Bourne, H. R. et al 1974. Modulation of inflammation and immunity by cyclic AMP. *Science* 184:19–28
18. Boushey, H. A., Richardson, P. S. 1973. The reflex effects of intralaryngeal carbon dioxide on the patterns of breathing. *J. Physiol. London* 228:181–91
19. Boushey, H. A., Richardson, P. S., Widdicombe, J. G. 1972. Reflex effects of laryngeal irritation on the pattern of breathing and total lung resistance. *J. Physiol. London* 224:501–13
20. Brocklehurst, W. E. 1960. The release of histamine and formation of a slow-reacting substance (SRS-A) during anaphylactic shock. *J. Physiol. London* 151:416–35
21. Brokaw, C. J. 1966. Mechanics and energetics of cilia. *Am. Rev. Resp. Dis.* 93:32–40
22. Bucher, K. 1958. Pathophysiology and pharmacology of cough. *Pharmacol. Rev.* 10:43–58
23. Busse, W. W., Reed, C. E., Hoehne, J. H. 1972. Where is the allergic reaction in ragweed asthma? II. Demonstration of ragweed antigen in airborne particles smaller than pollen. *J. Allergy Clin. Immunol.* 50:289–93
24. Butler, W. T., Waldman, T. A., Rossen, R. D., Douglas, R. G. Jr., Couch, R. B. 1970. Changes in IgA and IgG concentrations in nasal secretions prior to the appearance of antibody during viral respiratory infection in man. *J. Immunol.* 105:584–91
25. Cabezas, G. A., Graf, P. D., Nadel, J. A. 1971. Sympathetic versus parasympathetic nervous regulation of airways in dogs. *J. Appl. Physiol.* 31:651–55
26. Casarett, L. J., Milley, P. S. 1964. Alveolar reactivity following inhalation of particles. *Health Phys.* 10:1003–11
27. Cate, T. R. 1973. Interferons. In *Viral and Mycoplasmal Infections of the Respiratory Tract,* ed. V. Knight, 53–64. Philadelphia: Lea & Febiger. 250 pp.
28. Cate, T. R., Buckley, C. E. III, McMahon, S. M., Halprin, G. M., Zitt, M. J. 1970. Interferon activity from serum and lymphocytes during influenza. *Clin. Res.* 18:85 (Abstr.)
29. Cate, T. R., Douglas, R. G. Jr., Couch, R. B. 1969. Interferon and resistance to upper respiratory virus illness. *Proc. Soc. Exp. Biol. Med.* 131:631–36
30. Cate, T. R., Kelly, J. R. 1970. Hong Kong influenza antigen sensitivity and decreased interferon response to peripheral lymphocytes. *Antimicrob. Ag. Chemother.* 10:156–60
31. Cate, T. R., Rossen, R. D., Douglas, R. G. Jr., Butler, W. T., Couch, R. B. 1966. The role of nasal secretion and serum antibody in the rhinovirus common cold. *Am. J. Epidemiol.* 84:352–363
32. Chamberlain, D. W., Nopajaroonsri, C., Simon, G. T. 1973. Ultrastructure of the pulmonary lymphoid tissue. *Am. Rev. Resp. Dis.* 108:621–31
33. Chanock, R. M. 1968. Possible role of immunological factors in pathogenesis of R. S. virus in lower respiratory tract disease. In *Virus-Induced Immunopathology,* ed. E. Pollard, 125–39. New York: Academic. 344 pp.
34. Claman, H. N., Mosier, D. Z. 1972. Cell-cell interactions in antibody production. *Progr. Allergy* 16:40–80
35. Clarke, S. W., Graf, P. D., Nadel, J. A. 1970. In vivo visualization of small-airway constriction after pulmonary microembolism in cats and dogs. *J. Appl. Physiol.* 29:646–50
36. Cohen, A. B., Cline, M. J. 1971. The human alveolar macrophage: isolation, cultivation in vitro, and studies of morphologic and functional characteristics. *J. Clin. Invest.* 50:1390–98
37. Cohen, A. B., Geczy, D. 1973. Purification of two populations of human alveolar macrophages from surgical specimens. *Am. Rev. Resp. Dis.* 108:972–75
38. Cohn, Z. A. 1963. The fate of bacteria within phagocytic cells. I. The degradation of isotopically labeled bacteria by polymorphonuclear leukocytes and macrophages. *J. Exp. Med.* 117:(I)27–42, (II) 43–53
39. Cohn, Z. A. 1968. The structure and function of monocytes and macrophages. *Advan. Immunol.* 9:163–214
40. Colebatch, H. J. H., Olsen, C. R., Nadel, J. A. 1966. Effect of histamine, serotonin, and acetylcholine on the pe-

ripheral airways. *J. Appl. Physiol.* 21:217–26
41. Colebatch, H. J. H., Olsen, C. R., Nadel, J. A. 1966. Effects of 48/80 on the mechanical properties of the lungs. *J. Appl. Physiol.* 21:379–82
42. Corn, M. 1972. Urban aerosols: problems associated with evaluation of inhalation risk. See Ref. 14, 465–79
43. Corn, M., Demaio, L. 1965. Particulate sulfates in Pittsburgh air. *J. Air Pollut. Contr. Assoc.* 15:26–30
44. Corn, M., Montgomery, T. L., Reitz, R. J. 1968. Atmospheric particulates: specific surface areas and densities. *Science* 159:1350–51
45. Cornforth, J., D'Arcy Hart, P., Rees, R., Stock, J. 1951. Antituberculous effect of certain surface active polyoxyethylene ethers in mice. *Nature* 168:150–53
46. D'Arcy Hart, P. 1968. Mycobacterium tuberculosis in macrophages: effect of certain surfactants and other membrane-active compounds. *Science* 162: 686–89
47. Dautrebande, L., Lovejoy, F. W. Jr., McCredie, R. M. 1962. New studies on aerosols XVII. Effects of atropine microaerosols on the airway resistance in man. *Arch. Intern. Pharmacodyn.* 139: 198–211
48. Dautrebande, L., Robillard, E., Stone, H. 1960. New studies on aerosols: Effect of sympathomimetic aerosols upon the respiratory reflexes induced by dusting of the supraglottic airways in the dog. *Arch. Intern. Pharmacodyn.* 129: 455–68
49. Davenport, F. M. 1961. Pathogenesis of influenza. *Bacteriol. Rev.* 25:294–300
50. Davis, B. D., Delbecco, R., Eisen, H. N., Ginsberg, H. S., Wood, W. B. 1967. Host-parasite relations in bacterial diseases. In *Microbiology,* 620–21. New York: Harper & Row. 1464 pp.
51. Davis, B. D., Delbecco, R., Eisen, H. N., Ginsberg, H. S., Wood, W. B. 1967. Bacteria indigenous to man. See Ref. 50, 924
52. DeKock, M. A., Nadel, J. A., Zwi, S., Colebatch, H. J. H., Olsen, C. R. 1966. New method for perfusing bronchial arteries: histamine bronchoconstriction and apnea. *J. Appl. Physiol.* 21:185–94
53. Dennis, W. L. 1971. The effect of breathing rate on the deposition of particles in the human respiratory system. In *Inhaled Particles and Vapours, III,* ed. W. Walton, 1:91–102. Surrey: Gresham. 570 pp.
54. Donovan, R., Johansson, S. G. O., Bennich, H., Soothill, J. F. 1970. Immunoglobulins in nasal polyp fluid. *Int. Arch. Allergy* 37:154–66
55. DuBois, A. B., Dautrebande, L. 1958. Acute effects of breathing inert dust particles and of carbachol aerosol on the mechanical characteristics of the lungs in man. Changes in response after inhaling sympathomimetic aerosols. *J. Clin. Invest.* 37:1746–55
56. Duthie, E. S. 1930. Phagocytosis by bronchial epithelium in the lungs of mice. *J. Pathol. Bacteriol.* 33:547–551
57. Ehrenkranz, N. Y. 1966. Nasal rejection of experimentally inoculated *Staphylococcus aureus:* evidence for an immune reaction in man. *J. Immunol.* 96:509–17
58. Eichenwald, H. F., Kotsevalov, O., Fasso, L. A. 1961. Some effects of viral infection on aerial dissemination of staphylococci and on susceptibility to bacterial colonization. *Bacteriol. Rev.* 25:274–81
59. Fillenz, M., Widdicombe, J. G. 1972. Receptors of the lungs and airways. In *Enteroceptors: Handbook of Sensory Physiology III,* ed. E. Neil, 81–112. Berlin: Springer. 233 pp.
60. Fillenz, M., Woods, R. I. 1970. Sensory innervation of the airways. In *Breathing: Hering-Breuer Centenary Symposium,* a Ciba Foundation Symposium, ed. R. Porter, 101–7. London: Churchill. 402 pp.
61. First, M. W. 1973. Aerosols in Nature. *Arch. Intern. Med.* 131:24–32
62. Fleisch, J. H., Kent, K. M., Cooper, T. 1973. Drug receptors in smooth muscle. In *Asthma: Physiology, Immunopharmacology and Treatment,* ed. K. A. Austen, L. M. Lichtenstein, 139–67. New York: Academic. 314 pp.
63. Frank, N. R., Amdur, M. O., Worchester, J., Whittenberger, J. L. 1962. Effects of acute controlled exposure to SO_2 on respiratory mechanics in healthy male adults. *J. Appl. Physiol.* 17:252–58
64. Gamsu, G., Weintraub, R. M., Nadel, J. A. 1973. Clearance of tantalum from airways of different caliber in man evaluated by a roentgenographic method. *Am. Rev. Resp. Dis.* 107:214–24
65. Gerber, M. A., Paronetti, F., Kochwa, S. 1971. Immunohistochemical localization of IgE in asthmatic lungs. *Am. J. Pathol.* 62:339–52
66. Godwin, M. C., Jagatic, J. 1970. Asbes-

tos and mesotheliomas. *Environ. Res.* 3:391–416
67. Golbert, T. M., Patterson, R. 1970. Pulmonary allergic aspergillosis. *Ann. Intern. Med.* 72:395–403
68. Gold, W. M. 1973. Cholinergic pharmacology in asthma. In *Asthma: Physiology, Immunopharmacology and Treatment,* ed. K. F. Austen, L. M. Lichtenstein, 169–84. New York: Academic. 314 pp.
69. Gold, W. M., Kessler, G.-F., Yu, D. Y. C. 1972. Role of vagus nerves in experimental asthma in allergic dogs. *J. Appl. Physiol.* 33:719–25
70. Gold, W. M., Kessler, G.-F., Yu, D. Y. C., Frick, O. L. 1972. Pulmonary physiologic abnormalities in experimental asthma in dogs. *J. Appl. Physiol.* 33:496–501
71. Goldberg, I. S., Lourenco, R. V. 1973. Deposition of aerosols in pulmonary disease. *Arch. Intern. Med.* 131:88–91
72. Goldsmith, J. R., Nadel, J. A. 1969. Experimental exposure of human subjects to ozone. *J. Air Pollut. Contr. Assoc.* 19:329–30
73. Gottschalk, A. 1960. Correlation between composition, structure, shape, and function of a salivary mucoprotein. *Nature* 186:949–51
74. Green, L. H., Green, G. M. 1968. Differential suppression of pulmonary antibacterial activity as the mechanism of selection of a pathogen in mixed bacterial infection of the lung. *Am. Rev. Resp. Dis.* 98:819–24
75. Green, G. M., Kass, E. H. 1964. The role of the alveolar macrophage in the clearance of bacteria from the lung. *J. Exp. Med.* 119:167–75
76. Greenert, S., Bernstein, I. L., Michael, J. G. 1971. Immune responses of nonatopic individuals to prolonged immunization with ragweed extract. *Lancet* 2:1121–23
77. Grossberg, S. E. 1972. The interferons and their inducers: molecular and therapeutic considerations. *New Engl. J. Med.* 287:(I) 13–19, (II) 79–85, (III) 122–28
78. Guarneri, J. J., Laurenzi, G. A. 1968. Effect of alcohol on the mobilization of alveolar macrophages. *J. Lab. Clin. Med.* 72:40–51
79. Halliwell, R. E. W. 1973. The localization of IgE in skin: an immunofluorescent study. *J. Immunol.* 110:422–30
80. Hebb, C. 1968. Motor innervation of the pulmonary blood vessels of mammals. In *The Pulmonary Circulation and Interstitial Tissue,* ed. A. P. Fishman, H. H. Hecht, 195–222. Chicago, Ill.: Univ. Chicago Press. 432 pp.
81. Heise, E. R., Han, S., Weiser, R. S. 1968. In vitro studies on the mechanism of macrophage migration inhibition in tuberculin sensitivity. *J. Immunol.* 101:1004–15
82. Henney, C. S., Waldman, R. H. 1970. Cell-mediated immunity shown by lymphocytes from the respiratory tract. *Science* 169:696–97
83. Hidy, G. M. 1972. The dynamics of aerosols in the lower troposphere. See Ref. 14, 81–115
84. Hilding, A. 1931. Ciliary activity and course of secretion currents of the nose. *Proc. Staff Meet. Mayo Clin.* 6:285–87
85. Hirsch, J. A., Tokayer, J. L. 1973. The effects of dry air and subsequent humidification on tracheal mucous velocity in dogs. *Physiologist* 16:342 (Abstr.)
86. Hobday, J. D., Townley, R. G. 1971. Deposition of inhaled pollen grains in the lower respiratory tract of the guinea pig. *J. Allergy Clin. Immunol.* 48: 254–56
87. Hoehne, J. H., Reed, C. E. 1971. Where is the allergic reaction in ragweed asthma? *J. Allergy Clin. Immunol.* 48:36–39
88. Holub, M., Hauser, R. E. 1969. Lung alveolar histiocytes engaged in antibody production. *Immunology* 17:207–26
89. Hung, K.-S., Hertweck, M. S., Hardy, J. D., Looslj, C. G. 1973. Innervation of pulmonary alveoli of the mouse lung: an electron microscopic study. *Am. J. Anat.* 135:477–96
90. Hurlimann, J. 1971. Immunoglobin synthesis and transport by human salivary glands: immunological mechanisms of the mucous membrane *Curr. Top. Pathol.* 55:69–108
91. Ingelstedt, S. 1956. Studies on the conditioning of air in the respiratory tract. *Acta Oto Laryngol. Suppl.* 131:1–42
92. Ishizaka, K., Ishizaka, T. 1970. The significance of immunoglobulin E in reaginic hypersensitivity. *Ann. Allergy* 28:189–202
93. Ishizaka, K., Ishizaka, T. 1973. Role of IgE and IgG antibodies in reagenic hypersensitivity in the respiratory tract. See Ref. 68, 55–70
94. Ishizaka, K., Ishizaka, T., Lee, E., Fudenberg, H. 1965. Immunochemical properties of human γA-isohemagglutinin. I. Comparisons with γG and γM-globulin antibodies. *J. Immunol.* 95: 197–208

95. Jacobson, A. R. 1962. Natural sources of air pollution. In *Air Pollution,* ed. A. C. Stern, 1:175–208. New York: Academic. 586 pp.
96. Karczewski, W. 1962. The electrical activity of the vagus nerve in anaphylactic shock. *Acta Allergol.* 17:334–42
97. Karczewski, W., Widdicombe, J. G. 1969. The role of the vagus nerves in the respiratory and circulatory reactions to anaphylaxis in rabbits. *J. Physiol. London* 201:293–304
98. Kaufman, J., Wright, G. W. 1969. The effect of nasal and nasopharyngeal irritation on airway resistance in man. *Am. Rev. Resp. Dis.* 100:626–30
99. Kempe, C. H. 1960. Studies on smallpox and complications of smallpox vaccination. *Pediatrics* 26:176–89
100. Kessler, G.-F., Austin, J. H. M., Graf, P. D., Gamsu, G., Gold, W. M. 1973. Airway constriction in experimental asthma in dogs: tantalum bronchographic studies. *J. Appl. Physiol.* 35: 703–8
101. Kessler, G.-F., Frick, O. L., Gold, W. M. 1974. Immunologic and physiologic characterization of the role of reagenic antibodies in experimental asthma in dogs. *Int. Arch. Allergy Appl. Immunol.* In press
102. Kilburn, K. H., Ed. 1974. Pulmonary reactions to organic materials *Ann. NY Acad. Sci.* 221:1–390
103. Klosterkötter, W., Einbrodt, H. J. 1967. Retention, penetration and elimination of inhaled dusts. In *Inhaled Particles and Vapours II,* ed. C. N. Davies, 2:215–27. Oxford/New York: Pergamon. 605 pp.
104. Knight, V., Kasel, J. A. 1973. Influenza virus—M. See Ref. 27, 98–99
105. LaBelle, C., Brieger, H. 1961. Patterns and mechanisms in the elimination of dust from the lung. See Ref. 103, 356–65
106. LaForce, F. M., Kelly, W. J., Huber, G. L. 1973. Inactivation of staphylococci by alveolar macrophages with preliminary observations on the importance of alveolar lining materal. *Am. Rev. Resp. Dis.* 108:784–90
107. Lall, A., Graf, P. D., Nadel, J. A., Edmunds, L. H. Jr. 1973. Adrenergic reinnervation of the reimplanted dog lung. *J. Appl. Physiol.* 35:439–42
108. Laurenzi, G. A., Berman, L., First, M., Kass, E. H. 1964. A quantitative study of the deposition and clearance of bacteria in the murine lung. *J. Clin. Invest.* 43:759–68
109. Leach, L. J. 1970. A five-year inhalation study with natural uranium dioxide (UO_2) dust—I. Retention and biologic effect in the monkey, dog, and rat. *Health Phys.* 18:599–612
110. Lee, R. E. Jr. 1972. The size of suspended particulate matter in air. *Science* 178:567–75
111. Levine, B. B. 1968. Genetic factors in hypersensitivity reactions to drugs. *Ann. NY Acad. Sci.* 151:988–96
112. Levine, B. B., Stember, R. H., Fotimo, M. 1972. Ragweed hay fever: genetic control and linkage to HL-A haplotypes. *Science* 178:1201–3
113. Lichtenstein, L. M. 1973. The control of IgE-mediated histamine release: Implications for the study of asthma. See Ref. 68, 91–107
114. Lichtenstein, L. M., Osler, A. G. 1964. Studies on the mechanisms of hypersensitivity phenomena: IX. Histamine release from human leukocytes by ragweed pollen antigen. *J. Exp. Med.* 120:507–30
115. Lieberman, J., Kurnick, N. B. 1963. Proteolytic enzyme activity and the role of desoxyribose nucleic acid (DNA) in cystic fibrosis sputum. *Pediatrics* 31: 1028–32
116. Lucas, A. M., Douglas, L. C. 1934. Principles underlying ciliary activity in the respiratory tract. II. A comparison of nasal clearance in man, monkey and other mammals. *Arch. Otolaryngol.* 20:518–41
117. Mackaness, G. B. 1954. Artificial cellular immunity against tubercle bacilli: an effect of polyoxyethylene ethers (Triton). *Am. Rev. Tuberc. Pulm. Dis.* 69:690–704
118. Mackaness, G. B. 1970. Cell-mediated immunity to infection. *Hosp. Pract.* 5:73–86
119. Mackaness, G. B. 1971. The J. Burns Amberson Lecture—the induction and expression of cell-mediated hypersensitivity in the lung. *Am. Rev. Resp. Dis.* 104:813–28
120. Macklem, C. C. 1955. Pulmonary sumps, dust accumulations, alveolar fluid and lymph vessels. *Acta Anat.* 23:1–33
121. Macklem, P. T. 1971. Airway obstruction of collateral ventilation. *Physiol. Rev.* 51:368–436
122. Macklem, P. T., Hogg, W. E., Brunton, J. 1973. Peripheral airway obstruction and particulate deposition in the lung. *Arch. Intern. Med.* 131:93–97

123. McCombs, R. P. 1965. Systemic "allergic" vasculitis: clinical and pathological relationships. *J. Am. Med. Assoc.* 194: 1059–64
124. McCombs, R. P. 1972. Diseases due to immunologic reactions in the lungs. *N. Engl. J. Med.* 286:(I) 1186–94, (II) 1245–52
125. McCormick, D. P., Wenzel, R. P., Davies, J. A., Beam, W. E. 1972. Nasal secretion protein responses in patients with wild-type adenovirus disease. *Infec. Immunol.* 6:282–88
126. McDevitt, H. O., Bodmer, W. F. 1972. Histocompatibility antigens, immune responsiveness and susceptability to disease. *Am. J. Med.* 52:1–8
127. Mann, S. P. 1971. The innervation of mammalian bronchial smooth muscle: the localization of catecholamines and cholinesterases. *Histochem. J.* 3:319–31
128. Marin, M. G., Davis, B., Olver, R. E., Nadel, J. A. 1974. Chloride transport across canine tracheal epithelium. *Am. Rev. Resp. Dis.* 109:731 (Abstr.)
129. Mason, R. J., Huber, G., Vaughan, M. 1972. Synthesis of dipalmitoyl lecithin by alveolar macrophages. *J. Clin. Invest.* 51:68–73
130. Massing, H. 1917. Pathophysiology of the nasal airflow. *Int. Rhinol.* 5:63–67
131. Matacic, S., Loewy, A. G. 1968. The identification of isopeptide crosslinks in insoluble fibrin. *Biochem. Biophys. Res. Commun.* 30:356–62
132. Mercer, T. T. 1967. On the role of particle size in the dissolution of lung burdens. *Health Phys.* 13:1211–21
133. Mills, J. E., Sellick, H., Widdicombe, J. G. 1969. Activity of lung irritant receptors in pulmonary microembolism, anaphylaxis and drug-induced bronchoconstriction. *J. Physiol. London* 203: 337–57
134. Mills, J. E., Sellick, H., Widdicombe, J. G. 1970. Epithelial irritant receptors in the lungs. See Ref. 60, 77–92
135. Mills, J. E., Widdicombe, J. G. 1970. Role of the vagus nerves in anaphylaxis and histamine-induced bronchoconstrictions in guinea pigs. *Brit. J. Pharmacol.* 39:724–31
136. Morrow, P. E. 1971. Lymphatic drainage of the lung in dust clearance. *Ann. NY Acad. Sci.* 200:46–65
137. Murphy, S. D., Ulrich, C. E., Frankowitz, S. H., Xintaras, C. 1964. Altered function in animals inhaling low concentrations of ozone and nitrogen dioxide. *Am. Ind. Hyg. Assoc. J.* 25:246–53
138. Nadel, J. A. 1965. Structure-function relationships in the airways: bronchoconstriction mediated via vagus nerves or bronchial arteries; peripheral lung constriction mediated via pulmonary arteries. *Med. Thorac.* 22:231–42
139. Nadel, J. A. 1973. Neurophysiologic aspects of asthma. See Ref. 68, 29–38
140. Nadel, J. A. 1974. Physiology of airway smooth muscle. *Physiol. Rev.* In press
141. Nadel, J. A., Cabezas, G. A., Austin, J. H. M. 1971. In vivo roentgenographic examination of parasympathetic innervation of small airways: use of powdered tantalum and a fine focal spot X-ray tube. *Invest. Radiol.* 6:9–17
142. Nadel, J. A., Colebatch, H. J. H., Olsen, C. R. 1964. Localization and mechanism of airway constriction after barium sulfate microembolism. *J. Appl. Physiol.* 19:387–394
143. Nadel, J. A., Comroe, J. H. Jr. 1961. Acute effects of inhalation of cigarette smoke on airway conduction. *J. Appl. Physiol.* 16:713–16
144. Nadel, J. A., Corn, M., Zwi, S., Flesch, J., Graf, P. 1967. Location and mechanism of airway constriction after inhalation of histamine aerosol and inorganic sulfate aerosol. See Ref. 103, 55–67
145. Nadel, J. A., Salem, H., Tamplin, B., Tokiwa, Y. 1965. Mechanism of bronchoconstriction during inhalation of sulfur dioxide. *J. Appl. Physiol.* 20: 164–67
146. Nadel, J. A., Widdicombe, J. G. 1962. Reflex effects of upper airway irritation on total lung resistance and blood pressure. *J. Appl. Physiol.* 17:861–65
147. Nadel, J. A., Widdicombe, J. G. 1962. Effect of changes in blood gas tensions and carotid sinus pressure on tracheal volume and total lung resistance to airflow. *J. Physiol. London* 163:13–33
148. Nagaishi, C. 1972. *Functional Anatomy and Histology of the Lung,* 5–6. Baltimore/London: Univ. Park Press. 205 pp.
149. Nail, B. S., Sterling, G. M., Widdicombe, J. G. 1969. Epipharyngeal receptors responding to mechanical stimulation. *J. Physiol. London* 204: 91–98
150. Nakashima, M. 1965. Studies on the resistance of rabbit alveolar macrophages to the toxicity of tubercle bacilli in tissue culture. *Acta Tuberc. Jap.* 14:75–88
151. Novey, H. S., Wilson, A. F., Surprenant, E. L., Bennett, L. R. 1970. Early ventilation-perfusion changes in asthma. *J. Allergy* 46:221–30

152. Olsen, C. R., Colebatch, H. J. H., Mebel, P. E., Nadel, J. A., Staub, N. C. 1965. Motor control of pulmonary airways studied by nerve stimulation. *J. Appl. Physiol.* 20:202–8
153. Owen, P. R. 1969. Turbulent flow and particle deposition on the trachea. In *Circulation and Respiratory Mass Transport,* a Ciba Foundation Symposium, ed. G. E. W. Wolstenholme, J. Knight, 236–255. London: Churchill. 310 pp.
154. Paintel, A. S. 1973. Vagal sensory receptors and their reflex effects. *Physiol. Rev.* 53:159–227
155. Patterson, R. 1960. Investigation of spontaneous hypersensitivity of the dog. *J. Allergy* 31:351–63
156. Patterson, R., Head, L. R., Suszko, I. M., Zeiss, C. R. Jr. 1972. Mast cells from human respiratory tissues and their in vitro reactivity. *Science* 175:1012–14
157. Patterson, R., Suszko, I. M., Zeiss, C. R. Jr. 1972. Reactions of primate respiratory mast cells. *J. Allergy Clin. Immunol.* 50:7–17
158. Pepys, J. 1973. Disodium cromoglycate in clinical and experimental asthma. See Ref. 68, 279–94
159. Pflug, A. E., Cheney, F. W. Jr., Butler, J. 1970. The effects of an ultrasonic aerosol on pulmonary mechanics and arterial blood gases in patients with chronic bronchitis. *Am. Rev. Resp. Dis.* 101:710–14
160. Potter, J. L., Spector, S., Matthews, L. W., Lemm, J. 1969. Studies on pulmonary secretions. III. The nucleic acids in whole pulmonary secretions from patients with cystic fibrosis, bronchiectasis, and laryngectomy. *Am. Rev. Resp. Dis.* 99:909–16
161. Proctor, D. F. 1974. The upper respiratory tract and the ambient air. *Clin. Notes Resp. Dis.* 12:2–10
162. Proctor, D. F., Andersen, I., Lundqvist, G. 1973. Clearance of inhaled particles from the human nose. *Arch. Intern. Med.* 131:132–39
163. Proetz, A. W. 1933. Studies of nasal cilia in the living mammal. *Ann. Otol. Rhinol. Laryngol.* 42:778–88
164. Reasor, M. J., Adams, G. K. III, Rubin, R. J., Proctor, D. F. 1974. Effect of cholinergic stimulation on canine tracheobronchial secretions. *Fed. Proc.* 33:365 (Abstr.)
165. Rees, R. J. W., D'Arcy Hart, P. 1961. Analysis of the host-parasite equilibrium in chronic murine tuberculosis by total and viable bacillary counts. *Brit. J. Exp. Pathol.* 42:83–88
166. Richardson, J. B., Hogg, J. C., Bouchard, T., Hall, D. L. 1973. Localization of antigen in experimental bronchoconstriction in guinea pigs. *J. Allergy Clin. Immunol.* 52:172–81
167. Robertson, O. H. 1941. Phagocytosis of foreign material in the lung. *Physiol. Rev.* 21:112–39
168. Rodgers, R., Merigan, T. C. 1972. Interferon and its inducers: antiviral and other effects. *CRC Crit. Rev. Clin. Lab. Sci.* 3:131–62
169. Rossen, R. D. 1966. The sedimentation behaviour of rhinovirus neutralizing activity in nasal secretion and serum following the rhinovirus common cold. *J. Immunol.* 97:532–38
170. Rossen, R. D., Alford, R. H., Butler, W. T., Vannier, W. E. 1966. The separation and characterization of proteins intrinsic to nasal secretion. *J. Immunol.* 97:925–38
171. Rossen, R. D., Butler, W. T. 1973. Immunologic responses to infection at mucosal surfaces. See Ref. 27, 23–52
172. Rossen, R. D., Butler, W. T., Cate, T. R., Szwed, C. F., Couch, R. B. 1965. Protein composition of nasal secretions during respiratory virus infection. *Proc. Soc. Exp. Biol. Med.* 119:1169–76
173. Rossen, R. D. et al 1970. The proteins in nasal secretion. II. A longitudinal study of IgA and neutralizing antibody levels in nasal washings from men infected with influenza virus. *J. Am. Med. Assoc.* 211:1157–61
174. Rossen, R. D., Kasel, J. A., Couch, R. B. 1971. The secretory immune system: its relation to respiratory viral infection. *Progr. Med. Virol.* 13:194–238
175. Rossen, R. D., Schade, A. L., Butler, W. T., Kasel, J. A. 1966. The proteins in nasal secretions: A longitudinal study of the γ A-globulin, γ G-globulin, albumin, siderophilin, and total protein concentrations in nasal washing from adult male volunteers. *J. Clin. Invest.* 45: 768–76
176. Salmon, S. E. 1970. IgE globulin in secretions. *Clin. Res.* 18:135 (Abstr.)
177. Salvaggio, J., Castro-Murillo, E., Kundur, V. 1969. Immunologic response of atopic and normal individuals to keyhole limpet hemocyanin. *J. Allergy* 44:344–54
178. Schild, H. 1963. Histamine release and anaphylactic shock in isolated lungs of guinea-pigs. *Quart. J. Exp. Physiol.* 26:165–79

179. Schild, H. O., Hawkins, D. F., Monger, J. L., Herxheimer, H. 1951. Reactions of isolated human asthmatic lung and bronchial tissue to specific antigen; histamine release and muscular contraction. *Lancet* 2:376–82
180. Schultz, H. E., Heremans, J. F. 1966. *Molecular Biology of Human Proteins,* I:816–30. Amsterdam/New York: Elsevier. 879 pp.
181. Sellick, H., Widdicombe, J. G. 1969. The activity of lung irritant receptors during pneumothorax, hyperpnea and pulmonary vascular congestion. *J. Physiol. London* 203:359–81
182. Sellick, H., Widdicombe, J. G. 1971. Stimulation of lung irritant receptors by cigarette smoke, carbon dust and histamine aerosol. *J. Appl. Physiol.* 31:15–19
183. Sim, V. M., Pattle, R. E. 1957. Effect of possible smog irritants on human subjects. *J. Am. Med. Assoc.* 165:1908–13
184. Simonsson, B. G., Jacobs, F. M., Nadel, J. A. 1967. Role of autonomic nervous system and the cough reflex in the increased responsiveness of airways in patients with obstructive airway disease. *J. Clin. Invest.* 46:1812–18
185. Smith, C. B., Purcell, R. H., Bellanti, J. A., Chanock, R. M. 1966. Protective effect of antibody to parainfluenza Type I virus. *N. Engl. J. Med.* 275:1145–52
186. Soloviev, V. D. 1968. Some results and prospects in the study of endogenous and exogenous interferon. In *The Interferons, An International Symposium,* ed. G. Rita, 233–43. New York: Academic. 269 pp.
187. South, M. A., Cooper, M. D., Wollheim, F. A., Hong, R., Good, R. A. 1966. The IgA system. I. Studies of the transport and immunochemistry of IgA in the saliva. *J. Exp. Med.* 123:615–27
188. Speizer, F. E., Frank, N. R. 1966. A comparison of changes in pulmonary flow resistance in healthy volunteers acutely exposed to SO_2 by mouth and by nose. *Brit. J. Ind. Med.* 23:75–79
189. Stähelin, H., Karnovsky, M. L., Suter, E. 1956. Studies on the interaction between phagocytes and tubercle bacilli. II. The action of phagocytes upon C^{14}-labeled tubercle bacilli. *J. Exp. Med.* 104:137–50
190. Sterling, G. M. 1967. Mechanism of bronchoconstriction caused by cigarette smoking. *Brit. Med. J.* 3:275–77
191. Stillman, E. G. 1923. The presence of bacteria in the lungs of mice following inhalation. *J. Exp. Med.* 38:117–26
192. Stone, S. H., Liacopoulos, P., Liacopoulos-Briot, M., Neveu, T., Halpern, B. N. 1964. Histamine: differences in amount available for release in lungs of guinea pigs susceptible and resistant to acute anaphylaxis. *Science* 146:1061–62
193. Strecker, F. J. 1967. Tissue reactions in rat lungs after dust inhalation with special regard to bronchial dust elimination and to the penetration of dust into the lung interstices and lymphatic nodes. See Ref. 103, 141–53
194. Stuart, B. O. 1973. Deposition of inhaled aerosols. *Arch. Intern. Med.* 131:60–73
195. Study of Man's Impact on Climate (SMIC). *Inadvertent Climate Modification.* 1971. Cambridge, Mass.: MIT Press. 308 pp.
196. Sullivan, A. L., Grimby, P. M., Metzgen, H. 1971. Electron microscopic localization of immunoglobulin E on the surface membrane of human basophils. *J. Exp. Med.* 134:1403–16
197. Tada, T., Ishizaka, K. 1970. Distribution of gamma E-forming cells in lymphoid tissues of the human and monkey. *J. Immunol.* 104:377–87
198. Tees, E. O., Milner, F. H. 1962. The allergens of asthma. *Acta Allergy Köbenhavn* 17:536–46
199. Thomas, R. G. 1968. Transport of relatively insoluble materials from lung to lymph nodes. *Health Phys.* 14:111–17
200. Tomasi, T. B. Jr., Bienenstock, J. 1968. Secretory immunoglobulins. *Advan. Immunol.* 9:1–96
201. Tomasi, T. B., Grey, H. M. 1972. Structure and function of immunoglobulin A. *Progr. Allergy* 16:81–213
202. Tomioka, H., Ishizaka, K. 1971. Mechanisms of passive sensitization: II. Presence of receptors for IgE on monkey mast cells. *J. Immunol.* 107:971–78
203. Tomori, Z., Korec, R. 1964. Le reflexe d'aspiration comme réaction semblable ar "gasping" chez les chats. *J. Physiol. Paris* 54:661–62
204. Tomori, Z., Widdicombe, J. G. 1969. Muscular, bronchomotor and cardiovascular reflexes elicited by mechanical stimulation of the respiratory tract. *J. Physiol. London* 200:25–49
205. Tourville, D. R., Adler, R. H., Bienenstock, J., Tomasi, T. B. 1968. The human secretory immunoglobulin system: Immunohistological localization of γ A secretory "piece" and lactoferrin in normal human tissues. *J. Exp. Med.* 129:411–23

206. Trimbrell, V. 1965 The inhalation of fibrous dusts. *Ann. NY Acad. Sci.* 132:255–73
207. Trimbrell, V., Pooley, F., Wagner, J. C. 1970. Characteristics of respirable asbestos fibres. In *Pneumoconiosis: Proceedings of the International Conference,* ed. H. A. Shapiro, 120–25. Capetown: Oxford Univ. Press. 652 pp.
208. Truitt, G. L., Mackaness, G. B. 1971. Cell-mediated resistance to aerogenic infection of the lung. *Am. Rev. Resp. Dis.* 104:829–43
209. Tse, K. S., Wicher, K., Arbesman, C. E. 1970. IgE antibodies in nasal secretions of ragweed-allergic subjects. *J. Allergy* 46:352–58
210. VanHouten, P. D., Hashimoto, B., Wilson, A. F. 1973. A technique for intense radiolabeling of pollen and pollen extract with ^{99m}Tc. *J. Allergy Clin. Immunol.* 52:115–21
211. Waldman, R. H., Henney, C. S. 1971. Cell-mediated immunity and antibody responses in the respiratory tract after local and systemic immunization. *J. Exp. Med.* 134:482–94
212. Waldman, R. H., Spencer, C. S., Johnson, J. E. III. 1972. Respiratory and systemic cellular and humoral immune responses to influenza virus vaccine administered parenterally or by nose drops. *Cell Immunol.* 3:294–300
213. Watson, H. H. 1953. Dust sampling to stimulate the human being. *Brit. J. Ind. Med.* 10:93–100
214. Wernet, P., Breu, H., Knop, J., Rowley, D. 1971. Antibacterial action of specific IgA and transport of IgM, IgA, and IgG from serum into the intestine. *J. Infec. Dis.* 124:223–26
215. West, G. B., Harris, J. M. 1964. Pharmacogenetics—a fresh approach to the problem of allergy. *Ann. NY Acad. Sci.* 118:441–51
216. White, J. C., Elmes, P. C. 1960. Some rheological properties of bronchial mucus and mucoprotein. In *Flow Properties of Blood and Other Biological Systems,* ed. A. L. Copley, G. Stainsby, 259–81. New York: Pergamon. 446 pp.
217. Widdicombe, J. G. 1954. Respiratory reflexes from the trachea and bronchi of the cat. *J. Physiol. London* 123:55–70
218. Widdicombe, J. G. 1961. Action potentials in vagal efferent nerve fibers to the lungs of the cat. *Arch. Exp. Pathol. Pharmakol.* 241:415–32
219. Widdicombe, J. G. 1964. Respiratory reflexes. *Handb. Physiol. Sect. 3. Respiration,* ed. W. O. Fenn, H. Rahn, 1:585–630. Washington D.C.: Am. Physiol. Soc. 926 pp.
220. Widdicombe, J. G. 1966. Action potentials in parasympathetic and sympathetic efferent fibers to the trachea and lungs of dogs and cats. *J. Physiol. London* 186:56–88
221. Widdicombe, J. G., Kent, D. C., Nadel, J. A. 1962. Mechanism of bronchoconstriction during inhalation of dust. *J. Appl. Physiol.* 17:613–16
222. Widdicombe, J. G., Sellick, H. 1970. Vagal deflation and inflation reflexes mediated by lung irritant receptors. *Quart. J. Exp. Physiol.* 55:153–63
223. Widdicombe, J. G., Sterling, G. M. 1970. The autonomic nervous system and breathing. *Arch. Intern. Med.* 126:311–29
224. Wilkin-Jensen, K. 1959. The diagnosis of allergic diseases. In *International Textbook of Allergy,* ed. J. M. Jamar, 121–41. Springfield, Ill.: Thomas. 639 pp.
225. Williams, R. C., Gibbons, R. J. 1972. Inhibition of bacterial adherence by secretory immunoglobulin. A mechanism of antigen disposal. *Science* 177:697–99
226. Wilson, A. F., Novey, H. S., Berke, R. A., Surprenant, E. L. 1973. Deposition of inhaled pollen and pollen extract in human airways. *New Engl. J. Med.* 288:1056–58
227. Wilson, A. F., Novey, H. S., Surprenant, E. L., Bennett, L. R. 1971. Fate of inhaled whole pollen in asthmatics. *J. Allergy* 47:107–8
228. Wilson, I. B., LaMer, V. K. 1948. The retention of aerosol particles in the human respiratory tract as a function of particle radius. *J. Ind. Hyg. Toxicol.* 30:265–80
229. Wilson, I. D. 1972. Studies on the opsonic activity of human secretory IgA using an in vitro phagocytosis system. *J. Immunol.* 108:726–30
230. Woolcock, A. J. et al 1969. Effect of vagal stimulation on central and peripheral airways in dogs. *J. Appl. Physiol.* 26:806–13

Copyright 1975. All rights reserved

HEMOGLOBIN FUNCTION, OXYGEN AFFINITY, AND ERYTHROPOIETIN[1]

❖1134

John W. Adamson[2] *and Clement A. Finch*
Division of Hematology, Department of Medicine, University of Washington
School of Medicine, Seattle, Washington 98195

The molecular vehicle for oxygen transport in mammals is hemoglobin, which, in most animals, consists predominantly of a single molecular species. This review focuses on the structure and function of human hemoglobin, how both hemoglobin concentration and function are modified in response to physiologic need, and, finally, how hemoglobin interrelates with other components of the oxygen transport system.

THE HEMOGLOBIN MOLECULE

Structure of the Hemoglobin Molecule

In man, over 96% of circulating hemoglobin is composed of two α and two β chains united in a tetrameric conformation. The individual chains are called α^1, α^2, β^1, and β^2 to distinguish their individual placements within the molecule. The amino acid sequence for each polypeptide chain is known: 141 amino acids for the α chain and 146 for the β chain. Also, the three-dimensional structure of the intact protein and the placement of its prosthetic heme groups have been defined through X-ray crystallography (108). The molecule is globular in shape, with each of its four polypeptide chains being folded and twisted on itself. In this configuration, each chain contains eight relatively straight regions consisting of α helices, denoted by the letters A through H (beginning at the aminoterminus and ending at the carboxyterminus). The helices are separated from one another by major turns or twists in the direction of the globin chain—the interhelical regions. Thus each amino acid may be designated by two numbers: one for its sequence in the chain, and the other for its relation to a helical or nonhelical region.

[1]Supported by research grant HL–06242 from the National Institutes of Health.
[2]Dr. Adamson is the recipient of Research Career Development Award AM–70222 of the NIAMDD.

The hemoglobin molecule is highly symmetrical, with the globin chains arranged about a central cavity and two axes of symmetry running through the molecule at right angles to one another.[3] In general, hydrophilic amino acids are concentrated on the outside of the molecule while amino acids with uncharged and hydrophobic side chains are found in the interior or wedged into small spaces on the surface. Molecular stability is provided by inter- and intrachain bonds (109). Important contacts occur at the interfaces between the unlike chains. Thus between the α^1 and β^1 chains there are 34 amino acids, or 110 atoms in contact in the oxy form. Nineteen amino acids have contacts at the $\alpha^1\beta^2$ interface, including one hydrogen bond between aspartic acid G1 [94]α and asparagine G4 [102]β. Each heme lies in a hydrophobic pocket formed by an individual chain and makes about 60 nonpolar contacts with amino acids of the chain's interior. The invariance among mammalian hemoglobins of nearly all of the residues surrounding the heme group implies their critical importance for normal hemoglobin function.

Allosteric Effects and Ligand Binding

An understanding of hemoglobin function begins with an appreciation of the structural changes occurring with oxygenation and deoxygenation of the molecule (106). This "molecular respiration" includes major changes within the heme pockets and between the β chains. It is believed that oxygenation of the hemoglobin molecule begins with the α subunits. Triggering oxygenation at the heme pocket, there is a position shift of the iron atom and heme-linked histidine relative to the porphyrin ring. As the iron atom moves into the plane of the ring, helix F moves toward the center of the molecule closing the FH pocket of the chain, expelling the penultimate tyrosine HC2, which is otherwise held in place there. As the tyrosines are displaced, the C-terminal residues are pulled along, breaking their anchoring salt bridges and releasing Bohr protons. These changes are associated with stress at the $\alpha^1\beta^2$ contact, which is "dove-tailed," so that the CD region of α^1 fits into the FG region of β^2. In the change from deoxy to oxy conformation, the subunits at the $\alpha^1\beta^2$ contact slide in relation to one another and the H bond between aspartate G1 [99]β and tyrosine C7 [42]α "jumps" to asparagine G4 [102]β and aspartate G1 [94]α (109). As oxygenation of the chains progresses, constraining bonds become weaker, the quaternary structure of the molecule "clicks" to the liganded form, and the affinity of heme iron for oxygen increases greatly, as reflected by the sigmoid nature of the oxygen-hemoglobin dissociation curve (Figure 1).

This functional behavior of the hemoglobin molecule can be modified in vitro by the presence of other ligands produced by body tissues and by an intraerythrocytic regulating system. These effects are seen as shifts in the oxygen-hemoglobin dissociation curve that reflect altered release of oxygen to tissue for any given oxygen tension. Carbon dioxide is probably the most important physiological modifier of tissue oxygen delivery. The carbon dioxide generated by tissue metabolism diffuses into the red cell and is converted along with water by erythrocytic carbonic anhydrase to H^+ and HCO_3^-. An increase in H ions resists oxygenation of the hemoglobin

[3]An excellent graphic depiction of hemoglobin conformation can be found in reference 39.

molecule and shifts the oxygen-hemoglobin dissociation curve to the right (Bohr effect), while a decrease in H ion concentration shifts the dissociation curve to the left. At the molecular level, H ions strengthen salt bridges between the β chain C-terminal histidines and aspartate FG1 [94] of the same chain and to lysine C5 [40] of the α chain (106). Linkages also involve the α chain C-terminal argenines, which form two inter-α salt bridges. One of these salt bridges extends from the α^2 arginine to aspartate H9 [126] of α^1; the other extends from a carboxyl group of α^2 arginine to a cluster of three ionizable groups composed of valine NA1 [1], aspartate A4 [6], and lysine H10 [127] on α^1. Alpha chains may also contribute to the Bohr effect by participating in H^+-dependent links extending from arginine HC3 [141]α^2 to aspartate H9 [126]α^1, causing charge rearrangements that include histidine H5 [122]α^1. By increasing the positive charges of valine 1 α and histidine 122 α, H ions oppose the rupture of salt bridges between the α chains and raise the energy requirements for expulsion of the penultimate tyrosines from their pockets. Similarly, in the β chains H ions increase the charge of the C-terminal histidines, thereby strengthening their salt bridges with aspartate FG1 [94] and opposing expulsion of the tyrosines.

The rapidity of the Bohr effect is such that increased accumulation of carbon dioxide in tissues can enhance local oxygen release (51, 114). Thus, while the mean pH difference between arterial and venous blood pH is only 0.04, the difference may be as high as 0.1 in actively metabolizing tissues, and even greater differentials occur when decreased blood flow is combined with increased tissue metabolism. The accumulation of fixed acids and an overall increase in carbon dioxide also exert a differential effect on oxygen release, provided oxygen loading occurs on the upper, flat portion of the dissociation curve (63).

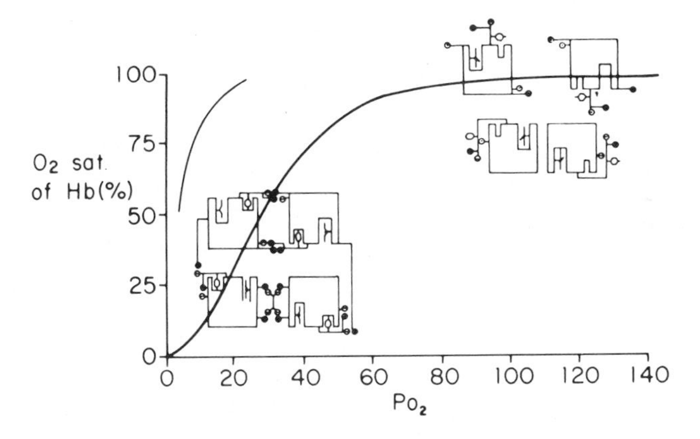

Figure 1 The oxygen dissociation curve of hemoglobin as performed in vitro on whole blood under standard conditions is shown. Superimposed on the lower portion of the curve is a diagrammatic portrayal of the interchain bonding of deoxyhemoglobin, as compared to oxyhemoglobin on the upper portion of the curve (taken from Perutz, reference 106). At the upper left is shown the curve for myoglobin.

Although the main effect of carbon dioxide on molecular hemoglobin function lies in the generation of H^+, carbon dioxide also binds directly to the four aminoterminal valines of the globin chains to reduce oxygen affinity and thus affect the oxygen dissociation curve (15, 70, 96). Ordinarily this effect is modest when compared to the pH effect; however, the valine binding is enhanced at low oxygen saturations or in the presence of low concentrations of inorganic phosphates (135).

Various organic phosphates within the red cell interact with hemoglobin to reduce its affinity for oxygen (22, 33). Inositol hexaphosphate is most important for this effect in avian red cells, but in mammals the effect is largely due to 2,3-diphosphoglycerate (DPG) (23). In the absence of DPG it is estimated that the standard P_{50}[4] would be decreased from the normal value of 27 to less than 20 mm Hg. Adenosine phosphates, including ATP, ADP, and AMP, also bind hemoglobin and affect oxygen affinity. In man, ATP is the most effective of these compounds, but it has only one fifth the concentration of DPG as well as a lower binding affinity for hemoglobin, perhaps due to the inability to make contact with all of the DPG-binding sites (106). In addition, ATP has a high binding constant within the red cell to Mg^{2+} and is therefore less available to interact with hemoglobin (23).

DPG affects hemoglobin affinity for oxygen in two ways. The first is by binding together the two β chains of the molecule. DPG is stereochemically complementary to six positively charged groups in the two β chains facing the central cavity of the molecule (106). These groups are provided by valine NA1 [1], histidine H21 [143], and lysine EF6 [82]. In this position DPG stabilizes the quaternary deoxy structure of the hemoglobin molecule by introducing additional salt bridges which cross-link the β subunits. This interaction probably has no effect on the tertiary structure of the individual chains and the sigmoid nature of the oxygen dissociation curve is maintained. The second mechanism by which DPG influences oxygen affinity is through a reduction in intraerythrocytic pH due to the acidity of the DPG molecule itself, i.e. by the Bohr effect (16). At low red cell levels of DPG, direct binding to hemoglobin is thought to be the more important influence on oxygen affinity, whereas the influence of pH change predominates at high DPG levels (40). Together, these affect the velocity constants for oxygen exchange (20).

DPG plays an important regulatory role in oxygen exchange (27, 38). In a variety of situations where tissue oxygen supply is impaired, the DPG level rises, producing a proportionate increase in the standard P_{50}. Such changes have been reported with cardiac failure (89, 133), in anemia (125), and with arterial oxygen desaturation (42, 81, 101, 111, 128). The mechanism of response has been explained in the following manner: when the oxygen supply falls, deoxyhemoglobin accumulates and binds larger amounts of DPG and H^+ ions. The reduction in free DPG within the cell, along with the increase in intracellular pH, stimulates glycolysis and thereby DPG synthesis (59). Under these conditions, the in vivo rise in DPG has a $T_{1/2}$ of about 4–8 hr, as illustrated by the rise in DPG of stored red cells following transfusion (25) and in subjects taken rapidly to high altitude (80).

[4]The standard P_{50} is the most convenient notation characterizing the oxygen-hemoglobin dissociation curve. It represents the partial pressure of oxygen (mm Hg) at which 50% of the hemoglobin is saturated under standard in vitro conditions of pH and temperature.

Changes in DPG also occur in compensation for pH-induced alterations in hemoglobin affinity. When the red cell pH rises, phosphofructokinase activity is stimulated, resulting in increased glucose consumption and DPG production (92). Conversely, with acidosis, glycolysis is impaired and DPG concentration falls. The net result of the interaction of pH and DPG, given sufficient time, is the precise counterbalancing by DPG of the Bohr effect (21). However, since the Bohr effect is almost instantaneous, while the change in DPG requires several hours, a rapid pH change or a rapid correction of an abnormal pH is associated with a lag period of altered hemoglobin affinity and tissue oxygen delivery.

In recent years, most studies of molecular hemoglobin function have examined the standard P_{50}. Here a good correlation would be expected between DPG and P_{50} because other factors influencing the P_{50}, such as temperature and pH, have been controlled. At physiologic pH, a 50% increase above normal in DPG is associated with an increase in P_{50} of 3.75–5 mm Hg. However, the in vivo P_{50}, which is of greater physiologic importance, has not been examined so extensively in hypoxemia or anemia and is not an easy matter to evaluate, since pH differs in various parts of the circulation and is constantly changing, depending on local circulation and metabolism.

In a variety of situations, including ascent to high altitude (79), febrile states, hypotension, myocardial infarction (83), anemia, and perhaps in chronic cardiac failure (17), in vivo pH may rise due to hyperventilation. In such a setting, the DPG response may be largely compensatory for the pH change rather than a direct response to hypoxia. Particularly in anemia there is impressive evidence relating the DPG change to a pH change of antecubital venous blood (82). It has also been demonstrated that the DPG response during ascent to high altitude is partly, at least, a response to hyperventilation alkalosis, since treatment with either ammonium chloride or with a carbonic anhydrase inhibitor to maintain a normal pH greatly dampens the DPG response (126). There are situations where the combination of hyperventilation and DPG correction of alkalosis-dependent increased hemoglobin-oxygen affinity may be beneficial. For example, ascent to high altitude requires hyperventilation for optimal oxygen loading, and the accompanying DPG response permits release of oxygen at a more normal oxygen tension.

Thus regulation of tissue oxygenation by H^+, carbon dioxide, and DPG occurs largely through the changes they produce in the affinity of hemoglobin for oxygen. These ligands have important interactions among themselves and their concentrations are modulated appropriately in the presence of a limited oxygen supply so that oxygen availability is improved at the cellular level (19, 54, 88, 118, 135).

Structural Abnormalities of Hemoglobin That Modify Function

To date almost 200 mutants of the hemoglobin molecule have been described. Most of these are functionally inert and are recognized only on population screening. However, some variants have profound effects on molecular behavior, through altering either the valence of heme iron, the binding of oxygen or other ligands, or the structural stability of the molecule (121).

Modification of the heme environment may render the iron molecule inert as an oxygen carrier. Five mutations have been described involving amino acid substitutions (107) that promote the ferric state of iron resulting in methemoglobin; these are the so-called hemoglobins M. In four mutants the α or β histidines at F8 or E7 are replaced by tyrosine. With such replacement of the "distal" histidines in Hb M Boston (E7 [58]α) and Hb M Saskatoon (E7 [63]β), the phenolic oxygen of tyrosine appears close enough to form an ionic link with iron, eliminating the normal space for ligand. In Hb M Iwate (F8 [87]α) and Hyde Park (F8 [92]β), the "proximal" histidines are replaced. Ionic links are formed between iron and tyrosine phenolic oxygen at position 87α or 92β, and there is covalent binding to the histidines at E7 (58α or 63β). Valine E11 [67]β is replaced by glutamic acid in Hb Milwaukee, where the carboxyl group of glutamic acid forms an ionic link with the iron atom, thereby stabilizing it in the ferric form. Oxygen affinity of the Hb M group appears to be variable, having been reported as decreased with the α substitutions of histidine and nearly normal with the β chain substitutions of histidine (62, 122). However, the oxygen-carrying capacity of theses molecules is more profoundly affected by the extent of ferriheme formation.

Alterations in oxygen affinity may also be caused by substitutions that change the allosteric equilibrium of the hemoglobin molecule. Most information on this subject has been derived by examining stable mutants with increased oxygen affinity, of which over 10 are now known. These amino acid substitutions frequently occur at the $\alpha^1\beta^2$ interface (Hbs Chesapeake, Capetown, Yakima, Kempsey, Ypsilanti, Malmo, and Hirose); they are characterized by a shift to the left in their oxygen dissociation curve and usually a marked reduction of heme-heme interaction, as reflected by loss of the sigmoid shape of the curve.

An explanation of the mechanism by which such substitutions alter hemoglobin function has been provided in a number of instances (95). For example, substitution of histidine (Hb Yakima) or asparagine (Hb Kempsey) for aspartate at G1 [99]β removes a hydrogen bond that normally stabilizes the deoxy quaternary structure, displacing the equilibrium to the oxy form. Changes at the $\alpha^1\beta^1$ interface, although locally less critical, may be translated into larger changes in quaternary structure. This may apply to Hb San Diego, in which methionine is substituted for valine at G11 [109]β, eliminating an important hydrogen bond at the interface. As a result, the constrained or deoxy conformation of the tetramer may be destabilized (99).

Other important substitutions have been found away from the interfaces between unlike chains. Most interesting of these are Hbs Rainier and Bethesda, in which cysteine and histidine, respectively, replace tyrosine at HC2 [145]β. The loss of these penultimate tyrosines produces considerable disturbance of function, with marked increase in oxygen affinity and virtual absence of heme-heme interaction (58, 61).

Mutations at or near the DPG binding sites have also been reported. Such an example is Hb Little Rock with glycine replacing histidine H21 [143]β (18). Fetal hemoglobin ($\alpha^2\gamma^2$) has a lower natural affinity for oxygen than Hb A (28), but its in vitro and in vivo dissociation curves are shifted to the left of that of Hb A due to decreased binding with DPG (100, 127). This decrease is probably related to the presence in the γ chain of alanine instead of histidine at position H21 [143] of the β chain.

The affinity of hemoglobin for oxygen can be altered by introducing foreign ligands. Cyanate, studied recently because of its possible use in the treatment of sickle cell anemia, reacts irreversibly with the free amino group of the terminal valine of all polypeptide chains. Since the amino terminal valines are involved in the formation of salt bridges that stabilize the quaternary structure of deoxyhemoglobin, it is not surprising that carbamylation increases the oxygen affinity of hemoglobin and reduces the Bohr effect (71).

In Hb Kansas, the only known stable mutant with decreased oxygen affinity, asparagine is replaced by threonine at G4 [102]β, a site just three residues removed from position G1 where mutations of Hbs Kempsey, Yakima, and Ypsilanti occur (95). The threonine substitution eliminates a hydrogen bond normally formed between asparagine G4 β^2 and aspartate G1 α^1 in the oxy form, thus destabilizing the quaternary structure. Hb Kansas has the most marked decrease in oxygen affinity of any known hemoglobin, with a P_{50} of 70 as compared to the normal of 27 mm Hg. With this degree of shift, full saturation of hemoglobin cannot occur at normal arterial Po_2 (110). Hb Seattle is a mildly unstable hemoglobin with aspartate replacing alanine at E14 [70]β. This substitution allegedly alters linkage with pyrrols I and IV of the porphyrin ring and thus the heme environment, although the precise mechanism of the decreased oxygen affinity is unknown (13).

Many amino acid substitutions associated with altered oxygen affinity also cause molecular instability, often sufficient to be expressed as hemolytic anemia. In Hb Zurich, for example, the replacement by arginine of histidine E7 [63]β opens the heme pocket and facilitates oxygen binding (95). With Hbs Hammersmith and Bucuresti, substitutions of serine and leucine, respectively, for phenylalanine CD1 [42]β result in the loss of a "spacer" that normally maintains the heme group in an inclined position corresponding to the oxy conformation. Loss of this spacer favors the deoxy conformation and thus reduced oxygen affinity (95). The increased molecular degradation observed with these hemoglobins is thought to be related to instability of the heme group position.

Metabolic Abnormalities Affecting Hemoglobin Function

Hemoglobin affinity for oxygen is affected by metabolic changes that disturb glycolysis and thereby the erythrocytic level of DPG (36, 137). With genetic abnormalities of enzymes in the glycolytic series located above the Leubering-Rapaport pathway, DPG is reduced. Hexokinase deficiency is the best known example, where there is also decreased ATP and shortened red cell survival. With defects of such enzymes as pyruvate kinase below the Leubering-Rapaport pathway, DPG is increased. The result is a reduction in hemoglobin affinity for oxygen and a shortened red cell survival due to failure of ATP maintenance. While alterations in aerobic glycolysis (hexosemonophosphate shunt defects) render hemoglobin susceptible to oxidative denaturation, oxygen affinity is unchanged, since anaerobic glycolysis, and thus DPG production, is unchanged.

Maintenance of DPG depends upon the organic phosphate level within the red cell as well as normal glycolysis. Temporary or acute changes in plasma inorganic phosphate have little effect on intraerythrocytic DPG because of the slow exchange

(85); however, chronic depletion of plasma inorganic phosphate decreases red cell DPG and may also prevent the normal DPG response to an increased pH (10, 136). In situations where inorganic phosphate is inadequate for the needs of glycolysis, ATP may also be depleted to a point of impairing cell viability (84).

Recently the influence of in vitro blood preservation on oxygen transport function has been of particular interest. Storage of red cells for three weeks in standard acid-citrate-dextrose solution produces a marked fall in DPG, paralleled by the expected decrease in P_{50} (29, 117, 129). When these cells are transfused, normal affinity is regained only after many hours. The potential harm of impaired oxygen release is most obvious in patients requiring transfusions since they are often hypoxic and already have a compensatory decrease in oxygen affinity. Concern about this potential hazard has led to development of methods whereby DPG may be maintained during storage or increased immediately before transfusion (9, 26, 41, 102). Increased inorganic phosphate [CPD (citrate-phosphate-dextrose) preservative] and the addition of inosine have been shown to be a practical means of improving DPG maintenance.

Several hormones have been reported to influence DPG synthesis; e.g. thyroxine has shown to elevate red cell DPG in vitro (119), and decreased in vitro oxygen affinity has been reported in patients with hyperthyroidism (91), although the latter does not appear to be a consistent finding. Increased DPG levels have also been reported in patients with chronic renal failure treated with testosterone (104).

THE ERYTHRON

Hemoglobin Concentration

In normal man, erythropoiesis is regulated by a glycoprotein hormone, erythropoietin (ESF, erythropoiesis stimulating factor), which is present in the circulating blood and urine. ESF has an estimated molecular weight of 46,000 (55) and contains approximately 30% carbohydrate, of which 11% is sialic acid. The size of the active portion of the molecule is not known. Sialic acid appears to be necessary to maintain hormone activity in vivo, since removal of sialic acid results in the rapid uptake of ESF by hepatic parenchymal cells; however, sialic acid residues are not required for in vitro hormone activity. To date, the available amount of highly purified ESF has been so limited as to preclude detailed studies of molecular structure or the development of useful immunologic or biochemical assays. As a result, cumbersome biological methods for ESF measurement are still required.

Erythropoietin Assays

The most reliable and widely used method for measuring ESF is a bioassay. The test animals are mice whose endogenous level of erythropoiesis has been suppressed by polycythemia, induced either by hypertransfusion or by intermittent exposure to low oxygen tensions (75). Erythropoiesis in groups of control animals or in animals receiving injections of test materials is expressed as the percent incorporation of radioiron into newly formed red cells. The provision of an International Reference Preparation (IRP) of ESF and its unit (U) has facilitated interlaboratory comparison

(14). The major problems of the bioassay are its inconvenience, imprecision, and insensitivity. Most bioassays have a minimum sensitivity of about 0.025 to 0.04 IRP U/assay animal, near the basal level estimated for normal sera (93). Thus subnormal levels in human blood cannot be identified. A more useful assay is made possible by concentrating urine against a large molecular weight material (polyethylene glycol or methylcellulose) or by ultrafiltration. Assay of urinary concentrates has permitted the detection of a diurnal variation in ESF excretion (3), sex differences in excretion (11), and the demonstration of subnormal excretion when the hemoglobin concentration is increased by hypertransfusion (1).

Recent attempts have been made to develop immunoassays for ESF. A hemagglutination inhibition (HAI) technique has been described (78) that is precise and sensitive to 0.005 IRP U/ml. However, it cannot be said to reflect consistently the biologic activity of ESF since discrepancies are found between the bioassay and immunoassay, particularly at low ESF levels. Using highly purified preparations of ESF, Fisher developed a radioimmunoassay for ESF that is sensitive to 1×10^{-5} IRP units (49). The validity of this assay for biologic activity also has not been established, again due to the question of purity of the ESF employed for antibody stimulation, and the question of the relationship between immunologic and biologic parameters. An in vitro method that appears promising for measuring the biologic activity of ESF utilizes hemoglobin synthesis by cultured marrow cells (131). Modified from the original technique of Krantz and co-workers (73, 74), the method is sensitive to small doses of ESF ($1-2 \times 10^{-4}$ IRP U) and is considerably more sensitive and reproducible than the bioassay. However, the interpretation of assay results in such a system is made difficult by the presence in different sera of nonspecific stimulators and inhibitors of hemoglobin synthesis. Also, when radioiron is used as an indicator, it is essential to maintain a constant relationship between the iron pool and the cell population. The technique has particular advantages in serial observations on material from the same source (4).

Mechanism of Erythropoietin Production

The classic work of Jacobson and co-workers (69) localized the main site of ESF production in normal animals to the kidney. A number of early perfusion studies more directly demonstrated the role of the kidney by showing that the isolated organ increases ESF production in response to perfusion with anemic or hypoxic blood (76).

The mechanism of ESF formation has been investigated principally by Gordon and associates (56). They reported that a light mitochondrial fraction extracted by differential centrifugation of kidney homogenates became erythropoietically active upon incubation with homologous plasma. Neither the renal factor, called erythrogenin, nor the plasma substrate, believed to come from the liver, were erythropoietically active in the polycythemic mouse bioassay or were recognized by the HAI assay (87). These studies have not been reproducible in all laboratories (44), and an alternate model of ESF biogenesis has been advanced. Erslev and co-workers have reported that an extractable lipid material from kidney tissue interacts or complexes with ESF to neutralize it, and that normal plasma contains a protein factor that releases ESF (45). Thus hypoxia may release the hormone-inhibitor complex from the kidney, exposing the complex to the plasma factor.

In chronic renal failure, ESF output is less than that expected for the degree of anemia (5). Uremic toxins may play some role in suppressing erythropoiesis, but the presence of active red cell production in patients with certain types of renal disease (hemolytic-uremic syndrome) indicates that uremia per se does not interfere significantly with the marrow response. The exact site of ESF production within the kidney remains unclear. Erythrogenin appears to be widely distributed in renal cortex and medulla (56). While production of ESF is clearly separate from that of angiotensin, changes in the juxtaglomerular apparatus associated with abnormalities in production of both hormones have suggested that this might be the production site (37). Other work suggests that the glomerular tuft may be implicated (31).

Major attention has been directed to the kidney, but extrarenal sites of ESF production also exist as shown by the fact that exposure of nephrectomized animals or man to severe hypoxia results in increased ESF levels (52, 97, 98). The functional capacity of the extrarenal system is limited compared to that of the kidney, but studies in patients with chronic renal failure supported by hemodialysis suggest that extrarenal production may increase with time and may ultimately be capable of supporting a hemoglobin of about 10 g% (46). The similar behavior of the extrarenal ESF in in vitro and bioassay systems suggests that the material produced is identical to that from the kidney (52).

Mechanism of Erythropoietin Action

The primary target of ESF action in the erythron is an early precursor cell referred to as a committed or unipotential stem cell. This cell, while probably capable of self-replication (86), is to be distinguished from the pluripotential stem cell on which ESF is thought to have little or no effect (72). After ESF stimulation, the unipotential stem cell undergoes several divisions that amplify the initial induction step at least 16-fold. The increase in total number of cells undergoing maturation is largely responsible for the increased erythropoiesis. In addition, the intermitotic interval is shortened and the amount of hemoglobin synthesized within developing erythroblasts is increased upon ESF stimulation (103).

ESF also has an effect on reticulocyte release from the marrow. Normally the reticulocyte spends two to three days in the marrow before entering circulation. Premature release of reticulocytes occurs during in vitro perfusion of marrow with ESF-rich material (50) and is seen in vivo with anemia in animals and man (77). The degree of premature reticulocyte release or "shift" may be quantified by determining the marrow radioiron transit time (i.e. the time for radioiron taken up by marrow cells to appear in circulation). This time is shortened in proportion to the increase in plasma and urinary ESF level and usually in proportion to the degree of anemia. The prematurely released reticulocytes, or "shift" cells, are identified in the circulating blood as large polychromatic erythrocytes; their presence on the blood smear is a useful indicator of increased ESF activity (105).

Regulation of Erythropoiesis

The oxygen content of arterial blood appears to be a primary determinant of ESF production. For example, when a normal individual is transfused to a high hematocrit level, ESF production falls below the measurable level (1), while with phlebotomy, urinary ESF increases exponentially. When arterial oxygen is decreased by ascent to high altitude, ESF increases (47) and a predictable increase in hemoglobin concentration occurs (68). These findings support the general concept that hemoglobin concentration is determined by ESF.

A physiologic understanding of polycythemic states may be reached by following ESF changes induced by phlebotomy. In hypoxic polycythemia, the ESF response curve is displaced to the right of normal, i.e. a higher ESF excretion for any given hemoglobin concentration. Patients with increased affinity of hemoglobin for oxygen also have a right-shifted ESF response curve (7). On the other hand, an autonomous ESF production may be responsible for polycythemia; this occurs in association with a number of neoplasms and also as a recessively expressed genetic disorder (8). In polycythemia vera ESF excretion has been shown to be greatly reduced or absent at high hematocrits, resuming only when a normal or subnormal hematocrit is reached. This finding provides physiologic evidence that the erythroid marrow in polycythemia vera does not depend on ESF for red cell production (1).

The rate of erythropoietic response to ESF stimulation does not bear any clear relation to the ESF level because blood production is often restricted by inadequate iron or by marrow dysfunction in hematologic disease. For example, in patients with acute hemolysis, marrow production may increase to 5 times normal within one week because of the abundant iron supply derived from red cell destruction (116); however, after acute blood loss the red cell production rate is usually less than 2 times normal due to the slow rate of mobilization of iron from storage depots (34). When additional iron is given orally, the production rate usually rises significantly (60, 64). In patients with compensated hemolytic anemia, where both marrow function and iron supply are intact, a small increase in ESF may be sufficient to support a rate of red cell production several times normal.

It has been appreciated only recently that ESF production also depends on hemoglobin affinity for oxygen. When the affinity is altered by a hemoglobin structural abnormality (2), by a change in pH (90), or by a rise or fall in red cell DPG concentration (137), the amount of oxygen available to the renal regulating center at the tissue level is altered and the output of ESF changes accordingly. In contrast, ESF regulation is quite insensitive to changes in arterial blood supply. A decrease in renal blood flow to about one third normal occurring in individuals with cardiac failure is unassociated with changes in hemoglobin concentration and therefore, by inference, with ESF production. This insensitivity to flow may be explained by parallel changes in renal oxygen consumption, consistent with Jacobson and associates' early hypothesis that ESF output was dependent on the relationship between renal oxygen supply and tissue requirements (69). If renal blood flow falls to a point at which sodium retention and plasma volume expansion occur, the resulting dilutional anemia stimulates erythropoiesis and increases red cell mass until a normal hemoglobin concentration is regained.

While regulation of hemoglobin concentration in any individual is highly precise, the hemoglobin level established in different individuals may vary by several grams per 100 ml of blood. This variation may reflect differences in availability of oxygen or special influences on ESF output. In childhood, higher inorganic phosphate levels lead to a greater availability of oxygen, which may contribute to the lower hemoglobin concentration of this age group (32). Undoubtedly other factors such as variations in red cell glycolysis and testosterone level may affect the individual's hemoglobin concentration.

A number of hormones have been shown to alter hemoglobin concentration through mechanisms that may involve ESF. Anemia has been described in hypopituitarism, hypothyroidism, hypoadrenalism, and after castration (6). Indeed, the pituitarectomized animal was used at one time for the bioassay of ESF, since pituitary ablation suppressed endogenous ESF production (53). The influence of adrenoglucocorticoids on hemoglobin concentration is exemplified by erythrocythemia of Cushing's disease and mild anemia of Addison's disease. In such conditions it is difficult to separate primary ESF effects from those secondary to plasma volume changes, and even more difficult to separate changes in ESF due to altered oxygen consumption from the direct action of hormones on ESF production. Alterations in thyroid function, which produce marked changes in oxygen consumption, are associated with relatively modest changes in hemoglobin concentration. Estrogen and progestational hormones may influence erythropoiesis by altering the marrow response to ESF, a property claimed for estradiol (57).

Testosterone in physiologic amounts affects ESF output. Differences in testosterone levels between men and women are thought to be responsible for the 1–2 g difference in hemoglobin concentration (11). Larger doses of androgens increase ESF output (12) and hemoglobin concentration of normal individuals and reestablish erythropoiesis in some patients with aplastic anemia (115). Since such patients already have very high EFS levels, it seems likely that recovery from anemia is produced through some other mechanism than a further increase in ESF production (124). Recent studies implicate a direct action of certain steroids on bone marrow cells to stimulate hemoglobin synthesis (94). One nonandrogenic steroid is believed to increase the number of ESF-responsive cells, thereby increasing the cellular response to a given amount of ESF (24).

General Comments

The physiologic role of the erythron is to provide an adequate amount of available oxygen in arterial blood at a suitable oxygen tension. If the arterial oxygen saturation is decreased, there is a compensatory increase in hemoglobin concentration; this compensation is best seen in the direct relationship between hemoglobin concentration and high altitude (68). It has been customary to equate arterial hemoglobin saturation with oxygen supply, but recent studies of hemoglobin affinity underline its importance in influencing the availability of oxygen. Laboratory differences in hemoglobin concentration between men and women and between adults and children are compensated by differences in oxygen availability (67). Patients with a hemoglobinopathy characterized by increased hemoglobin-oxygen affinity have a proportionate increase in hemoglobin concentration to counteract the decreased tissue availability of oxygen. Conversely, hemoglobinopathies with decreased affinity are associated with lowered hemoglobin concentration. Thus a patient with Hb Seattle with 11 g Hb/100 ml blood and a P_{50} of 44 mm Hg, has essentially normal tissue oxygen supply (123). With Hb Kansas the expected decrease in hemoglobin concentration does not occur since the P_{50} of 70 mm Hg desaturates arterial hemoglobin (110). In a variety of hemolytic anemias associated with altered hemoglobin-oxygen affinity, whether due to an abnormal hemoglobin or to an abnormality in red cell metabolism, the hematocrit is more closely correlated with the oxygen affinity than with the rate of hemolysis (66). This suggests that the availability of oxygen is a more important variable than the degree of hemolysis in determining the eventual hemoglobin concentration, and shows that in defining anemia or polycythemia in a physiologic context, it is necessary to consider measurements of hemoglobin concentration, hemoglobin saturation with oxygen, and hemoglobin affinity for oxygen.

It is difficult to evaluate the functional significance of alterations in hemoglobin concentration. Anemia reduces maximum work performance in man (120), and animal studies suggest that this may be a linear function demonstrable even with a moderate decrease in hemoglobin concentration (134). It is even more of a problem to define the limitations imposed by an increased affinity of hemoglobin for oxygen. Work performance in rats was little affected by a reduction in DPG that shifted the in vitro P_{50} from 36 to 21 mm Hg (134); however, more severe reductions limited work capacity. Ischemic changes in the heart have been produced by transfusing animals with blood low in 2,3-DPG (65).

These considerations of red cell and erythron function cannot be separated from other components of oxygen flow: the loading of oxygen in the lungs, cardiac output, and distribution of blood to tissues (48). Since the success of oxygen transport is dependent on the sum of these individual processes, it is necessary to relate the erythron to these other transport functions. This can be done by briefly characterizing their interactions in various states of tissue hypoxia. As previously discussed, individuals with abnormal hemoglobins having increased oxygen affinity compensate by increasing hemoglobin concentration. An increase in tissue oxygen requirement as seen in hyperthyroidism is corrected principally by an increase in cardiac output (35). Ascent to high altitude provides a more complex problem. Initially, hyperventilation improves oxygen loading, but at the same time the increased pH interferes with oxygen release (81). The DPG response counteracts the effects of alkalosis within one or two days (126), and within a week the kidney has corrected extracellular pH by the excretion of excess base. With additional time at high altitude, erythropoiesis effects an increase in hemoglobin concentration proportionate to the amount of arterial oxygen desaturation (68, 132). At normal pH and decreased arterial oxygen saturation, the increase in DPG has little effect on oxygen exchange at altitudes above 15,000 ft.

In other disorders of oxygen loading, such as cyanotic heart disease or pulmonary arteriovenous fistulae, increased hemoglobin and DPG are usually found in the presence of a normal pH (30, 101). With chronic pulmonary disease associated with arterial oxygen desaturation, respiratory acidosis may modify both the hemoglobin and DPG response (43). Similar effects on the erythron of hypoxic man are produced experimentally by pH manipulation (90).

In anemia, oxygen loading is decreased due to the decreased oxygen-carrying capacity of the blood. DPG (125) and ESF are increased, but frequently, because of impairment in red cell production, there is no change in hemoglobin concentration. Decreased viscosity of the blood is presumably responsible for the increased cardiac output that becomes increasingly important as anemia becomes more severe (113). Blood distribution is also modified in anemia so as to maintain flow in critical areas. True anemia, with its physiologic compensations, is to be differentiated from certain hemoglobinopathies and endocrinopathies in which there is a reduced hemoglobin concentration but no tissue oxygen deficit.

When tissue oxygen delivery is impaired as the result of decreased cardiac output, DPG increases and blood redistribution occurs so as to maintain flow to critical areas (112, 130). These compensatory mechanisms permit maintenance of oxygen consumption despite a cardiac output reduction of one third to one half. Other changes in the patient with cardiac failure include decreased physical activity and, ultimately, a decrease in oxygen requirement through atrophy of muscle mass.

From such examples it becomes clear that adjustments to any impairment in oxygen supply are determined by the nature of the disturbance, and that the behavior of the marrow and the erythrocyte must ultimately be judged in the context of the total oxygen transport system. However, it is evident that elegant control systems exist for maintaining an optimum supply of oxygen by altering hemoglobin concentration and/or hemoglobin affinity for oxygen.

Acknowledgments

We gratefully acknowledge the helpful suggestions of Drs. Eloise Giblett and George Stamatoyannopoulos in the preparation of this manuscript.

Literature Cited

1. Adamson, J. W. 1968. The erythropoietin/hematocrit relationship in normal and polycythemic man: implications of marrow regulation. *Blood* 32:597–609
2. Adamson, J. W. 1970. Oxygen delivery by abnormal hemoglobins: effects on erythropoietin production. *Hemopoietic Cellular Proliferation,* ed. F. Stohlman, 112–21. New York: Grune & Stratton
3. Adamson, J. W., Alexanian, R., Martinez, C., Finch, C. A. 1966. Erythropoietin excretion in normal man. *Blood* 28:354–64
4. Adamson, J. W., Dale, D. C., Elin, R. J. 1974. Hematopoiesis in the grey collie dog: studies of the regulation of erythropoiesis. *J. Clin. Invest.* In press
5. Adamson, J. W., Eschbach, J. W., Finch, C. A. 1968. The kidney and erythropoiesis. *Am. J. Med.* 44:725–33
6. Adamson, J. W., Finch, C. A. 1974. Hormones and the formed elements of the blood. *Textbook of Endocrinology,* ed. R. H. Williams, 963–69. Philadelphia: Saunders. 5th ed.
7. Adamson, J. W., Parer, J. T., Stamatoyannopoulos, G. 1969. Erythrocytosis

associated with hemoglobin Rainier: oxygen equilibria and marrow regulation. *J. Clin. Invest.* 48:1376–86

8. Adamson, J. W., Stamatoyannopoulos, G., Kontras, S., Lascari, A., Detter, J. 1973. Recessive familial erythrocytosis: aspects of marrow regulation in two families. *Blood* 41:641–52
9. Åkerblom, O., de Verdier, C.-H., Garby, L., Högman, C. 1968. Restoration of defective oxygen-transport function of stored red blood cells by addition of inosine. *Scand. J. Clin. Lab. Invest.* 21:245–48
10. Alberti, K. G. M. M., Darley, J. H., Emerson, P. M., Hockaday, T. D. R. 1972. 2,3-diphosphoglycerate and tissue oxygenation in uncontrolled diabetes mellitus. *Lancet* 2:391–95
11. Alexanian, R. 1966. Urinary excretion of erythropoietin in normal men and women. *Blood* 28:344–53
12. Alexanian, R. 1969. Erythropoietin and erythropoiesis in anemic man following androgens. *Blood* 33:564–72
13. Anderson, N. L., Perutz, M. F., Stamatoyannopoulos, G. 1973. Site of the amino-acid substitution in Haemoglobin Seattle (α_2^A β_2^{70Asp}). *Nature* 243:274–75
14. Annable, L., Cotes, P. M., Mussett, M. V. 1972. The second international reference preparation of erythropoietin, human, urinary, for bioassay. *Bull. WHO* 47:99–112
15. Arnone, A. 1974. X-ray studies of the interaction of CO_2 with human deoxyhaemoglobin. *Nature* 247:143–45
16. Astrup, P. 1970. Red-cell pH and oxygen affinity of hemoglobin. *N. Engl. J. Med.* 283:202–4
17. Awamura, M. 1969. Clinical studies on the acid-base balance disturbance in congestive heart failure. *Jap. Circ. J.* 33:275–91
18. Bare, G. H. et al 1974. Hemoglobin Little Rock (β143 (H21) His $\longrightarrow$ Gln). Effects of an amino acid substitution at the 2,3-diphosphoglycerate binding site. *J. Biol. Chem.* 249:773–79
19. Bauer, C. 1970. Reduction of the carbon dioxide affinity of human haemoglobin solutions by 2,3-diphosphoglycerate. *Resp. Physiol.* 10:10–19
20. Bauer, C., Klocke, R. A., Kamp, D., Forster, R. E. 1973. Effect of 2,3-diphosphoglycerate and H^+ on the reaction of O_2 and hemoglobin. *Am. J. Physiol.* 224:838–47
21. Bellingham, A. J., Detter, J. C., Lenfant, C. 1971. Regulatory mechanisms of hemoglobin oxygen affinity in acidosis and alkalosis. *J. Clin. Invest.* 50: 700–6
22. Benesch, R., Benesch, R. E. 1967. The effect of organic phosphates from the human erythrocyte on the allosteric properties of hemoglobin. *Biochem. Biophys. Res. Commun.* 26:162–67
23. Berger, H., Jänig, G.-R., Gerber, G., Ruckpaul, K., Rapoport, S. 1973. Interaction of haemoglobin with ions. Interactions among magnesium, adenosine 5'-triphosphate, 2,3-bisphosphoglycerate, and oxygenated and deoxygenated human haemoglobin under simulated intracellular conditions. *Eur. J. Biochem.* 38:553–62
24. Besa, E. C., Gorshein, D., Hait, W. A., Gardner, F. H. 1973. Effective erythropoiesis induced by 5β-pregnane-3β-hydroxy-20-one in squirrel monkeys. *J. Clin. Invest.* 52:2278–82
25. Beutler, E., Wood, L. 1969. The in vivo regeneration of red cell 2,3-diphosphoglyceric acid (DPG) after transfusion of stored blood. *J. Lab. Clin. Med.* 74:300–4
26. Brake, J. M., Deindoerfer, F. H. 1973. Preservation of red blood cell 2,3-diphosphoglycerate in stored blood containing dihydroxyacetone. *Transfusion* 13:84–88
27. Brewer, G. J., Eaton, J. W. 1971. Erythrocyte metabolism: interaction with oxygen transport. *Science* 171:1205–11
28. Bunn, H. F., Briehl, R. W. 1970. The interaction of 2,3-diphosphoglycerate with various human hemoglobins. *J. Clin. Invest.* 49:1088–95
29. Bunn, H. F., May, M. H., Kocholaty, W. F., Shields, C. E. 1969. Hemoglobin function in stored blood. *J. Clin. Invest.* 48:311–21
30. Bürkmann, I., Behn, P., Herold, B., Rosenkranz, U. 1971. Zum Verlauf der O_2-Dissoziationskurve bei Gesunden sowie bei Kranken mit angeborenem zyanotischem Herzfehler bzw. chronischem obstruktivem Lungenemphysem. *Respiration* 28:36–53
31. Busuttil, R. W., Roh, R. L., Fisher, J. W. 1971. The cytological localization of erythropoietin in the human kidney using the fluorescent antibody technique. *Proc. Soc. Exp. Biol. Med.* 137:327–30
32. Card, R. T., Brain, M. C. 1973. The "anemia" of childhood. Evidence for a physiologic response to hyperphosphatemia. *N. Engl. J. Med.* 288:388–92

33. Chanutin, A., Curnish, R. R. 1967. Effect of organic and inorganic phosphates on the oxygen equilibrium of human erythrocytes. *Arch. Biochem. Biophys.* 121:96–102
34. Coleman, D. H., Stevens, A. R. Jr., Dodge, H. T., Finch, C. A. 1953. Rate of blood regeneration after blood loss. *Arch. Intern. Med.* 92:341–49
35. deGroot, W. J., Leonard, J. J. 1970. Hyperthyroidism as a high cardiac output state. *Am. Heart J.* 79:265–75
36. Delivoria-Papadopoulos, M., Oski, F. A., Gottlieb, A. J. 1969. Oxygen-hemoglobin dissociation curves: effect of inherited enzyme defects of the red cell. *Science* 165:601–2
37. Demopoulos, H. B., Highman, B., Altland, P. D., Gerving, M. A., Kaley, G. 1965. Effects of high altitude on granular juxtaglomerular cells and their possible role in erythropoietin production. *Am. J. Pathol.* 46:497–507
38. de Verdier, C.-H., Garby, L., Hjelm, M., Astrup, P., Rörth, M. 1970. The erythrocyte as a vehicle for oxygen with self-regulating adjustment of unloading. *Scand. J. Clin. Lab. Invest.* 26:193–98
39. Dickerson, R. E., Geis, I. 1969. *The Structure and Action of Proteins.* New York: Harper and Row. 120 pp.
40. Duhm, J. 1973. 2,3-DPG-induced displacements of the oxyhemoglobin dissociation curve of blood: mechanisms and consequences. *Advan. Exp. Med. Biol.* 37A:179–86
41. Duhm, J., Deuticke, B., Gerlach, E. 1971. Complete restoration of oxygen transport function and 2,3-diphosphoglycerate concentration in stored blood. *Transfusion* 11:147–51
42. Eaton, J. W., Brewer, G. J., Grover, R. F. 1969. Role of red cell 2,3-diphosphoglycerate in the adaptation of man to altitude. *J. Lab. Clin. Med.* 73:603–9
43. Edwards, M. J., Canon, B. 1972. Normal levels of 2,3-diphosphoglycerate in red cells despite severe hypoxemia of chronic lung disease. *Chest* 61:(Suppl.) 25S–26S
44. Erslev, A. J., Kazal, L. A. 1969. Renal erythropoietic factor. Lack of effect on hypertransfused mice. *Blood* 34:222–29
45. Erslev, A. J., Kazal, L. A., Miller, O. P. 1971. The action and neutralization of a renal lipid inhibitor of erythropoietin. *Proc. Soc. Exp. Biol. Med.* 138:1025–29
46. Eschbach, J. W. et al 1967. Erythropoiesis in patients with renal failure undergoing chronic dialysis. *N. Engl. J. Med.* 276:653–58
47. Faura, J. et al 1969. Effect of altitude on erythropoiesis. *Blood* 33:668–76
48. Finch, C. A., Lenfant, C. 1972. Oxygen transport in man. *N. Engl. J. Med.* 286:407–15
49. Fisher, J. W. 1972. Erythropoietin: pharmacology, biogenesis and control of production. *Pharmacol. Rev.* 24:459–508
50. Fisher, J. W., Lajtha, L. G., Buttoo, A. S., Porteous, D. D. 1965. Direct effects of erythropoietin on the bone marrow of the isolated perfused hind limbs of rabbits. *Brit. J. Haemat.* 11:342–49
51. Forster, R. E., Roughton, F. J. W., Kreuzer, F., Briscoe, W. A. 1957. Photocalorimetric determination of rate of uptake of CO and O_2 by reduced human red cell suspensions at 37°C. *J. Appl. Physiol.* 11:260–68
52. Fried, W., Kilbridge, T., Krantz, S., McDonald, T. P., Lange, R. D. 1969. Studies on extrarenal erythropoietin. *J. Lab. Clin. Med.* 73:244–48
53. Fried, W., Plzak, L., Jacobson, L. O., Goldwasser, E. 1956. Erythropoiesis. II. Assay of erythropoietin in hypophysectomized rats. *Proc. Soc. Exp. Biol. Med.* 92:203–7
54. Garby, L., Robert, M., Zaar, B. 1972. Proton- and carbamino-linked oxygen affinity of normal human blood. *Acta Physiol. Scand.* 84:482–92
55. Goldwasser, E., Kung, C. K.-H. 1972. The molecular weight of sheep plasma erythropoietin. *J. Biol. Chem.* 247: 5159–60
56. Gordon, A. S. 1970. *Regulation of Hematopoiesis. Vol. 1. Red Cell Production,* ed. A. S. Gordon, Chap. 19. New York: Appleton. 765 pp.
57. Gordon, A. S., Zanjani, E. D., McLaurin, W. D. 1968. The renal erythropoietic factor (REF). VII. Relation to sex steroid hormone effects on erythropoiesis. *Proc. Soc. Exp. Biol. Med.* 129: 871–74
58. Greer, J., Perutz, M. F. 1971. Three dimensional structure of haemoglobin Rainier. *Nature New Biol.* 230:261–64
59. Hamasaki, N., Asakura, T., Minakami, S. 1970. Effect of oxygen tension on glycolysis in human erythrocytes. *J. Biochem. Tokyo* 68:157–61
60. Hamstra, R. D., Block, M. H. 1969. Erythropoiesis in response to blood loss in man. *J. Appl. Physiol.* 27:503–7
61. Hayashi, A., Stamatoyannopoulos, G. 1972. Role of penultimate tyrosine in

haemoglobin β subunit. *Nature New Biol.* 235:70–72

62. Hayashi, A., Suzuki, T., Imai, K., Morimoto, H., Watari, H. 1969. Properties of hemoglobin M, Milwaukee-I variant and its unique characteristic. *Biochim. Biophys. Acta* 194:6–15
63. Hermansen, L., Osnes, J.-B. 1972. Blood and muscle pH after maximal exercise in man. *J. Appl. Physiol.* 32:304–8
64. Hillman, R. S., Henderson, P. A. 1969. Control of marrow production by the level of iron supply. *J. Clin. Invest.* 48:454–60
65. Holsinger, J. W. Jr., Salhany, J. M., Eliot, R. S. 1973. Evidence for a relationship between 2,3-diphosphoglycerate-depleted red blood cells, slow oxygen release and myocardial ischemia. *Advan. Exp. Med. Biol.* 37A:179–86
66. Huehns, E. R., Bellingham, A. J. 1969. Diseases of function and stability of haemoglobin. *Brit. J. Haematol.* 17: 1–10
67. Humpeler, E., Amor, H. 1973. Sex differences in the oxygen affinity of hemoglobin. *Pfluegers Arch.* 343: 151–56
68. Hurtado, A., Merino, C., Delgado, E. 1945. Influence of anoxemia on the hemopoietic activity. *Arch. Intern. Med.* 75:284–323
69. Jacobson, L. O., Goldwasser, E., Fried, W., Plzak, L. 1957. Role of the kidney in erythropoiesis. *Nature* 79:633–34
70. Kilmartin, J. V., Fogg, J., Luzzana, M., Rossi-Bernardi, L. 1973. Role of the α-amino groups of the α and β chains of human hemoglobin in oxygen-linked binding of carbon dioxide. *J. Biol. Chem.* 248:7039–43
71. Kilmartin, J. V., Rossi-Bernardi, L. 1969. Inhibition of CO_2 combination and reduction of the Bohr effect in haemoglobin chemically modified at its α-amino groups. *Nature* 222:1243–46
72. Korn, A. P., Henkelman, R. M., Ottensmeyer, F. P., Till, J. E. 1973. Investigations of a stochastic model of haemopoiesis. *Exp. Hematol.* 1:362–75
73. Krantz, S. B. 1965. The effect of erythropoietin on human bone marrow cells in vitro. *Life Sci.* 4:2393–97
74. Krantz, S. B., Gallien-Lartigue, O., Goldwasser, E. 1963. The effect of erythropoietin upon heme synthesis by marrow cells in vitro. *J. Biol. Chem.* 238:4085–90
75. Krantz, S. B., Jacobson, L. O. 1970. *Erythropoietin and the Regulation of Erythropoiesis.* Chicago: Univ. Chicago Press. 330 pp.
76. Kuratowska, Z., Lewartowski, B., Michalak, E. 1961. Studies on the production of erythropoietin by isolated perfused organs. *Blood* 18:527–34
77. Labardini, J. et al 1973. Marrow radioiron kinetics. *Haematologia* 7:301–12
78. Lange, R. D., McDonald, T. P., Jordan, T. 1969. Antisera to erythropoietin: partial characterization of two different antibodies. *J. Lab. Clin. Med.* 73:78–90
79. Lenfant, C., Sullivan, K. 1971. Adaptation to high altitude. *N. Engl. J. Med.* 284:1298–1309
80. Lenfant, C. et al 1968. Effect of altitude on oxygen binding by hemoglobin and on organic phosphate levels. *J. Clin. Invest.* 47:2652–56
81. Lenfant, C., Torrance, J. D., Reynafarje, C. 1971. Shift of the O_2-Hb dissociation curve at altitude: mechanism and effect. *J. Appl. Physiol.* 30:625–31
82. Lichtman, M. A. 1973. Oxygen binding to hemoglobin in hypoproliferative anemia: adaptation to alkalosis, not hemoglobin deficit. *Blood* 42:996 (Abstr.)
83. Lichtman, M. A., Cohen, J., Young, J. A. 1974. Reduced arterial oxygen flow and respiratory alkalosis following myocardial infarction: role of hemoglobin-oxygen affinity in the maintenance of oxygen consumption. *Clin. Res.* 23:554A (Abstr.)
84. Lichtman, M. A., Miller, D. R., Cohen, J., Waterhouse, C. 1971. Reduced red cell glycolysis, 2,3-diphosphoglycerate and adenosine triphosphate concentration, and increased hemoglobin-oxygen affinity caused by hypophosphatemia. *Ann. Intern. Med.* 74:562–68
85. Lichtman, M. A., Murphy, M. S., Byer, B. J., Freeman, R. B. 1974. Hemoglobin affinity for oxygen in chronic renal disease: the effect of hemodialysis. *Blood* 43:417–24
86. McCulloch, E. A. 1970. Control of hematopoiesis at the cellular level. *Regulation of Hematopoiesis. Vol. 1. Red Cell Production,* ed. A.S. Gordon, Chap 7. New York: Appleton. 765 pp.
87. McDonald, T. P., Zanjani, E. D., Lange, R. D., Gordon, A. S. 1971. Immunological studies of the renal erythropoietic factor (erythrogenin). *Brit. J. Haematol.* 20:113–21
88. Messier, A. A., Schaefer, K. E. 1973. The Bohr effect in chronic hypercapnia. *Resp. Physiol.* 19:26–34
89. Metcalfe, J., Dhindsa, D. S., Edwards, M. J., Mourdjinis, A. 1969. Decreased

affinity of blood for oxygen in patients with low-output heart failure. *Circ. Res.* 25:47–51
90. Miller, M. E. et al 1973. pH effect on erythropoietin response to hypoxia. *N. Engl. J. Med.* 288:706–10
91. Miller, W. W., Delivoria-Papadopoulos, M., Miller, L., Oski, F. A. 1970. Oxygen releasing factor in hyperthyroidism. *J. Am. Med. Assoc.* 211: 1824–26
92. Mills, G. C. 1969. The physiologic regulation of erythrocyte metabolism. *Tex. Rep. Biol. Med.* 27:773–86
93. Mirand, E. A., Weintraub, A. H., Gordon, A. S., Prentice, T. C., Grace, J. T. Jr. 1965. Erythropoietic activity of untreated and deproteinized normal human plasma. *Proc. Soc. Exp. Biol. Med.* 118:823–26
94. Mizoguchi, H., Levere, R. D. 1971. Enhancement of heme and globin synthesis in cultured human marrow by certain 5β-H steroid metabolites. *J. Exp. Med.* 134:1501–12
95. Morimoto, H., Lehmann, H., Perutz, M. F. 1971. Molecular pathology of human haemoglobin: stereochemical interpretation of abnormal oxygen affinities. *Nature London* 232:408–13
96. Naeraa, N., Petersen, E. S., Boye, E., Severinghaus, J. W. 1966. pH and molecular CO_2 components of the Bohr effect in human blood. *Scand. J. Clin. Lab. Invest.* 18:96–102
97. Naets, J. P., Wittek, M. 1968. Presence of erythropoietin in the plasma of one anephric patient. *Blood* 31:249–51
98. Nathan, D. G., Schupak, E., Stohlman, F. Jr., Merrill, J. P. 1964. Erythropoiesis in anephric man. *J. Clin. Invest.* 43:2158–65
99. Nute, P. E., Stamatoyannopoulos, G., Hermodson, M. A., Roth, D. 1974. Hemoglobinopathic erythrocytosis due to a new electrophoretically silent variant, Hemoglobin San Diego (β109 (G11) Val $\longrightarrow$ Met). *J. Clin. Invest.* 53:320–28
100. Oski, F. A. 1973. The unique fetal red cell and its function. *Pediatrics* 51:494–500
101. Oski, F. A., Gottlieb, A. J., Delivoria-Papadopoulos, M., Miller, W. W. 1969. Red-cell 2,3-diphosphoglycerate levels in subjects with chronic hypoxemia. *N. Engl. J. Med.* 280:1165–66
102. Oski, F. A., Travis, S. F., Miller, L. D., Delivoria-Papadopoulos, M., Cannon, E. 1971. The in vitro restoration of red cell 2,3-diphosphoglycerate levels in banked blood. *Blood* 37:52–58
103. Papayannopoulou, T., Finch, C. A. 1972. On the in vivo action of erythropoietin: a quantitative analysis. *J. Clin. Invest.* 51:1179–85
104. Parker, J. P., Beirne, G. J., Desai, J. N., Raich, P. C., Shahidi, N. T. 1972. Androgen-induced increase in red-cell 2,3,-diphosphoglycerate. *N. Engl. J. Med.* 287:381–83
105. Perrotta, A. L., Finch, C. A. 1972. The polychromatophilic erythrocyte. *Am. J. Clin. Pathol.* 57:471–77
106. Perutz, M. F. 1970. Stereochemistry of cooperative effects in haemoglobin. *Nature London* 228:726–41
107. Perutz, M. F., Lehmann, H. 1968. Molecular pathology of human haemoglobin. *Nature London* 219:902–9
108. Perutz, M. F., Muirhead, H., Cox, J. M., Goaman, L. C. G. 1968. Three-dimensional Fourier synthesis of horse oxyhaemoglobin at 2.8 Å resolution: the atomic model. *Nature London* 219:131–39
109. Perutz, M. F., TenEyck, L. F. 1971. Stereochemistry of cooperative effects in hemoglobin. *Cold Spring Harbor Symp. Quant. Biol.* 36:295–310
110. Reissmann, K. R., Ruth, W. E., Nomura, T. 1961. A human hemoglobin with lowered oxygen affinity and impaired heme-heme interactions. *J. Clin. Invest.* 40:1826–33
111. Rosenthal, A. et al 1971. The role of red blood cell organic phosphates in adaptation to congenital heart disease. *Pediatrics* 47:537–47
112. Rowell, L. B. 1974. Human cardiovascular adjustments to exercise and thermal stress. *Physiol. Rev.* 54:75–159
113. Roy, S. B., Bhatia, M. L., Mathur, V. S., Virmani, S. 1963. Hemodynamic effects of chronic severe anemia. *Circulation* 28:346–56
114. Salhany, J. M. 1972. Effect of carbon dioxide on human hemoglobin. Kinetic basis for the reduced oxygen affinity. *J. Biol. Chem.* 247:3799–3801
115. Sánchez-Medal, L., Gomez-Leal, A., Duarte, L., Guadelupe Rico, M. 1970. Anabolic-androgenic steroids in the treatment of aplastic anemia. *Blood* 34:283–300
116. Sánchez-Medal, L., Pizzuto, J., Rodriguez-Moyado, H., Expósito, L. 1969. Haemolysis and erythropoiesis. II. Reticulocytosis and rate of haemoglobin rise in haemolytic and deficiency anaemias. *Brit. J. Haematol.* 17:343–50

117. Shafer, A. W., Tague, L. L., Welch, M. H., Guenter, C. A. 1971. 2,3-diphosphoglycerate in red cells stored in acid-citrate-dextrose and citrate-phosphate-dextrose: implications regarding delivery of oxygen. *J. Lab. Clin. Med.* 77:430–37
118. Siggaard-Andersen, O., Garby, L. 1973. The Bohr effect and the Haldane effect. *Scand. J. Clin. Lab. Invest.* 31:1–8
119. Snyder, L. M., Reddy, W. J. 1970. Mechanism of action of thyroid hormones on erythrocyte 2,3-diphosphoglyceric acid synthesis. *J. Clin. Invest.* 49:1993–98
120. Sproule, B. J., Mitchell, J. H., Miller, W. F. 1960. Cardiopulmonary physiological responses to heavy exercise in patients with anemia. *J. Clin. Invest.* 39:378–88
121. Stamatoyannopoulos, G. 1972. The molecular basis of hemoglobin disease. *Ann. Rev. Genet.* 6:47–70
122. Stamatoyannopoulos, G., Bellingham, A. J., Lenfant, C., Finch, C. A. 1971. Abnormal hemoglobins with high and low oxygen affinity. *Ann. Rev. Med.* 22:221–34
123. Stamatoyannopoulos, G., Parer, J. T., Finch, C. A. 1969. Physiologic implications of a hemoglobin with decreased oxygen affinity (hemoglobin Seattle). *N. Engl. J. Med.* 281:915–19
124. Stohlman, F. Jr. 1972. Aplastic anemia (editorial). *Blood* 40:282–86
125. Torrance, J. et al 1970. Intraerythrocytic adaptation to anemia. *N. Engl. J. Med.* 283:165–69
126. Torrance, J. D., Lenfant, C., Cruz, J., Marticorena, E. 1970. Oxygen transport mechanisms in residents at high altitude. *Resp. Physiol.* 11:1–15
127. Tyuma, I., Shimizu, K. 1970. Effect of organic phosphates on the difference in oxygen affinity between fetal and adult human hemoglobin. *Fed. Proc.* 29:1112–14
128. Valeri, C. R., Fortier, N. L. 1969. Red-cell 2,3,-diphosphoglycerate and creatine levels in patients with red-cell mass deficits or with cardiopulmonary insufficiency. *N. Engl. J. Med.* 281:1452–55
129. Valeri, C. R., Fortier, N. L. 1970. Red cell 2,3-DPG, ATP, and creatine levels in preserved red cells and in patients with red cell mass deficits or with cardiopulmonary insufficiency. *Advan. Exp. Med. Biol.* 6:289–303
130. Wade, O. L., Bishop, J. M. 1962. *Cardiac Output and Regional Blood Flow,* Philadelphia: Davis. 268 pp.
131. Wardle, D. F. H., Baker, I., Malpas, J. S., Wrigley, P. F. M. 1973. Bioassay of erythropoietin using foetal mouse liver cells. *Brit. J. Haematol.* 24:49–56
132. Weil, J. V., Jamieson, G., Brown, D. W., Grover, R. F. 1968. The red cell mass—arterial oxygen relationship in normal man. *J. Clin. Invest.* 47:1627–39
133. Woodson, R. D., Torrance, J. D., Shappell, S. D., Lenfant, C. 1970. The effect of cardiac disease on hemoglobin-oxygen binding. *J. Clin. Invest.* 49:1349–56
134. Woodson, R. D., Wranne, B., Detter, J. C. 1973. Effect of increased blood oxygen affinity on work performance of rats. *J. Clin. Invest.* 52:2717–24
135. Wranne, B., Woodson, R., Detter, J. 1972. The two Bohr effects: physiological consequences of ligand interaction with hemoglobin. *Advan. Exp. Med. Biol.* 28:449–55
136. Young, J. A., Lichtman, M. A., Cohen, J. 1973. Reduced red cell 2,3-diphosphoglycerate and adenosine triphosphate, hypophosphatemia, and increased hemoglobin-oxygen affinity after cardiac surgery. *Circulation* 47: 1313–18
137. Zürcher, C., Loos, J. A., Prins, H. K. 1965. Hereditary high ATP content of human erythrocytes. *Folia Haematol. Leipzig* 83:366–73

Copyright 1975. All rights reserved

KIDNEY

❖1135

William E. Lassiter
Department of Medicine, University of North Carolina School of Medicine, Chapel Hill, North Carolina 27514

INTRODUCTION

The literature of renal physiology has continued its exponential growth in the two years since kidney was last reviewed in this series (57), and a comprehensive survey of the entire field is obviously impossible if a critical perspective is to be maintained. Partly because of important recent developments in these areas, and certainly because of personal interest, I have elected to limit this review to the following four topics: dynamics of glomerular filtration, control of sodium reabsorption in the proximal tubule, functions of the loop of Henle, and uric acid excretion. Even so, the space limitations have forced selectivity and many relevant contributions have been left uncited. This review necessarily reflects personal prejudices, but I have tried to be fair and hope that I have provided the reader with a reasonably comprehensive and critical survey of these areas of controversy.

DYNAMICS OF GLOMERULAR FILTRATION

Homer Smith suggested some years ago that filtration equilibrium may be achieved in the glomerular capillaries, but the conventional view has been that disequilibrium persists and filtration continues along the entire length of the capillaries. If filtration equilibrium, defined as that condition in which forces favoring and opposing filtration are equal, does exist, then at some point along the capillaries

$$(P_G - P_{BS}) - (\pi_G - \pi_{BS}) = 0$$

where P is hydrostatic pressure, π is colloid osmotic pressure, and G and BS refer to the glomerular capillaries and Bowman's space respectively. Under these conditions, in which a relatively large hydraulic permeability of the glomerular capillaries is implied, the glomerular filtration rate (GFR) is proportional to the glomerular plasma flow (GPF), and the filtration fraction (FF) is constant as long as net hydrostatic pressure ($P_G - P_{BS}$) and afferent arteriolar oncotic pressure (π_a) are unchanged. If, as has been conventionally believed, filtration equilibrium is not achieved, GFR is less dependent on changes in GPF, and FF is variable. This conventional view rests entirely on indirect estimates of glomerular capillary pressure and permeability.

Permeability estimates have been based largely on the porosity of the filtration membrane to molecules of varying sizes that appear in the urine; estimates of glomerular capillary pressure have been either outright guesses or extrapolations from such indirect measurements as the maximum ureteral pressure during ureteral occlusion. More recently Gertz et al (32) estimated glomerular capillary pressure from the pressure in individual nephrons during stop flow and reported surprisingly high values of approximately 75 mm Hg. Their method of measurement of intratubular stop-flow pressure, however, was inadequate for the purpose and would probably yield spuriously high estimates of the pressures in this particular circumstance.

The development of a servo-nulling system for measurement of hydrostatic pressure in microvascular structures and the discovery of rats with glomeruli on the surface of their kidneys have made possible direct measurement of the operative forces. Brenner and his associates in San Francisco (12, 13, 23, 25, 61) have provided most of the recent information, but similar work has been performed in the micropuncture laboratory in Dallas (6). The hydrostatic pressure in the capillaries of the most superficial glomeruli has been measured directly, and blood has been taken from the ends of single efferent arterioles, the "star" vessels, for protein determination. Presumably minimal fluid reabsorption occurs between the end of the glomerular capillaries and the star vessels on the surface of the kidney; any reabsorption that might occur would of course result in a lower protein concentration and apparent deviation from filtration equilibrium.

These direct measurements indicate that in hydropenic rats P_G averages approximately 45 mm Hg, some 40% of mean arterial pressure, P_{BS} equals 10 mm Hg, π_a 20 mm Hg, and π_e (efferent arteriolar oncotic pressure) 35 mm Hg. Thus the net filtration pressure is 15 mm Hg at the afferent end of the glomerular capillaries and 0 at the efferent end; i.e. filtration equilibrium is achieved. [There must be some fall in hydrostatic pressure along the glomerular capillaries, but Brenner et al presented theoretical arguments that this is quite small, perhaps of the order of 1–2 mm Hg (24)].

Filtration equilibrium was also observed in rats expanded with plasma equivalent to 2.5% of the body weight (bw), but not with further plasma expansion to 5% of the body weight. In this latter circumstance Deen et al (25) were able to calculate the glomerular ultrafiltration coefficient, K_f. The rate of glomerular filtration is defined as

$$\mathrm{GFR} = K_f \times P_{uf} = k \times S \times P_{uf}$$

where K_f is a product of the specific hydraulic permeability (k) and the surface area (S) of the glomerular capillaries, and P_{uf}, the net ultrafiltration pressure, equals $(P_G - P_{BS} - \pi_G)$. The validity of this calculation depends on the value assigned to mean colloid osmotic pressure. The colloid osmotic pressure almost certainly rises in an exponential fashion as a result of filtration as blood flows along the glomerular capillaries; therefore, the mean colloid osmotic pressure in the capillaries when filtration equilibrium has been achieved may be greatly overestimated if taken as half the sum of the afferent and efferent colloid osmotic pressures. The point at which equilibrium is achieved is flow-dependent, and the earlier it is reached, the greater the potential for error in the estimate. It is only under conditions of disequilibrium, when the rise in colloid osmotic pressure along the capillaries is more nearly linear, that K_f can be estimated in this fashion. K_f per glomerulus was estimated to be 0.08 nl sec^{-1} (mm Hg)$^{-1}$ and, utilizing the previously determined filtration surface of 0.0019 cm^2/rat glomerulus, $k = 4$ nl sec^{-1} cm^2 (mm Hg)$^{-1}$. This is approximately 10 times larger than earlier estimates of glomerular permeability based on indirect evidence, and 50 times greater than recent direct estimates of capillary permeability in rat skeletal muscle. Interestingly, in rats loaded with plasma to 5% of bw, K_f was unchanged over a range of single nephron plasma flows (SNGPF) from 173 nl/min (when renal perfusion pressure was reduced by an aortic clamp) to 309 nl/min (after carotid artery occlusion). These results indicate that the strong dependency of GFR on plasma flow reported by both the San Francisco and Dallas workers results from flow-induced changes in mean P_{uf} and not from large changes in K_f.

How general is the applicability of this finding of filtration equilibrium in the surface glomeruli of a mutant strain of white rats? Are these few most superficially located glomeruli representative of the more than 30,000 other glomeruli situated in the deeper parts of the kidney cortex? Is filtration equilibrium regularly achieved in the glomeruli of other strains and other species [Deen et al (24) state that direct observations by Maddox, Troy, and Brenner indicate that filtration equilibrium also exists in the surface glomeruli of squirrel monkeys], and does it occur in diseased glomeruli? The concept is so attractive that one is tempted to generalize the findings, but unfortunately there is little information from which to construct an opinion. No detailed morphological observations on these particular glomeruli have been reported, and there are few published data on the simultaneous measurement of comparable functions in the whole kidney and at the level of the individual glomerulus.

Allison, Wilson & Gottschalk (3) reported that in rats with autologous immune-complex nephritis and antiglomerular basement membrane nephritis, filtration equilibrium apparently was reached in only those nephrons with very low SNGFR. Glomerular hydrostatic pressure was estimated from tubular stop-flow pressure, however, and efferent arteriolar colloid osmotic pressure was estimated from whole kidney filtration fraction; neither procedure has been proven to be adequate for this purpose in the diseased kidney. Although the authors recognized the uncertainty of their methodology and the need for direct measurements, the estimated disequilibrium that they found was so large that it is difficult to believe that filtration equilibrium was achieved in most of the nephrons; their conclusions seem reasonable. Moreover, it is likely that because of variability of the disease process the magnitude of disequilibrium may differ not only in different glomeruli but also in different capillary loops of a single glomerulus. Since SNGFRs are so variable in experimentally diseased kidneys, there must also be great heterogeneity of SNGPF and/or SNFF in these kidneys. The fall in hydrostatic pressure along the glomerular capillaries may be greater than normal, also complicating the analysis of the situation. For these reasons all the pertinent direct observations must be made on the same individual nephron and the corresponding efferent arteriole, a very difficult technical feat. Normal rats with reduced filtration fraction resulting from high glomerular plasma flows failed to achieve filtration equilibrium, although glomerular permeability was normal, as discussed above. Since a common finding in patients with chronic kidney disease is a reduced filtration fraction, it is not unreasonable to suggest that filtration equilibrium is not achieved in diseased kidneys, at least not in those glomeruli with high plasma flow.

The micropuncture literature of the past two decades is replete with examples of erroneous conclusions resulting from inadequate technology; thus some consideration of the special technical problems encountered in the study of glomerular dynamics is appropriate, since an uncommonly high level of technical competence is required. Although the glomeruli on the surface of the kidney are clearly visible, the direct measurement of P_G is not done under visual control. The tip of the pipette filled with colorless fluid must be small (1–3 μm OD), and it must pass through Bowman's space before a capillary lumen can be impaled. Successful puncture is signaled by the recording of a pulsatile pressure in phase with the arterial pulse pressure and higher than that in Bowman's space. Apparently a high pressure may be recorded if the tip is in the glomerular mesangial region, but it is out of phase with arterial pulse pressure. A microtip, especially one with too long a bevel, might easily partially penetrate the capillary wall and record a pressure intermediate between the mesangium and capillary lumen. Furthermore, entry of the micropipette sometimes induces visible constriction of the glomerular capillary tuft, and sufficient time must elapse for this to disappear before a valid pressure can be recorded.

If it could be shown that stop-flow pressure (SFP) plus π_a always equals the directly measured P_G, this might often be the preferred methodology. This indirect procedure for estimating P_G is technically much simpler than the direct measurement, and nephrons with deeper glomeruli can be studied. As Allison et al pointed out, the estimation of P_G in this fashion involves three important assumptions (3). First, glomerular filtration must be completely stopped, so that the protein concentration in the glomerular capillaries is the same as that in the systemic circulation. Second, any possible hemodynamic effects of the reduction of flow at the macula densa after blockage of the tubule with oil must be negligible. Third, appropriate alterations in the afferent and efferent arteriolar resistances must have occurred in order to accommodate the increased capillary flow due to cessation of filtration without change in glomerular hydrostatic pressure. It will be necessary for indirect measurement of P_G such as this to be proven adequate in each new physiological circumstance before it can be accepted. The need for caution is evident from the only published systematic comparison of directly measured and estimated P_G. Blantz et al (6) reported that obstruction of the proximal tubule caused a significant rise in directly measured P_G that returned to control levels within 25 sec in normally hydrated rats but remained elevated indefinitely in volume-expanded rats unless tubular fluid was collected proximal to the blockade.

Collection of sufficient plasma from the star vessels for protein determination, and the ultramicro determination itself, is also technically difficult. Insertion of a pipette into a star vessel might conceivably change pressures and flows in the glomerular capillaries that feed that efferent arteriole and result in changes in glomerular dynamics; the chemical determination itself is technically challenging. Indeed, non-reproducibility of results has led several laboratories to abandon their use of it. Finally, the natural variability in P_G and efferent arteriolar protein concentration among individual collections is unfortunately not apparent in the published data, since for the most part only animal's mean values have been presented.

CONTROL OF SODIUM REABSORPTION IN THE PROXIMAL TUBULE

Water and electrolyte transport in the proximal tubule was extensively reviewed four years ago by Orloff & Burg (59), who ended their discussion of the regulation of sodium excretion on this discouraging note: "One fact is certain. The kidney knows how to regulate sodium excretion and we do not." Despite the intense investigative activity of the past four years, we are reluctantly forced to conclude that this assessment is still valid, and the mechanisms whereby proximal sodium reabsorption is regulated continue to elude precise definition.

Oncotic Pressure

Interest in recent years has centered on the role of the peritubular environment in the control of sodium excretion, stimulated by the demonstration by Earley and co-workers (29) and Lewy & Windhager (54) that changes in such factors as hydrostatic and oncotic pressure of the peritubular capillary blood were associated with altered sodium reabsorption. These workers were appropriately circumspect in their conclusions, but some of their followers have been led, incorrectly in our opinion, to suggest that physical factors are the chief determinants of the magnitude of sodium reabsorption in the proximal tubule, although most concede that salt and water reabsorption from the proximal tubule requires active transport of solute, and that hydrostatic and oncotic pressures are not the primary driving forces.

Brenner & Troy (10) attempted to alter the peritubular environment by perfusing Ringer's solution, containing albumin in concentrations varying from 0 to 15 g/100 ml, into efferent arterioles on the surface of the kidney. They collected fluid by micropuncture from adjacent proximal tubules. Infusion of colloid-free Ringer's was associated with decreased absolute and fractional absorption, whereas hyperoncotic capillary perfusion increased absorption. The effects were rapidly reversible. Aortic clamping produced a fall in both GFR and filtration fraction, and postglomerular capillary protein concentration and the absolute rate of proximal reabsorption were decreased in parallel. If postglomerular protein concentration was then increased by capillary perfusion, absolute reabsorption increased toward normal. In a subsequent study (11) the inhibition of proximal reabsorption induced by acute volume expansion was reversed when the protein concentration in peritubular capillaries was restored to normal by capillary perfusion with isoncotic albumin Ringer's solution.

In contrast (22), chronically salt-loaded rats achieved sodium homeostasis by an increase in GFR and not by a decrease in absolute proximal sodium reabsorption; however, these animals responded in the same manner as controls to a superimposed acute saline load, and the absolute magnitude of proximal sodium reabsorption paralleled the tubular capillary protein concentration. Brenner et al (11) concluded that "the bulk of inhibition in absolute proximal reabsorption after volume expansion with colloid-free solutions is causally mediated by the parallel decline in post-glomerular vascular protein concentration," a conclusion that seems unnecessarily strong.

Although not emphasized by workers in this field, it is obvious that efferent arteriolar protein concentration cannot be the sole determinant of the magnitude of proximal reabsorption, since the capacity of the peritubular capillaries to absorb water before the colloid osmotic pressure is reduced to a limiting value depends not only on entering protein concentration but also on the volume of plasma flowing through the capillaries.

Imai & Kokko (41) and Grantham et al (35) studied the influence of peritubular protein concentration on sodium and water reabsorption in fragments of proximal tubules isolated by microdissection from rabbit kidneys, and although their techniques were somewhat different, the results are qualitatively similar. Imai & Kokko perfused convoluted tubules in a bath derived from rabbit serum and found that when protein concentration in the bath was increased to twice normal, net efflux of both sodium and water was increased by almost a third; however, when the bath was replaced by a colloid-free ultrafiltrate of rabbit serum, efflux was markedly reduced. No change was observed in the transtubular potential or in the passive permeability to sodium or urea, but permeability to sucrose was significantly increased.

Grantham et al used a preparation in which the tubule was occluded at one end and perfused at the other under a constant head of hydrostatic pressure. Net water absorption was estimated from the rate of delivery of tritiated water out of the perfusion pipette into the bathing medium. A marked decline in the rate of absorption was observed when the bathing medium was changed from rabbit serum containing 6% protein to a colloid-free ultrafiltrate of serum. In contrast to Imai & Kokko, however, they observed no increase in absorption when the bath was hyperoncotic. The transport rate was relatively insensitive to small increases in hydrostatic pressure and was markedly inhibited by ouabain. Since in these preparations no capillary wall is interposed, it is reasoned that the effect of oncotic pressure must be exerted directly across the tubular basement membrane.

Oncotic pressure, whether acting across capillary walls or directly across the tubular basement membrane, is presumed to modulate net reabsorption by serving as a driving force for the removal of salt and water that has been transported by the tubular epithelium into the intercellular spaces. When oncotic pressure is reduced, the intercellular spaces widen and hydrostatic pressure in them increases slightly, permitting increased back-diffusion across the apical tight junctions into the tubular lumen. Evidence that this may be a reasonable postulate is derived from several sources. Lorentz, Lassiter & Gottschalk (55) observed that under conditions of increased intrarenal pressure induced by elevation of ureteral pressure, partial renal vein constriction, or massive saline diuresis, the permeability of the tubule to a variety of small molecules (creatinine, mannitol, sucrose, and iothalamate) was increased. This was true whether the tubules were dilated, as with increased ureteral pressure, or unchanged in diameter or actually compressed, as in renal vein constriction.

Bulger et al (14) examined the morphology of the tight junctions of rat proximal tubules after fixation with osmium tetroxide. All the tight junctions were fused in control animals that were subjected only to moderate mannitol diuresis. However, when kidneys were fixed in states of increased intratubular pressure, induced either by elevation of ureteral pressure or by renal vein constriction, some tight junctions in every animal showed nonfusion of the adjacent cell membranes, while others were normal. Increased tubular pressure was thus shown to be associated with an alteration in the morphology of the tight junction even when gross dilatation of the tubule was absent.

Boulpaep & Seely (9) examined the electrical properties of proximal and distal tubules in the dog kidney and concluded that an important paracellular pathway for fluid and electrolyte transport exists across the proximal epithelium. They cited several lines of evidence for this, which I shall not attempt to summarize. Their conclusion derives chiefly from the small magnitude of the observed transepithelial resistance, which is several orders of magnitude lower than the specific resistance of the cell membranes, and the relative ranking of permeability coefficients for various ions and the small range of their differences, which again is at variance with that observed for cell membranes. Subsequently Boulpaep (8) investigated the effect of saline loading on the permeability of the proximal tubule of Necturus and found that the transepithelial electrical conductance was increased threefold by volume expansion. Permeability to NaCl was increased to a similar extent, and an even greater increase in permeability to raffinose, a solute to which the tubule is normally impermeable, was observed. He concluded that saline loading increases the backflux through paracellular channels, thus decreasing net sodium reabsorption. A similar conclusion was reached by Seely from studies on the rat (69). He perfused peritubular capillaries with various concentrations of albumin or dextran and found that hypo-oncotic perfusion and systemic saline loading both produced a small but statistically significant decrease in electrical resistance of the proximal tubules, whereas resistance was increased by hyperoncotic perfusion and unchanged when the perfused fluid was isoncotic.

It remains to be determined whether these functional changes in the paracellular pathway, induced by alterations in oncotic pressure, are accompanied by parallel morphologic changes, as was demonstrated by Bulger et al (14) in the case of hydrostatic pressure. Tisher & Yarger (78) perfused tubules with colloidal lanthanum, and on electron microscopy found no morphological differences between hydropenic and volume-expanded animals. The tight junctions in the proximal tubule were permeable to the lanthanum in both groups of animals. This observation is not easily reconciled with the findings of Bulger et al. However, the size of the colloidal particles of lanthanum, which may vary from experiment to experiment, is uncertain, and without direct monitoring it is impossible to be certain that a small but possibly important increase in hydrostatic pressure might have occurred at some time during perfusion of the tubule with the lanthanum solution. Simple observation of luminal diameter is not adequate for this purpose; thus it is possible that the findings of Tisher & Yarger are due in part to artifact.

In spite of the seemingly compelling evidence cited above, the role of oncotic pressure in the modulation of salt and water reabsorption in the proximal tubule remains a topic of active debate, and several recent studies suggest that oncotic pressure may not be the sole, or for that matter even a very important, determinant of the magnitude of reabsorption. Horster et al (40) perfused isolated rabbit proximal convoluted tubules bathed either in rabbit serum or in protein-free ultrafiltrates of rabbit serum, prepared with membranes of various degrees of selectivity. When the bath consisted of a protein-free ultrafiltrate of serum prepared with membranes that nominally exclude only solutes of molecular weight greater than 50,000, the rate of fluid absorption from the tubule was markedly reduced, in agreement with results previously cited (35, 41), but in contrast to the earlier studies; restoration of oncotic pressure by addition of bovine serum albumin to the ultrafiltrate failed to restore transport to control values. Ultrafiltrates prepared with membranes that exclude all solutes of molecular weight greater than 10,000 or 14,000, on the other hand, supported reabsorption as readily as normal serum, as did protein-free artificial saline buffers that had been previously dialyzed across one of these membranes against normal rabbit serum. The authors concluded that factors other than colloid osmotic pressure are necessary for the maintainance of fluid reabsorption, and that changes in fluid absorption previously ascribed to the presence or absence of protein colloid osmotic pressure are in fact due instead to the presence or absence of one of these other unidentified factors. On the basis of their results they suggest that at least 3 serum factors may be involved: (*a*) substrate(s) or accelerator(s), of molecular weight less than 14,000, that are necessary for fluid absorption and are lacking in artificial saline buffers; (*b*) inhibitor(s) of fluid absorption, of molecular weight between 14,000 and 50,000; and (*c*) inactivator(s) of the inhibitor, of molecular weight greater than 50,000.

These results suggest that protein colloid osmotic pressure per se is not the critical determinant of fluid absorption in isolated tubules, but a role for oncotic pressure in the more complicated situation in vivo is not excluded. Plasma protein concentration might still be a determinant of the rate of fluid uptake into capillaries, and hence influence net absorption by modulating interstitial fluid pressure. Even this is questioned in a recent report by Conger, Bartoli & Earley (20), who perfused rat peritubular capillaries with pooled plasma made protein-free or hyperoncotic by ultrafiltration. Re-collection of proximal tubular fluid was used to determine the effect on volume absorption and nephron filtration when perfusate replaced blood flow. Trace amounts of tritium-labelled PAH and mannitol-^{14}C were added to the perfusate to exclude leakage into the punctured tubules and to assure that the perfusate was actually reaching the tubules under study. Varying the protein concentration between 0 and 13 g% produced no changes in tubular reabsorption, although acetazolamide perfused in the same manner markedly inhibited absorption. The authors concluded that peritubular protein concentration is of minor importance in regulating proximal reabsorption.

The reasons for the difference between these results and those of Brenner's group are not immediately apparent. The capillary perfusion rate (130 nl/min) was somewhat lower than that employed by Brenner & Troy (10), but it still should have been adequate to produce an effect. One important difference in the protocols is that the perfusates employed by Conger et al were prepared from rabbit serum, whereas Brenner & Troy used artificial solutions that might have lacked some component critical to the support of reabsorption.

Bartoli, Conger & Earley (4) employed an ingenious technique to demonstrate that proximal tubular reabsorption is at least in part dependent on the luminal flow rate. Flow of tubular fluid between early and late proximal sites was reduced an average of 45% by partial diversion of the glomerular filtrate by aspiration at the early proximal site. Tubular reabsorption in the intervening segment was simultaneously reduced an average of 29%; this reduction occurred in the absence of changes in hemodynamics or nephron GFR. The authors concluded that changes in intraluminal load play a direct role in glomerulotubular balance. They suggested that the flow rate might have a direct effect on unstirred layers in the brush border, or that sodium reabsorption might be dependent on reabsorption of some other unidentified substance in the tubular fluid, the absorption of which is in turn concentration-limited. Support for this latter possibility was obtained in microperfusion studies (5). When proximal tubules in the rat kidney were perfused in situ with artificial solutions, the rate of reabsorption decreased with time, but reabsorption of an ultrafiltrate of plasma remained constant. In long nephron segments, changes in the perfusion rate were accompanied by parallel but smaller changes in the reabsorptive rate. The results suggested to the investigators that unidentified constituents of normal glomerular filtrate as well as intraluminal flow rate can influence proximal reabsorption.

The role, if any, of colloid osmotic pressure in the modulation of proximal reabsorption thus remains controversial. It is apparent, however, that whatever its role, the relationship between oncotic pressure and reabsorption is complex and not one of simple cause and effect.

Parathyroid Hormone and Sodium Reabsorption

Agus et al (1, 2) demonstrated by micropuncture that administration of purified parathyroid hormone (PTH) to dogs was followed by striking and parallel reductions in sodium and calcium reabsorption in the proximal tubule, unassociated with a rise in either total kidney or single nephron glomerular filtration rate. Similar effects were produced by infusion of dibutyryl cyclic AMP. Inhibition of phosphate reabsorption was somewhat greater than sodium or calcium, and Wen has shown that the phosphaturic effect of PTH may be partially dissociated from its effect on sodium reabsorption (80). In the studies of Agus et al the bulk of rejected phosphate was excreted in the urine, but sodium excretion was only slightly increased and calcium excretion fell despite the proximal inhibition. Thus PTH administration also results, either directly or indirectly, in an increase in calcium and sodium reabsorption in more distal parts of the nephron.

The relation of PTH to the inhibition of sodium absorption induced by hyperoncotic albumin infusion has been investigated by Knox and Schneider and their associates. Inhibition of proximal sodium reabsorption by PTH was confirmed, but changes in sodium reabsorption and phosphate excretion similar to those induced by PTH were also observed after albumin infusion (68). This led to an investigation of the role of PTH in the response to acute plasma volume expansion (45). Infusion of salt-poor hyperoncotic albumin into dogs significantly decreased the plasma ionized calcium concentration, increased circulating levels of immunoreactive PTH, decreased proximal tubular sodium reabsorption, and increased phosphate excretion. In contrast, infusion of albumin in which the ionized calcium was restored to normal plasma levels had no significant effect on any of these parameters. Similarly, albumin failed to alter proximal sodium reabsorption or phosphate clearance in parathyroidectomized animals given a constant replacement infusion of PTH. These findings suggest that PTH may play a significant role in the control of sodium reabsorption in the proximal tubule, and specifically that the hormone is involved in the mediation of the response to acute plasma volume expansion induced by hyperoncotic albumin infusion. It would be unwise to conclude, however, that PTH is the long sought but elusive "natriuretic hormone," since the natriuresis produced is relatively small.

Anesthetic Agents

Since physiological studies require the use of anesthetized animals, a brief consideration of the effects of anesthetics on salt and water movement is appropriate. Several years ago Hadfield & Ramsay (39) reported that the antidiuretic effect of Pitressin was significantly reduced in water-loaded dogs when anesthetized with thiobarbiturates, but not with oxybarbiturates. Also thiopental, but not pentobarbital, significantly inhibited the effect of Pitressin on the short circuit current of isolated frog skin. Since Inactin, a thiobarbiturate, is widely used in renal physiology, consideration of its effects on transport is particularly pertinent.

Conflicting views have been presented by Leyssac and his co-workers in Copenhagen, and by Schnermann and associates in Munich. Elmer et al (30) compared renal function in rats anesthetized with Inactin and Amytal, an oxybarbiturate. Using an indirect method to estimate proximal reabsorption that involves measurement of occlusion time and transit time, they calculated that proximal fluid reabsorption averaged 0.72 ml min^{-1} g^{-1} (kidney weight) in the Amytal anesthetized animals, and only 0.46 in the Inactin group. Although there was some overlap in individual values, the number of animals in each group was large and the differences statistically highly significant. The proximal reabsorptive rate, moreover, varied inversely with the circulating plasma concentration of Inactin, but was unrelated to the concentration of Amytal. They concluded that Inactin directly depresses and limits proximal reabsorption. Dev et al in Munich (26), on the other hand, were able to achieve satisfactory anesthesia with administration of somewhat smaller amounts of Inactin, and they found no differences in GFR or in tubular reabsorption when the Inactin-anesthetized rats were compared with a group of rats at a similar level of anesthesia after Amytal administration. Plasma anesthetic concentrations were not measured; hence, their observations are not necessarily incompatible with the Copenhagen results.

Recently Christensen et al (19) compared the effects of Amytal and Inactin on isosmotic net fluid transport in the isolated rabbit gall bladder in vitro. Measurable inhibition of fluid absorption was demonstrable at an Inactin concentration of 1×10^{-4} M, whereas a tenfold higher concentration of Amytal was required. At concentration of 5×10^{-4} M, previously found to be the median plasma concentration of both anesthetics in anesthetized rats, Inactin produced 40% inhibition of transport, whereas Amytal produced no inhibition. Changes in fluid reabsorption induced by Amytal were accompanied by parallel changes in oxygen consumption, but Inactin appeared to uncouple reabsorption and oxygen consumption. Whether these observations in the isolated gall bladder are relevant to solute transport in the intact kidney is not clear, but obviously the possibility that anesthesia itself may induce unrecognized alterations in the functional state of the experimental animal must be a matter of continuing concern.

LOOP OF HENLE FUNCTION

The role of the loop of Henle in the mechanism of urine concentration was reviewed in detail by Morel and de Rouffignac in the 1973 *Annual Review of Physiology* (57), but the subject deserves further consideration because of new developments. Consideration is limited to the more recent papers.

Function of the Thin Segments of Henle's Loop in Countercurrent Multiplication

It is now universally accepted that the elaboration of a concentrated urine involves osmotic equilibration of collecting duct urine with a medullary interstitium that becomes progressively more hypertonic as one proceeds from the corticomedullary junction to the tip of the papilla, and that this osmotic gradient is generated by countercurrent multiplication in Henle's loop. Classical countercurrent theory requires that the descending and ascending loops have different permeability characteristics, and the "single effect," or initial concentration difference that is multiplied in the loop is presumed to be generated by the active transport of solute out of the entire length of the water-impermeable ascending limb (33). The existence of active solute transport in the thick portion of the ascending limb is not in doubt (vide infra), and it is generally recognized that both anatomical and functional differences exist between the descending and ascending thin limbs, particularly in regard to their permeability properties. However, firm evidence that the thin ascending limb is capable of active directional transport of solute is lacking. Interest has been stimulated, therefore, in theoretical models that might predict the concentration gradients known to exist in the inner medulla without requiring active transport.

Stephenson (74) proposed a model in which descending and ascending limbs of Henle's loop and collecting ducts all exchange with a central vascular core, formed of vasa recta, which is assumed to be so highly permeable that it functions as a single tube open at the cortical end and closed at the papillary end. Solute supplied to the vascular core, primarily from the ascending limb of Henle, increases the osmolality of the core and therefore extracts water from the descending limb and collecting ducts, increasing their osmolality while at the same time diluting ascending limb fluid. The single effect is multiplied by the counterflow arrangement and leads to a high papillary osmolality in all structures. To this point, the model does not differ fundamentally from the classical countercurrent theory of urine concentration. An essential requirement of the system is that the total solute concentration at each point along the ascending limb of Henle's loop be lower than the adjacent concentration in the vascular core, and Stephenson has shown theoretically that in a single solute system this is possible only if there is active transport of solute out of the ascending limb (75). In a two solute system, on the other hand, it is possible for concentration to occur with all net transport of individual solutes occurring down concentration gradients (i. e. passive transport), provided appropriate permeability properties are assigned to the tubules (76). Thus urea derived from collecting ducts and salt derived from loops of Henle both contribute significantly to the total osmolality of the vascular core. If the ascending thin limb of Henle is much more permeable to salt than to water or urea, diffusion of salt out of the limb down its concentration gradient leaves the remaining fluid hypotonic to its environment. Passive diffusion of salt along its concentration gradient out of the ascending limb, and not active transport, may therefore produce the "single effect."

Another model, similar to the Stephenson model in most of its essentials, has been independently proposed by Kokko & Rector (49). This model also assumes that all solute and water movement across both the descending and ascending thin segments of the loop of Henle is passive, and that active salt transport occurs out of the water and solute-impermeable thick ascending limb. The following permeability characteristics are required of the thin segments: The descending limb is relatively impermeable to all solutes but is highly permeable to water. In the thin ascending loop, by contrast, permeability to sodium chloride is greater than the permeability to urea, and this segment is nearly totally impermeable to water. The distal tubule and cortical collecting ducts are impermeable to urea but permeable to water when ADH is present, and the medullary collecting duct is permeable to both water and urea in the presence of ADH. Salt transport out of the thick ascending loop of Henle leads, if ADH is present, to water loss by osmotic equilibration in more distal nephron segments, with a large increase in the urea concentration in the tubular fluid finally delivered to the medullary collecting ducts. This urea is then able to diffuse out of the collecting ducts into the medullary interstitium, contributing significantly to the interstitial osmolality. Potential energy generated by active solute transport by the thick ascending limb in the outer medulla is thus transferred to the inner medulla, with urea serving as the "messenger." Meanwhile, tubular fluid entering the descending limb of the loop achieves osmotic equilibrium with the hypertonic medullary interstitium primarily by loss of water, since this segment is presumed to be highly permeable to water and relatively impermeable to solute. The solute in this segment is primarily NaCl, and fluid reaching the bend of the loop, although in osmotic equilibrium with its surroundings, contains NaCl in higher concentration and urea in lower concentration than the medullary interstitium. The thin ascending limb is impermeable to water, but both NaCl and urea can diffuse across the tubule along their concentration gradients. However, since this segment is more permeable to NaCl than to urea, the rate at which NaCl leaves the tubule is greater than the rate of urea entry, and the fluid in this segment thus becomes hypotonic to its surroundings. Stewart & Valtin (77) have undertaken a computer simulation of the model and have shown that it is capable of producing medullary gradients of total solute, sodium chloride, and urea concentrations about the same as those observed experimentally, provided appropriate permeability constants are assumed.

Kokko and associates examined the permeability properties of isolated fragments of loops of Henle dissected from rabbit kidneys, and their findings are in remarkably good agreement with the requirements of the theory (48). The thin descending limb was found to have a high osmotic permeability to water and low passive permeabilities for sodium (46), potassium (63), and urea (47). By contrast, the diffusional permeability to water of the thin ascending limb was only a tenth that of the descending limb, and hydraulic permeability was almost immeasurably small (42). Permeability to both sodium and chloride in the thin ascending limb was greater than to urea, and was higher than in any other nephron segment. No net transtubular movement of solute or water was observed, no osmotic gradient developed, and no transtubular potential differences were generated when fragments of either thin descending or ascending limb were perfused with solutions identical in composition to the bathing medium; thus there was no evidence for active transport in either segment under these conditions. When the thin ascending loop was perfused with a 600 mosm solution containing chiefly NaCl and bathed in an isosmotic solution in which half the osmolality was due to NaCl and half to urea, the osmolality of collected fluid was decreased significantly below that of both the bath and the initial perfusate because the efflux of NaCl was greater than the influx of urea.

For maximum efficiency these passive models for countercurrent multiplication in the inner medulla require that osmotic equilibration in the descending loop occur primarily by water loss and not by solute entry. There is an abundance of data in the older literature, however, suggesting that the urea concentration, in particular, at the bend of the loop of Henle is greater than can be accounted for by water removal in the descending loop alone (34, 53, 56). de Rouffignac and co-workers (66, 67) measured concentrations of total solute, urea, and various electrolytes at the bend of loops of Henle in Psammomys and found concentrations that are difficult to explain if osmotic equilibration in the descending loop occurred solely by water loss. Furthermore, they found no correlation between tubular fluid: plasma inulin ratios in early distal tubules and the final urine osmolality, as might be expected if water loss in the descending loop varied with inner medullary solute concentration. These investigators suggested that osmotic equilibration in the descending loop, in this species at least, occurs primarily by solute entry and not by water loss. Unfortunately no firm conclusions can be drawn from their data because assumptions are required regarding the composition of fluid entering the loops that cannot be directly verified. However, they also observed that water reabsorption in loops of Henle of superficial nephrons was less than would be expected if osmotic equilibration occurred solely by water loss, since in this species the loops of even the most superficial nephrons dip into a markedly hypertonic region of the inner medulla (66). Jamison et al (44) studied the composition of fluid in Henle's loops in rats with hereditary hypothalamic diabetes insipidus. From comparisons of inulin concentration ratios, osmolality, and sodium and potassium concentrations in loop fluid before and after ADH administration, they estimated that the increase in osmolality along the descending limb that occurs after induction of antidiuresis was accounted for in approximately equal measure by water removal and addition of nonelectrolyte, presumably urea. In more recent studies Jamison revised his estimate slightly; he found that roughly two thirds of the osmotic equilibration is due to water removal and one third to solute addition (60).

The demonstration of solute entry into the descending loop of Henle does not necessarily invalidate the passive countercurrent multiplier hypothesis, but it does place a limitation on the efficiency of the system. Whether a purely passive countercurrent multiplier system is still theoretically capable of producing the observed concentration gradients when allowance is made for solute entry of reasonable magnitude into the descending loop, or whether at least a small element of active solute transport is still required, awaits determination. Even with this reservation the hypothesis has many attractive features, although it must be acknowledged that almost all the experimental data offered in its support have been generated in a single laboratory using tubule fragments from a single species, and further confirmation from other laboratories is needed. As has been noted by Kokko (47), permeability characteristics of the tubules may change when the osmolality of the bathing solution is altered; thus it would be desirable to study the permeability properties of the loops of Henle when exposed to osmotic concentrations equal to the maximum achieved in vivo.

I would like to suggest an additional experiment that might be useful as a test of validity of the hypothesis. It has been previously demonstrated (43) that fluid in the ascending limb of the loop of Henle is normally hypotonic to fluid at the same level in the descending limb, as predicted both by classical countercurrent theory and by the passive models. Passive models of countercurrent multiplication require a high interstitial urea concentration in the inner medulla for generation of the concentration difference; thus the difference should disappear under conditions in which the medullary urea concentration is decreased, as in water or osmotic diuresis. On the other hand, if the thin ascending limb is capable of active solute transport as predicted by classical theory, a concentration difference should persist under these circumstances.

Active Chloride Transport in the Thick Ascending Limb

Solute transport in the thick ascending limb of Henle's loop has been studied by the Dallas group (62) and at the National Institutes of Health (15); although their findings differ somewhat in detail, the two groups agree that the water-impermeable thick ascending limb of Henle has the capacity for active outward solute transport as a consequence of an electrogenic chloride pump. In both laboratories isolated segments of thick ascending limb obtained by microdissection from rabbit kidneys were perfused, either with artifical solutions or with ultrafiltrates of rabbit serum, and both groups found this segment to have a very low permeability for water. Burg & Green (15) estimated the segment to be 100 times less permeable to water than the proximal tubule, while Rocha & Kokko (62) found the hydraulic permeability too small to measure. They agreed that the passive permeability to sodium is greater than to chloride. When the tubules were perfused with solutions containing sodium and chloride, net outward movement of both ions against a concentration gradient was observed, and a transtubular potential of approximately 7 mV, lumen positive, was generated. Burg et al found that the potential was abolished when sulfate was substituted for chloride, but was increased to 14 mV when choline chloride was substituted for NaCl. Rocha et al, on the other hand, found that substitution of choline for sodium reduced the potential difference. One possible reason for this discrepancy is that different portions of the thick ascending limb were used in the two laboratories.

The Dallas group utilized only medullary segments, while the NIH investigators employed that portion of the limb just proximal to the macula densa, which included cortical ascending limb as well. While the existence of active sodium transport could not be excluded, both groups agreed that its magnitude must be small. Both also found that ouabain decreased chloride transport, but it is not clear whether this is due to direct inhibition by the drug of a chloride-dependent ATPase or whether the decreased chloride transport is an indirect effect of altered Na-K transport. Active chloride transport appears to be the principal energy source for production of the "single effect" in the operation of the countercurrent multiplier system in the outer medulla. If the passive models of the concentrating mechanism in the inner medulla are correct, active chloride transport in the outer medulla would also indirectly provide the driving force for countercurrent multiplication in the inner medulla.

Subsequent studies by Burg and associates (17, 18) have shown that small concentrations of intraluminal furosemide and ethacrynic acid markedly and reversibly decrease the transtubular potential and net chloride transport. The activity of ethacrynic acid is greatly increased if it is first complexed with cysteine, a maneuver that incidentally abolishes its effect on Na+K-ATPase. Mersalyl reduces but does not abolish chloride transport (16). All three drugs appear to be effective only from the intraluminal side of the tubule. Burg suggested that the natriuretic effect of these drugs may be primarily related to inhibition of chloride transport in the thick ascending limb of the loop and not dependent on direct inhibition of Na transport. This may explain why these drugs appear to cause relatively little disturbance in sodium transport in cells elsewhere in the body.

URIC ACID EXCRETION

Renal excretion of uric acid is generally considered to be regulated by a three-component system, involving glomerular filtration, tubular reabsorption, and tubular secretion (37), but the nature and anatomical location of the various transport functions are still controversial. Apparently contradictory data obtained in various animal species, as well as inconsistencies in data acquired by different techniques in the same species, has added to the confusion. The historical evolution of popular concepts of uric acid homeostasis is admirably summarized in a review by Gutman & Yü (38). The present review is primarily, although not exclusively, limited to more recent studies. I have not attempted to include all relevant papers, but have limited the discussion to those that seem to offer greatest insight into the renal handling of urate.

Micropuncture and Microperfusion Studies

Uric acid transport in the proximal tubule of the anesthetized rat was studied by micropuncture by Greger, Lang & Deetjen (36). Under normal free-flow conditions and at physiological levels of plasma uric acid concentration (0.7–2 mg%), the urate tubular fluid:plasma concentration ratios were greater than the corresponding ratios for inulin in a majority of cases, demonstrating net secretion of uric acid in the proximal tubule. These observations were made under conditions in which the clearance ratio of urate to inulin was in the neighborhood of 0.4; hence net reabsorption of urate took place in the kidney, but apparently at a site distal to that portion of the proximal tubule accessible to micropuncture. These findings were confirmed in subsequent microperfusion studies (51, 52) that revealed secretion and reabsorption of urate along the entire accessible portion of the proximal tubule. Both influx and efflux appeared to obey first order kinetics (i.e. were proportional to concentration) over the range of concentrations studied, and at equal concentrations influx was 2.5 times as great as efflux. Net secretion of urate was found along the entire accessible portion of the proximal tubule, but the authors postulated that under free-flow conditions, as intratubular urate increases both as a result of secretion and indirectly as a consequence of water reabsorption, the contribution of the reabsorptive flux to net transport would become progressively greater, so that ultimately reabsorption would predominate in the pars recta of the proximal tubule or more distally in the loop of Henle.

Qualitative confirmation of the results of Deetjen and his collaborators was provided by the microperfusion studies in rats reported in abstract by Roch-Ramel & Boudry (64). These investigators perfused urate 2-^{14}C at 10–12 nl/min into various segments of the nephron and found evidence of urate reabsorption in the proximal tubule and loop of Henle, but not in the distal tubule. Influx of urate into the proximal tubule was also demonstrated but not quantified.

Kramp, Lassiter & Gottschalk (50) studied the recovery of urate in the urine after microinjection at various locations along the tubule of small volumes of fluid containing urate 2-^{14}C and tritium-labelled inulin. Their results were qualitatively consistent with the findings of the Deetjen group and of Roch-Ramel, although they suggested a somewhat smaller role for the loop of Henle in overall urate reabsorption. The whole kidney urate clearances of urate reported in this study were unusually high and averaged approximately 70% of GFR. We now know that these clearance determinations were in error. The clearances were measured with urate 2-^{14}C, and it is probable that a major fraction of the labelled urate was converted by liver urate oxidase to labelled allantoin before it reached the kidney. Since allantoin is handled by the kidney much like inulin, this results in a spurious increase in the apparent urate clearance.

This problem has been studied in detail by Cook in my laboratory (unpublished observations). When urate is oxidized to allantoin, the 6-carbon is lost as CO_2. Therefore, if urate labelled in the 6 position is infused, all the radioactivity excreted in the urine should be unchanged urate, since any allantoin formed as a result of urate metabolism would be unlabelled. The clearance of urate 6-^{14}C averaged approximately 25% of GFR, only slightly greater than the simultaneous clearance of urate measured chemically. In contrast, the apparent clearance of urate 2-^{14}C was much larger, and thin-layer chromatography of the urine indicated that 70% of the isotope excreted after urate 2-^{14}C infusion was not uric acid, but allantoin.

The studies of Deetjen and co-workers (36, 51, 52) indicated that the secretion of urate by the proximal tubule in the rat involves active transport, since net secretion occurred against an electrochemical gradient. The nature of proximal urate reabsorption is not clearly defined by their studies, however. They calculated a transport coefficient for unidirectional efflux of uric acid of 11×10^{-5} cm/sec (51), in remarkably good agreement with the permeability coefficient calculated by Sonnenberg, Oelert & Baumann (71). Although the latter authors assumed reabsorption was passive, nonionic diffusion was excluded as the avenue of reabsorption since the apparent permeability was insensitive to changes in pH. They attributed this to the low lipid solubility of unionized uric acid. Dantzler (21) studied urate transport in isolated perfused proximal tubules obtained by microdissection from kidneys of garter snakes. Urate is a major end product of nitrogen metabolism in these snakes, and secretion predominates and clearly involves active transport. Intracellular urate concentration was higher than that in either the bath or the lumen of the tubule, and Dantzler postulated, therefore, that the locus of active transport in the secretory direction was at the peritubular cell membrane. He found in addition that the tubular fluid:bath concentration ratio varied inversely with the rate of perfusion, and the apparent net secretion of urate increased linearly with increases in perfusion rate, suggesting the existence of concentration-dependent back-diffusion of urate out of the tubular lumen. Direct measurement of urate efflux led to the calculation of a permeability coefficient of 7.5×10^{-6} cm/sec, about an order of magnitude lower than reported values in the rat (51, 71). Considering the difference in the species and the arbitrary assumptions regarding tubular radius made in all of these studies, the agreement seems remarkably close.

Although the above observations suggest passive reabsorption of urate in the proximal tubules, they are equally compatible with active or at least carrier-mediated transport, provided the transport system is operating at a level well below saturation. That the bulk of urate reabsorption is carrier mediated and not due to simple diffusion is suggested by the observation of Kramp et al (50) that efflux of urate from the proximal tubule is inhibited by a variety of drugs known to affect uric acid excretion. In addition, they found evidence of saturation of urate reabsorption at high intratubular loads, as is also suggested by the microperfusion study of Roch-Ramel & Boudry (64).

Roch-Ramel & Weiner (65) applied micropuncture methods to the study of urate transport in the Cebus monkey. In contrast to the rat, reabsorption, not secretion, was dominant in the proximal tubule, and no evidence was found of reabsorption in the loop of Henle. Although the data are inadequate to completely rule out urate transport in the loop of Henle or distal convolution, the results indicate that these processes must be small in magnitude. Net urate reabsorption from the proximal tubule was inhibited by 2-nitroprobenecid. Tubular fluid:plasma urate ratios were consistently less than 1.0 under control conditions, averaging 0.62 ± 0.05 (SE). Since binding of urate to plasma proteins is negligible in this species (70), these observations indicate that reabsorption must be effected by active transport if the proximal transtubular potential in this species, as in the rat, is not far from zero.

Studies of Urate Transport in Man and Chimpanzee

Except for the single study mentioned in the preceding paragraph, direct studies of urate transport in individual kidney tubules have been limited to rodents, and conclusions regarding the mode of urate transport in man and other primates have been largely derived indirectly from observation of the effects of various combinations of drugs known to alter urate excretion. The validity of this approach depends on the dual assumptions that urate reabsorption and secretion occur as mutually independent processes and that when two or more drugs are given in combination each quantitatively retains its original effect, independent of the others. Particular interest has centered on pyrazinamide and its active metabolite pyrazinoic acid (PZA) (79), a powerful inhibitor of urate secretion (81, 82). If PZA completely suppresses urate secretion, then any residual excretion after its administration is assumed to represent filtered urate that has escaped reabsorption; the relative contributions to excretion of the three components, filtration, reabsorption, and excretion, are thus determined. Very large doses of pyrazinoate are uricosuric in dogs (79) and chimpanzees (31), and even in modest doses diminish the reabsorptive flux out of the proximal tubule of the rat (50). Nevertheless, the chief effect of the drug in moderate doses in most mammals appears to be to inhibit secretion.

The assumptions that secretion and reabsorption are entirely independent processes, and that one drug cannot interfere with the action of another, are more difficult to justify. PZA, for example, blunts or abolishes the response to a number of uricosuric drugs; this is difficult to understand if it is true that there is no drug interaction and that the secretory and reabsorptive processes are truly independent of one another. Since secretion and reabsorption have been shown to be anatomically coextensive in the proximal tubule of the rat, it is not unreasonable to suppose that this might also be true in higher animals, including man. The true magnitude of tubular secretion should then be underestimated in studies in which only changes in urinary excretion are measured, since much of the secreted urate might be liable to subsequent reabsorption. As we shall see, the data are consistent with this interpretation.

Diamond et al (27) measured urate excretion at various levels of urine flow in 12 human subjects undergoing water diuresis. They found that the rate of urate excretion and the urate clearance, expressed as percent of GFR, were significantly greater at high rates of urine flow than at low. The response to water loading was attenuated after pyrazinamide administration, suggesting that water loading had altered specifically the secretory component of urate excretion. Since water and solute reabsorption in the proximal tubule is presumably unchanged in water diuresis, the authors postulated the existence of a postsecretory reabsorptive site in the distal tubule where concentration-dependent reabsorption would vary inversely with the rate of urine flow, thus altering apparent secretion. This interpretation is difficult to reconcile with observations in the rat (50, 58) indicating that urate reabsorption in the distal tubule is negligible, but the observations are consistent with changes in concentration-dependent reabsorption in the loops of Henle in the inner medulla.

Further evidence that urate reabsorption is distal to, or more likely coextensive with, secretion is provided by the numerous studies showing attenuation or abolition of the effects of uricosuric drugs by pyrazinamide or pyrazinoate. Of particular interest in this regard are the studies of Diamond & Paolino (28) and Steele & Boner (73) in man, and of Fanelli & Weiner (31) in the chimpanzee. The essential observation that is common to all of these studies is that the response to uricosuric drugs such as probenecid is markedly attenuated or abolished by pyrazinamide or pyrazinoate. The effect is the same whether the PZA is given before or after the uricosuric drug. If secretion is defined as the amount by which urate excretion is decreased after administration of PZA, then the magnitude of this decrease observed under conditions in which reabsorption is also presumably inhibited is much greater than the total excretion when no drugs are administered. This implies that the actual magnitude of secretion is much greater than excretion; thus a portion of secreted urate must be subsequently reabsorbed. An alternative explanation that has not been completely ruled out is that pyrazinoate in some way interferes with the action of uricosuric drugs, either by preventing their excretion into the tubular lumen or by directly blocking interaction with sites for urate reabsorption. Boner & Steele (7) have shown that only the uricosuric effect of chlorothiazide is blocked by PZA, while the natriuretic and phosphaturic actions of the drug are unimpaired; definitive studies to exclude drug interaction have not yet been reported.

It is not certain whether uric acid is secreted by the mechanism common to other organic acids, or whether a separate pathway is involved. Boner & Steele (7) and Fanelli & Weiner (31) both observed that doses of PZA that profoundly decreased urate excretion had little effect on para-amino hippurate (PAH) excretion, suggesting that PAH is a much better competitor than pyrazinoate for the common organic acid secretory pathway. Since PAH, the better competitor, has less effect on urate transport than pyrazinoate, they argued that urate is secreted by a separate pathway. This evidence cannot be considered definitive, however, since no systematic attempt was made to determine whether or not the tubular transport capacity for PAH (Tm) was changed by PZA. Below Tm, of course, T_{PAH} is primarily a measure of renal plasma flow, not of transport capacity.

In conclusion, I should like to suggest the following formulation to describe urate transport in the mammalian kidney. Derived in large measure from Fanelli & Weiner (31) and Steele (72), the following is consistent with the current state of knowledge:

1. Bidirectional transport of urate occurs along the entire length of the proximal tubule, including the pars recta, and possibly in more distal portions of the loop of Henle, although there is no direct proof of the latter. This transport is carrier mediated and possibly active in both directions; simple diffusion plays a relatively minor role in urate transport. At normal plasma urate concentrations and in the absence of drug intervention the transport system in neither direction is saturated, thus unidirectional fluxes are in general proportional to concentration. The magnitude of the secretory and reabsorptive fluxes may both be very large in comparison to urate excretion. While quantitative differences exist in the relative magnitudes of secretion and reabsorption in various species, thus accounting for differences in excretion, the mechanisms are qualitatively similar in all mammalian species.

2. Drugs altering urate transport generally inhibit secretion and/or reabsorption, and most drugs inhibiting transport in one direction also have a similar effect on transport in the opposite direction, but differing in magnitude. Quantitative, but probably not qualitative, differences exist between species in their response to these drugs.

3. There is inadequate evidence at present to settle the question whether uric acid shares the secretory pathway common to other organic acids or is secreted by a unique mechanism.

The beauty of this formulation is that almost all existing experimental data can be accommodated, and many of the previously confusing differences between various species can be explained without postulating fundamentally different mechanisms of urate excretion. This is at the same time its weakness. Since almost any experimental finding is consistent with the theory, it is difficult to devise a critical experiment to test it. Obviously studies of urate excretion in the intact animal will not be adequate. The critical test must await the extension of micropuncture and microperfusion methods to a study of urate fluxes in other species and the application of these techniques to the study of drug actions on individual nephrons.

Literature Cited

1. Agus, Z. S., Gardner, L. B., Beck, L. H., Goldberg, M. 1973. Effects of parathyroid hormone on renal tubular reabsorption of calcium, sodium and phosphate. *Am. J. Physiol.* 224:1143–48
2. Agus, Z. S., Puschett, J. B., Senesky, D., Goldberg, M. 1971. Mode of action of parathyroid hormone and cyclic adenosine 3',5'-monophosphate on renal tubular phosphate reabsorption in the dog. *J. Clin. Invest.* 50:617–26
3. Allison, M. E. M., Wilson, C. B., Gottschalk, C. W. 1974. Pathophysiology of experimental glomerulonephritis in rats. *J. Clin. Invest.* 53:1402–23
4. Bartoli, E., Conger, J. D., Earley, L. E. 1973. Effect of intraluminal flow on proximal tubular reabsorption. *J. Clin. Invest.* 52:843–49
5. Bartoli, E., Earley, L. E. 1973. Importance of ultrafilterable factors in maintaining tubular reabsorption. *Kidney Int.* 3:142–50
6. Blantz, R. C., Israelit, A. H., Rector, F. C. Jr., Seldin, D. W. 1972. Relation of distal tubular NaCl delivery and glomerular hydrostatic pressure. *Kidney Int.* 2:22–32
7. Boner, G., Steele, T. H. 1973. Relationship of urate and *p*-aminohippurate secretion in man. *Am. J. Physiol.* 225:100–4
8. Boulpaep, E. L. 1972. Permeability changes of the proximal tubule of Necturus during saline loading. *Am. J. Physiol.* 222:517–31
9. Boulpaep, E. L., Seely, J. F. 1971. Electrophysiology of proximal and distal

tubules in the autoperfused dog kidney. *Am. J. Physiol.* 221:1084–96
10. Brenner, B. M., Troy, J. L. 1971. Postglomerular vascular protein concentration: Evidence for a causal role in governing fluid reabsorption and glomerulotubular balance by the renal proximal tubule. *J. Clin. Invest.* 50: 336–49
11. Brenner, B. M., Troy, J. L., Daugharty, T. M. 1971. On the mechanism of inhibition in fluid reabsorption by the renal proximal tubule of the volume-expanded rat. *J. Clin. Invest.* 50:1596–1602
12. Brenner, B. M., Troy, J. L., Daugharty, T. M. 1971. The dynamics of glomerular ultrafiltration in the rat. *J. Clin. Invest.* 50:1776–80
13. Brenner, B. M.,Troy, J. L., Daugharty, T. M., Robertson, C. R. 1972. Dynamics of glomerular ultrafiltration in the rat. II. Plasma-flow dependence of GFR. *Am. J. Physiol.* 223:1184–90
14. Bulger, R. E., Lorentz, W. B. Jr., Colindres, R. E. Gottschalk, C. W. 1974. Morphologic changes in rat renal proximal tubules and their tight junctions with increased intraluminal pressure. *Lab. Invest.* 30:136–44
15. Burg, M. B., Green, N. 1973. Function of the thick ascending limb of Henle's loop. *Am. J. Physiol.* 224:659–68
16. Burg, M., Green, N. 1973. Effect of mersalyl on the thick ascending limb of Henle's loop. *Kidney Int.* 4:245–51
17. Burg, M., Green, N. 1973. Effect of ethacrynic acid on the thick ascending limb of Henle's loop. *Kidney Int.* 4:301–8
18. Burg, M., Stoner, L., Cardinal, J., Green, N. 1973. Furosemide effect on isolated perfused tubules. *Am. J. Physiol.* 225:119–24
19. Christensen, P. L., Kristensen, L. O., Leyssac, P. P. 1973. The effects of Amytal and Inactin on isosmotic net fluid transport in the rabbit gall-bladder in vitro. *Acta Physiol. Scand.* 87:455–64
20. Conger, J. D., Bartoli, E., Earley, L. E. 1973. No effect of peritubular plasma protein on proximal tubular volume absorption during capillary perfusion in situ. *6th Ann. Meet. Am. Soc. Nephrology, Washington DC,* p. 25 (Abstr.)
21. Dantzler, W. H. 1973. Characteristics of urate transport by isolated perfused snake proximal renal tubules. *Am. J. Physiol.* 224:445–53
22. Daugharty, T. M., Ueki, I. F., Nicholas, D. P., Brenner, B. M. 1973. Renal response to chronic intravenous saline loading in the rat. *J. Clin. Invest.* 52:21–31
23. Deen, W. M., Robertson, C. R., Brenner, B. M. 1972. A model of glomerular ultrafiltration in the rat. *Am. J. Physiol.* 223:1178–83
24. Deen, W. M., Robertson, C. R., Brenner, B. M. 1974. Glomerular ultrafiltration. *Fed. Proc.* 33:14–20
25. Deen, W. M., Troy, J. L., Robertson, C. R., Brenner, B. M. 1973. Dynamics of glomerular ultrafiltration in the rat. IV. Determination of the ultrafiltration coefficient. *J. Clin. Invest.* 52:1500–8
26. Dev, B., Häberle, D., Schnermann, J., Wunderlich, P. 1973. Effect of barbiturates on GFR and fluid reabsorption along proximal convoluted tubules and loops of Henle in rats. *Pfluegers Arch.* 344:21–32
27. Diamond, H. S., Lazarus, R., Kaplan, D., Halberstam, D. 1972. Effect of urine flow rate on uric acid excretion in man. *Arthritis Rheum.* 15:338–46
28. Diamond, H. S., Paolino, J. S. 1973. Evidence for a post-secretory absorptive site for uric acid in man. *J. Clin. Invest.* 52:1491–99
29. Earley, L. E., Martino, J. A., Friedler, R. M. 1966. Factors affecting sodium reabsorption by the proximal tubule as determined during blockade of distal sodium reabsorption. *J. Clin. Invest.* 45:1668–84
30. Elmer, M., Eskildsen, P. C., Kristensen, L. O., Leyssac, P. P. 1972. A comparison of renal function in rats anesthetized with Inactin and sodium Amytal. *Acta Physiol. Scand.* 86:41–58
31. Fanelli, G. M. Jr., Weiner, I. M. 1973. Pyrazinoate excretion in the chimpanzee. Relation to urate disposition and the actions of uricosuric drugs. *J. Clin. Invest.* 52:1946–57
32. Gertz, K. H., Brandis, M., Braun-Schubert, G., Boylan, J. W. 1969. The effect of saline infusion and hemorrhage on glomerular filtration pressure and single nephron filtration rate. *Pfluegers Arch.* 310:193–205
33. Gottschalk, C. W. 1964. Osmotic concentration and dilution of urine. *Am. J. Med.* 36:670–85
34. Gottschalk, C. W. et al 1963. Micropuncture study of composition of loop of Henle fluid in desert rodents. *Am. J. Physiol.* 204:532–35

35. Grantham, J. J., Qualizza, P. B., Welling, L. W. 1972. Influence of serum proteins on net fluid reabsorption of isolated proximal tubules. *Kidney Int.* 2:66–75
36. Greger, R., Lang, F., Deetjen, P. 1971. Handling of uric acid by the rat kidney. I. Microanalysis of uric acid in proximal tubular fluid. *Pfluegers Arch.* 324: 279–87
37. Gutman, A. B., Yü, T.-F. 1961. Regulation of renal excretion of uric acid in man. *Trans. Assoc. Am. Physicians* 74:353–65
38. Gutman, A. B., Yü, T.-F. 1972. Renal mechanisms of uric acid excretion, with special reference to normal and gouty man. *Semin. Arthritis Rheum.* 2:1–46
39. Hadfield, D. A., Ramsay, D. J. 1969. Inhibition of the action of antidiuretic hormone by thiobarbiturates in dogs and on isolated frog skin. *J. Physiol.* 200:120P–121P
40. Horster, M., Burg, M., Potts, D., Orloff, J. 1973. Fluid absorption by proximal tubule in the absence of a colloid osmotic gradient. *Kidney Int.* 4:6–11
41. Imai, M., Kokko, J. P. 1972. Effect of peritubular protein concentration on reabsorption of sodium and water in isolated perfused proximal tubules. *J. Clin. Invest.* 51:314–25
42. Imai, M., Kokko, J. P. 1974. Sodium chloride, urea, and water transport in the thin ascending limb of Henle. Generation of osmotic gradients by passive diffusion of solutes. *J. Clin. Invest.* 53:393–402
43. Jamison, R. L. 1968. Micropuncture study of segments of thin loop of Henle in the rat. *Am. J. Physiol.* 215:236–42
44. Jamison, R. L., Buerkert, J., Lacy, F. 1973. A micropuncture study of Henle's thin loop in Brattleboro rats. *Am. J. Physiol.* 224:180–85
45. Knox, F. G. et al 1974. Proximal tubule reabsorption after hyperoncotic albumin infusion. Role of parathyroid hormone and dissociation from plasma volume. *J. Clin. Invest.* 53:501–7
46. Kokko, J. P. 1970. Sodium, chloride and water transport in the descending limb of Henle. *J. Clin. Invest.* 49: 1838–46
47. Kokko, J. P. 1972. Urea transport in the proximal tubule and the descending limb of Henle. *J. Clin. Invest.* 51:1999–2008
48. Kokko, J. P. 1974. Membrane characteristics governing salt and water transport in the loop of Henle. *Fed. Proc.* 33:25–30
49. Kokko, J. P., Rector, F. C. Jr. 1972. Countercurrent multiplication system without active transport in the inner medulla. *Kidney Int.* 2:214–23
50. Kramp, R. A., Lassiter, W. E., Gottschalk, C. W. 1971. Urate 2–^{14}C transport in the rat nephron. *J. Clin. Invest.* 50:35–48
51. Lang, F., Greger, R., Deetjen, P. 1972. Handling of uric acid by the rat kidney. II. Microperfusion studies on bidirectional transport of uric acid in the proximal tubule. *Pfluegers Arch.* 335:257–65
52. Lang, F., Greger, R., Deetjen, P. 1973. Handling of uric acid by the rat kidney. III. Microperfusion studies on steady state concentration of uric acid in the proximal tubule. Consideration of free flow conditions. *Pfluegers Arch.* 338: 295–302
53. Lassiter, W. E., Gottschalk, C. W., Mylle, M. 1961. Micropuncture study of net transtubular movement of water and urea in nondiuretic mammalian kidney. *Am. J. Physiol.* 200:1139–46
54. Lewy, J. E., Windhager, E. E. 1968. Peritubular control of proximal tubular fluid reabsorption in the rat kidney. *Am. J. Physiol.* 214:943–54
55. Lorentz, W. B. Jr., Lassiter, W. E., Gottschalk, C. W. 1972. Renal tubular permeability during increased intrarenal pressure. *J. Clin. Invest.* 51:484–92
56. Marsh, D. J. 1970. Solute and water flows in thin limbs of Henle's loop in the hamster kidney. *Am. J. Physiol.* 218: 824–31
57. Morel, F., de Rouffignac, C. 1973. Kidney. *Ann. Rev. Physiol.* 35:17–54
58. Oelert, H., Baumann, K., Gekle, D. 1969. Permeabilitätsmessungen einiger schwacher organischer Säuren aus dem distalen Konvolut der Rattenniere. *Pfluegers Arch.* 307:178–89
59. Orloff, J., Burg, M. 1971. Kidney. *Ann. Rev. Physiol.* 33:83–130
60. Pennell, J. P., Lacy, F. B., Jamison, R. L. 1974. An in vivo study of the concentrating process in the descending limb of Henle's loop. *Kidney Int.* 5:337–47
61. Robertson, C. R., Deen, W. M., Troy, J. L., Brenner, B. M. 1972. Dynamics of glomerular ultrafiltration in the rat. III. Hemodynamics and autoregulation. *Am. J. Physiol.* 223:1191–1200
62. Rocha, A. S., Kokko, J. P. 1973. Sodium chloride and water transport in

the medullary thick ascending limb of Henle. *J. Clin. Invest.* 52:612–23
63. Rocha, A. S., Kokko, J. 1973. Membrane characteristics regulating potassium transport out of the isolated perfused descending limb of Henle. *Kidney Int.* 4:326–30
64. Roch-Ramel, F., Boudry, J. F. 1971. Tubular fate of 2–^{14}C urate: microperfusion experiments. *Fed. Proc.* 30:338 (Abstr.)
65. Roch-Ramel, F., Weiner, I. M. 1973. Excretion of urate by the kidneys of Cebus monkeys: a micropuncture study. *Am. J. Physiol.* 224:1369–74
66. de Rouffignac, C., Morel, F. 1969. Micropuncture study of water, electrolytes, and urea movements along the loops of Henle in Psammomys. *J. Clin. Invest.* 48:474–86
67. de Rouffignac, C., Morel, F., Moss, N., Roinel, N. 1973. Micropuncture study of water and electrolyte movements along the loop of Henle in Psammomys with special reference to magnesium, calcium, and phosphorus. *Pfluegers Arch.* 344:309–26
68. Schneider, E. G., Strandhoy, J. W., Willis, L. R., Knox, F. G. 1973. Relationship between proximal sodium reabsorption and excretion of calcium, magnesium, and phosphate. *Kidney Int.* 4:369–76
69. Seely, J. F. 1973. Effects of peritubular oncotic pressure on rat proximal tubule electrical resistance. *Kidney Int.* 4: 28–35
70. Simkin, P. A. 1972. Uric acid binding to serum proteins: differences among species. *Proc. Soc. Exp. Biol. Med.* 139: 604–6
71. Sonnenberg, H., Oelert, H., Baumann, K. 1965. Proximal tubular reabsorption of some organic acids in the rat kidney in vivo. *Pfluegers Arch.* 286:171–80
72. Steele, T. H. 1973. Urate secretion in man: The pyrazinamide suppression test. *Ann. Intern. Med.* 79:734–37
73. Steele, T. H., Boner, G. 1973. Origins of the uricosuric response. *J. Clin. Invest.* 52:1368–75
74. Stephenson, J. L. 1972. Concentration of urine in a central core model of the renal counterflow system. *Kidney Int.* 2:85–94
75. Stephenson, J. L. 1973. Concentrating engines and the kidney. I. Central core model of the renal medulla. *Biophys. J.* 13:512–45
76. Stephenson, J. L. 1973. Concentrating engines and the kidney. II. Multisolute central core systems. *Biophys. J.* 13: 546–67
77. Stewart, J., Valtin, H. 1972. Computer simulation of osmotic gradient without active transport in renal inner medulla. *Kidney Int.* 2:264–70
78. Tisher, C. C., Yarger, W. E. 1973. Lanthanum permeability of the tight junction (zonula occludens) in the renal tubule of the rat. *Kidney Int.* 3:238–50
79. Weiner, I. M., Tinker, J. P. 1972. Pharmacology of pyrazinamide: metabolic and renal function studies related to the mechanism of drug-induced urate retention. *J. Pharmacol. Exp. Ther.* 180: 411–34
80. Wen, S.-F. 1974. Micropuncture studies of phosphate transport in the proximal tubule of the dog. *J. Clin. Invest.* 53:143–53
81. Yü, T. F., Berger, L., Gutman, A. B. 1961. Suppression of tubular secretion of urate by pyrazinamide in the dog. *Proc. Soc. Exp. Biol. Med.* 107:905–8
82. Yü, T. F., Berger, L., Stone, D. J., Wolf, J., Gutman, A. B. 1957. Effect of pyrazinamide and pyrazinoic acid on urate clearance and other discrete renal functions. *Proc. Soc. Exp. Biol. Med.* 96:264–67

Copyright 1975. All rights reserved

REGIONAL BLOOD FLOW[1] ❖1136

Ove Lundgren and Mats Jodal
Department of Physiology, University of Göteborg, Göteborg, Sweden

This review was intended to cover the recent investigations within the field of circulatory physiology. Because of the large number of publications we have been forced to make a selection and, hence, only the vascular beds of the heart, the skeletal muscle, the brain, the splanchnic area, and the kidney are reviewed. However, even as regards these vascular circuits, the article may not be considered to be a comprehensive report and we apologize for omissions of important articles. The emphasis of the review is on local and "remote" (i.e. nervous and hormonal) control mechanisms of organ blood flow and on such circulatory adjustments that are of importance for the function of the organ in question. Some methodological questions are also commented upon. Central nervous or nervous reflex control of the circulation is not discussed and reports of mainly pathophysiological emphasis are not included.

HEART

The coronary vessels supply a tissue that may be considered to be in a lifelong state of exercise. Furthermore, an adequate blood supply to the heart is of vital importance for the proper functioning of the rest of the cardiovascular system. From a teleological point of view it therefore seems most appropriate that the heart itself "determines" its blood supply; the control of the coronary vessels is believed to be mainly exerted by local factors, i.e. the local chemical milieu and mechanical factors secondary to the beating of the heart.

As regards the local chemical control, discussion has centered on the extent to which oxygen per se is of importance as opposed to whether there occurs an extracellular accumulation of certain key metabolites, which, in turn, relax vascular smooth muscles. Berne (10) proposed adenosine to be one such metabolite. On the basis of experiments performed on isolated helical strips of coronary arteries from

[1]The work described herein as emanating from this laboratory was supported by grants from the Swedish Medical Research Council (14X–2855).

the rabbit (outer diameter 300–600 μm) Gellai and co-workers (40) proposed a hypothesis involving both oxygen and adenosine. According to this proposal, oxygen, diffusing across the walls of precapillary vessels (30, 31), is the main determinant of vascular tone during physiological circumstances. During myocardial hypoxia, on the other hand, adenosine is believed to be of greater importance, since the intracellular oxygen tension in this situation falls below the critical level for the formation of ATP and the accumulated adenosine then leaks out of the cells to induce a smooth muscle relaxation. It is an interesting hypothesis, but needs further confirmation in experiments performed under more physiological circumstances.

Bourdeau-Martini & Honig (18, 72) have developed a technique that makes possible the study of the effects of variations in arterial oxygen pressure (Pao_2) on the capillary circulation of the rat heart in situ. They determined the intercapillary distance (ICD) with a microscopic technique and provided evidence that ICD is decreased with decreasing Pao_2, reflecting an increased number of perfused capillaries secondary to a relaxation of "precapillary sphincters" (72). Variations in arterial pH on the other hand, did not change ICD (18), while lowering of $Paco_2$ possibly induced a slight relaxation of the sphincters that in turn decreased ICD.

The role of oxygen and carbon dioxide in the control of vascular smooth muscle tension has also been investigated with a microcirculatory technique by Duling (30, 31) in the golden hamster cheek pouch. Decreasing arterial Po_2 induced a vasodilatation that seemed to be so adjusted as to maintain tissue Po_2 fairly constant. An increased carbon dioxide tension in the tissue caused an increase of Po_2, partly induced by vasodilatation and partly caused by a Bohr shift in the oxyhemoglobin dissociation curve. This study and the above-mentioned one by Bourdeau-Martini & Honig have thus provided clear-cut evidence that variations in Pao_2 indeed induced changes in vivo in the different series-coupled vascular sections of the heart and the cheek pouch. However, these studies fail to answer the crucial question of whether the observed adjustments were caused by oxygen per se or by any "metabolite."

The beating of the heart imposes a further strain on the nutritional blood supply to the heart, increasing tissue pressure particularly in the subendocardial portion. The hemodynamic effects of this have been reviewed recently by Moir (76), who challenged the opinion that the subendocardial part is normally underperfused by blood, and proposed that a nutritionally adequate blood flow is supplied to all parts of the heart during each cardiac cycle. On the other hand, an uneven perfusion may occur during low pressure perfusion. Moir's views are corroborated by studies of tissue substrate levels in heart muscle (46) and by blood flow studies by Kjekshus (60). The latter author stressed the importance of tissue pressure in determining vascular tone. According to Kjekshus, vascular resistance in the subendocardium is comparatively low due to the high tissue-to-vessel transmural pressure gradient that relaxes the vascular smooth muscle as a consequence of the "myogenic" properties of the vascular smooth muscle cells. In an ischemic region this mechanism does not function since all vessels are maximally dilated under a dominating metabolic influence and, hence, flow passively follows perfusion pressure.

Another factor of importance, apart from blood flow, for the supply of nutrients to the heart is capillary permeability. Studying the horseradish peroxidase distribution by electron microscopy, Anversa and co-workers (3) demonstrated a higher permeability to this tracer in the subendocardial part than in the rest of the heart, reflecting in all probability a greater "porosity." This may make these capillaries more permeable to water-soluble compounds.

The nervous control of the coronary vessels is, as pointed out above, generally believed to be quantitatively comparatively insignificant. This is again demonstrated in a report by Nayler & Carson (77), who studied the effects of β-adrenergic blocking agents on the coronary vasculature. Stimulation of the chemoreceptors in the carotid arteries causes reflex coronary cholinergic vasodilatation via the vagal nerve fibers (47).

SKELETAL MUSCLE

Rubidium (or potassium) clearance or uptake is sometimes used for measuring "nutritional" blood flow in an organ or flow distribution in a whole animal. To judge from a report by Sheehan & Renkin (94), this is hardly possible since these authors showed that no transcapillary diffusion equilibrium of the ions was present in skeletal muscle even at low blood flows. The inadequancy of rubidium is even more clearly demonstrated in tissues with a high blood flow. Hence, Albrecht & Jansson (personal communication), measuring blood flow in the corpus luteum of the ovary, recorded a flow in this tissue of about 70 ml (min 100 g)$^{-1}$ with ^{86}Rb, while a flow of 1700 ml (min 100 g)$^{-1}$ was estimated with the more reliable microsphere technique.

Another method for estimating muscle blood flow is the ^{133}Xe washout technique. This is the only possible technique to use during exercise, the washout curve then being rather monoexponential. At resting skeletal muscle blood flow, the ^{133}Xe washout is multiexponential, and in this situation the technique offers great disadvantages. Sejrsen & Tønnesen (93) claimed that one explanation for the bending of the washout curve was a countercurrent exchange of the injected tracer. On the basis of four observations, they estimated the "gas-shunt" to be 11%. Since skeletal muscle blood flow was in the upper range of cat muscle flow, one wonders how much oxygen reaches the muscle at resting blood flow. To us it seems more probable that the bending of the washout curve reflects a heterogeneous blood flow due to the fact that skeletal muscle consists of red and white fibers with different flows. An inhomogeneous blood flow was also proposed by Kjellmer et al (61), and no convincing evidence against this view has since been published.

The search for a single substance causing exercise hyperemia is an old topic in circulatory physiology. Since metabolism and, hence, also "metabolites" vary in red and white muscle and in different types of exercise, there is every reason to believe that the functional hyperemia in skeletal muscle is due to multiple factors and that the importance of different vasodilator substances varies during different phases of exercise. This view is illustrated by Mohrman and co-workers (74, 75) in their studies on the time course of vascular resistance and P_{VO_2} following a brief tetanus.

Their results clearly identify at least two different mechanisms of local vascular control: one acting very rapidly and one acting so slowly that it may be related directly or secondarily to tissue oxidative metabolism. Thus, when exercise hyperemia is studied, it seems necessary to define also the exercise model used. An extensive study fullfilling this criterion was reported by Lundvall (70), who investigated the role of tissue hyperosmolarity in exercise vasodilatation. The author proposed that hyperosmolarity, induced by exercise was responsible for more than 40% of exercise hyperemia during light work and more than 60% of exercise hyperemia during heavy work. Furthermore, its relative importance was suggested to be greatest during the development of the vasodilatation and the subsequent early phases of exercise.

However, one important observation in Lundvall's work was not confirmed by Tominaga et al (106); using a constant flow perfusion of canine hindlimb muscles, they found no correlation between vascular resistance and venous effluent osmolarity. Two of the most studied candidates in exercise hyperemia, the potassium ion and oxygen, showed a significant correlation with the degree of hyperemia. The importance of the potassium ion in exercise hyperemia was also stressed by Hník and co-workers (52, 53), who reported a rapid increase in extracellular potassium concentration in venous effluent during and after a short tetanus; the increase was nicely correlated with the vascular response. This effect of the potassium ion on the resistance vessels was attributed by Anderson et al (2) and Biamino & Wessel (11) to changes in the membrane potential of the vascular smooth muscles. However, it can be questioned whether results from aorta strips (11) are representative for the smooth muscles of the multiunit type found in the arterioles, especially as the rythmical activity studied must be induced by norepinephrine.

The influence of Pa_{O_2} on vascular tone in skeletal muscle has been studied with a microscopic method by Hutchins et al (54). They found that a mild hypoxia caused a significant dilatation restricted to the arterioles with a diameter less than 40 μm and oriented transversely to the muscle fibers. However, these authors could not distinguish between a metabolically mediated effect and a direct effect of oxygen on the vascular smooth muscles. The same problem is met with when the vacular effects of adenosine compounds are studied (82, 110), since adenosine itself has metabolic effects. While measuring oxygen tissue tension and oxygen consumption in the cat soleus muscle, Whalen et al (111) were unable to obtain any clear-cut evidence supporting the hypothesis that oxygen plays a role in the regulation of muscle blood flow.

It has been generally accepted that a precapillary sphincter determines the blood flow through each single capillary according to the metabolic demand of the surrounding tissue. This concept is challenged, however, by Gentry & Johnson (41) in a microvascular study on reactive hyperemia in frog skeletal muscle. They found that peak flow in a single capillary after 1 min occlusion of that capillary was only a little above control. A flow increase of the same magnitude as the peak flow observed after occlusion of an arteriole was only seen when all the capillaries supplied by that arteriole were occluded. The authors concluded that blood flow in individual capillaries was not regulated by the metabolic environment surrounding each capillary but rather by the metabolic environment of the arteriole supplying the capillary.

Mechanisms affecting transcapillary fluid exchange have been studied in several papers. Lundvall et al (71) reported that during heavy exercise on a bicycle ergometer a substantial loss of fluid into the working muscle occurred, a loss which was kept within tolerable limits by a fluid gain from inactive muscle groups, due partly to a concomitant increase in arteriolar osmolarity and partly to a sympathetic nerve activation that lowered mean capillary hydrostatic pressure.

Another interesting observation on the control of the mean capillary pressure was described by Wiederhielm & Weston (112) in a study on the bat wing. In this unanesthetized preparation the capillary pressure, measured by micropuncture, exhibited large rythmic variations that probably resulted in a net outward filtration over the whole capillary length when the precapillary sphincter was opened, and a reverse of the fluid stream when the sphincter was closed. Hence, at any given moment there usually seemed to be a fluid transfer in one direction only between capillary and interstitium. Furthermore, this paper reported a tissue pressure of about 1–2 mm Hg, i.e. just above the pressure in the adjacent lymph capillary and at variance with Guyton's measurements. Since the authors used a very thin "needle" (outer diameter 0.2 μm) for measuring tissue pressure, invalidating the old criticism of tissue pressure recordings, these results revive the old controversy regarding the true value of interstitial tissue pressure.

The question of the possible existence of histaminergic vasodilator fibers in canine skeletal muscle has been reinvestigated (42, 67).

BRAIN

A number of techniques for measuring brain blood flow in man and animals have been developed during the last 20–25 yr, as reviewed by Posner (81). Most of these involve the use of an inert gas as a tracer, most recently argon drawn by vacuum from the blood via a gas-permeable membrane mounted on the tip of a flexible plastic tube and into a mass spectrometer. This sampling technique makes it possible to use Kety's original flow method without taking blood samples (32). The latter technique measures total cerebral blood flow, but the brain is obviously a very heterogeneously perfused organ. Attempts to record regional cerebral blood flow (CBF) have also been made. In man this usually implies the use of a large number of scintillation detectors that measure the washout of a radioactive tracer, often ^{133}Xe. Each detector records radioactivity from a large portion of the brain, including grey as well as white tissue. In animals this can be avoided by recording the washout of inhaled or injected hydrogen by locally implanted platinum electrodes, as was done in the baboon (80). Reimann et al (86) developed a technique on the unanesthetized goat that makes possible the measurement of total CBF by an electromagnetic flow meter.

The local chemical factors controlling brain circulation have been studied intensively during the last decade, and it is generally believed that the extracellular H^+ concentration is the main determinant of blood flow in the brain. However, nervous activity is accompanied by extracellular changes of potassium concentration, and, in certain invertebrates, it has been calculated that extracellular K^+ concentrations may increase twofold in the brain. Since K^+ has been proposed as a physiological dilator agent in other vascular beds, such as skeletal muscle, Kuschinsky et al (64) investigated the vascular effects of K^+ on the pial vessels of the cat brain. They applied to the perivascular space 1–3 μl of solutions with different K^+ concentrations and recorded microscopically the changes in diameter of the adjacent vessel. Increasing the potassium concentration from 0 to 10 meq/liter at varying pH always caused a vasodilatation. These authors also used the same technique to study the effects of variations in perivascular osmolarity (109) on the pial arteries. When osmolarity was varied with mannitol or NaCl, a vasodilatation was observed above, and a constriction below, 317 mosmol/liter. The pial arteries have thus been shown to be influenced by perivascular K^+ ions and osmolarity. However, this does not necessarily imply that these two factors are of physiological importance since the physiological range of variation of K^+ and osmolarity in the brain is not known. Furthermore, the vascular reactions of the intracerebral vessels may be quantitatively different from those of the pial vessels.

Vasodilating metabolites have been proposed to be responsible also for the autoregulation of the cerebral circulation. However, during recent years an increasing number of observations seem to suggest that myogenic properties of the vascular smooth muscles may play an important role, although, quite likely, both mechanisms are of relevance and work in synergism in most situations. Thus Symon and co-workers (103, 104) have demonstrated that the autoregulatory response in gray as well as white tissue was evoked within seconds upon changing perfusion pressure. Furthermore, changing transmural pressure by lowering intravascular pressure or by raising extravascular pressure produced a similar relationship between perfusion pressure and flow. Mchedlishvili et al (73), however, failed to find any evidence for a myogenic mechanism and proposed that autoregulation of the brain is nervously mediated.

The classical view that cerebral circulation is almost devoid of nervous vasoconstrictor fiber influence has lately been challenged in several reports. The circulatory studies were prompted by the histochemical demonstration of adrenergic neurons in the walls of the large extracerebral arteries and veins by means of Hillarp's fluorescent technique. The effects of an adrenergic influence on the cerebral circulation has been the subject of a number of reports. The reactions of pial resistance vessels, when exposed to norepinephrine, were studied with microscopic techniques by Wahl et al (108) and Raper et al (83). Wahl and co-workers, using the technique described above, demonstrated a constriction in response to norepinephrine of all vessels studied (outer diameter 25–208 μm) when the bicarbonate concentration of the injected solution was 0 or 11 meq/liter (pH 6.80 and 7.15 respectively). At a bicarbonate concentration of 22 meq/liter (pH 7.45) no vasoconstriction to norepinephrine was recorded. Raper et al, on the other hand, were unable to induce any vasoconstriction with norepinephrine using a technique in which the pial vessels of the parietal cortex were viewed through a window and solutions containing the drug were brought under the window with a constant infusion pump. The discrepancy in results reported by Wahl et al and by Raper et al is probably explained by the fact that the bicarbonate content of the solution used by Raper and co-workers was 21–27 meq/liter, a concentration at which Wahl et al also were unable to evoke any vascular effects of norepinephrine.

A constrictor effect on cerebral blood flow of intra-arterially administered epinephrine and norepinephrine was also shown on unanesthetized goats (68). However, the demonstration that a vessel reacts to norepinephrine does not necessarily imply that it is innervated. The most convincing demonstration of a nervous vasoconstrictor influence on the cerebral resistance vessels was reported in a study on dogs by D'Alecy & Feigl (26). These authors directed venous outflow from the brain through the retroglenoid vein so as to measure it with an electromagnetic flow meter. Stimulation of the stellate ganglion with 1–15 Hz caused a graded vasoconstriction, reducing flow up to 30% of control without any concomitant alterations of arterial Po_2, Pco_2, or pH. This constriction of the cerebral resistance vessels, which could be blocked by α-adrenergic blocking agents (25), was as great as that observed during maximal activation of the vasoconstrictor fibers to skeletal muscle.

The neural effect on the cerebral capacitance vessels was investigated by Edvinsson and co-workers (34, 35), who studied the cerebral blood volume (CBV) by means of intravascularly injected ^{131}I-labelled serum albumine. The results suggested that CBV could be reduced 15–20% upon maximal vasoconstrictor activation. The corresponding nervously induced reduction of blood volume in skeletal muscle and intestine, for instance, amounts to about 40% of the regional blood volume. Hence, the sympathetic vasoconstrictor influence on the cerebral veins was comparatively weak.

The physiological significance of the cerebral vasoconstrictor fiber influence is not known. The fibers seem not to fire during "normal" conditions, since Skinhøj (98) was unable to change cerebral blood flow in man by giving an α-adrenergic blocking agent. He proposes that the vasoconstrictor fibers may be of importance in hindering an excessive increase of mean capillary hydrostatic pressure and, hence, of capillary filtration during cerebral vasodilatation induced by hyperventilation.

The cholinergic innervation of the cerebral vessels was studied histochemically by Edvinsson et al (33). These types of nerves were abundantly distributed to the same vessels as the adrenergic nerves. In fact, the two types of autonomic nerves were found to be so closely intermingled on the outer boundery of the vascular media that some axon-axonal interaction may possibly occur between adrenergic and cholinergic axons, as well as between axons of the same type. Electrical stimulation of the facial nerve seems to activate the cholinergic nerves (89), but their functional significance is largely unknown. Giardini and co-workers (88, 92) have advanced a new and startling hypothesis, based on rat experiments in which cerebral blood flow was studied with the hydrogen washout technique. They proposed that the increases of cerebral flow elicited by increased Pco_2 are induced via a nervous cholinergic pathway, since the CO_2-induced hyperemia was abolished by atropine and potentiated by eserine. These findings should initiate further inquiries into the possible relationship between nervous and metabolic influences on the cerebral resistance vessels. In this context it should also be stressed that the nervous control of the cerebral circulation ought also be taken into consideration in circulatory studies of drug effects since different experimental procedures (e.g. blood pressure changes) may reflexly readjust a drug influence.

It is well documented that stimulation of the visual center is accompanied by discrete vasodilatation in this region, i.e. one may induce a functional hyperemia in the brain also. This has again been observed by Risberg & Ingvar (87) during memorizing and reasoning, by Sooriyamoorthy & Livingston (99) during the induction of a release of neurohypophysial hormone, and by Bondy (17) during visual stimulation.

THE SPLANCHNIC CIRCULATION

Stomach

The introduction by Jacobson et al (55) of the amidopyrine clearance technique for measuring gastric mucosal blood flow represented a major advancement in its field. Curwain & Holton (24) developed a similar technique utilizing radioactively labelled aniline, which is more easily determined than amidopyrine. A comparison between the two techniques revealed that aniline clearance was consistently lower than amidopyrine clearance, a difference the authors ascribed to the plasma binding of aniline.

One classical question in circulatory physiology is the relationship between blood flow and secretion. This problem can easily be studied with the above-mentioned clearance techniques. The most accepted view infers that changes in gastric secretion are accompanied by corresponding changes of mucosal blood flow, but an increase of blood flow cannot itself induce any active secretion. This opinion is corroborated by two recent studies (23, 113) in which the effects of glucagon, isoprenaline, and norepinephrine on pentagastrin- and/or histamine-stimulated secretion were investigated. These studies were primarily prompted by the observation that isoprenaline and glucagon inhibited the gastric secretion induced by pentagastrin, while no such effect was seen when the secretion was caused by histamine injections. The results obtained clearly suggested that blood flow changes were not the primary cause of the observed secretory responses.

In the discussion of the pathogenesis of gastric ulcer, it has been proposed that ischemia of the mucosa is one contributing factor. To study this problem Dorricott et al (29) and Davenport & Barr (27) induced ischemia in Heidenhain pouches in unanesthetized dogs by various means, such as injection of vasopressin and norepinephrine and by bleeding the animals. The condition of the gastric mucosa was judged by the net movements of H^+ and Na^+ across the mucosa: a diffusion of H^+ into the tissue and a net movement of Na^+ from the tissue indicating tissue damage. Despite the fact that large amounts of the drugs were infused during 2 hr, the authors were unable to produce any signs of mucosal damage. In fact, mucosal amidopyrine clearance was in several instances observed to increase in the face of a large infusion of vasoconstrictor material, probably due to a vasodilator effect of the accumulating tissue "metabolites" during low flow. On the basis of these and other similar experiments one can question the concept that vasoconstriction of an undamaged vessel per se can cause tissue damage, since metabolites that relax the vascular smooth muscles and increase blood flow will always accumulate in these situations before tissue damage has occurred. Quite another situation is at hand if vasoconstriction is accompanied by rheological disturbances (e.g. thrombocyte aggregation), or by increased diffusion distances (e.g. due to increased transcapillary filtration of fluid), or if the vessel itself is narrowed by the presence of an atheromatous plaque, for instance. In such situations tissue lesions may ensue during vasoconstriction.

Intestine

In most studies of the intestinal circulation, total blood flow is measured. However, the mucosal blood flow is the most interesting from a functional point of view. Biber et al (14) have developed an indicator-dilution technique for the study of mucosal and villous flow. It involved the use of β-emitting labelled plasma particles or red cells that were injected into the superior mesenteric artery as a "slug." Their transit through the mucosa was monitored by a detector placed in the intestinal lumen. With this technique the intestinal hemodynamics were investigated during drug-induced vasodilatation, during reduced perfusion pressure (69), and during sympathetic vasoconstrictor activation (101). A completely different technique was used by Levitt & Levitt (66), who followed the relative rates of absorption of different inert gases from the small and large intestines and from the stomach in the awake rat. The data obtained were fitted to a series of models for the interaction between perfusion and diffusion, and one of these seemed to predict the absorption rates of the gases from all organs investigated. Based on this, the authors concluded that absorption of gases from the gut was almost completely blood-flow limited, so that an "effective" mucosal blood flow could be calculated.

The intake of food leads to a moderate functional hyperemia in the splanchnic area, increasing blood flow 100–200% in the face of a largely unchanged perfusion pressure. The factors responsible for this vasodilatation have until recently been quite unknown. The controlling mechanism must by necessity be organized in another manner than as in skeletal muscle, for instance, since absorption, the major function of the gut, is carried out mainly by the epithelial cells of the villi, which are situated relatively far away from the mucosal-submucosal arterioles, the main determinants of intestinal flow resistance. This has been shown to be the case. Thus Fara and co-workers (37) showed in an extensive study that the intraduodenal instillation of corn oil, L-phenylalanine, or hydrochloric acid, after a short latency, induced a selective increase of pancreatic and jejunal blood flow, in all probability due to the physiological release of secretin and cholecystokinin. They also demonstrated that the vasodilatation was not mediated via adrenergic or cholinergic vascular receptors and suggested that the hyperemia was secondary to an increased metabolism.

Another mechanism that may be of importance in explaining the functional hyperemia of the gut was proposed by Biber and co-workers (15). They showed that slight mechanical stimulation of the mucosa of a denervated intestinal segment could increase gut blood flow more than twofold. From a pharmacological analysis, the authors concluded that mechanical stimulation of the mucosa elicited a vasodilatation via an intramural nervous reflex arch involving 5-HT receptors. In a subsequent study Biber et al (12) also stimulated apparently the same reflex by applying an electrical field across the intestinal wall. The same reflex arch may possibly be involved also in the intestinal vasodilatation observed by Chou et al (21) when hypertonic glucose was introduced into the intestinal lumen.

As regards the cellular events inducing a smooth muscle relaxation during intestinal vasodilatation, Shepherd et al (97) proposed from experiments performed in the dog mesenteric circulation that an increased intracellular cAMP concentration caused the vasodilatation observed after intra-arterial infusion of isoprenaline, prostaglandin E, and papaverine. What is lacking in this and many other similar investigations is the temporal relationship between cAMP concentration and smooth muscle response. Furthermore, in many in vitro studies (though not that of Shepherd et al), vascular smooth muscle tone is increased by "unphysiological" measures, e.g. by adding norepinephrine to the organ bath.

The effects of an activation of the regional sympathetic vasoconstrictor fibers on the intestinal vascular bed were studied in detail by Folkow et al (38). It was observed that a continuous, graded activation of the splanchnic nerves produced constriction of resistance and capacitance vessels as well as of precapillary sphincters. Within 2–4 min after the onset of constrictor fiber stimulation, intestinal blood flow again increased ("autoregulatory escape from vasoconstrictor fiber influence"), reaching a new steady state level only moderately below control, while the neurogenic effect on the capacitance vessels and on the precapillary sphincters remained largely unaltered throughout the stimulation period.

The eliciting mechanisms of this peculiar response pattern have aroused considerable interest. However, the studies of the "autoregulatory escape" are very confusing, in our opinion in part for semantic reasons. The fact that one names a fading effect of nervous- or drug-induced vasoconstriction "escape" does not a priori imply that these observations, made in different organs, have any bearing on what causes the "autoregulatory escape from the vasoconstrictor fiber influence" in the small intestine. The issue becomes even more confused when one proposes that observations on the escape from a vasodilatation in the gut induced by drugs may help to explain the autoregulatory escape during nervous vasoconstriction (51).

As regards the mechanisms underlying "the autoregulatory escape from nervous vasoconstriction" in the intestine, it was proposed by Fara & Ross (36) that the escape reflected an inherent property of the vascular smooth muscles, since these authors recorded escapes from the influence of norepinephrine when studying mesenteric arteries in vitro. If this hypothesis were true one would expect flow to be decreased more or less proportionally in all parts of the intestine. However, Svanik (102), using the above-mentioned indicator-dilution technique, showed that "villous" plasma flow was, if anything, increased slightly above prestimulatory control level during nervous vasoconstriction, although total venous outflow was lower than control.

A completely different explanation for the autoregulatory escape was offered by Shepherd and co-workers (95), who presented a system analysis of the intestinal blood flow control. This model was to some extent based on their own experimental work (96) and it attempted to explain not only the autoregulatory escape from the vasoconstrictor fiber influence but also autoregulation of gut blood flow. The analysis was founded on the assumption that intestinal Po_2 regulates smooth vascular tone in the precapillary vessels. This report represents an interesting attempt to make a physicomathematical model of the gut circulation. However, the model fails to explain several experimental observations. Thus the model treats the intestine as a homogeneous tissue, a gross oversimplification as the authors also point out (cf 102). Furthermore, the model fails to explain why a reduction in perfusion pressure, caused by elevating venous outflow pressure, lowers intestinal blood to a larger extent than lowering arterial inflow pressure, i.e. causing resistance vessel constriction. The model also assumes that intestinal oxygen consumption stays constant when arterial inflow pressure is lowered. However, Baker & Mendel (6) showed that intestinal oxygen consumption was reduced proportionally to blood flow.

Based on a series of studies of the intestinal mucosal circulation, Svanvik (101) proposed another hypothesis that may be looked upon as a modified "metabolic" hypothesis. It recognizes the heterogeneity of the intestinal vascular bed, but deals only with the vascular reactions in the mucosa, which receives the major portion of gut flow. The hypothesis infers that the vessels supplying the intestinal crypts are sensitive to changes in transmural pressure and dominated by sympathetic fibers, being less sensitive to vasodilating metabolites. The tone of villous arterial vessels, on the other hand, is largely determined by the chemical environment surrounding them as they pass between the crypts. Upon nervous stimulation both types of vessels constrict, the escape being explained by the dilatation of the villous vessels when metabolites accumulate in the crypt region.

The functional importance of blood flow for the rate of absorption of different substances has been investigated by Levitt & Levitt as discussed above. Winne and his research group have also been interested in this question, mainly studying passively absorbed solutes. The main trend of the different reports clearly suggests that the absorption of lipid-soluble compounds seems highly blood-flow dependent, while the absorption rates of water-soluble substances are largely unaffected by flow (for a review see 116). Winne ascribed these findings to the permeability characteristics of the intestinal epithelial cells, which allow a fairly free passage of lipophilic substances but restrict the hydrophilic ones. One exception from this rule is water itself, which is highly permeable; its absorption rate therefore appears to be very dependent on blood flow.

Svanvik and co-workers (16, 101), studying the effects of blood flow variations on the rate of intestinal absorption of ^{85}Kr, found that the absorption rate changed largely in proportion to total outflow. These observations suggested that the ^{85}Kr absorption was always blood-flow limited. However, Svanvik et al, on the basis of their detailed knowledge of the mucosal circulation of the cat, proposed that the main determinant of the absorption rate of ^{85}Kr was not volume flow of blood per se but mean transit time in the intestinal countercurrent exchanger. The importance of the countercurrent exchanger for the absorption of sodium, water, and fatty acids was studied by Jodal & Lundgren (48, 49, 56).

Several physicomathematical models have been proposed for the interaction between gut blood flow and rate of intestinal absorption. The most elaborate ones are those described by Winne (114, 117) that consist of up to four compartments (intestinal lumen, interstitial space, capillaries, serosal bath). However, models seem to offer a great temptation to their inventors. The model, which in the original report was discussed critically and dissected in detail with regard to its assumptions, strengths, and weaknesses, represents in the following publications the "truth," and farfetched conclusions are not seldom drawn from fitting experimental data into the model. Winne (78, 115), for example, claimed that the intestinal reflection coefficients for water, amidopyrine, and antipyrine are greater than 1, and discussed possible explanations, despite the fact that Wright & Diamond (120) and Tay & Findlay (105), testing 60 different substances, always obtained reflection coefficients within the usual range (0–1). Winne's findings would lead us to question the model used, at least until such surprising findings had been confirmed with independent techniques.

Pancreas

The chemical isolation and purification of secretin and cholecystokinin (CCK) has prompted a reinvestigation of their effects on pancreatic blood flow and exocrine secretion. The intravascular administration of secretin induced a steady increase of blood flow and secretion (4), while the secretory response to CCK was variable, blood flow being regularly augmented (107). The secretory response to the hormones was much larger during constant pressure perfusion than during constant flow perfusion when perfusion pressure was allowed to decrease upon vasodilatation. These observations could not be ascribed to any lack of oxygen during the constant flow experiments since the authors were unable to reveal any constant relationship between secretion rate and oxygen consumption (4). The increased secretion is usually believed to be induced by active transport mechanisms. The above-mentioned observations may also be explained if one assumes that the hormonally induced secretory response, particularly that of secretin, not only was caused by an active secretion but also to some extent by a transcapillary filtration of fluid into the pancreatic acini. Such a filtration may be induced by an increased mean capillary hydrostatic pressure due to a dilatation of the precapillary resistance vessels, and/or by a lowering of the effective colloid osmotic pressure due to an increased capillary permeability (cf 13). According to this speculative hypothesis a lowering of arterial inflow pressure to the pancreas (as during vasodilatation in constant flow experiments) would decrease mean capillary hydrostatic pressure and, hence, rate of secretion. This hypothesis would also explain the recent observations that the secretory effects of intravascularly administered acetylcholine or papaverine are "potentiated" by a concomitant infusion of secretin (65). Acetylcholine and papaverine are known to dilate precapillary vessels and increase capillary pressure without affecting capillary permeability, while secretin probably causes an increased capillary porosity. Hence, infusion of both drugs would affect the two above-mentioned factors in the direction of inducing secretion.

The sympathetic nervous control of pancreatic secretion and blood flow has been investigated by Barlow et al (9). The flow response seemed to be similar to that of the small intestine, i.e. an "autoregulatory escape from the vasoconstrictor fiber influence." Secretion was greatly reduced, probably secondary to the blood flow response.

Liver

Strandell and co-workers (100) described a promising new technique that allows the study of liver and/or splanchnic blood flow in awake humans. They reopened the umbilical vein and could introduce up to three catheters via this route. By infusing ^{133}Xe dissolved in saline through one catheter and collecting it at another "downstream," blood flow, as for instance in the portal vein, could be calculated.

Several basic facts regarding the liver circulation are still unknown. Greenway & Oshiro (44, 45) have shed light on one problem, namely the intrahepatic flow distribution, by utilizing radioactive microspheres in dogs and cats. Blood flow via the portal and arterial route was evenly distributed in the cat liver; in the dog, on the other hand, portal flow to the caudate lobe and arterial blood flow to the papillary process were significantly higher than mean blood flow of the liver. To any particular region there was a similar relative flow from the two supplies of the liver, that is, a relatively low portal flow to one region was not accompanied by a high arterial flow or vice versa. However, the occlusion of a portal branch to a liver lobe induced a compensatory increase of arterial blood to the same region.

The local regulatory mechanisms of liver flow are almost completely unexplored. In an attempt to investigate to what extent the autoregulation of blood flow in the hepatic artery was of "myogenic" or "metabolic" origin, Hanson (50) studied how a papaverine-induced hyperemia influenced autoregulation. This drug partly or wholly abolished the autoregulation, an observation Hanson believed favors the myogenic hypothesis. However, a drug-induced hyperemia also enhances oxygen delivery and may therefore also lower tissue levels of vasodilating metabolites. A more crucial test of the myogenic theory would be to study the hemodynamic effects of an increase of venous outflow pressure.

The effects of the sympathetic nervous system on liver flow distribution were investigated by Greenway & Oshiro (45) with microspheres. Upon electrical stimulation of the nerves an autoregulatory escape of arterial blood flow from the vasoconstrictor fiber influence was noted in the cat but not in the dog. The autoregulatory escape was not accompanied by any redistribution of blood flow. This conclusion was also corroborated by studies of liver hemodynamics and metabolism performed by Krarup (62, 63). Greenway & Oshiro (45) also studied the nervous control of the hepatic capacitance vessels. About 40% of the liver blood volume, measuring about 30 ml/100 g tissue, could be maximally expelled by stimulation of the nerves. In an interesting discussion the authors calculated that $\sim$25% of the animal's total blood volume can be "mobilized" at maximal sympathetic activation, representing the maximum blood volume that can be removed from the anesthetized animal without causing marked hypotension. They also pointed out that the liver, and the splanchnic region as a whole, is one of the most important contributors in such a mobilization. This was also demonstrated in a study of Brooksby & Donald (20).

KIDNEY

For many years great efforts have been made to develop techniques for measuring blood flow in different regions of the kidney. This interest was stimulated by Barger's proposal (8) that a functional difference existed between glomeruli, depending on their localization within the renal cortex. One of the most common methods for studying intrarenal flow distribution is the inert gas washout technique. This method has the advantage of being usable on awake animals. However, sometimes the inert gas clearance technique is used uncritically (cf 19); great care should be taken to control in each experimental situation the localization of the different components of the washout curve. Radioactively labelled microspheres have lately been used to an increasing extent in the study of renal flow distribution. This method has recently been applied to the study of flow to a single glomerulus (7, 58).

The mechanisms underlying the well established ability of the renal vascular bed to autoregulate its blood flow are still being discussed. Abe et al (1) showed that the autoregulation was strongly correlated with changes in transmural pressure elicited by either reduction of the arterial inflow pressure or elevation of interstitial pressure induced by increasing the venous outflow pressure. During autoregulation a blood flow redistribution to the inner parts of the cortex occurred. Since a similar flow distribution was recorded during vasodilatation caused by acetylcholine, bradykinin, and prostaglandin E_2, it was concluded that this renal redistribution was a general response to vasodilatation. The authors suggested that their observations may be explained by intrarenal differences as regards the "resting" blood-flow rate in relation to its maximum, i.e. in "resting" basal vascular smooth muscle tone. Hence, these observations support the myogenic hypothesis. According to an alternative explanation, the renin-angiotensin system plays a significant role in renal autoregulation. Two recent reports (5, 90) failed to find any evidence for this hypothesis. A study on animals depleted of renin showed no autoregulation, however (19). This discrepancy is difficult to explain, but the treatment employed in the last-mentioned study may have caused other effects than only a depletion of renin.

The existence of autoregulation of cortical blood flow is generally accepted, but there are divergent results concerning autoregulation in the medulla. This is largely explained by the great difficulty of measuring the blood flow in the medulla, since diffusible tracers cannot be used due to the countercurrent system. However, Grängsjö & Wolgast (43), utilizing local detection of indicator-dilution curves of ^{32}P-labelled red cells, demonstrated an autoregulation in the medulla of the same order of magnitude as in the cortex. The same conclusion was also reached by Galskov & Nissen (39).

Autoregulation of total renal blood flow obviously also implies an autoregulation of glomerular blood flow. This is of great significance for renal function since recent studies seem to indicate that the glomerular filtration rate is mainly plasma-flow dependent, as discussed in an excellent review by Brenner et al (28). This view is based on findings of a high filtration fraction (33%) and low glomerular hydrostatic pressure in superficial nephrons in the rat kidney, the filtration equilibrium normally being achieved fairly early in the glomerular capillaries. Thus an increase in renal plasma flow, acting to keep the effective filtration pressure constant, would result in an augmented glomerular filtration rate. According to this hypothesis, the rising plasma colloid osmotic pressure (up to about 34 mm Hg) is the factor that limits transcapillary filtration at the venous end of the glomerular capillary. This osmotic pressure has been suggested to be the main driving force for tubular reabsorption. Hence, the peritubular Starling equilibrium, not an active transport mechanism across the tubule epithelium, may control the rate of isotonic fluid transport across the renal proximal tubule (28, 59, 119, 121). Blood flow, therefore, seems not only to be of prime importance for glomerular filtration but also for tubular reabsorption.

A peculiar feature of the renal circulation is the possible existence of plasma skimming, which originally was proposed to be very pronounced in the cortex by Pappenheimer & Kinter (79). However, their ingenious hypothesis was not corroborated by experiments in which the intrarenal distribution of red cells and plasma protein was studied. These experiments suggested instead that the medulla was perfused with blood of a low hematocrit; this observation has been reinvestigated by Rasmussen (85) using ^{125}I-γM-immunoglobulin as plasma marker. This high molecular weight protein stayed intravascular for a considerable length of time; a constant plasma volume in the medulla was recorded during the first 10 min after an intravenous administration. The reported intrarenal hematocrit was based on red cell and plasma volumes determined in tissue slices. The hematocrit in the inner medulla amounted to 40–50% of arterial hematocrit. Such a low hematocrit can be explained either by a plasma skimming or by an axial streaming of the red cells in small vessels. One way to differentiate between these two possibilities is to estimate hematocrit from red cell and plasma flow values, which are unaffected by axial streaming. The flow hematocrit in the medulla, observed by Wolgast (118) with an indicator-dilution technique, was of the same order of magnitude as that reported by Rasmussen. Thus these observations strongly support the hypothesis that plasma skimming in the kidney leads to a low hematocrit blood flow in the medulla.

The possible importance of a low hematocrit in the renal medulla was illustrated in reports by Rasmussen (84) and Schmid-Schönbein et al (91). They measured the alterations in the in vivo and in vitro blood viscosity when plasma osmolarity and/or plasma protein concentration was increased to mimic the conditions present in the renal medulla. The red cell crenation induced by plasma hypertonicity and the red cell aggregation caused by the high fibrinogen concentration resulted in a considerable increase of apparent viscosity. The authors proposed that hypertonicity through its effect on red cell rheology is an important factor in explaining the relatively low linear rate of flow in the vasa recta during antidiuresis. Had it not been for the low hematocrit of the medullary blood, a pronounced increase of viscosity would have been expected.

The effect of renal sympathetic nerve stimulation on total renal blood flow was reported by Coote et al (22) in a study primarily performed to investigate factors involved in the release of renin. They confirmed the results obtained by Johansson et al (57), i.e. an initial marked flow reduction followed by an increase to near control blood flow. The vascular response was, therefore, similar to the autoregulatory escape from the vasoconstrictor fiber influence described in the intestine (see above). However, if the nervous stimulation to the kidney was repeated within 5 min, the vasoconstrictor response was drastically reduced (57). This was never observed in the intestine, again underlining the fact that so-called escape mechanisms are different in different organs. Coote et al observed a release of renin that was most pronounced during the initial vasoconstriction. β-blocking agents abolished the renin release but not the autoregulatory escape.

Literature Cited

1. Abe, Y., Kishimoto, T., Yamamoto, K., Ueda, J. 1973. Intrarenal distribution of blood flow during ureteral and venous pressure elevation. *Am. J. Physiol.* 224:746–51
2. Anderson, D. K. et al 1972. Effect of hypokalemia and hypomagnesemia produced by hemodialysis on vascular resistance in canine skeletal muscle. *Circ. Res.* 31:165–73
3. Anversa, P., Giacomelli, F., Wiener, J. 1973. Regional variation in capillary permeability of ventricular myocardium. *Microvasc. Res.* 6:273–85
4. Augier, D., Boucard, J. P., Pascal, J. P., Ribet, A., Vaysse, N. 1972. Relationships between blood flow and secretion in the isolated perfused canine pancreas. *J. Physiol. London* 221:55–69
5. Bailie, M. D., Loutzenhiser, R., Moyer, S. 1972. Relation of renal hemodynamics to angiotensin II in renal hilar lymph of the dog. *Am. J. Physiol.* 222:1075–78
6. Baker, R., Mendel, D. 1967. Some observations on autoregulatory escape in cat intestine. *J. Physiol. London* 190: 229–40
7. Bankir, L., Farman, N., Grünfeld, J.-P., Huet de la Tour, E., Funck-Grentano, J.-L. 1973. Radioactive microsphere distribution and single glomerular blood flow in the normal rabbit kidney. *Pfluegers Arch.* 342:111–23
8. Barger, A. C. 1966. Renal hemodynamic factors in congestive heart failure. *Ann. NY Acad. Sci.* 139:276–84
9. Barlow, T. E., Greenwell, J. R., Harper, A. A., Scratcherd, T. 1974. The influence of the splanchnic nerves on the external secretion, blood flow and electrical conductance of the cat pancreas. *J. Physiol. London* 236:421–33
10. Berne, R. M. 1963. Cardiac nucleotides in hypoxiae: possible role in regulation of coronary blood flow. *Am. J. Physiol.* 204:317–22
11. Biamino, G., Wessel, H.-J. 1973. Potassium-induced relaxation of vascular smooth muscle: A possible mechanism of exercise hyperaemia. *Pfluegers Arch.* 343:95–106
12. Biber, B., Fara, J., Lundgren, O. 1973. Intestinal vasodilatation in response to transmural electrical field stimulation. *Acta Physiol. Scand.* 87:277–82
13. Biber, B., Fara, J., Lundgren, O. 1973. Vascular reactions in the small intestine during vasodilatation. *Acta Physiol. Scand.* 89:449–56
14. Biber, B., Lundgren, O., Stage, L., Svanvik, J. 1973. An indicator-dilution method for studying intestinal hemodynamics in the cat. *Acta Physiol. Scand.* 87:433–47
15. Biber, B., Lundgren, O., Svanvik, J. 1971. Studies on the intestinal vasodilatation observed after mechanical stimulation of the mucosa of the gut. *Acta Physiol. Scand.* 82:177–90
16. Biber, B., Lundgren, O., Svanvik, J. 1973. The influence of blood flow on the rate of absorption of ^{85}Kr from the small intestine of the cat. *Acta Physiol. Scand.* 89:227–38
17. Bondy, S. C. 1973. The regulation of regional blood flow in the brain by visual input. *J. Neurol. Sci.* 19:425–32
18. Bourdeau-Martini, J., Honig, C. R. 1973. Control of coronary intercapillary distance: Effect of arterial Pco_2 and pH. *Microvasc. Res.* 6:286–96
19. Brech, W. J. et al 1973. The influence of renin on the intrarenal distribution of blood flow and autoregulation. *Nephron* 12:44–58
20. Brooksby, G. A., Donald, D. E. 1972. Release of blood from the splanchnic circulation in dogs. *Circ. Res.* 31: 105–18
21. Chou, C. C., Burns, T. D., Hsieh, C. P., Dabney, J. M. 1972. Mechanisms of local vasodilatation with hypertonic

glucose in the jejunum. *Surgery* 71: 380–87

22. Coote, J. H., Johns, E. J., Macleod, V. H., Singer, B. 1972. Effect of renal nerve stimulation, renal blood flow and adrenergic blockade on plasma renin activity in the cat. *J. Physiol. London* 226:15–36
23. Curwain, B. P., Holton, P. 1972. The effects of isoprenaline and noradrenaline on penta-gastrin-stimulated gastric acid secretion and mucosal blood flow in the dog. *Brit J. Pharmacol.* 46: 225–33
24. Curwain, B. P., Holton, P. 1973. The measurement of dog gastric mucosal blood flow by radioactive analine clearance compared with amidopyrine clearance. *J. Physiol. London* 229:115–31
25. D'Alecy, L. G. 1973. Sympathetic cerebral vasoconstriction blocked by adrenergic alpha receptor antagonists. *Stroke* 4:30–37
26. D'Alecy, L. G., Feigl, E. O. 1972. Sympathetic control of cerebral blood flow in dogs. *Circ. Res.* 31:267–83
27. Davenport, H. W., Barr, L. L. 1973. Failure of ischemia to break the dog's gastric mucosal barrier. *Gastroenterology* 65:619–24
28. Deen, W. M., Robertson, C. R., Brenner, B. M. 1973. Transcapillary fluid exchange in the renal cortex. *Circ. Res.* 33:1–8
29. Dorricott, N. J., Eisenberg, H., Silen, W. 1973. Effect of intraarterial vasopressin on canine gastric mucosal permeability. *Gastroenterology* 65:625–29
30. Duling, B. R. 1972. Microvascular responses to alterations in oxygen tension. *Circ. Res.* 31:481–89
31. Duling, B. R. 1973. Changes in microvascular diameter and oxygen tension induced by carbon dioxide. *Circ. Res.* 32:370–76
32. Dyken, M. L. 1972. Cerebral blood flow and metabolism studies comparing krypton 85 desaturation technique with argon desaturation technique using the mass spectrometer. *Stroke* 3:279–85
33. Edvinsson, L., Nielsen, K. C., Owman, C., Sporrong, B. 1972. Cholinergic mechanisms in pial vessels. *Z. Zellforsch. Histochem. Electron Microsc. Pharmacol.* 134:311–25
34. Edvinsson, L., Nielsen, K. C., Owman, C., West, K. A. 1972. Sympathetic neural influence on norepinephrine vasoconstriction in brain vessels. *Arch. Neurol.* 27:492–95
35. Edvinsson, L., Nielsen, K. C., Owman, C., West, K. A. 1973. Evidence of vasoconstrictor sympathetic nerves in brain vessels of mice. *Neurology* 23:73–77
36. Fara, J. W., Ross, G. 1972. Escape from drug-induced constriction of isolated arterial segments from various vascular beds. *Angiologica* 9:27–33
37. Fara, J. W., Rubinstein, E. H., Sonnenschein, R. R. 1972. Intestinal hormones in mesenteric vasodilation after intraduodenal agents. *Am. J. Physiol.* 223:1058–67
38. Folkow, B., Lewis, D., Lundgren, O., Mellander, S., Wallentin, I. 1964. The effect of graded vasoconstrictor fibre stimulation on the intestinal resistance and capacitance vessels. *Acta Physiol. Scand.* 61:445–57
39. Galskov, A., Nissen, O. I. 1972. Autoregulation of directly measured blood flows in the superficial and deep venous drainage areas of the cat kidney. *Circ. Res.* 30:97–103
40. Gellai, M., Norton, J. M., Detar, R. 1973. Evidence for direct control of coronary vascular tone by oxygen. *Circ. Res.* 32:279–89
41. Gentry, R. M., Johnson, P. C. 1972. Reactive hyperemia in arterioles and capillaries of frog skeletal muscle following microocclusion. *Circ. Res.* 31: 953–65
42. Graham, B. H., Lioy, F. 1973. Histaminergic vasodilatation in the hindlimb of the dog. *Pfluegers Arch.* 342:307–18
43. Grängsjö, G., Wolgast, M. 1972. The pressure-flow relationship in renal cortical and medullary circulation. *Acta Physiol. Scand.* 85:228–36
44. Greenway, C. V., Oshiro, G. 1972. Intrahepatic distribution of portal and hepatic arterial blood flows in anaesthetized cats and dogs and the effects of portal occlusion, raised venous pressure and histamine. *J. Physiol. London* 227:473–85
45. Greenway, C. V., Oshiro, G. 1972. Comparison of the effects of hepatic nerve stimulation on arterial flow, distribution of arterial and portal flows and blood content in the livers of anaesthetized cats and dogs. *J. Physiol. London* 227:487–501
46. Griggs, D. M., Tchokoev, V. V., Chen, C. C. 1972. Transmural differences in ventricular tissue substrate levels due to coronary constriction. *Am. J. Physiol.* 222:705–9
47. Hackett, J. G., Abboud, F. M., Mark, A. L., Schmid, P. G., Heistad, D. D.

1972. Coronary vascular responses to stimulation of chemoreceptors and baroreceptors. *Circ. Res.* 31:8–17
48. Haglund, U., Jodal, M., Lundgren, O. 1973. An autoradiographic study of the intestinal absorption of palmitic and oleic acid. *Acta Physiol. Scand.* 89: 306–17
49. Haljamäe, H., Jodal, M., Lundgren, O. 1973. Countercurrent multiplication of sodium in intestinal villi during absorption of sodium chloride. *Acta Physiol. Scand.* 89:580–93
50. Hanson, K. M. 1973. Dilator responses of the canine hepatic vasculature. *Angiologica* 10:15–23
51. Henrich, H., Singbartl, G. 1973. Vascular adjustments in dilatory reactions. *Angiologica* 10:185–97
52. Hník, P., Vyskočil, F., Kriz, N., Holas, M. 1972. Work-induced increase of extracellular potassium concentration in muscle measured by ion-specific electrodes. *Brain Res.* 40:559–62
53. Hník, P. et al 1973. Work-induced potassium changes in muscle venous effluent blood measured by ion-specific electrodes. *Pfluegers Arch.* 338:177–81
54. Hutchins, P. M., Bond, R. F., Green, H. D. 1974. Participation of oxygen in the local control of skeletal muscle microvasculature. *Circ. Res.* 34:85–93
55. Jacobson, E. D., Linford, R. H., Grossman, M. I. 1966. Gastric secretion in relation to mucosal blood flow studied by a clearance technic. *J. Clin. Invest.* 45:1–13
56. Jodal, M., Lundgren, O. 1973. The distribution of absorbed ^{3}H-palmitic acid in the intestinal villi of the cat during various circulatory conditions. *Acta Physiol. Scand.* 89:318–26
57. Johansson, B., Sparks, H., Biber, B. 1970. The escape of the renal blood flow response during sympathetic nerve stimulation. *Angiologica* 7:333–43
58. Källskog, Ö., Ulfendahl, H. R., Wolgast, M. 1972. Single glomerular blood flow as measured with carbonized 141-Ce labelled microspheres. *Acta Physiol. Scand.* 85:408–13
59. Källskog, Ö., Wolgast, M. 1973. Driving forces over the peritubular capillary membrane in the rat kidney during antidiuresis and saline expansion. *Acta Physiol. Scand.* 89:116–25
60. Kjekshus, J. K. 1973. Mechanism for flow distribution in normal and ischemic myocardium during increased ventricular preload in the dog. *Circ. Res.* 33:489–99
61. Kjellmer, I., Lindbjerg, I., Přerovský, I., Tønnesen, H. 1967. The relation between blood flow in an isolated muscle measured with the Xe^{133} clearance and a direct recording technique. *Acta Physiol. Scand.* 69:69–78
62. Krarup, N. 1973. The effect of noradrenaline and adrenaline on hepatosplanchnic hemodynamics, functional capacity of the liver and hepatic metabolism. *Acta Physiol. Scand.* 87:307–19
63. Krarup, N. 1973. The effect of hemorrhage on hepatosplanchnic hemodynamics, liver function and hepatic metabolism. *Acta Physiol. Scand.* 89:269–77
64. Kuschinsky, W., Wahl, M., Bosse, O., Thurau, K. 1972. Perivascular potassium and pH as determinants of local pial arterial diameter in cats. *Circ. Res.* 31:240–47
65. Lenninger, S. 1973. Effects of acetylcholine and papaverine on the secretion and blood flow from the pancreas of the cat. *Acta Physiol. Scand.* 89:260–68
66. Levitt, M. D., Levitt, D. G. 1973. Use of inert gases to study the interaction of blood flow and diffusion during passive absorption from gastrointestinal tract of the rat. *J. Clin. Invest.* 52:1852–62
67. Lioy, F., White, K. P. 1973. ^{14}C-histamine release during vasodilatation induced by lumbar ventral root stimulation. *Pfluegers Arch.* 342:319–24
68. Lluch, S., Reimann, C., Glick, G. 1973. Evidence for the direct effect of adrenergic drugs on the cerebral vascular bed of the unanesthetized goat. *Stroke* 4:50–56
69. Lundgren, O., Svanvik, J. 1973. Mucosal hemodynamics in the small intestine of the cat during reduced perfusion pressure. *Acta Physiol. Scand.* 88:551–63
70. Lundvall, J. 1972. Tissue hyperosmolality as a mediator of vasodilatation and transcapillary fluid flux in exercising skeletal muscle. *Acta Physiol. Scand.* Suppl. 379
71. Lundvall, J., Mellander, S., Westling, H., White, T. 1972. Fluid transfer between blood and tissues during exercise. *Acta Physiol. Scand.* 85:258–69
72. Martini, J., Honig, C. R. 1969. Direct measurement of intercapillary distance in beating rat heart in situ under various conditions of O_2 supply. *Microvasc. Res.* 1:244–56
73. Mchedlishvili, G. I., Mitagvariia, N. P., Ormotsadze, L. G. 1973. Vascular mechanisms controlling a constant

blood supply to the brain ("autoregulation"). *Stroke* 4:742–50
74. Mohrman, D. E., Cant, J. R., Sparks, H. V. 1973. Time course of vascular resistance and venous oxygen changes following brief tetanus of dog skeletal muscle. *Circ. Res.* 33:323–36
75. Mohrman, D. E., Sparks, H. V. 1973. Resistance and venous oxygen dynamics during sinusoidal exercise of dog skeletal muscle. *Circ. Res.* 33:337–45
76. Moir, T. W. 1972. Subendocardial distribution of coronary blood flow and the effect of antianginal drugs. *Circ. Res.* 30:621–27
77. Nayler, W. G., Carson, V. 1973. Effect of stellate ganglion stimulation on myocardial blood flow, oxygen consumption, and cardiac efficiency during beta-adrenoceptor blockade. *Cardiovasc. Res.* 7:22–29
78. Ochsenfahrt, H., Winne, D. 1972. Solvent drag influence on the intestinal absorption of basic drugs. *Life Sci.* 11:1115–22
79. Pappenheimer, J. R., Kinter, W. B. 1956. Hematocrit ratio of blood within mammalian kidney and its significance for renal hemodynamics. *Am. J. Physiol.* 185:377–90
80. Pasztor, E., Symon, L., Dorsch, N. W. C., Branston, N. M. 1973. The hydrogen clearance method in assessment of blood flow in cortex, white matter and deep nuclei of baboons. *Stroke* 4: 556–67
81. Posner, J. B. 1972. Newer techniques of cerebral blood flow measurement. *Stroke* 3:227–37
82. Raberger, G., Weissel, M., Kraupp, O., Chirikdjian, J. J. 1973. Circulatory and metabolic effects of adenosine in the hind limb of intact dogs. *Naunyn-Schmiedeberg's Arch. Pharmakol. Exp. Pathol.* 277:227–37
83. Raper, A. J., Kontos, H. A., Wei, E. P., Patterson, J. L. 1972. Unresponsiveness of pial precapillary vessels to catecholamines and sympathetic nerve stimulation. *Circ. Res.* 31:257–66
84. Rasmussen, S. N. 1972. Influence of plasma hypertonicity on blood viscosity studied in vitro and in an isolated vascular bed. *Acta Physiol. Scand.* 84:472–81
85. Rasmussen, S. N. 1973. Intrarenal red cell and plasma volumes in the non-diuretic rat. *Pfluegers Arch.* 342:61–72
86. Reimann, C., Lluch, S., Glick, G. 1972. Development and evaluation of an experimental model for the study of the cerebral circulation in the unanesthetized goat. *Stroke* 3:322–28
87. Risberg, J., Ingvar, D. H. 1973. Patterns of activation in the grey matter of the dominant hemisphere during memorizing and reasoning. *Brain* 96: 737–56
88. Rovere, A. A., Scremin, O. U., Beresi, M. R., Raynald, A. C., Giardini, A. 1973. Cholinergic mechanism in the cerebrovascular action of carbon dioxide. *Stroke* 4:969–72
89. Salanga, V. D., Waltz, A. G. 1973. Regional cerebral blood flow during stimulation of seventh cranial nerve. *Stroke* 4:213–17
90. Schmid, H. E. 1972. Renal autoregulation and renin release during changes in renal perfusion pressure. *Am. J. Physiol.* 222:1132–37
91. Schmid-Schönbein, H., Wells, R. E., Goldstone, J. 1973. Effect of ultrafiltration and plasma osmolarity upon the flow properties of blood: A possible mechanism for control of blood flow in the renal medullary vasa recta. *Pfluegers Arch.* 338:93–114
92. Scremin, O. U., Rovere, A. A., Raynald, A. C., Giardini, A. 1973. Cholinergic control of blood flow in the cerebral cortex of the rat. *Stroke* 4:232–39
93. Sejrsen, P., Tønnesen, K. H. 1972. Shunting by diffusion of inert gas in skeletal muscle. *Acta Physiol. Scand.* 86:82–91
94. Sheehan, R. M., Renkin, E. M. 1972. Capillary, interstitial and cell membrane barriers to blood-tissue transport of potassium and rubidium in mammalian skeletal muscle. *Circ. Res.* 30:588–607
95. Shepherd, A. P., Granger, H. J. 1973. Autoregulatory escape in the gut: A systems analysis. *Gastroenterology* 65: 77–91
96. Shepherd, A. P., Mailman, D., Burks, T. F., Granger, H. J. 1973. Effects of norepinephrine and sympathetic stimulation on extraction of oxygen and ^{86}Rb in perfused canine small bowel. *Circ. Res.* 33:166–74
97. Shepherd, A. P., Mao, C. C., Jacobson, E. D., Shanbour, L. L. 1973. The role of cyclic AMP in mesenteric vasodilation. *Microvasc. Res.* 6:332–41
98. Skinhøj, E. 1972. The sympathetic nervous system and the regulation of cerebral blood flow in man. *Stroke* 3:711–16
99. Sooriyamoorthy, T., Livingston, A. 1973. Blood flow changes in the pituitary neural lobe of the rabbit associa-

ted with neurohypophysial hormone-releasing stimuli. *J. Endocrinol.* 57: 75–85

100. Strandell, T. et al 1973. Measurement of the dual hepatic blood flow in awake patients. *J. Appl. Physiol.* 35:755–61
101. Svanvik, J. 1973. Mucosal blood circulation and its influence on passive absorption in the small intestine. *Acta Physiol. Scand. Suppl.* 385
102. Svanvik, J. 1973. Mucosal hemodynamics in the small intestine of the cat during regional sympathetic vasoconstrictor activation. *Acta Physiol. Scand.* 89:19–29
103. Symon, L., Held, K., Dorsch, N. W. C. 1973. A study of regional autoregulation in the cerebral circulation to increased perfusion pressure in normocapnia and hypercapnia. *Stroke* 4:139–147
104. Symon, L., Pasztor, E., Dorsch, N. W. C., Branston, N. M. 1973. Physiological responses of local areas of the cerebral circulation in experimental primates determined by the method of hydrogen clearance. *Stroke* 4:632–42
105. Tay, D. K. C., Findlay, G. P. 1972. Permeability of the duodenum of the toad to non-electrolytes. *Aust. J. Biol. Sci.* 25:931–39
106. Tominaga, S., Suzuki, T., Nakamura, T. 1973. Evaluation of roles of potassium, inorganic phosphate, osmolarity, pH, P_{CO_2}, P_{O_2} and adenosine or AMP in exercise and reactive hyperemias in canine hindlimb muscles. *Tohoku J. Exp. Med.* 109:347–63
107. Vaysse, N., Martinel, C., Lacroix, A., Pascal, J. P., Ribet, A. 1973. Effet de la cholécystokinine-pancréozymine GIH sur la vaso-motricité du pancréas isolé du chien. Relations entre l'effet vasomoteur et la réponse sécrétoire. *Biol. Gastroenterol.* 6:33–40
108. Wahl, M. et al 1972. Effect of 1-norepinephrine on the diameter of pial arterioles and arteries in the cat. *Circ. Res.* 31:248–56
109. Wahl, M., Kuschinsky, W., Bosse, O., Thurau, K. 1973. Dependency of pial arterial and arteriolar diameter on perivascular osmalarity in the cat. *Circ. Res.* 32:162–69
110. Weissel, M., Raberger, G., Kraupp, O. 1973. The effects of intra-arterial adenosine infusion on substrate levels and blood flow in skeletal muscle of the dog. *Naunyn-Schmiedeberg's Arch. Pharmakol. Exp. Pathol.* 277:239–52
111. Whalen, W. J., Buerk, D., Thuning, C. A. 1973. Blood flow-limited oxygen consumption in resting cat skeletal muscle. *Am. J. Physiol.* 224:763–68
112. Wiederhielm, C. A., Weston, B. V. 1973. Microvascular, lymphatic and tissue pressures in the unanesthetized mammal. *Am. J. Physiol.* 225:992–96
113. Wilson, D. E., Ginsberg, B., Levine, R. A., Washington, A. 1972. Effect of glucagon on histamine- and pentagastrin-stimulated canine gastric acid secretion and mucosal blood flow. *Gastroenterology* 63:45–50
114. Winne, D. 1970. Formal kinetics of water and solute absorption with regard to intestinal blood flow. *J. Theor. Biol.* 27:1–18
115. Winne, D. 1972. The influence of blood flow and water net flux on the absorption of tritiated water from the jejunum of the rat. *Naunyn-Schmiedeberg's Arch. Pharmakol. Exp. Pathol.* 272: 417–36
116. Winne, D. 1972. Durchblutung und enterale Resorption. *Gastroenterologie* 9:429–41
117. Winne, D., Ochsenfahrt, H. 1967. Die formale Kinetik der Resorption unter Berücksichtigung der Darmdurchblutung. *J. Theor. Biol.* 14:293–315
118. Wolgast, M. 1973. Renal medullary red cell and plasma flow as studied with labelled indicators and internal detection. *Acta Physiol. Scand.* 88:215–25
119. Wolgast, M., Persson, E., Schnermann, J., Ulfendahl, H., Wunderlich, P. 1973. Colloid osmotic pressure of the subcapsular interstitial fluid of rat kidneys during hydropenia and volume expansion. *Pfluegers Arch.* 340:123–31
120. Wright, E. M., Diamond, J. M. 1969. Patterns of non-electrolyte permeability. *Proc. Roy. Soc. B* 172:227–71
121. Wunderlich, P., Persson, E., Schnermann, J., Ulfendahl, H., Wolgast, M. 1971. Hydrostatic pressure in the subcapsular interstitial space of rat and dog kidneys. *Pfluegers Arch.* 328:307–19

Copyright 1975. All rights reserved

TEMPERATURE REGULATION ❖1137

Michel Cabanac
Université Claude Bernard, U.E.R. Médicale Lyon-Sud-Ouest, Laboratoire de Physiologie, B.P. 12, 69600 Oullins, France

The study of temperature physiology is a very active field. Since the last review on temperature regulation in this journal, that by Hammel (47), "Regulation of internal body temperature," four *Annual Review of Physiology* volumes have had chapters on temperature physiology and aspects of temperature regulation: in 1971, "Temperature acclimation in birds and mammals" by Chaffee & Roberts (26); in 1973, "The physiology of exercise under heat stress" by Wyndham (160) and "Neuroendocrine aspects of thermoregulation" by Gale (40); and in 1974, "Thermoreceptors" by Hensel (55a). In addition, eleven international conferences have met during this period dedicated entirely or in part to temperature physiology and regulation: IUPS congresses in Washington (1968) and Munich (1971); biometeorology congresses in Montreux (1968) and Noordwijk (1972); IUPS temperature regulation symposia in New Haven (1968), Lyon (1970), Dublin (1971), and Strasbourg (1973) on "Physiological and psychological effects of thermal environment on man"; symposia in Prague (1971) on "Non-shivering thermogenesis" and in San Francisco (1972) on the "Pharmacology of thermoregulation"; and finally, in London (1970) the *Ciba Symposium on Pyrogens and Fever.*

Most of these conferences have resulted in a book, proceedings, or both. In addition, other books have appeared that focus on temperature physiology: *Comparative Physiology of Thermoregulation* in three volumes, edited by Whittow, Academic Press, 1970, 1971, and 1973; *The Stress of Hot Environment,* by Kerslake (80); *Temperature Regulation in Mammals and Other Vertebrates,* by Bligh (11); and *International Review in Science, Environmental Physiology,* edited by Robertshaw, Buttersworth, 1974.

This list is probably incomplete, but it gives an idea of the prodigious development of our knowledge of temperature regulation in recent years. As already pointed out by Hammel in 1968 (47), it is not necessary to repeat badly what has been well described by previous reviewers. In the following pages specialized aspects of temperature physiology are not examined, and this review is limited to reports on temperature regulation *sensu stricto* that have appeared since Hammel's review. Only the mechanisms involved in the control of body temperature are examined. Important problems such as long-term adaptation, hibernation, ontogeny, exercise, fever, comparative physiology, single unit recording, pharmacology and transmitters, anatomy, aging, etc, are studied here only to the extent that they add information about the short-term mechanism of temperature regulation. Fortunately, as listed above, several of these topics have been recently reviewed.

Data acquired before 1968 are accepted without discussion and are recalled without bibliographic reference. Even with these restrictions the very strict space limits given by the editors render hazardous any attempt to make a comprehensive review of the literature.

Another event within the time span of this review should be called to the reader's attention. The International Union of Physiological Sciences has established a commission on temperature physiology under J. D. Hardy's chairmanship. Among other tasks, this commission has recommended the use of the International System of Units (S.I.) and has published a standard system of symbols for thermal physiology (39) and a glossary of terms for thermal physiology (12). The recommendations contained in both of these publications will be observed in the following review. In particular, "temperature regulation" will be used rather than "thermoregulation."

INTRODUCTION

The term "temperature regulation" means that there are mechanisms defending the temperature of one or several definable regions of the body with the result that these temperatures remain within a restricted range.

This very concept of temperature regulation has been challenged. It has been proposed that temperature is not regulated, and that its constancy is merely fortuitous, the regulated variable being the rate of heat stored (58). Since this theory questions the nature of the mechanisms that result in a constant inner body temperature, it is necessary to examine it before going further.

Starting with the observation that average body temperature and heat storage remain constant under a wide range of conditions (30, 107, 124), and that there is a good correlation between these variables and sweat rate, Houdas et al (58) proposed a model in which body heat content rather than body temperature is the important factor. Signals sent from the temperature sensors located throughout the body are integrated by the central nervous system to provide information about the level of body heat storage; the activating signal for thermoregulatory responses is the instantaneous rate of heat storage. According to this theory, the thermoregulatory control system would act more as a servomechanism of thermal exchange than as a regulator of internal temperature.

Almost identical is the theory advanced by Snellen (135), according to whom average body temperature is the proper input signal. The regulating mechanism operates as if there were heat content regulation instead of temperature regulation. This heat content regulation, according to Snellen, may be achieved if there exists an interaction between blood osmolarity, which he suggests may be an indicator of body mass, and average body temperature. In both theories rectal and skin temperature would be open-loop passive results of local heat balance.

If one considers the organism from outside as a black box, the model of heat content regulation is certainly as valid as a model of temperature regulation, because temperature is proportional to heat when mass and specific heat are constant. While this viewpoint provides a correct description of physical events, it is not necessarily correct at the level of the physiological mechanism, where it is desirable to specify cause and effect. If a constant temperature were a side effect of heat control there would be no reason for the system to stabilize at almost the same temperature in species living in polar, tropical humid, and aquatic thermal environments. Furthermore, mass from species to species varies in many ways in a single individual during his own growth or after dramatic amputations. Another problem is to explain how average body temperature is sensed. Temperature sensors may be spread all over the body and their information integrated. But, if so, then it becomes impossible to account for the constancy of core temperature in paraplegic and quadriplegic patients or in animals completely deafferented except for the head. These patients and animals manage to keep their internal temperature constant across a range of environmental temperatures if their limited response capacity is not overtaxed. Finally, although this hypothesis describes correctly the thermoregulatory response in a warm environment, it has not been verified that it describes the response in a cold environment. Because of these considerations, the classical view that temperature rather than heat content is regulated is accepted in the following pages.

If the homeothermic organism is a system that regulates its temperature, it must receive information about its temperature and produce regulatory defense reactions. The temperature inputs and the responses are related by laws. The new findings concerning the responses, inputs, and laws are next examined in turn.

RESPONSES

Any study of the temperature control system depends on the measurement of corrective responses. It is only when he observes a thermoregulatory response that the physiologist can conclude that the organism under observation is not at its thermoneutral point. Since measurement of thermoregulatory responses is the only way to probe the controller, it is essential to take into account all effects taking place at the periphery and to sort out the precise extent to which thermoregulatory responses depend on thermal or other factors. It is therefore necessary to start by reviewing the outputs first.

There have been very few fundamental changes since the last review, and new students of temperature regulation will find in textbooks the description of basic patterns of thermoregulatory responses. These responses are (*a*) heat production through shivering and other metabolic processes, (*b*) vasomotor responses resulting in a modification of heat transfer from core to skin and, in turn, of heat loss to the environment, (*c*) evaporative heat loss, and (*d*) behavior.

Thermogenesis

The capacity to adjust heat production was thought to be the privilege of homeotherms, but in fact there are a few examples of ectotherms, such as the brooding python, which are capable of increasing their thermogenesis to raise body temperature. The list of these species should be extended to include a fish, the tuna (22), and, among insects, bees and moths (52, 53, 64, 79, 112, 140).

Moderate hypoxia diminished cold thermogenesis in dogs (9). This reduction might be explained by reduced heat loss due to peripheral vasoconstriction resulting from hypocapnia (118).

Free fatty acids seem to be the major fuel of the shivering muscle. This fuel represents as much as 50 (109) to 75% (95) of total energy expenditure of dogs placed in cold environments.

Nonshivering thermogenesis is a slower process that probably plays a role in cold adaptation rather than in temperature regulation in the short term. The reader will find this question reviewed elsewhere (26, 40, 56, 68).

Vasomotor and Other Vascular Mechanisms

The vasomotor response is the cheapest of all thermoregulatory defense reactions. The only energy expenditure is in the form of cardiac work, which constitutes only a small portion of total energy expenditure. The priority of the needs of temperature regulation over circulatory equilibrium have been clearly demonstrated in subjects submitted to a heat load and at the same time to a negative pressure of the lower body (54, 77). During severe hyperthermia even brain blood flow is reduced (46) in favor of increased peripheral circulation. Although the blood volume increases during heat stress (130, 131), this increase is limited. It has always been assumed that skin vasoconstriction as a cold defense reaction and skin vasodilatation as a warm defense reaction were compensated by simultaneous opposite responses in the thermal core. This has been confirmed by a series of experimental studies (3, 45, 83, 123, 129, 151). The balance between vascular beds is under sympathetic control, and the tonus of visceral and cutaneous nerves appears to respond oppositely to the same stimuli (63, 83, 121, 150). All the vascular reactions are appropriate to, that is, they act against, the stimuli received, whether these stimuli are central or peripheral. They persist in spite of general anesthesia.

The thermoregulatory role of arteriovenous anastomoses has been demonstrated in the sheep (45) and the dog (162). The proportion of the cardiac output passing through arteriovenous anatomoses is increased markedly during heat stress. Vasodilation in the cold is also due to opening of arteriovenous anastomoses (38). These structures thus appear to have a clear-cut role in controlling skin temperature.

The possibility of a peripheral effect of cold on skin blood flow has been proposed. The influence of skin temperature could be mediated by a temperature-dependent change in blood viscosity and thus would be a strictly passive effect (110). This hypothesis was not confirmed by an in vitro study of blood flow (147). A different effect of peripheral temperature on peripheral circulation has been demonstrated, however: noradrenergic vasoconstriction was considerably increased by a cool (25°C) temperature and reduced by a warm (42°C) temperature. This remained true after prolonged sympathectomy (148).

There is some evidence of a local cooling of brain temperature based on vascular peculiarities in some species. In the dog the blood from the dorsal nasal, angularis oculi, and facial veins returns via the ophthalmic vein to the cavernous sinus and cools the base of the brain. Changing the temperature of this venous blood was followed by shivering or panting, demonstrating the effectiveness of this mechanism. The presence of smooth muscles arranged in circular layers within the wall of these vessels (91) suggests that local blood flow in this region, and thus local temperature, is controlled. Blatt et al (8) have described a nasal gland that responds like a sweat gland and may also contribute to this control of local brain temperature. Other species such as the cat and the sheep possess within the cavernous sinus a carotid rete mirabile that could very well act as a heat exchanger (51).

The role of these mechanisms is not quite clear since the species possessing them do not appear to be more tolerant of heat than do others during ordinary life conditions. These mechanisms may protect the brain from overheating during escape running, when general temperature regulation is sacrificed and large quantities of heat build up rapidly. In the antelope, which has a rete mirabile, the brain remains 2.7°C cooler than the core during running (143).

Mechanisms that control local cephalic temperature seem to be well developed in ectotherms. In tuna fish (87), lizards (33, 76, 152, 153), and turtles, vascular shunts, and presumably a countercurrent heat exchange mechanism, provide a relative stability of brain temperature when these animals are exposed to warm as well as cool environments. In ectotherms the utility of this response is obvious. However, the fact that local control of brain temperature has apparently been lost in some phyla leads one to assign a minor role to this kind of mechanism.

Evaporative Heat Loss

Water used as an evaporative coolant is produced either by the salivary glands or by the sweat glands, depending on the species.

SALIVA SECRETION Saliva is secreted during heat stress in species which pant, such as the dog (133). The rat (which does not pant) increases its secretion of saliva and spreads it on its body surface (43). Saliva secretion is proportional to ambient temperature (43) and to inner body temperature (132, 133). In the rat the submaxillary gland is specially adapted for thermoregulatory secretion (44), while in the dog, all salivary glands apparently respond to heat stress (132).

SWEAT SECRETION Sweat secretory processes have been studied in detail. In amphibians, mucus is discharged on the skin surface in a way comparable to sweat secretion in mammals. The frequency of mucus discharge is proportional to body temperature (85). The sweat glands of the sheep and goat do not discharge continuously; rather, they discharge spontaneously, briefly, and synchronously over all the skin surface. The frequency increases with increased ambient temperature. The sweat gland of the horse and donkey, on the other hand, respond continuously (4).

When sweat is secreted there is a delay before it appears on the skin surface due to the time necessary to fill the sweat ducts (14). Then sweat spreads over the skin surface and the presence of sodium chloride, which accumulates with evaporation, increases the surface area of the liquid film on the skin surface (7). Finally, drinking seems capable of triggering sweat secretion in dehydrated man (106a).

SWEATING "FATIGUE" During sustained exposure to a warm environment the amount of sweat secreted increases to a maximum, then decreases to a lower level. The reason for this "fatigue" of the secretory response is not clear and several explanations may be advanced.

There are good reasons to think that the presence of a liquid film on the skin itself inhibits sweat secretion. Everything happens as if sweating fatigue were due to the presence of water on the skin surface. When sweating skin is wiped dry it sweats more (106) and the fatigue immediately disappears if the ambient air is dried (55). This effect is important from a theoretical viewpoint, as we shall see later. Although this influence by itself seems sufficient to account for sweating fatigue, other factors may also be involved.

The pattern of sweat excretion during prolonged exposure to heat depends not only on the rate of secretion, but also on the amount of preformed sweat locally stored in the gland lumen (78).

General dehydration can inhibit evaporative heat loss. Thermal panting was suppressed in the rabbit (146) and the gazelle (142) during dehydration. In these species hyperthermia is tolerated in order to curtail water loss, as has been described previously in camels and donkeys.

Local temperature itself may modulate the sweat response, since a decrease of local temperature inhibits sweat secretion in vitro (128). Local skin temperature has been shown to have a multiplicative interaction with mean skin temperature in the determination of local sweating rate (105). Therefore, a local negative feedback may exist in which evaporation of the sweat secreted decreases local temperature and in turn decreases the local secretion.

Behavior

A new trend in physiological investigation is the recognition of behavior as a physiological response. Hardy long ago had emphasized this fact, and many workers have confirmed it in recent years. Behavior can be more or less sophisticated.

SIMPLE BEHAVIORS The simplest behavior is a change in orientation to the direction of wind or sun. This is seen in as simple an organism as the insect. A complementary behavior is modification of posture. These behaviors result in modification of the surface/mass ratio and therefore in the rate of heat exchange between the subject and his environment. For example, the surface area of the human silhouette will be increased by a factor of 3 when a person changes from crouching to an expanded body position. This response in itself can be very efficient when the subject is exposed to solar radiation, evaluated at about 1039 W m^{-2} at noontime in a summer desert climate. In less severe conditions a clothed manikin can gain 95 W m^{-2} from solar radiation, i.e. about twice the basal metabolic rate.

Another simple behavior is avoidance of dangerous or hostile temperatures and search of favorable temperatures. This behavior has been described in a multitude of species belonging to all classes of animals. For this reason the distinction between homeotherm and poikilotherm should be abandoned in favor of endotherm [or tachymetabolic species (12) that make use of an internal heat source in addition to external sources] and ectotherm (or bradymetabolic species that can gain heat almost exclusively from the environment). One consequence of the recognition of the role of behavior in maintaining a constant body temperature is that more and more studies of temperature regulation are being performed on ectothermic species.

MICROCLIMATES While avoidance or search behavior is certainly very efficient in dealing with the animal's thermal problems, it has the disadvantage that all the animal's activity is devoted to improving its thermal environment. It is therefore competitive with other forms of behavior and its presence at a given time means that temperature is at that time the most important motivation for the subject.

The construction of microenvironments is an improvement over search and avoidance, but only in a few species, such as social insects, beaver, and man, is it sophisticated enough to free the behavior for other purposes.

OPERANT BEHAVIOR Since the original work by Weiss (154a) the operant response has been widely used in a multitude of species, including fishes and reptiles, to study thermoregulatory behavior in a quantitative fashion. It must be remembered in considering experiments using this method that increase or decrease in bar pressing can be a nonspecific response resulting from general excitation or apraxia. An experimental result should be considered to be specific only when a symmetrical response is also obtained (e.g. increased bar pressing for heat and decreased bar pressing for cold), and when the response is a quantitative function of temperature. Operant responding for temperature change has been shown to be proportional to environmental temperature.

INGESTIVE BEHAVIORS Although the signals responsible for thermoregulatory responses are also capable of triggering food and water intake, and although these behaviors may improve the subject's thermal condition and energy balance, their effects on body temperature appear to be minor or delayed in time. Therefore, strictly speaking, food and water intake should not be considered as thermoregulatory behaviors unless ingestion leads to an immediate change in heat storage, as is the case when ice (48) or cold water are ingested in great amounts.

INPUTS

Nervous structures can be sensitive to temperature or to temperature change. Ström (139a) proposed that, when histological description is lacking, such structures be called *detectors* and that the term receptors be kept for those structures that have been histologically described. The more recent name *temperature sensor* seems more widely used in speaking about both kinds of afferents. As already pointed out by Hammel (47), an input can be considered to play a role in temperature regulation only if its activation by specific stimuli is followed by a regulatory response of the opposite sign; e.g. warming the hypothalamus results in polypnea, which in turn decreases hypothalamic temperature.

In recent years attention has been drawn more and more toward extrahypothalamic temperature sensors and to a better quantification of the relationship between temperature and the electrical response of the sensor, on the one hand, and between the temperature of the sensor and the thermoregulatory response, on the other. These kinds of studies lead to the construction of mathematical models of temperature regulation. When more than one temperature is involved in the control of a response, the relationship will be considered below in the section on the laws of temperature regulation.

Temperature sensors are found both on the body surface and in the core.

Skin Sensors

In ignorance of the density of temperature sensors it was usual to weight skin influence in man according to the surface area of each segment. This weighted average skin temperature has been corrected by Nadel et al (104) by measuring the sweat secreted when selective areas of the skin were heated for a short period of time, all other conditions remaining constant. Their results show that of the total influence on sweating, the face accounts for 21%, the chest and back for 21%, the abdomen for 17%, the upper legs for 15%, the lower legs for 8%, the upper arms for 12%, and the lower arms for 6%. Comparable experimental research remains to be done on the response to cold.

The heterogeneity of the skin influence has been long recognized. The scrotum of the ram and the udder of the goat are particularly efficient in triggering polypnea. This has been confirmed in another species, the pig (61). Similarly, the rabbit's nose and upper respiratory tract contain warmth sensors that are more important than the total skin surface in the control of panting rate, and that account for about one third of the total increase in panting frequency occurring during heat stress (90).

The fact that peripheral sensors are sensitive to the rate of change of local temperature has been known since the firing rates of temperature sensors were first recorded. The involvement of this particular sensitivity in the control of temperature regulation has always been assumed, but no model includes it clearly. As a matter of fact, the phasic neural response to temperature change disappears in a matter of seconds, a period apparently too short to be significant in regulating body temperature. There is, however, evidence for an influence of this time-dependant response. When hyperthermic human subjects were subjected to a sudden drop in ambient temperature, sweating decreased faster than skin temperature during 5–10 min. The sweating response correlated well with $\overline{T}_s + \mathrm{d}\overline{T}_s/\mathrm{d}t$ (159).

Internal Sensors

The sensitivity of the hypothalamus to cold as well as to warm stimulation is no longer questioned. The ability of the hypothalamic sensors to trigger the total pattern of autonomic and behavioral thermoregulatory responses in proportion to stimulus intensity has been repeatedly shown. This evidence has been extended to a variety of species, including reptiles (16, 99), teleost (34) and chondrichthyes (34) fishes, birds (48, 94), and a hibernating rodent (155, 156). The locus of greatest temperature sensitivity seems to be primarily the preoptic area, but the whole base of the brain seems to be capable of commanding one or another of the defenses against thermal stress. Stimulation of the posterior hypothalamus, mesencephalon, and medulla were followed by some corrective behavioral responses (89, 122), by shivering (20), and by less specific reactions (28, 141). The functional role of these sensors is not obvious, since their anatomic proximity to the anterior hypothalamus makes it likely that their temperatures are quite close to and vary in parallel with hypothalamic temperature.

The function of nonencephalic sensors is less enigmatic, since the temperatures of different parts of the thermal core are not necessarily homogeneous, particularly during transient temperature changes and in animals with large bodies.

SPINAL CORD TEMPERATURE The most well recognized extrahypothalamic temperature sensor is found in the spinal cord. The studies conducted initially, by the Bad Nauheim team in the dog (143a) have been extended to other species and, more importantly, have become increasingly quantitative.

Warm stimulation Warm stimulation of the spinal cord in frog (36), pigeon (112–115), rat (86), guinea pig (158), rabbit (42, 62, 82, 150), dog (32, 72, 73, 75, 83), cat (150), pig (60), goat (71), ox (74), and monkey (28) was followed by all the warmth defense reactions, including skin vasodilatation, reduction of heat production, increase in evaporative heat loss, and behavioral responses. Whenever it has been quantitatively measured, the response intensity was proportional to the spinal cord temperature.

The sensitivity of the spinal cord was generally found to be lower than that of the hypothalamus by a factor of ¼ (32), ⅓ (42), or ½ (60). These low measures of spinal sensitivity are perhaps due to the use of inadequate stimuli. Often few segments of the spinal cord are stimulated. In ignorance of the precise location of the sensors and the thermodes within the spinal cord, investigators usually use thermode temperature or a conservative average spinal temperature, which minimizes the apparent spinal sensitivity. When several thermodes are used, the slope of the response as a function of temperature is identical for spinal heating and hypothalamic heating in the dog (73). If the open-loop gain is considered, the effect of spinal heating on core temperature is of the same order of magnitude as the effect hypothalamic heating (74).

Cold stimulation Cold stimulation of the spinal cord leads to less homogeneous results. It is certain that cooling of the spinal cord in unanesthetized dogs is capable of inducing shivering, peripheral vasoconstriction, and piloerection (72, 73, 75, 83, 150). These responses are proportional to the magnitude of the stimulus.

Although comparable results have been obtained in pigeons (113) and in monkeys (28), the only effect in several cases was a simple inhibition of warmth defense reactions (59–61, 86). Cooling was followed by an incomplete pattern of cold defense reactions or by no reaction at all (42), even in unanesthetized animals (31, 71, 74). It is possible that cold stimulation of the spinal cord interacts in a multiplicative fashion with skin stimuli and therefore would be effective only in a cool or cold environment (24, 71).

Cooling the spinal cord has been observed to cause a time-dependent behavioral warming response (25). In the absence of information on the possible intervention of other sensors and autonomic responses, it is wise to await confirmation of this finding before concluding that there in fact exists a spinal sensitivity to the rate of temperature change.

TEMPERATURE SENSORS IN THE ABDOMEN Intra-abdominal heating in the ewe by means of chronically implanted electrical thermodes initiated panting in a neutral environment and inhibited metabolic heat production in a cold environment with no change, and sometimes even a depression, of extra-abdominal body temperatures (116). In the rabbit a 0.9°C increase of intra-abdominal thermode temperature was followed by vasodilatation (134). There is evidence that the input from temperature sensors in the walls of the intestine and rumen is carried by the splanchnic nerves, since section of one splanchnic nerve suppressed the response to ipsilateral heating (117). There may be other pathways for visceral inputs since it known that section of the vagus nerves suppresses shivering in the hypothermic anesthetized cat.

In the rabbit, elevation of rectal temperature 0.2°C is equal to a 1°C increase in hypothalamic temperature in the control of vasodilatation; for panting, the rectal increase equivalent to a 1°C hypothalamic increase is 0.8°C (81). When studied by thermode stimulation of the abdominal cavity, the sensitivity of the abdominal thermosensors of monkeys appeared to be one third of the hypothalamic sensitivity (81) and one fourth of the spinal sensitivity (121a) in eliciting thermoregulatory responses. Squirrel monkeys responded to cold as well as warm abdominal stimuli, but the sensitivity to these stimuli was not great (1). It seems possible that this abdominal sensitivity is better developed in herbivorous species and ruminants, where the rumen's temperature can increase to 40.1°C (145) due to the active fermentation of cellulose. This would be consistent with the absence of evidence for an abdominal cold sensitivity in the ewe (117) and the rabbit (121a), and with the absence of any response to abdominal warm and cold stimuli in pigs (60).

TEMPERATURE SENSORS IN MUSCLE During muscular work, the great amount of heat produced within the limited muscular volume drives local temperature to 40°C or higher; this temperature becomes the highest in the body (125). Because of this observation it was tempting to suspect the existence of anticipatory temperature sensors in or near the large muscles. In fact, although local muscle temperature is high during positive work and even higher during negative work, it does not under either condition influence sweat rate (107, 108). Therefore, the existence of the hypothesized muscle temperature sensors is unlikely.

It is clear that the central nervous system receives information about the temperature of a variety of regions within the body. The information from these various sites must be combined in some way to initiate thermoregulatory responses. Some of the laws describing the stimulus-response relationships have already been reported in the above section. These laws are usually a simple proportionality, with some limited influence of the time derivative of temperature. In the following section more complex relationships are examined.

LAWS

There is no doubt that the way we should look at temperature regulation has changed little since Hammel's review (47). The hypothalamus remains the privileged locus where temperature regulation takes place. Recent studies of the effects of hypothalamic lesions (6) have confirmed the essential role of this structure, which was demonstrated in many older works. In addition, there is recent evidence that spinally transected dogs lack all but the vasomotor adjustments to cold and warm spinal stimuli (151), which shows that the spinal network is not completely self-sufficient. The fact that lesioned animals do not display an intact pattern of responses does not, of course, imply that the missing response is exclusively controlled by the missing structure.

Combined Signals

Is it possible to know how the information received from several inputs is used by the central nervous system and combined to produce the thermoregulatory responses? This is a very difficult question to answer because of the multiplicity of the inputs and outputs. For example, the information from the skin has at least three relevant dimensions: surface area, time, and temperature. The general experimental method used in answering this question consists in holding constant the thermal state of the animal or human subject and in displacing only one variable at a time over the whole range of possible temperatures. Then another variable is selected for study until all the possible combinations are explored.

INTERACTION OF SKIN AND INTERNAL TEMPERATURES In man, direct measurement of hypothalamic temperature is not possible, nor is independent stimulation of various internal sensors. Thus the only combination that can be investigated in man is the interaction between mean skin and internal temperature. We have already noted that mean skin temperature is an inadequate measure of the peripheral signal and should be corrected according to the appropriate weighting factors. In general, skin and internal temperatures have individual influences of the same magnitude and sign. However, the way these inputs combine is not certain. The combination law may be additive, that is, the combined response is the sum of the two independent responses determined by the temperatures of the skin and core individually. On the other hand, the combination law may be multiplicative. This possibility is characterized by the absence of a response when one signal is zero—for example, in a neutral environment when the skin is neither warm nor cold. Another characteristic of multiplicative combination is that the curve describing the response as a function of one signal alone is not parallel to the response curve for the same signal when a second input is present. These two possibilities have been presented in Hammel's review (4). More recent arguments have been presented in favor of additive (2, 10, 31, 81, 105, 118, 133, 137, 156) and multiplicative (15, 21, 65, 98, 103, 161) combination laws.

The difference between additive and multiplicative models usually is obvious only for extreme temperatures. When an interaction is examined within the usual temperature range it is most often impossible to assess whether it is multiplicative or additive, at least as far as internal and mean skin temperatures are concerned. In addition, absence of a peripheral input is perhaps never realized. Therefore, the distinction between the two types of combinations has probably little importance.

From these experiments it is possible to deduce the relative influence of hypothalamic and peripheral signals on thermoregulatory responses. From the limited sample of the above works it may be concluded that the influence of internal sensors increases with body weight. There is some evidence that skin temperature is more important than hypothalamic temperature in the control of various thermoregulatory responses by a ratio of 3 in the rat (31), 1.2 in the guinea pig (13), 1.5 in the squirrel monkey (137), and 1.0 in the cat (65). In larger species, internal sensors are favored and the ratio is 0.25 in the dog (17), and in man 0.33 (154), 0.25 (10, 21), 0.2 (15, 161), and 0.14 (103). From a teleological viewpoint the predominant influence of internal sensors in larger species seems necessary in order to avoid the building of large heat deficits or surpluses due to the large mass. In addition, large species are threatened by their great inner heat production and low surface-to-mass ratio. In small species, such as arthropods, it is sufficient that the organism possess a single peripheral sensor in order to permit thermotropism toward a favorable ambient temperature, since the body mass is small and equilibration time is therefore short.

A special case in considering the relative roles of internal and peripheral sensors is found in birds. In these usually well-insulated animals, internal temperature is very stable and seems to be the essential factor in the control of warmth and cold reactions. Skin temperature apparently plays a minor or no role in controlling thermoregulatory responses (115, 119, 120, 157). Internal extrahypothalamic signals appear to modulate the response triggered by hypothalamic stimuli (119, 120), and spinal sensors may even predominate over hypothalamic sensors (115) in the control of shivering and tachypnea. Skin temperature has a small influence on heat production that is strictly additive to that of spinal temperature (115).

SPINAL CORD AND HYPOTHALAMUS Spinal cord and hypothalamus have individual influence of the same sign. In some experiments spinal cord sensitivity was only one third (42) or one half (74) the hypothalamic sensitivity, but in these experiments the spinal signal was usually considered to be the temperature of the water perfusing the spinal thermode. This conservative measurement tends to minimize the apparent spinal influence. Furthermore, in the rabbit experiments, not all the spinal cord was stimulated. It therefore seems logical to conclude, with Jessen & Simon (75), that these two temperature-sensitive areas in the dog have identical function and sensitivity.

The combination law for these two inputs seems to be solely additive. The spinal cord simply adds its influence to the thermoregulatory system during warm (24, 59, 72) stimulations. The simple additive law has also been found to describe the combination of hypothalamic and extrahypothalamic internal temperatures in the control of evaporative heat loss (49).

SPINAL CORD AND SKIN As pointed out above, there are unanimous results regarding spinal warmth sensitivity, but there are discrepancies regarding cold sensitivity. On several occasions a response to cold spinal stimuli could not be obtained unless the skin itself were also cold.

The response curves for spinal heating are parallel for various combinations of spinal with skin or ambient temperatures. This unchanged proportionality constant from condition to condition means that warmth skin and spinal signals are additive. In the control of panting (60) and of behavior (32), spinal and peripheral signals were additive, even when the peripheral inputs were limited to the scrotum (61). Cold response curves, when they can be obtained, are strictly parallel for various combinations of spinal and skin temperatures in the control of oxygen consumption or of behavior (24, 25).

From the evidence accumulated above, it is apparent that (*a*) several temperature sensors are capable of triggering defense reactions independently, and (*b*) the response is a function of several inputs combined at the same time. This is particularly evident from measurements of two-dimensional thresholds for regulatory responses (13, 17, 44, 81). The intimate link between the many inputs in the determination of regulatory responses leads to the question of what is regulated.

What is Regulated?

VOCABULARY Before trying to answer this question it seems necessary to start with a short discussion of terms borrowed by physiologists from the engineer's vocabulary and used to describe what is known about temperature regulation.

When in a system such as the body a physical value is constant, this constancy may be the result either of a passive equilibrium or of a regulated equilibrium (i.e. a regulation). A system is in equilibrium when the resultant of all forces acting on it is equal to zero. The equilibrium is stable when after a perturbation the system tends to return to its original position. If the perturbation lasts, a passive system reaches and maintains a new equilibrium position.

In a system where a variable is regulated, there exists a sensor of this variable. The signal emitted by this sensor is compared to a constant signal, the set point. The difference between the feedback signal and the set point is the error signal to be corrected by controller elements that act on the system and that are activated by the error signal itself. As a result of controller action, the regulated variable is kept close to, and may even return to, its original value even when submitted to a sustained perturbation.

It is not always easy to distinguish between a passive and a regulated system, since the latter may behave like the former if the corrective response in the regulation is overwhelmed. The only sure way to know that one is dealing with a regulatory system is to describe the feedback loop and the set point. The set point for the regulated variable can be identified only when the regulatory responses are put to work by activating the system. The set point is then identified with the value of the variable that just produced a threshold corrective response. To use the term "set point" for a temperature placed out of the actual normal range for the body should be regarded as a misuse of the word. When a central heating system is set for maintaining a temperature of 20°C, this temperature is the threshold for putting the furnace at work. The term "reference" should not be used in place of "set point." A reference is, strictly speaking, a physical or analog value used in setting up quantitative scales of measurements, e.g. melting ice temperature can be used as a reference for temperature measurements.

In the study of temperature regulation some confusion has been introduced by the simultaneous use of this vocabulary in describing three different approaches: (*a*) the measurement of physiological responses in relation to the temperatures activating them, (*b*) the theoretical representation of functions in block diagrams, and (*c*) the theoretical design of neuronal networks supporting these functions and permitting these responses. The physiologist's aim is certainly to reach a level of knowledge where circuits are expressed as neurons, but in temperature regulation this level of analysis is most often far from being reached.

For example, it is necessary to distinguish between the theory of the adjustable set point, based on the observation that there exists a variable threshold for panting and shivering in dogs placed at different ambient temperatures, on the one hand, and the tentative neuronal network postulated by Hammel to explain the observed facts, on the other. This neuronal hypothesis may be correct (57) but there may be other possible networks. The concept of the set point does not necessarily rely upon a reference made up of temperature-insensitive neurons.

One may consider as the regulated variable among several variables (*a*) the most constant, (*b*) any variable placed within a negative feedback loop, or (*c*) the variable for which the proportionality constant relating the response to stimulus intensity is greatest.

Among the multiple inputs, the proportionality constant seems to be greater for skin input than for internal inputs in species with a small mass. In these species it may therefore be considered that skin temperature is the regulated variable. In man and large animals internal temperature is without doubt more constant than skin temperature, and deep sensors are more sensitive than skin sensors. Although all the inputs are combined, it is logical to choose deep temperature as the regulated variable. The lack of information in man does not allow firm conclusions about a possible hierarchy of influence among the internal sensors in this species. In intact dogs the mass of evidence provided by Jessen et al (72, 73, 75) makes it clear that there is a functional equivalence between spinal and hypothalamic temperature sensors. It is probable that under most circumstances hypothalamic and extrahypothalamic deep temperatures vary in parallel. Lags between local temperatures may explain transient poor correlations between one deep temperature and thermoregulatory responses. As a matter of fact, the available experimental data suggest that when sensor temperatures do not vary in the same way, their signals add and the responses seem to depend upon several feedback loops more or less independent of each other. The effects of lesions in the CNS point to the hypothalamus as the critical structure in thermoregulation. Hypothalamic lesions and spinal cord sections in man and animals show that hypothalamic temperature is sufficient and hypothalamic integrity is necessary to the control of adequate thermoregulatory responses, while the spinal cord is neither sufficient nor necessary.

If the student of temperature regulation chooses hypothalamic temperature as the regulated variable, then he is forced to accept the theory of the adjustable set point.

SET POINT: ANALOGY OR REALITY? Any attempt to answer the question of whether the set point is an analogy or a reality must specify the level at which the system is analyzed, i.e. response measurement, block diagrams, or neuronal networks. What is true at one level may be false at another.

Responses It follows from the above considerations that the threshold hypothalamic temperature beyond which corrective responses are activated can be described as a set point for the system. The set point is therefore a reality at this level of analysis.

Block diagrams The description of temperature regulation in terms of block diagrams is a way to summarize the functional steps in the process leading from perturbation to response. Classical block diagrams include a set point. This feature has been challenged by Mitchell et al (96, 97), who proposed that temperature is not regulated *sensu stricto,* but rather is controlled by a dynamic equilibrium between antagonistic feedback loops without a set point. One loop includes a sensor of rise in brain temperature, the second loop a sensor of fall in brain temperature. These two signals simply subtract, resulting in an error signal. The signals originating from other sensors would in the same way be composed of rise sensors and fall sensors in multiple parallel loops, and would be summed up in a central controller.

Is this new model different from classical block diagrams, including a set point? This depends on the shape of the signal emitted by the sensors placed in each loop. If the signal has a threshold, then the model is not different from the classical model. The set point function is simply included in the sensor. If the signal emitted by the sensor has no threshold and is monotonic over the whole range of body temperatures, then the model is new. The error signal is the difference between the two feedback signals. This proposition is quite close to Hammel's hypothesis (46a) about the neuronal basis of the set point, in which the thermoregulatory signal is the difference between the activities of two populations of neurons with different Q_{10}. Is this equilibrium model a better representation of the facts than the regulation model? According to the former model, there is a permanent balance between warmth and cold signals resulting in a permanent balance between warmth and cold responses. In support of this view Jessen & Clough (70) have shown that evaporative or thermogenic responses are continuously present in the goat, and that the proportionality constants are identical for the two responses. This suggests that one error signal controls the two responses. On the other hand, as the authors point out, this model does exhibit a mathematical or analog set point. As long as the model has this property, it seems appropriate to include an explicit place for it in the model. In addition, a disadvantage of this model as well as the classic one is that it does not account for the possibility of dissociation of temperature regulation in the two independent networks responsible for cold defense and for warmth defense. This point is discussed below.

Neurons It has been reported that cats (136) and sheep (83) had a highly variable body temperature after hypothalamic lesion, but retained their capacity to shiver and pant. In addition the sheep responded to hypothalamic cooling and warming by appropriate responses (93). It is as if these preparations were normal except for the loss of a set point responsible for the overall maintenance of a constant inner temperature. This interpretation by Maskrey & Blight may perhaps be extended to many prior results on hypothalamic lesioned animals. These data suggest the existence of a real neuronal set point. It should be noted that while a stable body temperature was lost in these experiments, a threshold value could still be found for thermoregulatory responses activated by hypothalamic cold and warmth stimuli. Thus the set point, identified as the threshold value using stimulus response measures, may not correspond to the neural reference hypothetically eliminated in these experiments.

INDEPENDENT NETWORKS Warmth and cold responses can coexist at the same time in the same animal. This seemingly paradoxical observation for autonomic responses must be the result of a peripherally induced increase in the activity of one effector and a centrally controlled compensation by the other. This explanation does not hold up in accounting for the observation that animals will behaviorally demand simultaneous warmth and cold reinforcements (19, 98).

There exists a neutral region between the warm and cold thresholds in dogs (17) and monkeys (137). The breadth of this neutral zone is variable from dog to dog and in addition can be varied with pharmacological agents. Hypothalamic lesions can impair one or the other of the responses, as if there were two regulatory loops rather than one (84, among others). In the same way, pharmacologic suppression of hypothalamic warmth sensitivity eliminates all defenses against hyperthermia, but leaves temperature regulation unimpaired in a cold environment (66, 67).

All these observations suggest strongly that there exists some degree of independence between the networks responsible for cold and warmth defense all the way from sensors to effectors. Reciprocal inhibition between these networks may exist and has been included in most neuronal models, but the facts listed above show no evidence for it. The block diagrams made up today do not include this possibility and some even render it impossible. A correct representation of the thermoregulatory system should probably consist of two more-or-less independent block diagrams for warmth and for cold defense reactions.

Even this improvement would certainly be a gross oversimplification. It is probably more accurate to conceive of the control system for regulation as a number of networks independent of one another. The decision made at the outset of this review to consider all the responses as equivalent was acceptable as a first approximation but now needs modification, as follows.

Intact preparations It appears as though all thermoregulatory responses are complementary and interchangeable, and are activated by a unique thermoregulatory motivation or signal (137). There exists in the literature, however, some indication that this conclusion is not absolute. The study of behavior is the origin of this new complication.

Cooling the hypothalamus in pigs was followed by one kind of corrective behavior, operant responding for infrared heating, whereas cooling the spinal cord was followed by another, postural adaptation (25). Quite comparable are the results obtained by Roberts & Mooney (122), who found that a warmth stimulus placed in various areas of the brain stem was followed by peripheral vasodilatation in all cases, but by different thermoregulatory behaviors, depending on the locus of the stimulus. This suggests the existence of various circuits from sensor to effector that are completely independent of one another. Finally, in intact man, Bleichert et al (10) described different response slopes for sweating and behavior as a function of inner temperature. However, this latter result can perhaps be explained simply by the fact that the subjects were immersed in water. As seen above, the presence of water on the skin inhibits sweating and therefore reduces the proportionality constant for the response plotted against internal temperature.

Lesions in the CNS Lesions in the CNS produce a dissociation between behavioral and autonomic responses. Suppressed motivation for thermoregulatory behavior, with unaffected autonomic responses and normal body temperature, was observed after damage to the lateral hypothalamus in rats (127, 139). The opposite situation, suppression of the ability to keep a stable body temperature while thermoregulatory behavior was increased, has also been observed repeatedly (24, 88, 126, 144, 149). Once again, these results do not agree with the notion that the networks responsible for behavioral and autonomic responses are identical. On the contrary, they suggest the existence of independent feedback loops. If this independence does not show up in normal life in intact animals, the reason is that the loops work in parallel simultaneously.

Set Point and Exercise

There has been a long controversy about a possible change in the set point during exercise. First, the hypothesis of a raised set point should be abandoned, since this would diminish or suppress the error signal responsible for evaporative heat loss and in turn diminish or suppress this response, and this is not the case. New indirect evidence for this conclusion can be found in the fact that exercise brings about an improvement of thermoregulatory efficiency (heat acclimatization) (92), implying that the error signal has not been reduced.

The influence of the inertia of the passive system when placed under heat stress during muscular work has probably been underestimated. For example, it has been confirmed that internal temperature correlated better with circulatory capacity than with ambient temperature (29, 107, 111).

The possibility that the set point is lowered during exercise needs further discussion. Exercise lowers the threshold for evaporative heat loss in the dog. This has been recently confirmed in man for sweating (69) and in the dog for salivary secretion (50). This shift may be due to incorrect weighting of $\overline{T}_s$. The apparent lowered set point may result from failure to take into account temperature changes in regions such as the spinal cord (29a), which will influence the response measure. In addition, the increased glandular response may be a peripheral effect due to general sympathetic activation since sweat glands are sensitive to epinephrine, at least in vitro (128), as are salivary glands. In any event, increased sweating is transitory in man (138), and thus does not resemble a true resetting of the set point. The lower hypothalamic set point observed in some experiments may be explained on the basis of the possible existence of temperature inputs from various sensors that have additive or multiplicative effects on the response measured; this possibility should be considered before the hypothesis of a lowered set point during exercise is accepted.

There is now a growing array of observations showing no change in set point when several inputs are taken into account (5, 10, 18, 37). The presence of peripheral vasoconstriction (37, 81, 100) and the persistence of shivering (101, 102) at the onset of exercise also argue against a change of set point during exercise. Finally, since sweating was stimulated by exercise only if the subjects were already sweating (41), a role of the drying effect of convection on hydrated skin, which in itself releases sweating from inhibition, may be suspected here. Is it possible to reconcile the two viewpoints? Since there are several results showing no evidence for a nonthermal resetting of the thermostat during exercise, perhaps the discrepancies can be explained in terms of a resetting of the set point by as yet unaccounted-for temperature inputs, as suggested above.

CONCLUSION

The general way of looking at short-term temperature regulation has not fundamentaly changed since 1968. Some points nevertheless have been developed and deserve special attention:

1. The influence of water on the skin surface inhibits sweat secretion (55, 106). This fact may be the explanation of sweating fatigue and of discordant conclusions regarding the functioning of the regulator, particularly during exercise in man.
2. Since a large number of studies have shown that appropriate behaviors occur in response to all the stimuli that activate autonomic responses, behavior itself should be considered as an integral part of the thermoregulatory system (1, 2, 16, 18, 19, 21, 23, 25, 31, 32, 34–36, 48, 88, 89, 98, 99, 122, 126, 127, 137).
3. The description of the peripheral input for the control of sweating with regard to mean skin temperature (104) and time dependence (159) has been improved. Among internal temperature sensors those of the spinal cord have been extensively studied (25, 27, 32, 36, 42, 59–63, 71–75, 82, 83, 86, 113–115, 121, 150, 158) and demonstrated to have a sensitivity equal to that of the hypothalamic sensors (73, 75).
4. New hypotheses have been proposed describing the overall mechanism responsible for a constant temperature in the core (58, 96, 97, 135). These stimulating theories have been discussed briefly herein. Mechanisms for the defense against heat and against cold can be dissociated completely from one another. In the same way

the control of autonomic responses can be dissociated from the control of behavioral responses. This suggests that temperature regulation is brought about by multiple independent feedback loops. The overall system is well described, in the author's opinion, by the theory of the adjustable set point with proportional control (47).

ACKNOWLEDGMENT

The author is deeply indebted to Dr. E. F. Rabe for critically reading the manuscript and for the long hours he spent improving the English version.

Literature Cited

1. Adair, E. R. 1971. Displacements of rectal temperature modify behavioral. *Physiol. Behav.* 7(1):21–26
2. Adair, E. R., Casby, J. U., Stolwijk, J. A. J. 1970. Behavioral temperature regulation in the squirrel monkey: changes induced by shifts in hypothalamic temperature. *J. Comp. Physiol. Psychol.* 72(1):17–27
3. Alexander, G., Bell, A. W., Hales, J. R. S. 1973. Effect of cold exposure on tissue blood flow in the new born lamb. *J. Physiol. London* 234:65–77
4. Allen, T. E., Bligh, J. 1969. A comparative study of the temporal pattern of cutaneous water vapour loss from some domesticated mammals with epitrichial sweat glands. *Comp. Biochem. Physiol.* 31(2):347–63
5. Bainton, C. R., Mitchell, R. A. 1971. Effect of skin cooling on exercise ventilation in the awake dog. *J. Appl. Physiol.* 30(3):370–77
6. Bard, P., Woods, J. W., Bleier, R. 1970. The effects of cooling, heating, and pyrogen on chronically decerebrate cats. In *Physiological and Behavioral Temperature Regulation,* ed. J. D. Hardy, A. P. Gagge, J. A. J. Stolwijk, 519–45. Springfield, Ill.: Thomas. 944 pp.
7. Berglund, L. G., McNall, P. E. 1973. Human sweat film area and composition during prolonged sweating. *J. Appl. Physiol.* 35(5):714–18
8. Blatt, C. M., Taylor, C. R., Habal, M. S. 1972. Thermal panting in dogs: the lateral nasal gland, a source of water for evaporative. *Science* 177(4051): 804–5
9. Blatteis, C. M., Lutherer, L. O. 1973. Cold induced thermogenesis in dogs: its reduction by moderate hypoxia. *J. Appl. Physiol.* 35(5):608–12
10. Bleichert, A., Behling, K., Scarperi, M., Scarperi, S. 1973. Thermoregulatory behavior of man during rest and exercise. *Pfuegers Arch.* 338:303–12
11. Bligh, J. 1973. *Temperature Regulation in Mammals and Other Vertebrates.* Amsterdam: North-Holland. 436 pp.
12. Bligh, J., Johnson, K. G. 1973. Glossary of terms for thermal physiology. *J. Appl. Physiol.* 35(6):941–61
13. Brück, K., Wünnenberg, W. 1970. Meshed control of two effector systems: nonshivering and shivering thermogenesis. See Ref. 6, 562–80
14. Bullard, R. W. 1971. Studies on human sweat gland duct filling and skin hydration. *J. Physiol. Paris* 63:218–21
15. Bullard, R. W., Banerjee, M. R., Chen, F., Elizondo, R., McIntyre, B. A. 1970. Skin temperature and thermoregulatory sweating: a control system approach. See Ref. 6, 597–610
16. Cabanac, H. P., Hammel, H. T. 1971. Peripheral sensitivity and temperature regulation in *Tiliqua scincoides. Int. J. Biometeorol.* 15:239–43
17. Cabanac, M. 1970. Interaction of cold and warm temperature signals in the brain stem. See Ref. 6, 549–61
18. Cabanac, M., Cunningham, D. J., Stolwijk, J. A. J. 1971. Thermoregulatory set point during exercise: a behavioral approach *J. Comp. Physiol. Psychol.* 76(3):94–102
19. Cabanac, M., Duclaux, R., Gillet, A. 1970. Thermorégulation comportementale chez le chien. Effet de la fièvre et de la thyroxine. *Physiol. Behav.* 5(6):697–704
20. Cabanac, M., Hardy, J. D. 1968. Réponses unitaires et thermorégulatrices lors de réchauffements et refroidissements localisés de la région préoptique et du mésencéphale chez le lapin. *J. Physiol. Paris* 61:331–47
21. Cabanac, M., Massonnet, M., Belaiche, R. 1972. Preferred skin temperature as a function of internal and mean skin

temperature. *J. Appl. Physiol.* 33(6): 699–703
22. Carey, F. G., Lawson, K. D. 1973. Temperature regulation in free swimming bluefin tuna. *Comp. Biochem. Physiol.* 44(2A):375–92
23. Carlisle, H. J. 1969. Effect of preoptic and anterior hypothalamic lesions on behavioral thermoregulation in the cold. *J. Comp. Physiol. Psychol.* 69(2): 391–402
24. Carlisle, H. J., Ingram, D. L. 1973. The influence of body core temperature and peripheral temperature on oxygen consumption in the pig. *J. Physiol. London* 231:341–52
25. Carlisle, H. J., Ingram, D. L. 1973. The effects of heating and cooling the spinal cord and hypothalamus on thermoregulatory behaviour in the pig. *J. Physiol. London* 321:353–64
26. Chaffee, R. R. J., Roberts, J. C. 1971. Temperature acclimation in birds and mammals. *Ann. Rev. Physiol.* 33:155–202
27. Chai, C. Y., Lin, H. T. 1972. Effects of heating and cooling the spinal cord and medulla oblongata on thermoregulation in monkeys. *J. Physiol. London* 225(2)-:297–309
28. Chai, C. Y., Wang, S. C. 1970. Cardiovascular and respiratory responses to cooling the medulla oblongata of the cat. *Proc. Soc. Exp. Biol. Med.* 134:763–67
29. Clasing, D., Laumann, U. 1968. Das Verhalten der Körpertemperatur bei Fahrradergometerarbeit im Bereich der Ausdavergrenze. *Int. Z. Angew. Physiol.* 126(2):131–40
29a. Clough, D. P., Jessen, C. 1974. The role of spinal thermosensitive structures in the respiratory heat loss during exercise. *Pfluegers Arch.* 347:235–48
30. Colin, J., Houdas, Y. 1968. Déterminisme du déclenchement de la sudation thermique chez l'homme. *J. Physiol. Paris* 60:5–31
31. Corbit, J. D. 1973. Voluntary control of hypothalamic temperature. *J. Comp. Physiol. Psychol.* 83(3):394–411
32. Cormareche-Leydier, M., Cabanac, M. 1973. Influence de stimulations thermiques de la moëlle épinière sur le comportement thermorégulateur du chien. *Pfluegers Arch.* 341:313–24
33. Crawford, E. C. 1972. Brain and body temperatures in a panting lizard. *Science* 177(4047):431–33
34. Crawshaw, L. I., Hammel, H. T. 1971. Behavioral thermoregulation in two species of antarctic fish. *Life Sci.* 10(17):1009–20
35. Crawshaw, L. I., Hammel, H. T. 1973. Behavioral temperature regulation in the California Horn Shark *Heterodontus francisci. Brain Behav. Evol.* 7:447–52
36. Duclaux, R., Fantino, M., Cabanac, M. 1973. Comportement thermorégulateur chez *Rana esculenta.* Influence du réchauffement spinal. *Pfluegers Arch.* 342:347–58
37. Ekblom, B., Greenleaf, C. J., Greenleaf, J. E., Hermansen, L. 1971. Temperature regulation during continuous and intermittent exercise in man. *Acta Physiol. Scand.* 81(1):1–10
38. Forrester, A. C., Bell, G., McDowall, D. G. 1969. The effect of hypothermia on skin blood flow in the dog. *Clin. Sci.* 36:419–26
39. Gagge, A. P., Hardy, J. D., Rapp, G. M. 1969. Proposed standard system of symbols for thermal physiology. *J. Appl. Physiol.* 26(3):439–46
40. Gale, C. C. 1973. Neuroendocrine aspects of thermoregulation. *Ann. Rev. Physiol.* 35:391–430
41. Gisolfi, C., Robinson, S. 1970. Central and peripheral stimuli regulating sweating during intermittent work in men. *J. Appl. Physiol.* 29(6):761–68
42. Guieu, J. D., Hardy, J. D. 1970. Effects of preoptic and spinal cord temperature in control of thermal polypnea. *J. Appl. Physiol.* 28(4):540–42
43. Hainsworth, F. R., Stricker, E. M. 1970. Salivary cooling by rats in the heat. See Ref. 6, 611–26
44. Hainsworth, F. R., Stricker, E. M. 1971. Relationship between body temperature and salivary secretion by rats in the heat. *J. Physiol. Paris* 63:257–59
45. Hales, J. R. S. 1973. Effects of exposure to hot environments on the regional distribution of blood flow and on cardiorespiratory function in sheep. *Pfluegers Arch.* 344(2):133–48
46. Hales, J. R. S. 1973. Effects of exposure to hot environments on total and regional blood flow in the brain and spinal cord of the sheep. *Pfluegers Arch.* 344(3):327–38
46a. Hammel, H. T. 1965. Neurons and temperature regulation. *Physiological Controls and Regulations,* ed. W. S. Yamamoto, J. R. Brobeck, 5:71–97. Philadelphia: Saunders
47. Hammel, H. T. 1968. Regulation of internal body temperature. *Ann. Rev. Physiol.* 30:641–710

48. Hammel, H. T. 1971. Cited by Matthews, S. W. and Curtsinger—Antartica's nearer side. *Nat. Geogr.* 140: 622–55
49. Hammel, H. T. 1972. The set point in temperature regulation: analogy or reality. In *Essays on Temperature Regulation,* ed. J. Bligh, R. E. Moore, 121–37. Amsterdam: North-Holland. 190 pp.
50. Hammel, H. T., Sharp, F. 1971. Thermoregulatory salivation in the running dog in response to preoptic heating and cooling. *J. Physiol. Paris* 63:260–63
51. Hayward, J. N., Baker, M. A. 1969. A comparative study of the role of the cerebral arterial blood in the regulation of brain temperature in five mammals. *Brain Res.* 16:417–40
52. Heinrich, B. 1972. Patterns of endothermy in bumblebee queens, drones and workers. *J. Comp. Physiol.* 77: 49–65
53. Heinrich, B., Bartholomew, G. A. 1972. Temperature control in flying moths, certain insects must warm up before taking off. *Sci. Am.* 226(6):70–77
54. Heistad, D. D., Abboud, F. M., Mark, A. L., Schmid, P. G. 1973. Interaction of thermal and baroreceptor reflexes in man. *J. Appl. Physiol.* 35(5):581–86
55. Hénane, R. 1972. La dépression sudorale au cours de l'hyperthermie contrôlée chez l'homme. *J. Physiol. Paris* 64:147–63
55a. Hensel, H. 1974. Thermoreceptors. *Ann. Rev. Physiol.* 36:233–49
56. Himms-Hagen, J. 1972. Lipid metabolism during cold-exposure and during cold-acclimation. *Lipids* 7(5):310–23
57. Horowitz, J. M., Erkine, L. K. 1973. Central regulation of temperature in cold environments. A dynamic model with two temperature inputs. *Comput. Biomed. Res.* 6(1):57–73
58. Houdas, Y., Sauvage, A., Bonaventure, M., Guieu, J. D. 1973. Modèle de la résponse évaporatoire à l'augmentation de la charge thermique. *J. Physiol. Paris* 66:137–61
59. Ingram, D. L., Legge, K. F. 1971. The influence of deep body temperatures and skin temperatures on peripheral blood flow in the pig. *J. Physiol. London* 215(3):693–708
60. Ingram, D., Legge, K. F. 1972. The influence of deep body temperatures and skin temperatures on respiratory frequency in the pig. *J. Physiol. London* 220(2): 183–296
61. Ingram, D. L., Legge, K. F. 1972. The influence of deep body and skin temperatures on thermoregulatory responses to heating of the scrotum in pigs. *J. Physiol. London* 224(2):477–87
62. Iriki, M. 1968. Anderung der Mautdurchblutung bei unnarkitusierten Kaninchen durch isolierte Wärmung des Rückenmarkes. *Pfluegers Arch.* 299: 295–310
63. Iriki, M., Riedel, W., Simon, E. 1971. Regional differentiation of sympathetic activity during hypothalamic heating and cooling in anesthetized rabbits. *Pfluegers Arch.* 328:320–31
64. Ishay, J. 1972. Thermoregulatory pheromones in wasps. *Experientia* 28: 1185–86
65. Jacobson, F. H., Squires, R. D. 1970. Thermoregulatory responses of the cat to preoptic and environmental temperatures. *Am. J. Physiol.* 218(6):1575–82
66. Jancso-Gabor, A., Szolcsanyi, J., Jancso, N. 1970. Irreversible impairment of thermoregulation induced by capsaicin and similar pungent substances in rats and guinea-pigs. *J. Physiol. London* 206(3):495–508
67. Jancso-Gabor, A., Szolcsanyi, J. 1970. Stimulation and desensitization of the hypothalamic heat-sensitive structures by capsaicin in rats. *J. Physiol. London* 208(2):449–59
68. Jansky, L. 1973. Non-shivering thermogenesis and its thermoregulatory significance. *Biol. Rev.* 48(1):85–132
69. Jequier, E. 1970. Reduced hypothalamic set point temperature during exercise in man. *Experientia* 26:681
70. Jessen, C., Clough, D. P. 1973. Evaluation of hypothalamic thermosensitivity by feedback signals. *Pfluegers Arch.* 345:43–59
71. Jessen, C., Clough, D. P. 1973. Assessment of spinal temperature sensitivity in conscious goats by feedback signals. *J. Comp. Physiol.* 87:75–88
72. Jessen, C., Ludwig, O. 1971. Spinal cord and hypothalamus as core sensors of temperature in the conscious dog. II —Addition of signals. *Pfluegers Arch.* 324(3):205–16
73. Jessen, C., Mayer, E. Th. 1971. Spinal cord and hypothalamus as core sensors of temperature in the conscious dog. I—Equivalence of response. *Pfluegers Arch.* 324(3):189–204
74. Jessen, C., McLean, J. A., Calvert, D. T., Findlay, J. D. 1972. Balanced and unbalanced temperature signals generated in spinal cord of the ox. *Am. J. Physiol.* 222(6):1343–47

75. Jessen, C., Simon, E. 1971. Spinal cord and hypothalamus as core sensors of temperature in the conscious dog. III—Identity of functions. *Pfluegers Arch.* 324(1):217–26
76. Johnson, C. R. 1972. Head-body temperature differences in Varanus gouldii (Saurai: Vanaridae). *Comp. Biochem. Physiol.* 43(4):1025–29
77. Johnson, J. M., Niederberger, M., Rowell, L. B., Eisman, M. M., Brengelmann, G. L. 1973. Competition between cutaneous vasodilator and vasoconstrictor reflexes in man. *J. Appl. Physiol.* 35(6):798–803
78. Johnson, K. G. 1973. Sweat storage as a factor influencing sweat discharge in sheep. *J. Physiol. London* 235(2): 523–34
79. Kammer, A. E., Heinrich, B. 1972. Neural control of bumblebee fibrillar muscles during shivering. *J. Comp. Physiol.* 78(4):337–45
80. Kerslake, D. M. 1972. *The Stress of Hot Environment.* London: Cambridge Univ. Press. 376 pp.
81. Kluger, M. J., Gonzalez, R. R., Stolwijk, J. A. J. 1973. Temperature regulation in the exercising rabbit. *Am. J. Physiol.* 224(1):130–35
82. Kosaka, M., Simon, E., Thauer, R., Walther, O. E. 1969. Effect of thermal stimulation of spinal cord on respiratory and cortical activity. *Am. J. Physiol.* 217(3):858–63
83. Kullmann, R., Schonung, W., Simon, E. 1970. Antagonistic changes of blood flow and sympathetic activity in different vascular beds following central thermal stimulation. I—Blood flow in skin muscle and intestine during spinal cord heating and cooling in anesthetized dogs. *Pfluegers Arch.* 319:146–61
84. Lepkovsky, S., Snapir, N., Furuta, F. 1968. Temperature regulation and appetitive behavior in chickens with hypothalamic lesions. *Physiol. Behav.* 3: 911–17
85. Lillywhite, H. B. 1971. Thermal modulation of cutaneous mucus discharge as a determinant of evaporative water loss in the frog, *Rana catesbiana. Z. Vergl. Physiol.* 73:84–104
86. Lin, M. T., Yin, T. H., Chai, C. Y. 1972. Effects of heating and cooling of spinal cord on CV and respiratory responses and food and water intake. *Am. J. Physiol.* 223(3):626–31
87. Linthicum, D. S., Carey, F. G. 1972. Regulation of brain and eye temperatures by the bluefin tuna. *Comp. Biochem. Physiol.* 43(2):425–33
88. Lipton, J. M. 1968. Effects of preoptic lesions on heat escape responding and colonic temperature in the rat. *Physiol. Behav.* 3(1):165–69
89. Lipton, J. M. 1971. Behavioral temperature regulation in the rat: effect of thermal stimulation of the medulla. *J. Physiol. Paris* 63:325–28
90. Lyszczarz, J. 1972. Contribution des stimulations thermiques périphériques et centrales à l'apparition de la polypnée chez le lapin. *Acta Physiol. Polon.* 23(5): 781–87
91. Magilton, J. M., Swift, C. S. 1969. Responses of veins draining the nose to alar fold temperature changes in the dog. *J. Appl. Physiol.* 27:18–21
92. Marcus, P. 1972. Heat acclimatization by exercise induced elevation of body temperature. *J. Appl. Physiol.* 33:283–88
93. Maskrey, M., Bligh, J. 1972. The impairment of the thermoregulatory set point of a sheep in the apparent absence of any interference with the pathways between temperature sensors and thermoregulatory effectors. *Experientia* 29(7):792–93
94. Mills, S. H., Heath, J. E. 1972. Responses to thermal stimulation of the preoptic area in the house sparrow. *Am. J. Physiol.* 222(4):914–19
95. Minaire, Y., Vincent-Falquet, J. C., Pernod, A., Chatonnet, J. 1973. Energy supply in acute cold exposed dogs. *J. Appl. Physiol.* 35(1):51–57
96. Mitchell, D., Atkins, A. R., Wyndham, C. H. 1972. Mathematical and physical models of thermoregulation. See Ref. 49, 37–54
97. Mitchell, D., Snellen, J. W., Atkins, A. R. 1970. Thermoregulation during fever: change of set-point or change in gain. *Pfluegers Arch.* 321(4):293–304
98. Murgatroyd, D., Hardy, J. D. 1970. Central and peripheral temperatures in behavioral thermoregulation of the rat. See Ref. 6, 874–91
99. Myhre, K., Hammel, H. T. 1969. Behavioral regulation of internal temperature in the lizard *Tiliqua scincoides. Am. J. Physiol.* 217(5):1490–95
100. Myhre, K., Hellstrøm, B. 1973. Thermoregulation in exercising white rats. 1973. *Can. J. Physiol.* 51:814–24
101. Nadel, E. R., Bergh, U., Saltin, B. 1972. Body temperatures during negative work exercise. *J. Appl. Physiol.* 33(5): 553–58

102. Nadel, E. R., Holmer, I., Bergh, U., Astrand, P. O., Stolwijk, J. A. J. 1973. Thermoregulatory shivering during exercise. *Life Sci.* 13:983–89
103. Nadel, E. R., Horvath, S. M., Dawson, L. A., Tucker, A. 1970. Sensitivity to central and peripheral thermal stimulation in man. *J. Appl. Physiol.* 29(5): 603–9
104. Nadel, E. R., Mitchell, J. W., Stolwijk, J. A. J. 1973. Differential thermal sensitivity in the human skin. *Pfluegers Arch.* 340:71–76
105. Nadel, E. R., Stolwijk, J. A. J. 1971. Physiological control of local sweat secretion in man. *J. Physiol. Paris* 63:353–55
106. Nadel, E. R., Stolwijk, J. A. J. 1973. Effect of skin wettedness on sweat gland response. *J. Appl. Physiol.* 35(5):689–94
106a. Nicolaidis, S. 1970. Réflexe potohidrotique et son rôle dans la régulation thermique et hydro-minérale. *Arch. Sci. Physiol.* 24:397–408
107. Nielsen, B. 1969. Thermoregulation in rest and exercise. *Acta Physiol. Scand.* Suppl. 323
108. Nielsen, B., Nielsen, S. L., Petersen, F. B. 1972. Thermoregulation during positive and negative work at different environmental temperatures. *Acta Physiol. Scand.* 85(2):249–57
109. Paul, P., Holmes, W. L. 1973. FFA metabolism in thyroidectomized and normal dogs during rest and acute cold exposure. *J. Appl. Physiol.* 35(2):250–58
110. Pedersen, L. 1973. *The Thermoregulation of Man.* Copenhagen: H. C. Ørsted Institut Køбenhavn Universitet. 56 pp.
111. Pirnay, F., Petit, J. M., Deroanne, R. 1969. Evolution comparée de la fréquence cardiaque et de la température corporelle pendant l'exercice musculaire à haute température. *Int. Z. Angew. Physiol.* 28(1):23–31
112. Ploye, H., Buatois, A. 1969. Recherches sur la température interne du corps chez les femelles de *Blaberus craniifer* Burmeister. Relations avec l'activité et le poids. *C. R. Acad. Sci.* 269(6):728–30
113. Rautenberg, W. 1969. Die Bedeutung der Zentralnervösen Thermosensitivität für die Temperaturregulation der Taube. *Z. Vergl. Physiol.* 62:235–66
114. Rautenberg, W. 1971. The influence of the skin temperature on the thermoregulatory system of pigeons. *J. Physiol. Paris* 63:396–98
115. Rautenberg, W., Necker, R. May, B. 1972. Thermoregulatory responses of the pigeon to changes of the brain and the spinal cord temperatures. *Pfluegers Arch.* 338(1):31–42
116. Rawson, R. O., Quick, K. P. 1970. Evidence of deep-body thermoreceptor response to intra-abdominal heating of the ewe. *J. Appl. Physiol.* 28(6):813–20
117. Rawson, R. O., Quick, K. P. 1971. Unilateral splanchnotomy: its effect on the response to intra-abdominal heating in the ewe. *Pfluegers Arch.* 930:362–65
118. Raynaud, J., Varene, P., Viellefond, H., Durand, J. 1973. *Circulation cutanée et échanges thermiques en altitude (3800 m).* Presented at Colloque international "Prévisions quantitatives des effets physiologique et psychologique de l'environnement thermique sur l'homme." C.N.R.S., Strasbourg
119. Richards, S. A. 1970. The role of hypothalamic temperature in the control of panting in the chicken exposed to heat. *J. Physiol. London* 211(2):341–58
120. Richards, S. A. 1971. The significance of changes in the temperature of the skin and body core of the chicken in the regulation of heat loss. *J. Physiol. London* 216(1):1–10
121. Riedel, W., Iriki, M., Simon, E. 1972. Regional differentiation of sympathetic activity during peripheral heating and cooling in anesthetized rabbits. *Pfluegers Arch.* 332(3):239–47
121a. Reidel, W., Siaplauras, G., Simon, E. 1973. Intra-abdominal thermosensitivity in the rabbit as compared with spinal thermosensitivity. *Pfluegers Arch.* 340:59–70
122. Roberts, W. W., Mooney, R. D. 1974. Brain areas controlling thermoregulatory grooming, prone extension, locomotion, and tail vasodilation in rats. *J. Comp. Physiol. Psychol.* 86(3):470–80
123. Rowell, L. B., Detry, J. M., Profant, G. R., Wyss, C. 1971. Splanchnic vasoconstriction in hyperthermic man role of falling blood pressure. *J. Appl Physiol.* 31:864–69
124. Saltin, B., Gagge, A. P. 1971. Sweating and body temperatures during exercise. *Int. J. Biometeorol.* 15:189–94
125. Saltin, B., Gagge, A. P., Stolwijk, J. A. J. 1970. Body temperatures and sweating during thermal transients caused by exercise. *J. Appl. Physiol.* 28(3):318–27
126. Satinoff, E., Rutstein, J. 1970. Behavioral thermoregulation in rats with anterior hypothalamic lesions. *J. Comp. Physiol. Psychol.* 71(1):77–82

127. Satinoff, E., Shan, S. S. Y. 1971. Loss of behavioral thermoregulation after lateral hypothalamic lesions in rats. *J. Comp. Physiol. Psychol.* 77(2):302–12
128. Sato, K. 1973. Sweat induction from an isolated sweat gland. *Am. J. Physiol.* 225(5):1147–52
129. Schonung, W., Wagner, H., Jessen, C., Simon, E. 1971. Differentiation of cutaneous and intestinal blood flow during hypothalamic heating and cooling in anesthetized dogs. *Pfluegers Arch.* 328:145–54
130. Senay, L. C. Jr. 1970. Movement of water protein and crystalloids between vascular and extravascular compartments in heat-exposed men during dehydration and following limited relief of dehydration. *J. Physiol. London* 210: 617–35
131. Senay, L. C. Jr. 1972. Changes in plasma volume and protein content during exposures of working men to various temperatures before and after acclimatization to heat: separation of the roles of cutaneous and skeletal muscle circulation. *J. Physiol. London* 224: 61–81
132. Sharp, F. R., Hammel, H. T. 1972. Effects of fever on salivation response in the resting and exercising dog. *Am. J. Physiol.* 223:77–82
133. Sharp, F., Smith, D., Thompson, M., Hammel, H. T. 1969. Thermoregulatory salivation proportional to hypothalamic temperature above threshold in the dog. *Life Sci.* 8(Pt 1):1069–76
134. Slepchuk, N. A., Ivanov, K. P. 1972. On the thermo-sensitive interoceptors and their interaction with the hypothalamic thermo-sensitive structures. *Fiziol. Zh. SSSR* 58(10):1494–98
135. Snellen, J. W. 1972. Set point and exercise. See Ref. 49, 139–48
136. Squires, R. D., Jacobson, F. H. 1968. Chronic deficits of temperature regulation produced in cats by preoptic lesions. *Am. J. Physiol.* 214(3):549–60
137. Stitt, J. T., Adair, E. R., Nadel, E. R., Stolwijk, J. A. J. 1971. The relation between behavior and physiology in the thermoregulatory response of the squirrel monkey. *J. Physiol. Paris* 63(3): 424–27
138. Stolwijk, J. A. J., Nadel, E. R. 1973. Thermoregulation during positive and negative work exercise. *Fed. Proc.* 32:1607–13
139. Stricker, E. M., Hainsworth, F. R. 1970. Evaporative cooling in the rat: effects of hypothalamic lesions and chorda tympani damage. *Can. J. Physiol. Pharmacol.* 48(1):11–18
139a. Ström, G. 1960. Central nervous regulation of body temperature. *Handbook of Physiology, II Neurophysiology,* 1173
140. Stussi, Th. 1972. Réaction de thermogénèse au froid chez la guêpe ouvrière et autres hyminoptères sociaux. *C. R. Acad. Sci.* 274:2687–89
141. Tabatabai, M. 1972. Respiratory and cardiovascular responses resulting from cooling the medulla oblongata in cats. *Am. J. Physiol.* 223(1):8–12
142. Taylor, C. R. 1970. Strategies of temperature regulation: effect on evaporation in East African ungulates. *Am. J. Physiol.* 219:1131–35
143. Taylor, C. R., Lyman, C. P. 1972. Heat storage in running antelopes: independance of brain and body temperatures. *Am. J. Physiol.* 222(1):114–17
143a. Thauer, R. 1970. Thermosensitivity of the spinal cord. See Ref. 6, 472–92
144. Toth, D. M. 1973. Temperature regulation and salivation following preoptic lesions in the rat. *J. Comp. Physiol. Psychol.* 82(3):480–88
145. Trautmann, A., Hill, H. 1949. Temperaturmessungen im Pansen und Labmagen des Wiederkäuers (Ziege). *Pfluegers Arch.* 252:30–39
146. Turlejska-Stelmasiak, E. 1973. Thermoregulatory responses to hypothalamic heating in dehydrated rabbits. *Experientia* 29(1):51–52
147. Vanhoutte, P. M., Shepherd, J. T. 1970. Effect of temperature on reactivity of isolated cutaneous veins of the dog. *Am. J. Physiol.* 218:187–90
148. Vanhoutte, P. M., Shepherd, J. T. 1971. Thermosensitivity and veins. *J. Physiol. Paris* 63:449–51
149. Wakeman, K. A., Donovick, P. J., Burright, R. G. 1970. Septal lesions increase bar pressing for heat in animals maintained in the cold. *Physiol. Behav.* 5:1193–95
150. Walther, O. E., Iriki, M., Simon, E. 1970. Antagonistic changes of blood flow and sympathetic activity in different vascular beds following central thermal stimulation. II Cutaneous and visceral sympathetic activity during spinal cord heating and cooling in anesthetized rabbits and cats. *Pfluegers Arch.* 319:162–84
151. Walther, O. E., Simon, E., Jessen, C. 1971. Thermoregulatory adjustments of skin blood flow in chronically spinalized dogs. *Pfluegers Arch.* 332(4):323–35

152. Webb, G. J. W., Johnson, C. R. 1972. Head-body temperature differences in turtles. *Comp. Biochem. Physiol.* 43(3): 593–611
153. Webb, G. J. W., Johnson, C. R., Firth, B. 1972. Head-body temperature differences in lizards. *Physiol. Zool.* 45(2): 130–42
154. Webb, P., Annis, J. F. 1968. Cooling required to suppress sweating during work. *J. Appl. Physiol.* 25:489–94
154a. Weiss, B. 1957. Thermal behaviour of the subnourished pantothenic-acid-deprived rat. *J. Comp. Physiol. Psychol.* 50:481–85
155. Williams, B. A., Heath, J. E. 1970. Responses to preoptic heating and cooling in a hibernator *Citellus tridecemlineatus. Am. J. Physiol.* 218(6): 1654–60
156. Williams, B. A., Heath, J. E. 1971. Thermoregulatory responses of a hibernator to preoptic and environmental temperatures. *Am. J. Physiol.* 221(4): 1134–38
157. Woods, J. J., Whittow, G. C. 1974. The role of central and peripheral temperature changes in the regulation of thermal polypnea in the chicken. *Life Sci.* 14(1):199–206
158. Wünnenberg, W., Brück, K. 1968. Zur Funktionsweise thermoreceptiver Strukturen im Cervicalmark des Meerschweichens. *Pfluegers Arch.* 299: 1–10
159. Wurster, R. D., McCook, R. D. 1969. Influence of rate of change in skin temperature on sweating. *J. Appl. Physiol.* 27:237–40
160. Wyndham, C. H. 1973. The physiology of exercise under heat stress. *Ann. Rev. Physiol.* 35:193–220
161. Wyndham, C. H., Atkins, A. R. 1968. A physiological scheme and mathematical model of temperature regulation in man. *Pfluegers Arch.* 303:14–30
162. Zanick, O. C., Delaney, J. P. 1973. Temperature influences on anteriovenous anastomoses. *Exp. Biol. Med.* 144(2):616–91

Copyright 1975. All rights reserved

AVIAN PHYSIOLOGY ❖1138

William R. Dawson[1]
Department of Zoology, The University of Michigan, Ann Arbor, Michigan 48104

Research on the physiology of birds has grown enormously in recent years. Much of this growth is, of course, a manifestation of the importance of certain domesticated species in food production, and some of it also reflects the suitability of certain birds as experimental subjects in some types of physiological investigations. However, it also is a testimonial to the fact that birds are inherently interesting animals with frequently elaborate behaviors, spectacular powers of locomotion, and impressive regulatory capacities. Their evolution from a reptilian stock quite distinct from that giving rise to their fellow homeotherms, the mammals, makes consideration of certain of these regulatory capacities intriguing from a comparative standpoint.

Various facets of avian physiology have been extensively treated in monographs, symposia, and review articles or chapters over the past five years. The volumes of *Avian Biology* (64) represent a particularly useful source of information. With this wealth of material available, and considering limitations of space, it seems appropriate in this article to adopt an eclectic approach. The topics selected for discussion should provide a basis for examining the ways in which birds resemble or differ from other vertebrates, especially mammals, in the means by which they meet common functional requirements.

SOME ENERGETIC CONSIDERATIONS

Most aspects of avian physiology considered here are directly related to energetics or the consequences of catabolic processes, and it is thus pertinent to include a few statements on metabolic rates of birds. These rates tend to vary with a fractional power of body mass, as in most animals. Earlier analyses (29, 95) suggested that the exponent in the allometric equation relating basal metabolic rate (BMR) to body mass was lower than that reported for eutherian mammals (98). Subsequently, this was shown to be an artifact of lumping data for orders of birds differing substantially in metabolic level (107). When the data are analyzed properly an exponent near 0.75 is obtained. This is of interest in view of a recent analysis of physiological scaling

[1]Preparation of this review supported in part by Grant GB-25022 from the National Science Foundation.

(115) that suggests elastic stability and flexure ultimately determine that metabolic parameters of animals should vary with mass$^{0.75}$.

Metabolic rates of birds are subject to circadian oscillations, with the rate prevailing during the inactive (ρ) phase of the daily cycle running approximately 20% lower than that during the active (α) phase. The currently accepted equations (7) relating BMR ($\dot{H}_{bm}$ in W) to body mass in members of the order Passeriformes are $\dot{H}_{bm} = 6.82 \text{ kg}^{0.70}$ (for α) and $\dot{H}_{bm} = 5.56 \text{ kg}^{0.73}$ (for ρ). The corresponding equations for other birds are $\dot{H}_{bm} = 4.41 \text{ kg}^{0.73}$ and $\dot{H}_{bm} = 3.56 \text{ kg}^{0.73}$, respectively. These equations describe the lower boundary for the metabolic rates of euthermic animals at rest in a postabsorptive condition. The upper boundary for resting animals, the summit metabolism ($\dot{H}_{sum}$ in W), has not been investigated in many species. The equation based on existing data for both passeriform and nonpasseriform birds stimulated to maximum thermogenesis by severe cold is $\dot{H}_{sum} = 20.2 \text{ kg}^{0.65}$ (35). While substantially greater than $\dot{H}_{bm}$, summit metabolic rates do not approach the power inputs (P_i in W) associated with flight. One expression for these, based on data for several species, is $P_i = 52.9 \text{ kg}^{0.73}$ (79). Flight energetics is considered later in this review.

NEURAL CONTROL OF THERMOREGULATION AND FEEDING

Thermogenic, thermolytic, and behavioral activities contributing to homeothermy in birds have received extensive review over the past few years (36, 52, 53). A topic meriting further attention concerns the location and function of the neural components controlling thermoregulation. Some information on this has been obtained by selective destruction of tissue in the hypothalamic-preoptic area (H/POA). Production of lesions there impaired temperature regulation in the domestic fowl (66, 90, 112) and in the house sparrow *Passer domesticus* (122). Thermodes have been implanted in the anterior hypothalamus/POA of this latter bird (123). Cooling of this area elicited increases in O_2 consumption ($\dot{V}O_2$) and body temperature (T_b). Opposite effects were obtained with heating. The responses resembled those described for mammals (77). Extracranial receptors seemed involved in the response of the house sparrow, since changes in $\dot{V}O_2$ and T_b occurred only after a displacement of core temperature following heating or cooling with the thermode (123).

Earlier investigations (1) established that electrical stimulation of the medial POA elicited panting in the pigeon (*Columba livia*). Recent studies of domestic fowl indicate that extracranial deep body receptors, as well as peripheral units, affect this thermolytic process (147, 148).

Observations on pigeons with thermodes chronically implanted in the vertebral column and, in some cases, in the brain stem permit examination of where the primary control of avian thermoregulation resides. Selective heating or cooling of the vertebral column in unanesthetized birds produced distinct thermoregulatory responses without any change in hypothalamic temperature (T_h). At ambient temperatures (T_a) of 27–30°C and normal core and skin temperatures, cooling of the spinal cord induced shivering and a rise in T_b (144). Selective heating of the spinal cord at T_as of 27–30°C evoked thermal panting and cutaneous vasodilatation in the feet. On the other hand, cooling of the spinal cord of animals panting at T_as of 36–37°C lowered respiratory frequency to resting values (144).

Experimental manipulation of both skin and spinal cord temperatures provides evidence of a proportional control system in which the thermal set point for the spinal cord can be modified by changes in skin temperature (145). Manipulation of the temperatures of both the brain stem and the spinal cord provides further indication of the importance of the latter region in thermoregulation. Lowering the brain temperature to 36°C in pigeons maintained at T_as of 27–30°C did not produce shivering. Furthermore, neither simultaneous cooling of the brain and spinal cord nor heating the brain and cooling the spinal cord modified the intensity of shivering from that obtained with cooling of the spinal cord alone. Selective heating of the brain stem to 44°C seldom induced panting, whereas heating the spinal cord to 42–43°C generally resulted in polypnea under thermoneutral conditions. In hot environments, heating of the spinal cord and cooling the brain stem inhibited panting in only a quarter of the cases. On the other hand, cooling the spinal cord often inhibited panting. Ptiloerection and peripheral vasoconstriction followed simultaneous cooling of the spinal cord and brain stem. The contributions of the two regions to stimulation of these heat-conserving activities appeared similar in extent (146). Signals generated in the brain stem of the pigeon seem primarily to affect heat-conserving activities serving to stabilize T_b under mild thermal loads. Under stronger thermal stress, heating or cooling of the spinal cord serves to activate shivering or panting; this permits the bird to evade hyperthermia or hypothermia.

Despite the obvious importance of peripheral thermoreception in avian temperature regulation, relatively little is known of the units involved. Cold receptors exist in the tongues of the domestic fowl, pigeons, and ducks (97, 108). Those of the duck appear to be free nerve endings and are both less sensitive than cutaneous cold receptors of mammals and insensitive to mechanical stimulation.

Warmth receptors have been demonstrated in the internal face of the pigeon's bill (126, 127) during recording from all three branches of the trigeminal nerve. These showed an increased impulse frequency with warming, but no excitatory overshoot occurred. A special "warmth sensitive" receptor with a regular discharge rate at high skin temperature was totally inhibited by cooling. It regained its initial frequency without any overshoot after rewarming. The impulse frequency of this receptor did not respond to increasing skin temperature above a certain level, but remained constant. Slowly adapting mechanoreceptors were detected; most of these had regular high impulse frequencies that decreased during cooling without any excitatory overshoot and increased during warming without inhibition. Like temperature-sensitive mammalian mechanoreceptors, a few of the slowly adapting mechanoreceptors in the pigeon's bill were excited by cooling and inhibited by warming (127).

Thermally sensitive receptor units have also been observed in the bills of ducks (76, 108). These units appear to be free nerve endings with receptor fields of only a few square millimeters. Their responses to temperature have both static and dynamic components. Warming consistently produced a transient decrease or inhibition of firing rate if the temperature change was rapid. Cooling resulted in a transient, marked rise in firing rate. Following equilibration, this rate declined to a stable level characteristic for the temperature. The maximum stable rate tended to occur in the middle of the range of temperatures over which responses were present (76).

Aspects of fat metabolism and thermogenesis in birds are considered later in this review. It is thus useful to summarize briefly some of the information pertaining to neural control of food intake in these animals. Properly placed hypothalamic lesions have been known for some time to affect feeding behavior. Domestic fowl became aphagic following production of bilateral lesions in the mid and posterior hypothalamus (66). On the other hand, placement of lesions in approximately the ventromedial region of the hypothalamus resulted in hyperphagia that was sometimes accompanied by impairment of gonadotropin release (111). Ventromedial lesions in this portion of the brain also produced hyperphagia in the white-throated sparrow *Zonotrichia albicollis* (103). A dual hypothalamic system was characterized for this bird. Damage to the ventromedial hypothalamus was followed by hyperphagia and obesity, whereas bilateral lesions in the hypothalamus resulted in permanent aphagia (103). These observations and results of electrical stimulation indicate that the ventromedial and lateral hypothalamus inhibit and stimulate feeding, respectively, in a manner serving to regulate the size of fat deposits. However, these central neural components are only parts of a complex system that also seems to include peripheral receptors in the upper digestive tract (139) and such chemical factors as androgens (110) and cyclic AMP (3).

RESPIRATION OF BIRDS PRIOR TO HATCHING

Prehatching respiration of birds involves some special considerations without parallel in mammals, except in the monotremes. These considerations are indicated by the situation of chicks of the domestic fowl during the prehatching period. While gas exchange does not appear to be a problem initially (9), these developing birds increase their metabolic rates more than 1000-fold over the period of enclosure within a rigid shell of fixed area and thickness (149). Several recent summaries of gas exchange in the avian egg are available (8, 167, 184, 184a).

The overall pathway of gas diffusion between ambient air and the chorioallantoic capillary blood involves two components, the $CaCO_3$ shell and the proteinaceous shell membranes (see 185 for illustrations). This pathway is extended at the blunt end of the egg, as continued water loss permits the formation of an air cell there between the shell membranes. The shell is porous, being perforated in the egg of the domestic fowl by approximately 10,000 narrow funnel-shaped pores with an aggregate cross sectional area of approximately 2 mm^2 (185). The outer and inner shell membranes, which appear to contain gas rather than liquid in their interstices (104), and a thin tissue layer separating the inner shell membrane from the chorioallantoic capillaries constitute the entire diffusion pathway within the egg, except beneath the air cell (184). The chorioallantoic capillaries comprise the principal respiratory organ of the developing chick in all but the initial and terminal stages of incubation.

The diffusion capacity for CO along this pathway is affected by the ambient concentration of O_2; incubation of the egg in 60% O_2 substantially reduced this capacity from control values. This reduction is thought to result from a less extensive development of the chorioallantoic network, an increased thickness of the diffusion barrier between blood and air, or both (172). Experimental restriction of the shell surface area across which gas exchange can occur or exposing the chick to hypobaric conditions led to increases in hematocrit in the latter stages of incubation (33, 171). In normal chicks, the oxygen affinity of the blood is substantially higher prior to hatching than afterwards. The Bohr effect is similar in embryos and older birds (10, see section on oxygen transport).

The capillary network of the chorioallantois develops over the first half of incubation, coming to lie near the inner surface of the shell everywhere except beneath the air cell. It completely surrounds the embryo and egg contents by the twelfth day of incubation, covering the inner surface of the inner shell membrane (172, 184). The network has a fine reticulate formation unlike that of mammalian alveolar capillaries (171a). Near the end of incubation the lungs of the chick have developed sufficiently to assist in respiration and they do so after the chick makes a hole through the allantois allowing its bill to reach into the air space (49, 172). As hatching approaches, gas exchange between the air space and the chick becomes progressively more important. Hatching appears to be stimulated by the high P_{CO_2} and low P_{O_2} that ultimately develop in the air space (182).

Wangensteen et al (185) concluded from their determination of the coefficient for diffusion of O_2 across the egg shell of the domestic fowl that the main resistance to diffusion is the shell itself. They also calculated the diffusion coefficients for CO_2 and water vapor. Their belief that the egg shell is the principal barrier to diffusion was predicated on the assumption that the shell membranes are dry. Observations pertaining to this assumption have been made by Kutchai & Steen (104), who noted that the inital permeabilities of the shell and shell membranes are insufficient to permit the rates of gas exchange that must occur toward the end of incubation. The permeability increased with incubation in fertilized eggs, but not in unfertilized ones, reaching levels that by day 6 were compatible with completion of the prehatching phase of development. Contrary to Wangensteen et al's (185) interpretation, Kutchai & Steen (104) concluded that the resistance of O_2 diffusion is about equally divided between the shell and shell membranes from day 6 of incubation on. The changes in permeability occurring in fertilized eggs appeared to be associated with the drying of the shell membranes; the water content of these declined from 70% to 40% over the first 17 days of incubation, with almost two thirds of the loss occurring by day 6. Shell membranes of unfertilized eggs lost relatively little of their water over comparable periods (104).

Once the overall gas permeability of the shell and the shell membranes has stabilized, the increasing metabolic activity of the growing embryo inevitably leads to an increase in internal P_{CO_2}, until the approximate time of the onset of breathing near hatching (72). These trends have been documented by several groups (51, 60, 72). Although some disagreement exists concerning the maximum CO_2 tensions normally attained, there is some concensus that pH remains fairly stable over the entire incubation period. This stability results from a buildup of [HCO_3^-] and an increase in buffering capacity associated with increased concentrations of hemoglobin in the blood (60). The respiratory acidosis that develops over the incubation period may be completely compensated (60). Carbonate liberated with the mobilization of calcium from the shell over the incubation period assists in this compensation, but this mobilization can be depressed by hypercapnia (46a). It has been suggested that only partial compensation for respiratory acidosis occurs (75). The embryo has also been thought to encounter respiratory alkalosis with metabolic acidosis in the middle of the incubation period (170). The results of various studies on conditions within the fertile egg during incubation suggest that the developing chick must be well adjusted for operation at low oxygen tensions. Freeman & Mission (72) noted that the Pa_{O_2} for chicks prior to hatching is at a level not encountered in man until an altitude of 6096 m is reached. Under experimental conditions leading to asphyxia, increased P_{CO_2} in the fluids of the egg appears to constitute a more immediate threat to the chick than reduced P_{O_2} (50).

The ultimate factors that have influenced the evolution of the avian egg have led to a balance between the requirements for water conservation and for exchange of O_2 and CO_2. Over the 21 day incubation period of the domestic fowl, the developing chick consumes approximately 5 liters of O_2 and gives off 4 liters of CO_2 and 10 liters of water vapor (167). Water vapor conductance, shell thickness, and functional pore area of avian eggs vary with the 0.78, 0.46, and 1.24 powers of egg mass, respectively (6a). The relations of water vapor conductance, incubation, time, and rate of water loss in the nest to egg mass are such that the typical egg loses 18% of its mass as water during incubation (142a). The fact that the rates at which O_2 and CO_2 are exchanged rise dramatically over the incubation period, while water loss remains essentially constant, is influenced by the presence of a dry cuticle that constitutes a barrier around the shell to diffusion of water vapor (167).

RESPIRATION OF BIRDS AFTER HATCHING

Birds are active animals with extensive requirements for respiratory gas exchange in connection with thermoregulation and locomotion. In meeting these requirements they have evolved a respiratory system differing in some fundamental ways from the homologous system in mammals. A significant fraction of the literature concerning the physiology of avian respiration has been reviewed recently (105) and a detailed functional anatomic description of the respiratory system has been provided (56, 92). The operation of this system is sufficiently intriguing and distinct from that of mammals to make brief consideration of some of the recent literature on its properties worthwhile.

The avian respiratory tract includes relatively uncompliant lungs that undergo only minor volume changes during the respiratory cycle, owing in part to the attachment of their dorsal surfaces to the thoracic wall. The lungs are associated with anterior and posterior groups of air sacs. The trachea divides into two primary bronchi, each of which passes through a lung, ultimately connecting with one of the abdominal air sacs. In its posterior passage, the primary bronchus gives off at its hilus several craniomedial secondary bronchi and, posteriorly, 7–10 caudodorsal secondary bronchi, as well as some caudoventral secondary bronchi connecting with the ipsilateral caudal thoracic air sac. The craniomedial and caudodorsal bronchi are connected by tertiary bronchi, also called parabronchi. These are surrounded by rings of smooth muscle arranged in intervals of 100 μm or more and partially connected with adjacent rings by oblique strands. Atria emanate from the tertiary bronchi in these intervals, giving rise in turn to infundibula, from which air capillaries arise. These air capillaries are 3–10 μm in diameter and extensively anastamose with one another in all directions. They are surrounded by a network of blood capillaries that just fill the interstices. The interlaced blood and air capillaries form a mantle, 50–100 μm thick around each tertiary bronchus. The dense packing and small diameter of the air capillaries allows a very large exchange surface per unit volume in comparison with that of mammals, whose minimal alveolar diameter is approximately 35 μm (56). Collapse of the narrow air capillaries is prevented by surfactants (73), by a rigid tube-like structure, and by the relative constancy of the volume of the avian lung. The air capillaries evidently rely on diffusion with the tertiary bronchi, but dead space is minimized.

The respiratory motions serving to effect inspiration involve the ribs and sternum. During this phase of respiration, the coracoids, furcula, and sternal ribs are deflected forward and thereby produce a forward and downward movement of the sternum. This is accompanied by a strong lateral movement of the ribs lying caudal to the lungs. The internal pressure reduction produced within the body cavity by these movements leads to expansion of the air sacs. The muscles involved in these movements are dissociated from those involved in flight, and thus the respiratory movements can proceed without being disturbed by use of the wings (56). However, these movements do tend to be coordinated with wing movements in most birds, although the respiratory frequencies are often below wing beat frequencies (14, 178).

The system involving direct connection via tertiary bronchi between caudodorsal and craniomedial secondary bronchi is present in all birds and is the one to which the experimental analyses of air flow cited subsequently apply. However, it is the exclusive arrangement only in such "primitive" forms as penguins and emus and has in consequence been termed the "paleopulmo." Other birds have an additional connecting network of tertiary bronchi between the primary bronchi and posterior air sacs that has been termed the "neopulmo" (56). In its most extensive development this additional network occupies up to a quarter of the lung volume. In some species it can reach an extent in which its tertiary bronchi also originate from the initial segments of the caudodorsal secondary bronchi, and in others it is so developed that the neopulmo extends craniad and connects with lateral branches of the craniomedial secondary bronchi. This effectively connects the neopulmo with some of the anterior air sacs at the lateral margins of the lungs (see 56 for illustrations and more detailed description).

The avian respiratory system presents some distinct contrasts to its mammalian counterpart. The total lung capacity of birds is smaller than that of mammals (106) and the calculated dead space for the domestic fowl is 25% versus 40% in the dog (138). Despite somewhat more compact lungs, the total volume of the respiratory system is threefold greater in birds than in mammals of comparable size (106). This is primarily due to the air sacs, but it also reflects a greater tracheal volume in the birds (82). With respect to ventilation, tidal volume and respiratory frequency are approximately 1.7 and 0.3 times, respectively, those of mammals of comparable size (106).

Information permitting analysis of the pathway of air flow through the exchange areas of the avian lung has been obtained by a variety of ingenious techniques. Pressure fluctuations in the anterior and posterior air sacs of unanesthetized geese were found to be in phase and of similar amplitude; this led to the conclusion that these sacs filled and emptied simultaneously (46). Small pressure differences were subsequently noted between air sacs during the breathing of anesthetized geese (22). In unanesthetized domestic fowl, it was concluded that pressure differentials, which amount to approximately 10% of the parent pressure waves, are part of the equilibrium distribution of pressure within the respiratory system. These differentials appear to result from differences in resistances through the lung to the air sacs and differences in tidal volumes of these sacs. The resistances to air flow of the bronchial pathways to the posterior air sacs are generally greater than those to the anterior sacs. During vocalization, pressures in the coelom and air sacs may reach approximately 40 times normal as a result of occlusion of the upper airway (24). The overall amplitude of the pressure changes during respiration is quite small, approximating 0.3×10^{-3} atm in quiet breathing by the ostrich *Struthio camelus* (157). Pressure differences between anterior and posterior air sacs in this bird also were only about 10% of inhalation or exhalation pressures. Similarly, low pressure amplitudes have been noted in domestic fowl and ducks (21).

Concentrations of O_2 and CO_2 in posterior air sacs of several species have been found generally to be higher and lower, respectively, than those observed in the anterior air sacs (21, 23, 138). This has been interpreted as showing that air in the former structures has not passed over the exchange surfaces of the lungs, whereas that in the latter has. Studies of the ostrich afforded further insight concerning flows. Though incapable of flight, this large bird has extensively developed air sacs. Most of the anterior sacs showed higher CO_2 and lower O_2 concentrations than the posterior air sacs. However, oscillations in gas concentration could occur in a given sac. A slug of O_2 introduced into the system during inspiration appeared in the posterior air sacs in the same respiratory cycle. The O_2 concentration rose no higher in the subsequent breath, indicating that air arrives directly at the posterior sacs. More than one full respiratory cycle elapsed before the O_2 slug reached the anterior air sacs (157). A more elaborate experimental procedure employing slugs of argon and a mass spectrometer for sampling was employed with ducks (28); it yielded results consistent with those obtained for the ostrich. This is also the case for experiments in which gas mixtures rich in CO_2 were inhaled by domestic fowl and ducks (21). These experiments, following the passage of inhaled gases, provided presumptive evidence that a unidirectional flow of air occurred through the tertiary bronchi. Observations of washout times of certain of these gases allowed refutation of earlier notions that the anterior air sacs were not very actively ventilated, in contrast to the posterior ones. Recent measurements involving the washout of helium in domestic ducks indicate that, although the volumes of the interclavicular, prethoracic, postthoracic, and abdominal air sacs are similar, the prethoracic and postthoracic sacs are ventilated about three times as much as those of other air sacs (153a).

Details of the major flow pattern in the avian lung had to await use of small flow meters placed at various points within the respiratory tract (27, 151). This was accomplished in a particularly elegant fashion by Bretz & Schmidt-Nielsen (27), who used paired heated microthermistors positioned at selected points in the airways of Pekin ducks (primary bronchus, craniomedial secondary bronchus, caudodorsal secondary bronchus). Their results established that the flow of air is unidirectional through the paleopulmo and that the following overall flow pattern exists in resting unanesthetized birds: During inspiration, air flows to the posterior air sacs from the primary bronchus, bypassing the tertiary bronchi. In this phase of the respiratory cycle, air also flows toward the anterior air sacs via the caudodorsal secondary bronchi and the tertiary bronchi. A notable feature of the arrangement is that the craniomedial secondary bronchi, which constitute the direct connection between the primary bronchus and the anterior air sacs, convey only a small amount of air to these sacs. During expiration, air flows from the anterior sacs to the primary bronchus via these same craniomedial bronchi. At the same time, air flows from the posterior air sacs through the tertiary bronchi via the branches of the caudodorsal secondary bronchi (and caudoventral secondary bronchi in the case of the caudal thoracic air sacs), passing out to the primary bronchus by way of the craniomedial bronchi. The most direct route out of the posterior air sacs, via the primary bronchus, is effectively bypassed during expiration. Flow through those tertiary bronchi comprising the neopulmo (56), which represents a minor fraction of the exchange surface of the lung, appears bidirectional (see also 153). Duncker (56) has speculated that the neopulmo may be the primary region for gas exchange in birds at rest, with the paleopulmo being actively ventilated during activity when requirements for O_2 are high.

The achievement of unidirectional flow across the major fraction of the gas exchange surfaces in the avian lung and the intermittent bypassing or restriction of air flow in certain portions of the airway are particularly interesting phenomena in view of the absence of any anatomical valving in the respiratory system of birds. The air flow in the system appears laminar, of low velocity, and driven by small pressure differentials (27). Orientation of entrances into various parts of the system, curvatures of various air ways, and surface irregularities may be of crucial importance in controlling flow (23, 27). For example, Duncker (56) noted that the caudoventral secondary bronchi emanate from the primary bronchus in such a way that their return flow would tend to be directed into the caudodorsal secondary bronchi lying opposite them.

With the unidirectional flow through most of the tertiary bronchi, the possibility of a countercurrent arrangement involving the air and blood has been suggested (46, 154, 157). However, a crosscurrent exchange system has also been advanced (150). Experimental reversal of tertiary bronchial flow (by introducing gas into the system via the air sacs) failed to reveal a dependence of blood gas tensions on direction of air flow (152). In particular, Pa_{CO_2} was found to be lower than in the end-tidal air with either direction of flow. This is interpreted as support for a crosscurrent exchange arrangement.

OXYGEN TRANSPORT

Avian hemoglobin is present in multiple forms in many species. While five or more electrophoretically distinct forms have been claimed in the domestic fowl (80), two or three appear to be the usual number present where alteration of the native molecules is not a factor (30, 31, 181). The resistance of these hemoglobins to alkaline denaturation appears high. Somewhat lower heme-heme interactions have been reported for avian than for mammalian hemoglobin; single hemoglobin solutions from several birds showed Hill coefficients (n) of 2.3–2.6. Values obtained for solutions possessing two hemoglobins range from 2.1 to 2.6 (181). However, Lenfant et al (109) reported values for n of 2.9–3.0 for whole blood of Adélie penguins (*Pygoscelis adeliae*) and cited values for six other species ranging from 2.9 to 3.9. The Hill coefficient for the blood of the house sparrow is approximately 3.2 (calculated from 173).

Factors for the Bohr effect in birds ($\Delta\log P_{50}/\Delta pH$) show a certain amount of interspecific variation. Values for several species have been summarized (43). These and those of some other birds (124) lie between –0.35 and –0.55. The possibility of values outside this range representing adaptations for diving is considered subsequently.

Some of the factors affecting the function of hemoglobin in birds differ either qualitatively or quantitatively from those in mammals. The birds tend to operate at higher body temperatures (53) and maintain Pa_{CO_2}s at levels below 35 mm Hg and commonly below 30 mm Hg (37, 41, 42, 46, 102, 138). Arterial pHs typically run between 7.45 and 7.60 (37, 41, 42). Judging by results from experiments on the domestic fowl, in vivo buffering characteristics of avian blood appear similar to those of mammals, despite birds having lower concentrations of hemoglobin and plasma proteins and higher body temperatures (129).

Results of studies of oxygen transport in birds have produced a minor paradox. Measurements of several species suggest that arterial blood is incompletely saturated with oxygen even under normal conditions (42, 43, 47). This has been associated with the low oxygen affinities found for avian hemoglobins under physiological conditions (43). These low oxygen affinities are curious in view of the rather impressive resistance of certain birds to hypoxic environments (173). An explanation of this paradox appears to be provided by Lutz et al (113a, 114). The blood of pigeons with its nucleated erythrocytes and higher temperatures has a $\dot{V}_{O_2}$ roughly 10 times that of mammalian blood. With a technique eliminating delay between equilibration and analysis, Lutz et al (114) found pigeon blood to have a relatively high O_2 affinity ($P_{50} = 29.5$ mm Hg at pH of 7.5, P_{CO_2} of 35 mm Hg, and temperature of 41°C). The study of blood from six more species indicated O_2 affinities similar to those noted in mammals. The P_{50}s of these birds and of the pigeon varied with the -0.079 power of body mass (113a). The analytical problem identified by Lutz et al raises questions about work reported on O_2 affinities and Bohr effects of avian blood. The extent to which values obtained are distorted by alteration of oxygen tensions between equilibration and analysis should be determined for additional species.

One further point distinguishes the environments in which avian and mammalian hemoglobins operate. This concerns the nature of the organic phosphate compounds modulating the O_2 affinities of these molecules. Rather than 2,3-diphosphoglycerate, inositol hexaphosphate (IHP) has been specified as the principal compound in birds (13, 143). However, it now appears that inositol pentaphosphate (IPP) may be the actual compound present in the avian erythrocyte (see 86). The role of organic phosphate compounds in altitudinal acclimatization of birds remains to be characterized. These compounds appear to influence the respiratory properties of blood of the domestic fowl before and after hatching (86). The P_{50} declines during the 14th and 18th day of incubation; this is correlated with changes in intracellular concentrations of ATP. The intracellular concentration of IHP (IPP?) is negligible until the 18th day, after which it rises. At this time oxygen affinity becomes closely correlated with [IHP] (or [IPP]) until hatching. Following an unexplained rise in P_{50} at hatching (125), oxygen affinity continues to decline in a manner correlated with concentrations of organic phosphates in the erythrocytes over the next several weeks (see 86). The organic phosphate level in the erythrocytes of chicks of the Adélie penguin declines over the first 8 weeks after hatching; the decline is accompanied by a rise in the oxygen affinity of the blood (86). This appears to contribute to the preparation of these birds for the diving activities they will engage in as they enter the amphibious phase of their life.

PHYSIOLOGICAL ADJUSTMENTS FOR DIVING

Many birds make their living on and under the water. Unlike certain diving mammals that may remain submerged for as much as an hour, the vast majority of these birds appear to dive for only brief periods (100), although the emperor penguin (*Aptenodytes forsteri*) may be an exception (101). In their comprehensive review of avian cardiovascular physiology, Jones & Johansen (89) discussed the major cardiovascular adjustments to diving, including bradycardia and redistribution of blood flow in a manner insuring preferential perfusion of those tissues most sensitive to anoxic damage (brain, heart, sensory organs, certain endocrine glands).

Most data on diving in birds pertain to animals forced to submerge. Some information pertaining to voluntarily diving Adélie and gentoo (*Pygoscelis papua*) penguins is therefore of particular interest. Cardiovascular measurements obtained by radiotelemetry and supplemented by information on oxygen tensions and pH of the blood before and after the dives have now been published (121). The fall in heart rate during these voluntary dives was far less than reported for ducks (39) and other diving birds (89) during forced submergence, amounting to only a third of predive values. Femoral and carotid blood flows in the voluntarily diving penguins declined to 25 and 70%, respectively, of predive levels. The actual carotid flow exceeded that noted in penguins resting on land. Only minor changes in oxygen tension and pH of the blood were observed after voluntary dives lasting 20–40 sec. This is important, for these birds would often remain on the surface for only 1–3 sec between dives. Freely diving penguins seem to effect a compromise between exercise vasodilatation and induced muscle vasoconstriction. Thus a moderate perfusion of the muscles is continued, in contrast to the situation noted in ducks during enforced dives. This arrangement appears highly suitable for the pattern typically used by penguins, in which diving may be continued for hours, the time submerged possibly exceeding that spent on the surface by a factor of 30–40 (121). These animals dive on inspiration, and indications exist suggesting that gas exchange may continue between air sacs, lungs, and blood during submergence (102).

The results cited here differ profoundly from those obtained in experiments involving Adélie and gentoo penguins in forced dives. A combination of intermittent struggling and greater duration of submersion produced transient changes in heart rate and blood flow and substantial alteration of blood parameters. Several minutes were required before the blood parameters were restored to predive levels (121).

Mass-relative plasma, erythrocyte, and blood volumes of diving birds tend to be greater than those of nondiving ones (19). However, Lenfant et al (109) noted that the blood volume of Adélie penguins (86–99 ml/kg), while relatively high for birds, is lower than that of diving mammals. Hemoglobin concentrations of diving birds also tend to exceed those of their nondiving counterparts (19, 109, 124). Certain surface-feeding aquatic birds tend to have somewhat lower hemoglobin values than these diving birds (43, 124). It is of interest that penguin chicks, presumably confined to land, show values of 11.1–11.9 g Hb/100 ml blood, whereas adult values exceed 16.3 g Hb/100 ml (124).

Conservatism regarding interpretation of measurements of oxygen affinities of avian blood seems in order in view of the problems posed by the relatively rapid O_2 uptake by erythrocytes (114). However, it appears worthwhile to mention certain findings concerning diving birds. Milsom et al (124) noted that the blood of such species typically has a greater O_2 affinity than that of surface-feeding aquatic birds. They suggested that this relatively high affinity would facilitate reoxygenation of the blood during the often brief period between dives. It should be noted here that the most reliable value for the P_{50} of pigeon blood under physiological conditions is 29.5 mm Hg (114), as compared with values of 29.8–34.4 mm Hg for three species of penguins (*Pygoscelis adeliae, P. papua,* and *P. antarctica*) included in Milsom et al's analysis (124). The pigeon resembles diving birds in several other blood parameters and it has been suggested that this reflects its strong powers of flight (19).

Perhaps the most confusing matter relating to adaptations of blood respiratory properties in diving birds concerns the extent of the Bohr effect. Again, caution may be required in accepting the O_2 dissociation curves used to define this effect. Both unusually small and large Bohr effects have been regarded as adaptations for the diving habit in these animals (119, 124). Gentoo and chinstrap (*Pygoscelis antarctica*) penguins, which dive for relatively long periods, show larger Bohr effects than Adélie penguins, which dive for relatively short periods (124). A relatively large decline in O_2 affinity with increasing acidification of the blood over the course of a dive would seem advantageous in maintaining a relatively high Pa_{O_2} while extracting a maximum amount of O_2 bound to hemoglobin (6).

ADJUSTMENTS TO HYPOXIC SITUATIONS

Although most birds fly at heights well below 3000 m, records exist of some engaged in flapping flight at altitudes of nearly 8000 m (173, 177). In these latter animals, P_{O_2} and P_{CO_2} in the gas exchange regions of the lung would evidently be at levels below those tolerated by man. Birds might be expected to cope with hypoxic situations rather well, owing to the characteristics of their respiratory system (105). Dramatic documentation of this is afforded by Tucker's observations (173). After showing that unacclimatized house sparrows and budgerygahs (*Melopsittacus undulatus*) retained some powers of flight at simulated altitudes of 6100 m, he compared the responses of the sparrows and white mice in 1-hr exposures to this altitude at 5°C. At the end of the test period, the sparrows had $\dot{V}_{O_2}$s 2.2 times the basal rate and were normally active, although T_b had fallen 2°C. On the other hand, the mice had $\dot{V}_{O_2}$s below those observed at sea level and were moribund with T_b averaging 10°C below normal. Interspecific variation exists in avian tolerances of hypoxic situations (4). Acclimatization of birds to chronic hypoxic situations has largely been studied in domesticated species (see 89, 105). This process involves a number of changes in cardiovascular parameters, such as increases in hematocrit, hemoglobin concentration, total circulating erythrocyte volume, and total blood volume, as well as chronic pulmonary hypertension and ventricular hypertrophy. Shifts in blood gas tensions and pH also occur (16, 32, 34). These changes tend to be completely reversed in approximately three weeks following return of the birds to sea level conditions.

The question arises as to whether the responses to chronic hypoxia observed in domesticated birds are typical of those noted in wild ones. Presumptive evidence that similarities do exist is afforded by the greater heart masses noted in wild birds indigenous to or seasonally resident in montane situations (55, 57, 130) and experimental acclimatization of pintail ducks (*Anas acuta*) at barometric pressures of 310 mm Hg (equivalent to an altitude of 7000 m) (44, 45).

Details of oxygen transport in the process of adjustment of birds to high altitudes remain to be worked out. It would be particularly interesting to determine the extent of the involvement of changes in erythrocyte levels of organic phosphate compounds in the process.

ENERGETICS OF LOCOMOTION IN BIRDS

Any consideration of locomotion in birds must surely deal primarily with flight, for this activity has exerted a fundamental influence upon evolution of the form and physiology of these animals. Nevertheless, swimming and running also deserve consideration, for they are important activities in many species. Estimation of the power requirements for all these activities has involved some intriguing experimental efforts and considerable patience on the part of investigators. A very readable account of one laboratory's efforts in this area is provided by Schmidt-Nielsen (155).

Prange & Schmidt-Nielsen (140) analyzed the energetics of swimming by ducks. The cost of transport (the energy required to move 1 g of the animal over a unit distance) in this mode of locomotion is similar to that for walking, but nearly 10 times that for swimming by salmon of comparable size (156).

Certain large flightless birds, such as ostriches, rely on running for rapid locomotion. Power input during this activity varies linearly with velocity in the rhea (*Rhea americana*), with the same relation applying to results obtained at T_as of 25, 35, and 43°C (169). Interestingly, the cost of running in this bipedal animal is about twice that predicted for quadrapedal mammals of similar size, a situation also known for man (156). Running by rheas at 43°C is accompanied by storage of considerable amounts of heat, and evaporative water loss appears to play a minor role in thermal balance (169). Vascular arrangements promoting heat exchange in the head serve to maintain brain temperature somewhat below that of the body core (91). Below 1 kg the cost of transport of bipedal running by birds becomes progressively less than that of quadrapedal running by mammals (65).

Substantial progress has been made in the analysis of the physiology and energetics of avian flight (13a). The various methods by which measurements have been made are recounted by Farner (62) and Tucker (176). That providing the most useful information for quantitative analyses involves measurement of $\dot{V}O_2$ and, in some cases, $\dot{V}CO_2$ for birds flying in wind tunnels while fitted with transparent resporatory masks. Data are made available for three birds during flapping flight: the 0.035 kg budgerygah (174); the 0.26–0.36 kg laughing gull, *Larus atricilla* (177); and the 0.28 kg fish crow, *Corvus ossifragus* (15). Flight by these species requires metabolic rates approximately 6–8 times resting metabolic rates and 12–14 times basal rates. On the other hand, gliding flight by herring gulls (*Larus argentatus*) only requires a rate about twice the resting level (10a). Partial efficiencies of flapping flight (which don't reflect the work of overcoming drag) in these birds lie between approximately 0.2 and 0.3. The relation of power input to air speed in level flight differs among the budgerygah, laughing gull, and fish crow (15, 174, 177). Moveover, this input by the crow runs at about 1.3 times that for the gull despite the similarity in body mass of the two species (15).

Tucker's (174) analysis of power requirements of budgerygahs in horizontal, ascending, and descending flapping flight affords some interesting implications concerning the flight patterns of this bird. It requires little extra energy for the budgerygah to ascend at flight speeds lower than 7.5 m/sec, since the partial efficiency (E_p) for ascent is high. The budgerygah is a ground-feeding bird and many of its ascending flights are made on takeoffs, when flight speeds are low. At these slow speeds the E_p for ascent is greater than for descent. These considerations indicate that undulating flight would be more economical than level flight.

Tucker (179) has modified Pennycuick's (137) theory for the energetic requirements of flight in a manner improving the agreement between predictions and actual measurements for flying birds and bats. The striking thing emerging from estimation by the modified equation of the energetic costs of known long distance movements across water by land birds is the small margin of safety afforded by their energy reserves (180). Migratory flights such as those occurring in certain species between Alaska and Hawaii and between eastern North America and Bermuda may well require favorable winds or, at the very least, the absence of headwinds (180).

Flapping flight of birds is a vigorous process, but it allows them to move with costs of transport that are surprisingly economical in comparison with those for walking and running (175), though well above those for swimming by fish (156). Not only is flight relatively economical in relation to the forms of locomotion available to nonflying terrestrial vertebrates, it is also rapid, a key factor in permitting the long distance migrations employed by many birds. Interestingly, perhaps fortuitously, the costs of transport for flight of insects fall along the extrapolation of the body mass regression line fitted to data on birds (156).

THERMOGENIC MECHANISMS

Prusiner & Poe (142) provided a useful classification of documented and postulated biochemical mechanisms of thermogenesis in mammals. Of those listed, metabolic activity associated with shivering appears to overshadow any others in heat production by adult birds (78, 168, 188, 189). Energy for this is primarily obtained from catabolism of fatty acids (74). Catecholamines have not proved to be effective stimulants of thermogenesis in cold-acclimatized birds (40, 83). Furthermore, these substances do not appear to have a lipid-mobilizing action (38, 83). However, it has been suggested that an increased catecholamine and corticosterone release is required during initial response of turkeys to temperature stress (58). In various studies of thermogenesis in young birds, it usually seems to have been tacitly assumed that capacities for shivering were limited or absent in the period immediately after hatching. In interpreting these studies, it should be kept in mind that considerable variation concerning developmental state and thermoregulatory capacities exists among birds at hatching (see 53).

Like adult birds (88), chicks of the domestic fowl and neonates of several other species evidently lack brown fat (68, 88). In chicks of the domestic fowl, α- and β-adrenergic and ganglionic blockading agents impaired thermoregulation (186, 187). This was assumed to result from blockage of catecholamine release normally resulting from sympathetic neural activation. However, drugs such as propranolol may initially stimulate release of norepinephrine, which then exerts thermolytic effects or otherwise impairs temperature regulation (2, 70). Beta-adrenergic blockade produced by propranolol impairs thermoregulation in cool environments by 1- and 3-day-old skuas (*Catharacta skua*), an effect reduced by administration of the beta-activating aminoisoproterenol (125a). Catecholamines do not appear thermogenic in either young domestic fowl (2, 68, 69) or black-headed gulls, *Larus ridibundus* (132). Thiouracil-treated chicks of the former species show somewhat less effective control of T_b in cool surroundings (20°C) than do controls (71), suggesting the possibility of mediation of thermogenesis through an action of thyroid hormones on sodium transport, as suggested for mammals (85). Triiodothyronine and thyroxine stimulated thermogenesis in chicks of the domestic fowl (69). However, no differences in thyroid secretion rates were found in such chicks maintained on standardized diets over a T_a range of approximately 16–32°C (12). Thyroxine failed to stimulate $\dot{V}O_2$ in young black-headed gulls, whereas corticosterone administration did increase their thermogenesis (132). While lipolytic and glycogenolytic, glucagon did not increase $\dot{V}O_2$ of young domestic fowl (133), contrary to earlier suggestions concerning its possible role in stimulating thermogenesis of chicks.

The response of day-old chicks of the domestic fowl to moderate cold (20°C) is rather complex. Body temperature drops significantly, and there is an immediate mobilization of lipid (48, 69). However, no major change in total blood ketone bodies seems to occur (48). Blood levels of lactate and pyruvate are elevated. Plasma glucose concentration falls initially, increases after 6 hr, and essentially returns to normal after 24 hr despite virtually complete depletion of liver and muscle glycogen. Serum uric acid levels rise during exposure to cold, indicating increased protein catabolism. This, plus the restoration of blood glucose concentrations in the face of glycogen depletion, suggests the occurrence of gluconeogenesis. Both this process and protein catabolism would potentially be thermogenic (48).

Neither the site nor the actual mechanism(s) of any nonshivering thermogenesis in birds has been conclusively identified. The absence of brown fat in these animals suggests that it would not involve any significant uncoupling of oxidation from phosphorylation.

ADAPTIVE PERIODIC FAT STORAGE

Lipid metabolism and other facets of the intermediary metabolism of birds have recently been reviewed (81). In the general context of this article it still seems appropriate to mention two aspects of fat storage not ordinarily seen in domesticated species.

Various migratory birds show spectacular fat storage in advance of their vernal and autumnal movements. This occurs over a period of 6–10 days as a result of a hyperphagia that leads to the buildup of fat deposits equivalent to as much as 25–50% of the initial body weight (54, 131). Fattening tends to be greater preceding the vernal than the autumnal migration (93). King (93) regards the episodes of premigratory fattening as expressions of endogenous circannual rhythms, entrained by various environmental factors such as photoperiod.

In many small birds residing in cold climates, fat reserves are accumulated each winter day in sufficient amount to sustain the animal overnight and into the next day (61, 128). The extent of this fattening is rather precisely related to average temperature conditions for the time of year rather than to the actual conditions confronting the animals in a given year. This suggests that temperature is an ultimate rather than a proximate factor (61, 93, 96). The extent of the fat reserves of 12 species maintained in captivity at the same locality also correlates rather closely with the latitudes of their respective winter ranges (54). Considerable interspecific diversity exists in the two types of adaptive fat storage. Their relation to overall patterns of energy allocation by wild birds is reviewed by King (94).

OSMOREGULATION AND EXCRETION

Birds resemble mammals in being able to produce a urine hyperosmotic to the plasma. However, their renal function differs in several important respects from that of mammals. Moreover, the kidneys of many birds are supplemented in the task of electrolyte excretion by cephalic salt-secreting glands (see 158). Avian osmoregulation and excretion have been discussed by several authors over the last three years (84, 158, 161, 162).

The avian kidney contains both reptilian- (RT) and mammalian-type (MT) nephrons. The glomeruli and proximal and distal tubules of both types, collecting tubules, and associated vascular elements (including connections from the renal portal system) lie in a loosely subdivided cortical region. The loop structures of the MT nephrons in a given region project into a medullary cone along with the collecting tubules and associated vascular elements. In the cone the collecting tubules fuse to form increasingly larger ducts. These ultimately join with ducts from adjacent cones to form a secondary branch of the ureter. Such a group of cones constitutes a renal lobule (see 87 for illustration).

The osmotic-concentrating capacity of avian kidneys is modest by mammalian standards, generally resulting in a urine with no more than 2–3 times the concentration of the plasma, although a few species capable of slightly higher ratios are known (158, 163a). A countercurrent multiplier system appears to operate in the medullary cones (59, 166). However, no correlation was found between mean length of the medullary cones relative to kidney volume, a measure considered analogous with relative medullary thickness in mammals, and ability to concentrate urine in 26 species of 9 avian orders (87).

Birds control the rate of urine production through both adjustments of glomerular filtration rate (GFR) and tubular resorption of water. The GFR may drop to one third or one fourth during dehydration (161). Studies of the xerophilic Gambel quail (*Lophortyx gambelii*) indicate that this reduction is effected by a shutdown of the RT nephrons under control of arginine vasotocin (AVT), the antidiuretic hormone of birds (25, 26). Since these nephrons lack the loop structure, the shutdown enhances the production of a concentrated urine by the MT nephrons, which continue to function. The tubular resorption of water can vary widely in birds, and U/P ratios for inulin ranging from 3 to >100 have been observed (158, 165). Consequently, as little as 67% and more than 99% of the filtered water load would be resorbed. This fraction can be maximized by administration of AVT (5).

A summary of urinary excretion of Na^+, K^+, and Cl^- by birds is presented by Shoemaker (158). A distinctive feature of avian ion excretion relates to formation of the egg shell. Some of the calcium for this is obtained by resorption of $CaPO_4$ from medullary bone of the female. Acquisition of phosphate from this source and from increased intestinal absorption is accompanied by a net tubular secretion of this ion (141). Parathyroid hormone may act not only to facilitate mobilization of $CaPO_4$ from medullary bone but also to reduce tubular resorption of phosphate (120). Production of the $CaCO_3$ shell produces a metabolic acidosis in domestic fowl hens. This results in a drop in the pH of the urine from 8.0 to 6.0. Prior to the onset of lay, these birds show a rise in blood [HCO_3^-] (159).

The excretion of urates by avian kidneys presents some complex physicochemical relations. These substances are primarily introduced into the nephron by tubular secretion (158). Large amounts of urates are discharged from the ureters (116, 118), much of them in the form of small spheres (67) containing a soluble component (113). Perhaps the shape of these particles facilitates flow of the urinary suspension.

The concentrations of Na^+ and NH_4^+ (the other significant urinary nitrogenous product in birds) in the urine of the domestic fowl can be high enough to suggest that the urate present in the liquid fraction exists in the form of lyophilic colloids that possibly are stabilized by the glycoprotein or mucopolysaccharides present (117). Conditions favoring urate precipitation increase the Na^+ and K^+, but not the NH_4^+, contents of the precipitate, thereby preventing them from contributing to the osmotic pressure of the liquid fraction of the urine. The former two cations do not seem to precipitate in monobasic urate salts, possibly precipitating with urate instead as a result of physical rather than chemical interactions (117).

Birds lack certain enzymes of the urea cycle in their liver and kidneys and are unable to produce arginine. Arginase is present in high concentrations in the kidney, but not in the liver of most species. Tubular resorption of arginine apparently involves a transport mechanism shared in common by other cationic amino acids (20). The existence of this mechanism contributes to the importance of the kidney in regulation of arginine (183).

As urine emerges from the ureters into the urodeum, it commences a retrograde movement into the coprodeum and large intestine (99). This movement seems unaffected by the state of hydration of the bird (160). Within the coprodeum and large intestine the water content of the excrement, both fecal and urinary components, is reduced by solute-linked water flow across the mucosa (which increases during dehydration) (17, 18). It is estimated for budgerygahs that the hyperosmotic urine associated with the latter state can enter the cloaca without fostering a water loss (164). This has recently been verified in another xerophilic species, the galah (*Cacatua roseicapilla*). This bird appears capable of absorbing as much as 70% of the ureteral output of sodium and its cloacal resorption of water by solute-linked flow is greater than that of the domestic fowl (163).

CONCLUDING STATEMENT

Limitations of space have precluded comprehensive review here of all facets of avian physiology. This is regrettable, partially because it has prevented documentation of the key role that use of birds as experimental subjects has played in advancement of such fields as orientation, endocrinology, intermediary metabolism, and nutrition. In view of these necessary omissions, it seems appropriate to note that several recent works are available that provide a treatment of some or all of these fields (11, 63, 134–136).

Literature Cited

1. Åkerman, B., Andersson, B., Fabricius, E., Svensson, L. 1960. Observations on central regulation of body temperature and of food and water intake in the pigeon *Columba livia*. *Acta Physiol. Scand.* 50:328–36
2. Allen, D. J., Garg, K. N., Marley, E. 1970. Mode of action of α-methylnoradrenaline on temperature and oxygen consumption of young chickens. *Brit. J. Pharmacol.* 38:667–87
3. Allred, J. B., Roehrig, K. L. 1973. Metabolic oscillations and food intake. *Fed. Proc.* 32:1727–30
4. Altland, P. D. 1961. Altitude tolerance of chickens and pigeons. *J. Appl. Physiol.* 16:141–43
5. Ames, E., Steve, K., Skadhauge, E. 1971. Effects of arginine vasotocin on renal excretion of Na^+, K^+, Cl^-, and urea in the hydrated chicken. *Am. J. Physiol.* 221:1223–28
6. Andersen, H. T., Løvø, A. 1967. Indirect estimation of partial pressure of oxygen in arterial blood of diving ducks. *Resp. Physiol.* 2:163–67

6a. Ar, A., Paganelli, C. V., Reeves, R. B., Greene, D. G., Rahn, H. 1974. The avian egg: water vapor conductance, shell thickness, and functional pore area. *Condor* 76:153–58

7. Aschoff, J., Pohl, H. 1970. Rhythmic variations in energy metabolism. *Fed. Proc.* 29:1541–52
8. Bartels, H. 1970. *Prenatal Respiration.* Amsterdam: North-Holland. 199 pp.
9. Bartels, H., Baumann, F. 1972. Metabolic rate of early embryos (4–22 somites) at varying oxygen pressures. *Resp. Physiol.* 16:1–15
10. Bartels, H., Hiller, G., Reinhardt, W. 1966. Oxygen affinity of chicken blood before and after hatching. *Resp. Physiol.* 1:345–56

10a. Baudinette, R. V., Schmidt-Nielsen, K. 1974. Energy cost of gliding flight in herring gulls. *Nature* 248:83–84

11. Bell, D. J., Freeman, B. M., Eds. 1971. *Physiology and Biochemistry of the Domestic Fowl.* London/New York: Academic. 3 vols. 1488 pp.
12. Belnave, D. 1973. The influence of thyroxine and environmental temperature in the specific activity of hepatic malic enzyme in young male chicks. *Comp. Biochem. Physiol.* 44A:1069–74
13. Benesch, R., Benesch, R. E. 1969. Intracellular organic phosphates as regulators of oxygen release by haemoglobin. *Nature* 221:618–22

13a. Berger, M., Hart, J. S. 1974. Physiology and energetics of flight. See Ref. 64, 4:415–72

14. Berger, M., Roy, O. Z., Hart, J. S. 1970. The coordination between respiration and wing beats in birds. *Z. Vergl. Physiol.* 66:190–200
15. Bernstein, M. H., Thomas, S. P., Schmidt-Nielsen, K. 1973. Power input during flight of the fish crow, *Corvus ossifragus. J. Exp. Biol.* 58:401–10
16. Besch, E. L., Burton, R. R., Smith, A. H. 1971. Influence of chronic hypoxia on blood gas tensions and pH in domestic fowl. *Am. J. Physiol.* 220:1379–82
17. Bindslev, N., Skadhauge, E. 1971. Salt and water permeability of the epithelium of the coprodeum and large intestine in the normal and dehydrated fowl *(Gallus domesticus). J. Physiol. London* 216:735–51
18. Bindslev, N., Skadhauge, E. 1971. Sodium chloride absorption and solute-linked water flow across the epithelium of the coprodeum and large intestine in the normal and dehydrated fowl (*Gallus domesticus*). *In vivo* perfusion studies. *J. Physiol. London* 216:753–68
19. Bond, C. F., Gilbert, P. W. 1958. Comparative study of blood volume in representative aquatic and non-aquatic birds. *Am. J. Physiol.* 194:519–21
20. Boorman, K. N. 1971. The renal reabsorption of arginine, lysine and ornithine in the young cockerel *(Gallus domesticus). Comp. Biochem. Physiol.* 39A:29–38
21. Bouverot, P., Dejours, P. 1971. Pathway of inspired gas in the air sacs-lung apparatus of fowl and ducks. *Resp. Physiol.* 13:330–42
22. Brackenbury, J. H. 1971. Pressure-flow phenomena within the avian respiratory system. *J. Anat.* 108:609–10
23. Brackenbury, J. H. 1971. Airflow dynamics in the avian lung as determined by direct and indirect methods. *Resp. Physiol.* 13:319–29
24. Brackenbury, J. H. 1972. Lung-air sac anatomy and respiratory pressures in the bird. *J. Exp. Biol.* 57:543–50
25. Braun, E. J., Dantzler, W. H. 1972. Function of mammalian-type and reptilian-type nephrons in kidney of desert quail. *Am. J. Physiol.* 222:617–29

26. Braun, E. J., Dantzler, W. H. 1974. Effects of ADH on single-nephron glomerular filtration rates in the avian kidney. *Am. J. Physiol.* 226:1–8
27. Bretz, W. L., Schmidt-Nielsen, K. 1971. Bird respiration: flow patterns in the duck lung. *J. Exp. Biol.* 54:103–18
28. Bretz, W. L., Schmidt-Nielsen, K. 1972. The movement of gas in the respiratory system of the duck. *J. Exp. Biol.* 56:57–65
29. Brody, S., Proctor, R. C. 1932. Growth and development, with special reference to domestic animals. XXIII. Relation between basal metabolism and mature body weight in different species of mammals and birds. *Missouri Univ. Agr. Exp. Sta. Res. Bull.* No. 166:89–101
30. Brown, I. R. F., Bannister, W. H., DeLucca, C. 1970. A comparison of Maltese and Sicilian sparrow haemoglobins. *Comp. Biochem. Physiol.* 34: 557–62
31. Brush, A. H., Power, D. M. 1970. Electrophoretic studies on hemoglobins of Brewer's blackbird *Euphagus cyanocephalus. Comp. Biochem. Physiol.* 33:587–99
32. Burton, R. R., Besch, E. L., Smith, A. H. 1968. Effect of chronic hypoxia on pulmonary arterial blood pressure of the chicken. *Am. J. Physiol.* 214:1438–42
33. Burton, R. R., Smith, A. H. 1969. Induction of cardiac hypertrophy and polycythemia in the developing chick at high altitude. *Fed. Proc.* 28:1170–71
34. Burton, R. R., Smith, A. H., Carlisle, J. C., Sluka, S. J. 1969. Role of hematocrit, heart mass, and high-altitude exposure in acute hypoxia tolerance. *J. Appl. Physiol.* 27:49–52
35. Calder, W. A. 1974. The consequences of body size for avian energetics. *Avian Energetics,* ed. R. A. Paynter, Jr. Publ. Nuttall Ornithol. Club: In press
36. Calder, W. A., King, J. R. 1974. Thermal and caloric relations of birds. See Ref. 64, 4:259–413
37. Calder, W. A., Schmidt-Nielsen, K. 1968. Panting and blood carbon dioxide in birds. *Am. J. Physiol.* 215:477–82
38. Carlson, L. A., Liljedahl, S.-O., Verdy, M., Wirsén, C. 1964. Unresponsiveness to the lipid mobilizing action of catecholamines in vivo and in vitro in the domestic fowl. *Metabolism* 13:227–31
39. Catlett, R. H., Johnson, B. L. 1974. Cardiac response to diving in wild ducks. *Comp. Biochem. Physiol.* 47A:925–31
40. Chaffee, R. R. J., Mayhew, W. W., Drebin, M., Cassuto, Y. 1963. Studies on thermogenesis in cold-acclimated birds. *Can. J. Biochem. Physiol.* 41:2215–20
41. Chapot, G., Barrault, N., Müller, M., Dargnat, N. 1972. Comparative study of Pa_{CO_2} in several homeothermic species. *Am. J. Physiol.* 223:1354–57
42. Chiodi, H., Terman, J. W. 1965. Arterial blood gases of the domestic hen. *Am. J. Physiol.* 208:798–800
43. Clausen, G., Sanson, R., Storesund, A. 1971. The HbO_2 dissociation curve from the fulmar and the herring gull. *Resp. Physiol.* 12:66–70
44. Cohen, R. R. 1969. Total and relative erythrocyte levels of pintail ducks (*Anas acuta*) in chronic decompression hypoxia. *Physiol. Zool.* 42:108–19
45. Cohen, R. R. 1969. Recovery of erythrocyte levels following chronic decompression hypoxia in pintail ducks *Anas acuta. Physiol. Zool.* 42:120–25
46. Cohn, J. E., Shannon, R. 1968. Respiration in unanesthetized geese. *Resp. Physiol.* 5:259–68
46a. Crooks, R. J., Simkiss, K. 1974. Respiratory acidosis and egg shell resorption by the chick embryo. *J. Exp. Biol.* 61:197–202
47. Danzer, L. A., Cohn, J. E. 1967. The dissociation curve for goose blood. *Resp. Physiol.* 3:302–6
48. Davison, T. F. 1973. Metabolite changes in the neonate fowl in response to cold stress. *Comp. Biochem. Physiol.* 44A:979–89
49. Dawes, C. M. 1973. The effects of anoxia on the respiratory movements of the hatching chick. *Comp. Biochem. Physiol.* 46A:421–25
50. Dawes, C. M. 1974. The effects of restricting gaseous exchange across the eggshell on the pO_2, pCO_2, and pH values of the extraembryonic fluids of the chick embryo. *Comp. Biochem. Physiol.* 47A:233–41
51. Dawes, C., Simkiss, K. 1969. The acid-base status of the blood of the developing chick embryo. *J. Exp. Biol.* 50: 79–86
52. Dawson, W. R., Bartholomew, G. A. 1968. Temperature regulation and water economy of desert birds. *Desert Biology,* ed. G. W. Brown Jr., 357–94. New York/London: Academic
53. Dawson, W. R., Hudson, J. W. 1970. Birds. *Comp. Physiol. Thermoregul.* 1:223–310
54. Dolnik, W. R. 1971. Bioenergetische Anpassungen der Vögel and die Uber-

winterung in verscheidenen Breiten. *Falke* 14:305–6, 347–49
55. Dorst, J. 1972. Poid relatif du coeur chez quelques oiseaux des hautes Andes du Perou. *l'Oiseaux Rev. Fr. Ornithol.* 42:66–73
56. Duncker, H.-R. 1972. Structure of avian lungs. *Resp. Physiol.* 14:44–63
57. Dunson, W. A. 1965. Adaptation of heart and lung weight to high altitude in the robin. *Condor* 67:215–19
58. El-Halawani, M. E., Waibel, P. E., Appel, J. R., Good, A. L. 1973. Effects of temperature stress on catecholamines and corticosterone of male turkeys. *Am. J. Physiol.* 224:348–88
59. Emery, N., Poulson, T. L., Kinter, W. B. 1972. Production of concentrated urine by avian kidneys. *Am. J. Physiol.* 223:180–87
60. Erasmus, B. W., Howell, B. J., Rahn, H. 1970/71. Ontogeny of acid-base balance in the bullfrog and chicken. *Resp. Physiol.* 11:46–53
61. Evans, P. R. 1969. Winter fat deposition and overnight survival of yellow buntings (*Emberiza citrinella* L.). *J. Anim. Ecol.* 38:415–23
62. Farner, D. S. 1970. Some glimpses of comparative avian physiology. *Fed. Proc.* 29:1649–63
63. Farner, D. S., Ed. 1973. *Breeding Biology of Birds.* Washington DC: Nat. Acad. Sci. 515 pp.
64. Farner, D. S., King, J. R., Eds. 1971–1974. *Avian Biology.* New York/London: Academic. 4 vols.
65. Fedak, M. A., Pinshow, B., Schmidt-Nielsen, K. 1973. Energy cost of bipedal running. *Fed. Proc.* 32:422 (Abstr.)
66. Feldman, S. E., Larsson, S., Dimick, M., Lepkovsky, S. 1957. Aphagia in chickens. *Am. J. Physiol.* 191:259–61
67. Folk, R. L. 1969. Spherical urine in birds: petrography. *Science* 166: 1516–19
68. Freeman, B. M. 1967. Some effects of cold on metabolism of the fowl during the perinatal period. *Comp. Biochem. Physiol.* 20:179–93
69. Freeman, B. M. 1970. Thermoregulatory mechanisms of the neonate fowl. *Comp. Biochem. Physiol.* 33:219–30
70. Freeman, B. M. 1970. Some aspects of thermoregulation in the adult Japanese quail *(Coturnix coturnix japonica). Comp. Biochem. Physiol.* 34:871–81
71. Freeman, B. M. 1971. Impaired thermoregulation in the thiouracil-treated neonate fowl. *Comp. Biochem. Physiol.* 40A:553–55
72. Freeman, B. M., Misson, B. H. 1970. pH, pO_2, and pCO_2 of blood from the foetus and neonate of *Gallus domesticus. Comp. Biochem. Physiol.* 33:763–72
73. Fujiwara, T., Adams, F. H., Nozaki, M., Dormer, G. B. 1970. Pulmonary surfactant phospholipids from turkey lung: comparison with rabbit lung. *Am. J. Physiol.* 218:218–25
74. George, J. C., Berger, A. J. 1966. *Avian Myology.* New York/London: Academic. 500 pp.
75. Girard, H. 1971. Respiratory acidosis with partial metabolic compensation in chick embryo blood during normal development. *Resp. Physiol.* 13:343–51
76. Gregory, J. E. 1973. An electrophysiological investigation of the receptor apparatus of the duck's bill. *J. Physiol. London* 229:157–64
77. Hammel, H. T. 1968. Regulation of internal body temperature. *Ann. Rev. Physiol.* 30:641–708
78. Hart, J. S. 1962. Seasonal acclimatization in four species of small wild birds. *Physiol. Zool.* 35:224–36
79. Hart, J. S., Berger, M. 1972. Energetics, water economy and temperature regulation during flight. *Proc. XV Int. Ornithol. Congr.,* 189–99
80. Hashimoto, K., Wilt, F. H. 1966. The heterogeneity of chicken hemoglobin. *Proc. Nat. Acad. Sci. USA* 56:1477–83
81. Hazelwood, R. L. 1972. See Ref. 64, 2:471–526
82. Hinds, D. S., Calder, W. A. 1971. Tracheal dead space in the respiration of birds. *Evolution* 25:429–40
83. Hissa, R., Palokangas, R. 1970. Thermoregulation in the titmouse *(Parus major* L.). *Comp. Biochem. Physiol.* 33:941–53
84. Holmes, W. N. 1972. Regulation of electrolyte balance in marine birds with special reference to the role of the pituitary-adrenal axis in the duck *(Anas platyrhynchos). Fed. Proc.* 31:1587–98
85. Ismail-Beigi, F., Edelman, I. S. 1970. Mechanism of thyroid calorigenesis: role of active sodium transport. *Proc. Nat. Acad. Sci. USA* 67:1071–78
86. Johansen, K., Lenfant, C. 1972. A comparative approach to the adaptability of O_2-Hb affinity. *Proc. A. Benzon Symp.,* IV:750–80. Copenhagen: Munksgaard
87. Johnson, O. W. 1974. Relative thickness of the renal medulla in birds. *J. Morphol.* 142:277–84
88. Johnston, D. W. 1971. The absence of

brown adipose tissue in birds. *Comp. Biochem. Physiol.* 40A:1107–8

89. Jones, D. R., Johansen, K. 1972. See Ref. 64, 2:157–285
90. Kanematsu, S., Kii, M., Sonoda, T., Kato, Y. 1967. Effects of hypothalamic lesions on body temperature in the chicken. *Jap. J. Vet. Sci.* 29:95–104
91. Kilgore, D. L. Jr., Bernstein, M. H., Schmidt-Nielsen, K. 1973. Brain temperature in a large bird, the rhea. *Am. J. Physiol.* 225:739–42
92. King, A. S. 1966. Structural and functional aspects of the avian lungs and air sacs. *Int. Rev. Gen. Exp. Zool.* 2:171–267
93. King, J. R. 1972. Adaptive periodic fat storage by birds. *Proc. XV Int. Ornithol. Congr.*, 200–17
94. King, J. R. 1974. The seasonal allocation of time and energy resources in birds. *Avian Energetics,* ed. R. A. Paynter Jr. Publ. Nuttall Ornithol. Club. In press
95. King, J. R., Farner, D. S. 1961. Energy metabolism, thermoregulation and body temperature. *Biology and Comparative Physiology of Birds,* ed. A. J. Marshall, 2:215–88. New York/London: Academic
96. King, J. R., Farner, D. S. 1966. The adaptive role of winter fattening in the white-crowned sparrow with comments on its regulation. *Am. Natur.* 100:403–18
97. Kitchell, R. L., Ström, L., Zotterman, Y. 1959. Electrophysiological studies of thermal and taste reception in chickens and pigeons. *Acta Physiol. Scand.* 46:133–51
98. Kleiber, M. 1961. *The Fire of Life.* New York/London: Wiley. 454 pp.
99. Koike, T. I., McFarland, L. Z. 1966. Urography in the unanesthetized hydopenic chicken. *Am. J. Vet. Res.* 27: 1130–32
100. Kooyman, G. L. 1972. Deep diving behaviour and effects of pressure in reptiles, birds, and mammals. *The Effects of Pressure on Organisms,* ed. M. A. Sleigh, A. G. McDonald, Soc. Exp. Biol. Symp. 26:295–311
101. Kooyman, G. L., Drabeck, C. M., Elsner, R., Campbell, W. B. 1971. Diving behavior of the emperor penguin, *Aptenodytes forsteri.* *Auk* 88:775–95
102. Kooyman, G. L., Schroeder, J. P., Greene, D. G., Smith, V. A. 1973. Gas exchange in penguins during simulated dives to 30 and 68 m. *Am. J. Physiol.* 225:1467–71
103. Kuenzel, W. J. 1972. Dual hypothalamic feeding system in a migratory bird, *Zonotrichia albicollis.* *Am. J. Physiol.* 223:1138–42
104. Kutchai, H., Steen, J. B. 1971. Permeability of the shell and shell membranes of hens' eggs during development. *Resp. Physiol.* 11:265–78
105. Lasiewski, R. C. 1972. See Ref. 64, 2:287–342
106. Lasiewski, R. C., Calder, W. A. Jr. 1971. A preliminary allometric analysis of respiratory variables in resting birds. *Resp. Physiol.* 11:152–66
107. Lasiewski, R. C., Dawson, W. R. 1967. A re-examination of the relation between standard metabolic rate and body weight in birds. *Condor* 69:13–23
108. Leitner, L.-M., Roumy, M. 1974. Thermosensitive units in the tongue and in the skin of the duck's bill. *Pflueger's Arch.* 346:151–55
109. Lenfant, C., Kooyman, G. L., Elsner, R., Drabek, C. M. 1969. Respiratory function of the blood of the Adélie penguin, *Pygoscelis adeliae.* *Am. J. Physiol.* 216:1598–1600
110. Lepkovsky, S. 1973. Hypothalamic-adipose tissue interrelationships. *Fed. Proc.* 32:1705–8
111. Lepkovsky, S., Yasuda, M. 1966. Hypothalamic lesions, growth and body composition of male chickens. *Poultry Sci.* 45:582–88
112. Lepkovsky, S., Snapir, N., Furuta, F. 1968. Temperature regulation and appetitive behavior in chickens with hypothalamic lesions. *Physiol. Behav.* 3: 911–15
113. Lonsdale, K., Sutor, D. J. 1971. Uric acid dihydrate in bird urine. *Science* 172:958–59

113a. Lutz, P. L., Longmuir, I. S., Schmidt-Nielsen, K. 1974. Oxygen affinity of bird blood. *Resp. Physiol.* 20:325–30

114. Lutz, P. L., Longmuir, I. S., Tuttle, J. V., Schmidt-Nielsen, K. 1973. Dissociation curve of bird blood and effect of red cell oxygen consumption. *Resp. Physiol.* 17:269–75
115. McMahon, T. 1973. Size and shape in biology. *Science* 179:1201–4
116. McNabb, F. M. A., Poulson, T. L. 1970. Uric acid excretion in pigeons, *Columba livia.* *Comp. Biochem. Physiol.* 33:933–39
117. McNabb, R. A. 1974. Urate and cation interactions in the liquid and precipitated fractions of avian urine, and speculations on their physico-chemical

state. *Comp. Biochem. Physiol.* 48A: 45–54
118. McNabb, R. A., McNabb, F. M. A., Hinton, A. P. 1973. The excretion of urate and cationic electrolytes by the kidney of the male domestic fowl *(Gallus domesticus). J. Comp. Physiol.* 82:47–57
119. Manwell, C. 1958. Respiratory properties of the hemoglobin of two species of diving birds. *Science* 127:705–6
120. Martindale, L. 1969. Phosphate excretion in the laying hen. *J. Physiol. London* 203:82–83p
121. Millard, R. W., Johansen, K., Milsom, W. K. 1973. Radiotelemetry of cardiovascular responses to exercise and diving in penguins. *Comp. Biochem. Physiol.* 46A:227–40
122. Mills, S. H., Heath, J. E. 1972. Anterior hypothalamus/preoptic lesions impair normal thermoregulation in house sparrows. *Comp. Biochem. Physiol.* 43A:125–29
123. Mills, S. H., Heath, J. E. 1972. Responses to thermal stimulation of the preoptic area in the house sparrow, *Passer domesticus. Am. J. Physiol.* 222:914–19
124. Milsom, W. K., Johansen, K., Millard, R. W. 1973. Blood respiratory properties in some antarctic birds. *Condor* 75:472–74
125. Misson, B. H., Freeman, B. M. 1972. Organic phosphates and oxygen affinity of chick blood before and after hatching. *Resp. Physiol.* 14:343–52
125a. Murrish, D. E., Guard, C. L. 1973. Sympathetic control of nonshivering thermogenesis in south polar skua chicks. *Antarctic J. US* 8:197–98
126. Necker, R. 1972. Response of trigeminal ganglion neurons to thermal stimulation in the beak of pigeons. *J. Comp. Physiol.* 78:307–14
127. Necker, R. 1973. Temperature sensitivity of thermoreceptors and mechanoreceptors on the beak of pigeons. *J. Comp. Physiol.* 87:379–91
128. Newton, I. 1969. Winter fattening in the bullfinch. *Physiol. Zool.* 42:96–107
129. Nightingale, T. E., Fedde, M. R. 1972. Determination of normal buffer line for chicken blood. *Resp. Physiol.* 14:353–65
130. Norris, R. A., Williamson, F. S. L. 1955. Variation in relative heart size of certain passerines with increase in altitude. *Wilson Bull.* 67:78–83
131. Odum, E. P., Connell, C. E. 1956. Lipid levels in migrating birds. *Science* 123:892–94
132. Palokangas, R., Hissa, R. 1971. Thermoregulation in young black-headed gulls *Larus ridibundus* L. *Comp. Biochem. Physiol.* 38A:743–50
133. Palokangas, R., Vihko, V., Nuuja, I. 1973. The effects of cold and glucagon on lipolysis, glycogenolysis and oxygen consumption in young chicks. *Comp. Biochem. Physiol.* 45A:489–95
134. Paynter, R. A. Jr., Ed. 1974. *Avian Energetics. Publ. Nuttall Ornithol. Club.* In press
135. Peaker, M., Ed. 1974. Advances in avian physiology. *Symp. Zool. Soc. London* 35:In press
136. Pearson, R. 1972. *The Avian Brain.* New York/London: Academic. 636 pp.
137. Pennycuick, C. J. 1969. The mechanics of bird migration. *Ibis* 111:526–56
138. Piiper, J., Drees, F., Scheid, P. 1970. Gas exchange in the domestic fowl during spontaneous breathing and artificial ventilation. *Resp. Physiol.* 9:234–45
139. Polin, D., Wolford, J. H. 1973. Factors influencing food intake and caloric balance in chickens. *Fed. Proc.* 32:1720–26
140. Prange, H. D., Schmidt-Nielsen, K. 1970. The metabolic cost of swimming in ducks. *J. Exp. Biol.* 53:763–77
141. Prashad, D. N., Edwards, N. A. 1973. Phosphate excretion in the laying fowl. *Comp. Biochem. Physiol.* 46A:131–37
142. Prusiner, S., Poe, M. 1968. Thermodynamic considerations of mammalian thermogenesis. *Nature* 220:235–37
142a. Rahn, H., Ar, A. 1974. The avian egg: incubation time and water loss. *Condor* 76:147–52
143. Rapoport, S., Guest, G. M. 1941. Distribution of acid-soluble phosphorus in the blood cells of various vertebrates. *J. Biol. Chem.* 138:269–82
144. Rautenberg, W. 1969. Die Bedeutung der zentralnervösen Thermosensitivität für die Temperaturregulation der Taube. *Z. Vergl. Physiol.* 62:235–66
145. Rautenberg, W. 1971. The influence of the skin temperature on the thermoregulatory system of pigeons. *J. Physiol. Paris* 63:396–98
146. Rautenberg. W., Necker, R., May, B. 1972. Thermoregulatory responses of the pigeon to changes of the brain and spinal cord temperatures. *Pfleuger's Arch.* 338:31–42
147. Richards, S. A. 1970. The role of hypothalamic temperature in the control of panting in the chicken exposed to heat. *J. Physiol. London* 211:341–58
148. Richards, S. A. 1971. The significance of changes in the temperature of the

skin and body core of the chicken in regulation of heat loss. *J. Physiol. London* 216:1–10
149. Romijn, C., Lokhorst, W. 1960. Foetal heat production in the fowl. *J Physiol. London* 150:239–49
150. Scheid, P., Piiper, J. 1970. Analysis of gas exchange in the avian lung: theory and experiments in the domestic fowl. *Resp. Physiol.* 9:246–62
151. Scheid, P., Piiper, J. 1971. Direct measurement of the pathway of respired gas in duck lungs. *Resp. Physiol.* 11:308–14
152. Scheid, P., Piiper, J. 1972. Cross-current gas exchange in avian lungs: effects of reversed parabronchial air flow in ducks. *Resp. Physiol.* 16:304–12
153. Scheid, P., Slama, H., Piiper, J. 1972. Mechanisms of unidirectional flow in parabronchi of avian lungs: measurements in duck lung preparations. *Resp. Physiol.* 14:83–95
153a. Scheid, P., Slama, H., Willmer, J. 1974. Volume and ventilation of air sacs in ducks studied by inert gas wash-out. *Resp. Physiol.* 21:19–36
154. Schmidt-Nielsen, K. 1971. How birds breathe. *Sci. Am.* 225:72–79
155. Schmidt-Nielsen, K. 1972. *How Animals Work.* London/New York: Cambridge Univ. Press. 114 pp.
156. Schmidt-Nielsen, K. 1972. Locomotion: energy cost of swimming, flying and running. *Science* 177:222–28
157. Schmidt-Nielsen, K., Kanwisher, J., Lasiewski, R. C., Cohn, J. E., Bretz, W. L. 1969. Temperature regulation and respiration in the ostrich. *Condor* 71:341–52
158. Shoemaker, V. H. 1972. See Ref. 64, 2:527–74
159. Simkiss, K. 1970. Sex differences in the acid-base balance of adult and immature fowl. *Comp. Biochem. Physiol.* 34:777–88
160. Skadhauge, E. 1968. The cloacal storage of urine in the rooster. *Comp. Biochem. Physiol.* 24:7–18
161. Skadhauge, E. 1972. Salt and water excretion in xerophilic birds. *Symp. Zool. Soc. London* 31:113–31
162. Skadhauge, E. 1974. Renal and cloacal transport of salt and water. *Symp. Zool. Soc. London* 35:In press
163. Skadhauge, E. 1974. Cloacal resorption of salt and water in the galah (*Cacatua roseicapilla*). *J. Physiol. London* 240:763–73
163a. Skadhauge, E. 1974. Renal concentrating ability in selected West Australian birds. *J. Exp. Biol.* 61:269–76
164. Skadhauge, E., Kristensen, K. 1972. An analogue computer simulation of cloacal resorption of salt and water from ureteral urine in birds. *J. Theor. Biol.* 35:473–87
165. Skadhauge, E., Schmidt-Nielsen, B. 1967. Renal function in domestic fowl. *Am. J. Physiol.* 212:793–98
166. Skadhauge, E., Schmidt-Nielsen, B. 1967. Renal medullary electrolyte and urea gradient in chickens and turkeys. *Am. J. Physiol.* 212:1313–18
167. Steen, J. B. 1971. *Comparative Physiology of Respiratory Mechanisms.* New York/London: Academic. 182 pp.
168. Steen, J., Enger, P. S. 1957. Muscular heat production in pigeons during exposure to cold. *Am. J. Physiol.* 190:157–58
169. Taylor, C. R., Dmi'el, R., Fedak, M., Schmidt-Nielsen, K. 1971. Energetic cost of running and heat balance in a large bird, the rhea. *Am. J. Physiol.* 221:597–601
170. Tazawa, H., Mikami, T., Yoshimoto, C. 1971. Respiratory properties of chicken embryonic blood during development. *Resp. Physiol.* 13:160–70
171. Tazawa, H., Mikami, T., Yoshimoto, C. 1971. Effect of reducing the shell area on the respiratory properties of chicken embryonic blood. *Resp. Physiol.* 13: 352–60
171a. Tazawa, H., Ono, T. 1974. Microscopic observation of the chorioallantoic capillary bed of chicken embryos. *Resp. Physiol.* 20:81–89
172. Temple, G. F., Metcalfe, J. 1970. The effects of increased incubator oxygen tension on capillary development in the chick chorioallantois. *Resp. Physiol.* 9: 216–33
173. Tucker, V. A. 1968. Respiratory physiology of house sparrows in relation to high-altitude flight. *J. Exp. Biol.* 48: 55–66
174. Tucker, V. A. 1968. Respiratory exchange and evaporative water loss in the flying budgerigar. *J. Exp. Biol.* 48: 67–87
175. Tucker, V. A. 1969. Energetic cost of locomotion in animals. *Comp. Biochem. Physiol.* 34:841–46
176. Tucker, V. A. 1971. Flight energetics in birds. *Am. Zool.* 11:115–24
177. Tucker, V. A. 1972. Metabolism during flight in the laughing gull, *Larus atricilla. Am. J. Physiol.* 222:237–45
178. Tucker, V. A. 1972. Respiration during flight in birds. *Resp. Physiol.* 14:75–82
179. Tucker, V. A. 1973. Bird metabolism

during flight: evaluation of a theory. *J. Exp. Biol.* 58:689–709

180. Tucker, V. A. 1974. The energetics of natural avian flight. *Avian Energetics,* ed. R. A. Paynter, Jr. Publ. Nuttall Ornithol. Club. In press
181. Vandecasserie, C., Paul, C., Schnek, A. G., Léonis, J. 1973. Oxygen affinity of avian hemoglobins. *Comp. Biochem. Physiol.* 44A:711–18
182. Visschedijk, A. H. J. 1968. The air space and embryonic respiration. 3. The balance between oxygen and carbon dioxide in the air space of the incubating chicken egg and its role in stimulating pipping. *Brit. Poultry Sci.* 9:197–210
183. Wang, S., Nesheim, M. C. 1973. Effect of α-aminoisobutyric acid on arginine degradation and excretion by chickens. *Am. J. Physiol.* 225:724–28
184. Wangensteen, O. D. 1972. Gas exchange by a bird's embryo. *Resp. Physiol.* 14:64–74

184a. Wangensteen, O. D., Rahn, H., Burton, R. R., Smith, A. H. 1974. Respiratory gas exchange of high altitude adapted chick embryos. *Resp. Physiol.* 21:61–70

185. Wangensteen, O. D., Wilson, D., Rahn, H. 1970/1971. Diffusion of gases across the shell of the hen's egg. *Resp. Physiol.* 11:16–30
186. Wekstein, D. R., Zolman, J. F. 1968. Sympathetic control of homeothermy in the young chick. *Am. J. Physiol.* 214:908–12
187. Wekstein, D. R., Zolman, J. F. 1969. Ontogeny of heat production in chicks. *Fed. Proc.* 28:1023–28
188. West, G. C. 1965. Shivering and heat production in wild birds. *Physiol. Zool.* 38:111–20
189. West, G. C., Funke, E. R. R., Hart, J. S. 1968. Power spectral density and probability analysis of electromyograms in shivering birds. *Can. J. Physiol. Pharm.* 46:703–6

Copyright 1975. All rights reserved

THE EFFECTS OF LIGHT ON MAN AND OTHER MAMMALS[1]

❖1139

Richard J. Wurtman
Department of Nutrition and Food Science, Massachusetts Institute of Technology, Cambridge, Massachusetts 02139

INTRODUCTION: LIGHT AS AN ENVIRONMENTAL CONSTITUENT

Each human organism receives a finite number of inputs from the world beyond its integument. These inputs, collectively termed "the environment," include chemical, physical, biological, and informational factors; they presumably exerted the major influence on man's development throughout his evolutionary history, and continue to affect him now. The life of the individual human absolutely requires the presence of some environmental inputs (e.g. dietary protein, atmospheric oxygen, water) and the means of withstanding others (e.g. great extremes in temperature, predators, bacteria in drinking water). Some environmental inputs can be modified by choice; within limits, man can choose which solid and liquid chemicals will enter his gastrointestinal tract and whether on any particular day he will allow himself to be exposed to solar radiation. Other environmental inputs, such as cosmic rays, gravity, the magnetic field of the earth, and certain smells and noises, are, for all practical purposes, inescapable. A few specific physical and chemical inputs, notably sound waves, reflected visible light, and foodstuffs that can be tasted, are able to influence the individual both by virtue of their energy or chemical contents and as sources of information; highly specialized sensory cells transduce these inputs into neural signals, which are then sorted into patterns recognized by the brain.

Solar radiation constitutes a ubiquitous and essential component of man's environment. Besides serving as the ultimate source of his food and energy, it has also acted directly upon man to alter his chemical composition, control the rate of his maturation, and drive or entrain his biological rhythms. Until the advent of artificial light sources, reflected rays from the visible portion of the solar spectrum provided most of the raw data subserving man's capacity to see.

[1]Studies described in this report that were carried out in the author's laboratory were supported in part by grants from the United States Public Health Service (AM-11709 and ES-00616) and the National Aeronautics and Space Administration (NGR-22-009-627).

This article describes the best-studied extravisual effects of visible and ultraviolet light on humans and other mammals. It also considers the possible biological consequences to man of living in artificially lighted environments that differ significantly from the milieu in which he evolved.

CHARACTERISTICS OF NATURAL LIGHTING

Man evolved in an environment characterized by a particular kind of photic energy, i.e. the light of the sun, filtered through the atmosphere and its surrounding layer of ozone. This light is present, on the average, for 12 hr out of each 24 hr at every point on earth. The actual number of hours of daylight present on any particular day varies with an annual rhythm whose amplitude at any point on earth depends upon the angular distance between that point and the equator. In the northern hemisphere, the daylight period is longest on the first day of summer and shortest six months later.

Spectral Composition

The spectrum of the solar energies reaching the earth is highly characteristic. Essentially no wavelengths shorter than 290 nm (i.e. short-ultraviolet and some mid-ultraviolet photons) penetrate the atmospheric shield. The radiant flux at longer wavelengths increases sharply in the near-ultraviolet (320–380 nm) and visible (380–770 nm) portions of the spectrum, reaching a peak in the blue-green range between about 450 and 500 nm; it then decreases gradually into the infrared portion of the spectrum. The intensities of ultraviolet light that penetrate the atmosphere vary markedly with season; in the northern United States the total erythemal radiation (290–320 nm) reaching the earth's surface in December may be as little as one fifteenth of that present in June and may be essentially absent from the environment before 9 A.M. or after 3 P.M. The spectral composition and intensity of the visible solar radiation that reaches the earth shows much less tendency to seasonal variation. The illumination from direct sunlight (normal incidence) at noon in Boston in about 6400–8800 ft-c (34–47 mW/cm^2 for wavelengths between 290 and 770 nm), regardless of the time of year.

The spectral composition of sunlight at the earth's surface approximates that of the white light emitted by a theoretical black body heated to about 5600°K, minus the ultraviolet radiation below 290 nm that is unable to penetrate the ozone layer and atmospheric shield surrounding the earth. Hence the solar spectrum is continuous and the relative intensities of any of its component visible wavelengths do not differ by more than twofold; the ratios of the radiant fluxes of red, blue, and yellow bands contained in the white light of the typical midday sun approximate 1:1:1.

Incandescent light sources emit spectra that approximate those of heated black bodies. Their color temperature (the temperature to which a theoretical black body would have to be heated in order to emit a comparable spectrum) is considerably lower than that of sunlight, hence a larger fraction (about 90%) of their total radiant power consists of infrared radiation that provides heat rather than light (53). Within the visible portions of incandescent spectra, the relative fluxes at different wavelengths are, as expected, maximum in the red and minimum in the blue.

Fluorescent bulbs generate visible light by a different physical mechanism from that of the sun or incandescent bulbs. Their light output comes not as a consequence of heating but from the activation of chemical phosphors by ultraviolet emissions generated in a low-pressure mercury arc discharge. The spectra emitted by fluorescent sources can thus be modified at will, limited only by the ability of the chemist to devise novel phosphors. This freedom in programming spectra has been utilized to design bulbs that, for a given total output, are as bright as possible.

Brightness is a subjective phenomenon and depends upon the extent to which the photoreceptors in the retinas are stimulated. Since these photoreceptors are most sensitive to visible light in the yellow-green range (555 nm) (55), most fluorescent light sources have been designed to emit a considerably larger fraction of their total light output in this region of the visible spectrum than the fraction present in sunlight.

Fluorescent sources are also usually designed to minimize the emissions in the ultraviolet or infrared ranges. Because of the wide usage of fluorescent bulbs in offices, schools, and factories, most people in contemporary industrial societies spend most of their waking hours under light spectra that differ considerably from those characterizing natural sunlight and that were chosen by the lighting industry in accordance with the view that the only significant effect of visible light on man is on his retinas, i.e. to enable him to perceive objects by their relative brightness.

Considerable evidence, summarized in this article, indicates that environmental lighting in the visible and near-ultraviolet ranges does considerably more to man than simply to provide the substrate for his vision. Moreover, these other effects of visible light cannot be assumed to depend primarily on yellow-green emissions.

It should be noted that the near-universal propensity of biologists to express the intensity of a light emission in terms of "footcandles" reflects and perpetuates the bias that light's only significant effect upon man is to enable him to see. Footcandles (ft-c) are units of illumination and are defined subjectively in terms of lumens, a unit of brightness per square foot; therefore, the measurement of light from any source in footcandles depends largely upon its output of yellow-green emissions—the larger the proportion of emissions contained within the yellow-green range, the greater the footcandle rating. It should be apparent that for physiologists studying the metabolic effects of light that depend on other portions of the spectrum (e.g. the photoactivation of Vitamin D by ultraviolet light), footcandle measurements give misleading information. It seems much more appropriate that the intensities of visible light emissions be measured in absolute irradiance units, such as microwatts per square centimeter for each spectral band, instead of in subjective footcandle units. (Since much of the literature on biological effects of light provides only footcandle data, both footcandle and absolute energy units will be utilized in the remainder of this article.)

Intensity

The light intensity provided at eye level in most artificially lighted rooms is on the order of 50–100 ft-c (160–320 $\mu W/cm^2$ for cool-white fluorescent light). This level is, in general, less than 10% of that present outdoors in the shade. The decision that this particular intensity was appropriate for indoor use seems to have been based upon economic and technological considerations, rather than on any knowledge of man's biological needs. The amount of heat that would have been generated by incandescent bulbs providing more than 50 ft-c of light would have been burdensome in summertime. Fluorescent sources could provide higher light intensities without excessive heat production; however, the cost of the electric power used in the process would be greater than the amount that people are accustomed to spending for light. It should be recognized that if a citizen of Boston lives in a conventionally lighted indoor environment for 16 hr per day, the total amount of visible light to which he is exposed is considerably less than would impinge upon him were he to spend a single hour each day outdoors.

The responses of man to a particular lighted environment thus depend on three variables of the illumination, i.e. the spectrum of the light, its intensity, and the temporal pattern of the light exposure (e.g. the number of hours per day that the individual is exposed, regardless of day length). All three of these aspects have been changed drastically as man has moved indoors and taken advantage of artificial light sources.

RESPONSES OF HUMANS AND OTHER MAMMALS TO LIGHT

Direct and Indirect Effects of Light

Each of the various effects of light on mammalian tissues can be classified as direct or indirect, depending upon whether its immediate cause is a photochemical reaction occurring within that tissue or a nervous or neuroendocrine signal generated by a photoreceptor (57). The following discussion lists the best-studied effects in each group and describes some of the experimental criteria that can be used to determine the group to which any particular light effect belongs.

DIRECT EFFECTS The direct effects of light can be defined as the chemical changes in the composition of a tissue that result from the absorption of light energy within that tissue. The molecule that absorbs the photon may or may not be photochemically transformed in the process; more commonly it is not, and the photic energy is dissipated as heat. Moreover, through the process of photosensitization, light can also cause chemical changes in molecules other than those that actually absorb the photic energy. Certain photoabsorbent dyes and naturally-occurring body constituents (such as riboflavin) are reversibly converted to photosensitizers (17, 48) after they absorb photons of specific wavelengths. These high-energy intermediates can then catalyze the oxidation of a wide variety of circulating compounds and tissue constituents that would not themselves be capable of absorbing light.

In general, compounds containing conjugated double bonds easily absorb energy in the ultraviolet region (48). The amount absorbed and the wavelength of the photons absorbed maximally tend to increase as the size of the conjugated structure increases. The absorption spectrum of any particular compound is also influenced by the presence of charged side chains (e.g. amines, hydroxyl groups), by the polarity, temperature, and pH of its solvent, and by concentration of the compound in solution. The absorption of light by proteins occurs mostly within certain of the constituent aromatic amino acids (chiefly tyrosine and tryptophan), and is usually maximal at wavelengths of about 280 nm. The purines and pyrimidines in nucleic acids absorb maximally at wavelengths near 260 nm (48).

In order to prove that a particular chemical change in a tissue occurs as a direct response to light it must be shown that light energy of the required wavelength does, in fact, penetrate through the body to reach that tissue. Moreover, the postulated photochemical or photosensitization reaction should be fully characterized both in vitro (in simple solutions or tissue homogenates) and in vivo. This characterization requires that its in vivo and in vitro action spectra be defined, and that all of its reactants, intermediates, and products be isolated and identified. The visible portion of the solar spectrum apparently can penetrate into all of the metabolic compartments of the body—even into the brains of intact sheep (20). Ultraviolet light, which is far more active photochemically, penetrates tissues less effectively; however, even the erythemal irradiations (290–320 nm) are able to pass through the epidermis and into the dermis, where they have access to the blood circulating in dermal capillaries. The identification of in vivo action spectra is difficult and time consuming; few, if any, have been defined for tissue responses beneath the epidermis. The identification of the specific reactants, intermediates, and products involved in any in vivo photochemical reaction remains a future goal.

By studying the effects of controlled artificial light on dilute solutions of photoabsorbent compounds and photosensitizers it is possible to identify substances that might be chemically altered by light in vivo. Experiments can then be performed to determine whether light exposure does, in fact, modify the fate of the substance in the whole organism. However, even when such a modification can be shown to exist [e.g. in the rate at which plasma bilirubin levels fall when jaundiced, premature infants are exposed to sunlight, or artificial light (34)], it still cannot be concluded that the mechanisms of the in vivo and in vitro effects are the same until the action spectra and the reactants, intermediates, and products of the reaction have been characterized. [Indeed, in the case of bilirubin, it now appears that most of the material that is caused by light exposure to leave the body differs from the photodegradation products formed in vitro (4, 44). Some of the fall in plasma bilirubin may result from the absorption of photons by the photosensitizer riboflavin (29) and not by bilirubin itself.]

It should be noted that the demonstration that light exposure modifies the fates of any body constituents in vivo challenges the prevailing view that all chemical reactions occurring in mammals are catalyzed and controlled by enzymes. One can speculate as to why the evolutionary process, which could have provided man with a body surface less permeable to light, "allowed" nonenzymatic, open-ended reactions of this sort to continue to occur.

INDIRECT EFFECTS The indirect responses of a tissue to light result not from the absorption of light within that tissue but from the actions of chemical signals liberated by neurons (i.e. neurotransmitters) or delivered by the circulation (57). These signals, in turn, result ultimately from the responses of specialized photoreceptor cells to light. For example, when young rats are kept continuously under light, photoreceptive cells in their retinas respond by liberating neurotransmitter substances that activate other brain neurons; these neurons, in turn, transmit signals over complex neuroendocrine pathways that reach the anterior pituitary, where they stimulate the secretion of gonadotropin hormones that accelerate the maturation of the ovary. That the cells of the ovary are not responding directly to light can be shown by removing the eyes or the pituitary gland before placing the animals under continuous lighting; in such animals light no longer exerts any measurable influence on ovarian growth or function (57).

Photoreceptors

In order for an indirect effect of light to occur, (*a*) a photoreceptive cell must transduce light energy to a neural signal, (*b*) neurons and/or neuroendocrine transducer cells must transmit that signal via a chemical code along a chain of cells to the target organ, and (*c*) target organ cells must respond to the final neural or hormonal signal.

A particular mammalian cell must exhibit three characteristics to be categorized as a photoreceptor. These are: (*a*) *Anatomic*—Electron microscopy should show that the cell contains characteristic organelles ("outer segments") thought to be the locus of the photochemical transduction process (47). It should also be demonstrated that axons originating from the cell make synapses with true neurons. (*b*) *Chemical*—One of the Vitamin A photopigments (e.g. rhodopsin) should be identified within the cell. (*c*) *Physiological*—The presence of the putative photoreceiver should be shown to be essential in order that a known physiological response to light may occur. Such physiological evidence is necessary to identify a cell as photoreceptive; however, it does not in itself constitute sufficient proof. Thus, in the example cited above, both the retinas and the anterior pituitary gland must be intact in order for ovarian maturation to be stimulated by light; however, only the retina is the photoreceptor. The retina generates the internal signal in response to light; the pituitary is part of the chain of communications cells that is needed to transmit the signal to the ovary.

By applying these criteria, it is evident that only the retina clearly contains photoreceptor cells in mammals (e.g. the rods and cones). Indirect evidence has been presented that some indirect neuroendocrine effects of light persist in blinded immature animals (62); however, this evidence cannot as yet be regarded as compelling. In lower vertebrates, it appears that the retina is not the sole photoreceptive organ: in the blinded duck, light transmitted via quartz rods placed in the eye socket cause the hypothalamus to respond by liberating factors that cause the pituitary to secrete gonadotropins (5); in the frog, the pineal organ and several adjacent epithalamic structures respond to specific wavelengths of visible light by varying the rates at which they emit nerve impulses (13).

Effects of Light on the Skin and Subcutaneous Tissues

Natural sunlight acts directly on the cells of the skin and subcutaneous tissues to produce pathologic and protective responses. Examples of the former include sunburn and, in highly susceptible individuals exposed over many years, a particular variety of skin cancer, i.e. the squamous cell carcinoma. Examples of protective responses include accelerated melanin biosynthesis within epidermal melanocytes and accelerated cell division; these cause the ultraviolet-absorbing layers of the epidermis to thicken. Light also initiates photochemical and photosensitization reactions that affect compounds present in the extracellular spaces (e.g. the circulating blood) or stored in cells. These reactions may be beneficial to the organism, as in the photoactivation of Vitamin D precursors; however, they may also produce compounds toxic to tissues, as in photosensitive porphyria.

CELLULAR INJURY Mid-ultraviolet erythemal radiations (290–320 nm) cause sunburn to appear within several hours of exposure. It is generally believed that this inflammatory reaction, which may persist for several days, results from the release of vasoactive compounds from damaged epidermal cells. These compounds presumably diffuse into the dermis, where they damage the capillaries, causing erythema or reddening, heat, swelling, and pain. A variety of compounds have been proposed as the offending toxins (e.g. the biogenic amines serotonin and histamine; the polypeptide bradykinin).

Sunburn can be considered an affliction of civilization. If, weather permitting, people were to expose themselves to sunlight for 1 or 2 hr each day throughout the year, their skin's reaction to the gradual increase in erythemal solar energies that occurs during the winter and spring months would provide them with a protective layer of pigmentation for withstanding summertime intensities of ultraviolet light. Instead, most urban Americans spend virtually all of the daylight hours indoors during the winter and spring months and are thus highly vulnerable to sunlight on the first day of exposure in a bathing suit. The ensuing sunburn can be compared to the pancreatitis that develops in a starving man fed a large steak.

Chronic exposure to the sun for many hours each day over many decades can cause permanent changes in skin structure. In the epidermis, these changes include skin atrophy, the formation of keratin plaques, and, in susceptible individuals, the appearance of squamous cell carcinomas (28, 54). Dermal changes include the disintegration of collagen and elastic fibers. Genetic factors and the extent of skin pigmentation appear to be of major significance in determining the likelihood that an individual chronically exposed to sunlight will develop a carcinoma (54). Thus this disease is more common among people of Irish descent than would be anticipated if its distribution were random, yet it is reputed to be rare among Indians living high in the Andes who are exposed to considerably higher intensities of ultraviolet light.

Squamous cell carcinomas tend to develop on areas of the skin normally exposed to the greatest amounts of sunlight (for instance, the nose). Fortunately, most are readily curable surgically; just the same, they constitute a preventable, potentially lethal disease, and their manifest correlation with exposure to ultraviolet light has led some dermatologists to suggest that it would be best for humans to avoid ultraviolet light entirely. This conclusion seems extreme (6), especially in view of the growing evidence that most circulating Vitamin D is of endogenous origin (i.e. produced by solar ultraviolet emissions acting on the skin).

The threshold level of ultraviolet exposure beyond which man's general incidence of skin cancer would increase has not been determined. On intuitive grounds, however, it seems likely that this level is appreciably higher than that amount normally obtained from sunlight; otherwise, caucasians would have become extinct eons ago.

PROTECTIVE RESPONSES Immediately after people are exposed to sunlight the amount of pigment in their skin increases and they remain hyperpigmented for a few hours. This effect probably results from the photo-oxidation of a colorless melanin precursor; it can apparently be caused by all of the ultraviolet and visible radiations present in sunlight (49). After a day or two, when the initial response to sunlight has subsided, melanocytes in the epidermis begin to divide and increase their synthesis of melanin granules; the granules are then extruded, after which they are taken up into the keratinocytes. This secondary hyperpigmentation can persist for several weeks following exposure to an erythemal dose of mid-ultraviolet light; it provides considerable protection against further tissue damage by sunlight. It is lost as the keratinocytes slough off, explaining the disappearance of a suntan a week or two after vacation's end. Exposure to ultraviolet light also causes the thickness of the superficial stratum corneum (or horny layer) of the epidermis to increase. This effect helps to retard the passage of ultraviolet light into the deeper layers of the skin.

VITAMIN D AND LIGHT Vitamin D_3, or cholecalciferol, is formed in the skin and subcutaneous tissue when ultraviolet light is absorbed by its provitamin, 7-dehydrotachysterol; it can also be obtained by eating fish. The precise action spectrum for the activation of the provitamin in vivo is not known; it may include both mid-ultraviolet (290–320 nm) and long-wave ultraviolet (320–400 nm) irradiations. A related biologically-active compound, Vitamin D_2, can be obtained by consuming milk and other foods fortified with irradiated ergosterol (ergocalciferol); however, it remains to be demonstrated that this exogenous source is as biologically effective as the Vitamin D formed in the skin. In a population of caucasian adults from St. Louis, Missouri, 71–91% of the total Vitamin D activity in the blood was observed to be associated with Vitamin D_3 and its derivatives (23); hence sunlight remains vastly more important than food as a source of Vitamin D.

Recent studies by De Luca and others have shown that Vitamin D compounds are further transformed by the liver and kidneys to more active metabolites that are hydroxylated at the 1- and 25-positions; these metabolites act on the intestinal mucosa to facilitate calcium absorption and on bone to facilitate calcium exchange (12). Loomis has suggested that the term "Vitamin D" is a misnomer; the active compound is normally synthesized endogenously and thus is much more a hormone than a vitamin (32). Like the hormone thyroxine, which cannot be synthesized in the absence of the dietary constituent iodine, the hormone Vitamin D cannot be formed in the absence of the environmental light input. Just as one could substitute the consumption of irradiated milk for exposing oneself to sunlight, a person could replace his need for dietary iodine by consuming bovine thryoids. This does not mean that thyroxine should be considered a vitamin.

It has been recognized for some years that children chronically exposed to inadequate amounts of sunlight may develop rickets, a deforming disease characterized by undermineralization of the bones. This disease can be cured by irradiating the skin with ultraviolet light or by feeding afflicted children 200–400 international units of Vitamin D daily (32).

Recent studies in Boston showed that apparently normal, elderly males deprived of ultraviolet light for 3 months (by remaining indoors during the winter in environments illuminated by standard incandescent or fluorescent sources) developed an impairment in the ability of their intestinal mucosa to absorb calcium. Concurrent exposure of similar males for 8 hr per day to a lighting environment designed to simulate the solar spectrum in the visible and near-ultraviolet ranges blocked the 40% fall in calcium absorption observed in the control subjects (41). The amount of ultraviolet light impinging on these subjects was equivalent to the quantity that they might be expected to receive during a 15 min lunchtime walk in the summer. It seems possible that the appropriate design of artificial lighting environments may provide a powerful public health measure for the prophylaxis of bony undermineralization.

LIGHT AND PLASMA BILIRUBIN CONCENTRATIONS Bilirubin is a yellow compound produced from the degradation of the hemoglobin released when red blood cells die (46). Apparently bilirubin is harmful to human tissues (specifically, the brain) only during the first few days of life. An increase in the concentration of bilirubin in the blood causes the skin to exhibit a characteristic jaundiced color. Hyperbilirubinemia may reflect excessive production of bilirubin (e.g. because the rate of erythrocyte destruction is too great) or impaired removal of bilirubin from the body (a process initiated by the conversion of bilirubin to water-soluble metabolites in the liver).

A potentially dangerous form of hyperbilirubinemia occurs not infrequently among newborn premature infants whose livers are biochemically immature and whose red blood cells are being destroyed at a pathological rate because of a blood type (usually Rh) incompatibility between the infant and its mother. The lipid-soluble bilirubin becomes concentrated within certain parts of the brain, where it can destroy neurons and produce a clinical syndrome known as kernicterus ("yellow brain"). This toxicity is enhanced by a number of other factors including anoxia, acidosis, hypothermia, hypoglycemia, hypoproteinemia, and sepsis (1, 7, 21, 43). The cerebral damage resulting from kernicterus is irreversible; it can cause various degrees of motor and mental retardation leading to "cerebral palsy" and even death.

All present therapies for hyperbilirubinemia of the neonate are based on the premise that, if plasma bilirubin can be kept from attaining levels of 10–15 mg% until such time as the maturing liver becomes able to clear bilirubin from the blood (i.e. the end of the first postnatal week), brain damage will not occur. One widely-used mode of therapy involves "exchange transfusions," in which the jaundiced blood from the baby is completely replaced with normal blood from a donor (38).

Some years ago it was discovered that bilirubin in solution could, like the rhodopsin in retinal photoreceptors, be bleached by light. Unlike rhodopsin, however, the photodecomposition of bilirubin is not reversed by darkness. This observation prompted intensive clinical research on the possible use of light, or "phototherapy," to lower plasma bilirubin in neonatal hyperbilirubinemia. This possibility was supported by anecdotal evidence that newborn infants whose cribs had been placed near open windows tended to become jaundiced less often than infants whose cribs were at a distance from the windows; perhaps sunlight was accelerating the destruction of circulating bilirubin, and perhaps this effect could be reproduced by artificial light. This hypothesis has now been amply confirmed: literally thousands of jaundiced infants each year are now exposed to light for three or four days, or until their livers mature sufficiently to metabolize bilirubin, as the sole therapy for their hyperbilirubinemia (4, 33).

The final products of photodecomposition of bilirubin in vivo remain to be identified. They are generally believed to be nontoxic and, moreover, water-soluble, and thus can be excreted from the body. [Paradoxically, a major fraction of the excreted material may be unchanged bilirubin itself (26, 35, 44)].

Many questions remain concerning the mechanism and even the long-term safety of the phototherapy effect in hyperbilirubinemia. Blue light is most effective in vitro, using pure solutions of bilirubin, and the decomposition of bilirubin is proportional to the total radiant energy emitted. However, all full-spectrum light sources thus far tested in vivo appear to lower plasma bilirubin levels, regardless of the proportions of their radiant energy that fall in the blue part of the spectrum (52). Hence the mechanism by which light destroys bilirubin in vivo may not be the same as the simple photochemical reaction that occurs in pure solutions of bilirubin. [For example, it could involve a photosensitization reaction, perhaps mediated by circulating riboflavin (29), or even an effect of light on plasma albumin (42), the protein to which most of the circulating bilirubin is bound.] Alternatively, much smaller intensities of a particular spectral band than those currently thought to be necessary could be maximally effective in lowering plasma bilirubin; such intensities could be provided by all standard therapeutic regimens utilizing white-light sources. In any case, since "natural" white light apparently is as effective as pure blue light in treating jaundiced babies, and since exposure to blue light constitutes a novel and untested experience in man's evolutionary history, there seems to be little justification at the present time for treating infants with this narrow-band lighting environment.

The observation that environmental light from the sun or from artificial sources modifies the plasma levels of one endogenous compound opens a Pandora's box for the student of human biology; it raises the possibility that the plasma levels of many additional compounds will be found to be similarly affected. Some such direct responses to light may be advantageous to healthy or to sick people; some may not.

PHOTOSENSITIZING FOODS AND DRUGS A number of widely-used medicines (e.g. tetracyclines) and constituents of foods are potential photosensitizers; they can be activated within the body by light, producing intermediates that can cause tissue damage in sensitive persons. A characteristic sign of such a reaction in sensitive persons is the appearance of a rash on portions of the body most exposed to sunlight (the hands and the face); this disappears when the exposure to the sensitizer food or drug is terminated. In individuals with the congenital disease erythropoietic protoporphyria, unusually large amounts of photosensitizing porphyrins are released into the blood stream as a result of a biochemical abnormality in the cells. These compounds absorb long-wave ultraviolet radiation, generating intermediates that are toxic to the tissues. Patients complain of a burning sensation in portions of the skin exposed to light; this is soon followed by reddening and swelling. Since symptoms can be induced at will and without major hazards in patients suffering from relatively mild forms of this disease, erythropoietic protoporphyria constitutes one of the few clinical situations in which the action spectrum for a direct effect of light has been investigated in detail. The skin damage is produced by a relatively narrow band of light in the region of 400 nm; this coincides with one of the in vitro absorption peaks of the abnormal porphyrins.

The symptoms of this disease can be ameliorated by the use of photoprotective agents such as carotenoids (36), which may act by quenching the free radicals and the singlet-excited oxygen produced as intermediates of the photosensitization reactions.

Effects of Light Mediated via Retinal Photoreceptors

LIGHT AND BIOLOGICAL RHYTHMS The amount of time that all living things are exposed to light varies with two cycles: a 24 hr light-dark cycle of day and night and an annual cycle of changing day length, absent only at the equator. These light cycles correspond to many rhythmic changes in mammalian biological functions. Motor activity, sleep, food and water consumption, body temperature, and the rates at which many glands secrete their hormones all vary with rhythms whose periods approximate 24 hr. Thus the concentration of cortisol in the blood of human subjects varies with a characteristic 24 hr rhythm; it is maximal in the morning hours and attains its nadir in the evening. When people elect to reverse their activity cycles (for example, by working during the hours of darkness and sleeping during the daylight) their plasma cortisol rhythms require about 5–10 days to adapt to the new environmental conditions (16). The plasma glucocorticoid rhythm apparently persists in blinded rats (15), but not among animals kept under continuous illumination (11). The rhythm is perturbed in blind humans; the times of daily peaks and nadirs are out of phase with those of sighted individuals, and may vary from day to day (30).

Annual rhythms in sexual activity, hibernation, and migratory behavior are widespread among animal species. The physiological significance of these rhythms probably derives from their ability to synchronize the activities of individuals within a species with regard to one another and with regard to their changing environmental conditions. For example, sheep ovulate and are fertilized in the fall, thus anticipating by many months the spring when food will be available to the mother for nursing the newborn. For humans there is less pressure to adapt to the natural environment: psychosocial factors quite possibly are of greater importance than light cycles in generating or synchronizing biological rhythms. The biological utility of the sleep-wakefulness rhythm and of other consequent rhythms remains to be identified.

Cycles in environmental lighting may interact with biological rhythms in several ways. The light cycle might induce the rhythm. In this event, placing a mammal in an environment of continuous light or darkness should rapidly abolish the rhythm. Another cyclic environmental input—dietary protein—has been shown to generate a daily rhythm. The amino acids, constituents of protein, travel to the liver via the portal circulation after each meal and cause the protein-synthesizing units (polysomes) of hepatocytes to become aggregated; this accelerates the synthesis and increases the tissue levels of tyrosine transaminase enzyme protein (18, 60).

Rather than inducing the rhythm, the light cycle might simply entrain it, causing all animals in the same species to exhibit maxima and minima at the same time of day or night. The factor that generates the rhythmicity per se could be a different cyclic environmental input (such as dietary protein) or a hypothetical intrinsic oscillator (the mythic "biologic clock"). In either case, placing the mammal in an environment of continuous light or darkness should not extinguish the rhythm. If the rhythmic function can be sampled repeatedly in the same animal, it is possible to show that in the absence of a cyclic lighting input the rhythms in different animals become dissociated from each other. Presumably this dissociation occurs because the rhythm "free runs" or becomes "circadian" (2, 25, 45); that is, its precise period changes from exactly 24 hr to something more or less that is characteristic for each animal. If the rhythm does "free run," it is possibly not simply a "reflex" response to a cyclic environmental input exhibiting 24 hr periodicity (such as light, ambient temperature, humidity). The rhythm might then be generated by other cyclic environmental inputs (such as food and water) that also "free-run" in the absence of light, or it could result from intrinsic oscillators. In any case, only a few rhythms are amenable to this sort of experimental analysis in mammals, since only rhythms in behavior, body temperature, and the concentrations of plasma and urinary constituents can repeatedly be sampled in a single subject.

Relatively little information is available concerning the action spectra or intensities required for light to generate or entrain daily rhythms in mammals; it is known that light is the dominant environmental input affecting rhythms and that light exerts its effects immediately, via retinal photoreceptors. The action spectrum for the entrainment of body temperature rhythm in rats (37) is similar both to that required for the inhibition of the rat pineal (10) and to the absorption spectrum of rhodopsin (55). All peak in the yellow-green range.

LIGHT AND THE MAMMALIAN PINEAL ORGAN Probably the best-characterized indirect effect of light on any process other than vision is the inhibition of melatonin synthesis by the mammalian pineal organ (58). Experiments performed during the past decade have provided compelling evidence that nerve impulses, reaching the pineal via its sympathetic nerves, suppress the synthesis of this hormone (59). These impulses, in turn, are an inverse function of the amount of visible light impinging on the retinas (50). The effects of light on the pineal are mediated by a multisynaptic neuronal system involving the brain, spinal cord, and sympathetic nervous system. This circuitous pathway differs from the route taken by the nerve impulses responsible for vision, and apparently is unique to mammals.

If rats are maintained for several days under conditions of continuous illumination, the activities of two pineal enzymes [hydroxyindole-O-methyltransferase (HIOMT) and serotonin-*N*-acetyltransferase (NAT)] involved in melatonin biosynthesis decrease manifoldly; this effect is absent in animals in which the eyes have been removed or in which the nerves to the pineal have been cut. It appears simply to be an exaggeration of the normal daily response of the pineal to the naturally-occurring 24 hr light-dark cycle, since the rate at which melatonin is synthesized is also least at the end of the daily light period among animals kept in a cyclically lighted environment (3).

The precise role of melatonin, the major pineal hormone characterized thus far, in the physiology of the intact mammal remains to be identified. However, melatonin administration has been shown to affect both the brain (e.g. it induces sleep, modifies the electroencephalogram, and raises the levels of the neurotransmitter serotonin) and the secretion of various endocrine organs (e.g. the pituitary, gonads, and adrenals), probably via primary actions on neuroendocrine control centers in the brain (59). Melatonin administration blocks the cyclic release of luteinizing hormone (LH), the ovulating hormone, from the anterior pituitary gland. Immature rats and hamsters kept under continuous illumination become sexually mature at an earlier age than animals kept under a 24 hr light-dark cycle; this effect may be mediated by the photic inhibition of melatonin secretion. The pineal may provide one channel through which the lighting environment entrains rhythmic biologic processes that are not primarily dependent upon light.

In certain lower vertebrates, the pineal is directly responsive to environmental lighting (13); it serves as a photoreceptive "third eye" that sends messages about the state of environmental lighting to the brain. All traces of direct photoreceptive function are lost in the mammalian pineal organ. The retinal photoreceptor that mediates the control of the mammalian pineal by light awaits identification, as do the photoreceptors mediating all other neuroendocrine effects of light. However, recent studies suggest that this photoreceptor utilizes rhodopsin, and may thus be a rod cell (10).

The action spectrum for the photic inhibition of HIOMT is similar to the absorption spectrum for rhodopsin. If groups of rats are placed for several alternate periods under continuous darkness, light, darkness, and light, pineal HIOMT activity continues to respond appropriately (i.e. by increasing, decreasing, increasing, etc), in spite of the fact that histologic and electroretinographic examination of the eyes suggests that the light exposure has caused extensive damage to the retinal photoreceptive rod cells. This paradox cannot now be fully resolved, inasmuch as no other photoreceptor cells besides rods are known to exist in the rat eye, and the rod photopigment, rhodopsin, appears to mediate pineal responses to light.

LIGHT AND MAMMALIAN GONADAL FUNCTION Environmental lighting has been shown to influence the maturation and subsequent cyclic activity of the gonads in all mammalian and avian species thus far examined (39, 57). The particular responses of each species to light seem to depend on whether the species is monoestrous or polyestrous (that is, whether it normally ovulates once a year, in the spring or fall, or at regular intervals throughout the year). Examples of the latter are laboratory rats (every 4–5 days), guinea pigs (every 12–14 days); and humans (approximately every 29 days). The gonadal responses of each species to light also seem to depend on whether its members are physically active during the daylight hours or during the nighttime. Thus if weanling rats (a nocturnal, polyestrous species) are kept from birth under continuous illumination, they mature at a younger age than control animals kept under cyclic illumination, but then they fail to ovulate cyclically, exhibiting instead a state of "persistent estrus" (19). Blindness in humans (a diurnally active, polyestrous species) is also associated with early gonadal maturation (61).

The gonads of most birds (40, 56) and of most diurnally active, monoestrous mammals [e.g. the ferret (14, 51)] mature in the springtime, in response to the gradual increase in day length. Ovulation can be accelerated in these animals by exposing them to artificial "long days." The annual period of gonadal activity in domestic sheep (also a diurnally active, monoestrous species) occurs in the fall, in response to decreasing day length. The mechanisms that cause some species to be monoestrous and others polyestrous, or that cause some animals to sleep by day and others by night, are entirely unknown, as are those that cause the gonadal responses of various species to light to vary as widely as they do. Among polyestrous species, changes in day length can affect the period length of the estrous cycle (27), even to the point of suppressing cyclic LH release and ovulation [i.e. by continuous illumination in rats (8, 9, 19, 31)]. Exposure to "short days" of less than 12.5 hr of light per day causes hamster testes to atrophy (22, 27). However, baboons exposed for 3 yr to continuous illumination (1200 lux) exhibited no disruption of menstrual cycles (24).

In birds, photoreceptors capable of mediating gonadal responses apparently exist in the brain as well as in the eyes. Hence, light reaching the brain of the duck via quartz rods placed in the eye sockets can be used to accelerate gonadal enlargement (5). In adult mammals, however, only the retinas appear to contain the photoreceptor cells necessary for stimulating gonadal responses (or any other neuroendocrine effects, for that matter). In support of this conclusion, removal of the eyes completely blocks the ability of continuous illumination to accelerate maturation or to interfere with the mechanisms responsible for causing ovulation (57). The neural and neuroendocrine pathways connecting the retinas and the gonads are poorly defined; one such pathway probably involves the pineal organ and melatonin (59). Another may utilize cells in the hypothalamus that, by secreting "releasing factors," control the secretion of gonadotropin hormones from the anterior pituitary. The action spectra and dose-response relationships of the effects of light on mammalian gonads have not yet been identified.

Literature Cited

1. Ackerman, B., Dyer, G., Leydorf, M. 1970. Hyperbilirubinemia and kernicterus in small premature infants. *Pediatrics* 45:918–25
2. Aschoff, J., Ed. 1965. *Circadian Clocks.* Amsterdam: North-Holland
3. Axelrod, J., Wurtman, R. J., Snyder, S. H. 1965. Control of hydroxyindole-O-methyltransferase activity in the rat pineal gland by environmental lighting. *J. Biol. Chem.* 240:949–54
4. Behrman, R. E. et al 1974. Preliminary report of the Committee on Phototherapy in the Newborn Infant, NAS-NRC. *J. Pediat.* 84:135–43
5. Benoit, J., Assenmacher, I. 1959. The control by visible radiations of the gonadotrophic activity of the duck hypophysis. *Recent Progr. Horm. Res.* 15:143–64
6. Blum, H. F. 1964. Does sunlight cause skin cancer? *Univ. Mag.* 21:10–13
7. Boggs, T. R., Hardy, J. B., Frazier, T. M. 1967. Correlation of neonatal serum total bilirubin concentrations and developmental status at age eight months. *J. Pediat.* 71:553
8. Bradshaw, M., Critchlow, V. 1966. Pituitary concentration of luteinizing hormone in three types of "constant estrous" rats. *Endocrinology* 78:1007–14
9. Browman, L. G. 1937. Light in its relation to activity and estrous rhythms in the albino rat. *J. Exp. Zool.* 75:375–88
10. Cardinali, D. P., Larin, F., Wurtman, R. J. 1972. Control of the rat pineal gland by light spectra. *Proc. Nat. Acad. Sci. USA* 69:2003–5
11. Cheifetz, P., Gaffud, N., Dingman, J. F. 1968. Effects of bilateral adrenalectomy and continuous light on the circadian rhythm of corticotropin in female rats. *Endocrinology* 82:1117–24
12. De Luca, H. F. 1971. Role of the kidney tissue in metabolism of vitamin D. *New Engl. J. Med.* 284:554
13. Dodt, E., Heerd, E. 1962. Mode of action of pineal nerve fibers in frogs. *J. Neurophysiol.* 25:405–29
14. Donovan, B. T. 1967. Light and the control of the oestrous cycle in the ferret. *J. Endocrinol.* 39:105–13
15. Dunn, J., Bennett, M., Peppler, R. 1972. Pituitary-adrenal function in photic and olfactory-deprived rats. *Proc. Soc. Exp. Biol. Med.* 140:755–58
16. Eisenstein, A. B., Ed. 1969. *The Adrenal Cortex.* Boston: Little, Brown
17. Enns, K., Burgess, W. H. 1965. The photochemical oxidation of ethylenediamine-tetracetic acid and methionine by riboflavin. *J. Am. Chem. Assoc.* 87:5766–70
18. Fishman, B., Wurtman, R. J., Munro, H. N. 1969. Daily rhythms in hepatic polysome profiles and tyrosine transaminase activity: role of dietary protein. *Proc. Nat. Acad. Sci. USA* 64:677–82
19. Fiske, V. M. 1941. Effect of light on sexual maturation estrous cycles, and anterior pituitary of the rat. *Endocrinology* 29:187–96
20. Ganong, W. F., Shepherd, M. D., Wall, J. R., von Brunt, E. E., Clegg, M. T. 1963. Penetration of light into the brain of mammals. *Endocrinology* 72:962–63
21. Gartner, L. M., Snyder, R. N., Chabon, R. S., Berstein, J. 1970. Kernicterus: high incidence in premature infants with low serum bilirubin concentrations. *Pediatrics* 45:906–17
22. Gaston, S., Menaker, M. 1967. Photoperiodic control of hamster testis. *Science* 158:925–28
23. Haddad, J. G., Hahn, T. J. 1973. Natural and synthetic sources of circulating 25-hydroxyvitamin D in man. *Nature* 244:515–16
24. Hagino, N. 1971. Influence of constant light on the hypothalamic regulation of pituitary function in the baboon. *Endocrinology* 89:1322–24
25. Halberg, F. 1963. Circadian (about twenty-four hour) rhythms in experimental medicine. *Proc. Roy. Soc. Med.* 56:253–60
26. Hewitt, J. R., Klein, R. M., Lucey, J. F. 1972. Photodegradation of serum bilirubin in the Gunn rat. *Biol. Neonatorum* 21:112–19
27. Hoffman, R. A., Reiter, R. J. 1965. Pineal gland: influence on gonads of male hamsters. *Science* 148:1609–11
28. Kligman, A. M. 1969. Early destructive effect of sunlight on human skin. *J. Am. Med. Assoc.* 210:2377–80
29. Kostenbauder, H. B., Sanvordeker, D. R. 1973. Riboflavin enhancement of bilirubin photocatabolism in vivo. *Experientia* 3:282–83
30. Krieger, D. T., Rizzo, F. 1971. Circadian periodicity of plasma 11-hydroxycorticosteroid levels in subjects with partial and absent light perception. *Neuroendocrinology* 8:165–79

31. Lawton, I. E., Schwartz, N. B. 1965. Pituitary content in rats exposed to continuous illumination. *Endocrinology* 77:1140–42
32. Loomis, W. F. 1970. Rickets. *Sci. Am.* 223:77–91
33. Lucey, J. 1969. Phototherapy of jaundice. *Symposium on Bilirubin Metabolism* 6(No. 2):63–70. New York: Nat. Found. Birth Defects
34. Lucey, J. F., Ferreiro, M., Hewitt, J. 1968. Prevention of hyperbilirubinemia of prematurity by phototherapy. *Pediatrics* 41:1047–56
35. Lund, H. T., Jacobsen, J. 1972. Influence of phototherapy on unconjugated bilirubin in duodenal bile of newborn infants with hyperbilirubinemia. A preliminary study. *Acta Pediat. Scand.* 61:693–702
36. Mathews-Roth, M. M., Pathak, M. A., Fitzpatrick, T. B., Harber, L. C., Kass, E. H. 1970. Beta-carotene as a photoprotective agent in erythropoietic protoporphyria. *New Engl. J. Med.* 282:1231–34
37. McGuire, R. A., Rand, W. M., Wurtman, R. J. 1973. Entrainment of the body temperature rhythm in rats: effect of color and intensity of environmental light. *Science* 181:956–57
38. McKay, J. 1964. Current status of exchange transfusion in newborn infants. *Pediatrics* 33:763–73
39. Menaker, M. 1971. Rhythms, reproduction and photoreception. *Biol. Reprod.* 4:295–308
40. Morris, T. R., Fox, S. 1958. Artificial light and sexual maturity in the fowl. *Nature* 182:1522–23
41. Neer, R. M. et al 1971. Stimulation by artificial lighting of calcium absorption in elderly human subjects. *Nature* 229:255–57
42. Odell, G., Brown, R., Holtzman, N. 1970. Dye-sensitized photo-oxidation of albumin associated with a decreased capacity for protein-binding of bilirubin. *Symposium on Bilirubin Metabolism* 6 (No. 2):31–35. New York: Nat. Found. Birth Defects
43. Odell, G. B., Storey, G. N., Rosenberg, L. A. 1970. Studies in kernicterus. III. The saturation of serum proteins with bilirubin during neonatal life and its relationship to brain damage at five years. *J. Pediat.* 76:12–18
44. Ostrow, J. D. 1971. Photocatabolism of labeled bilirubin in the congenitally jaundiced (Gunn) rat. *J. Clin. Invest.* 50:707–18
45. Pittendrigh, C. S., Skopik, S. D. 1970. Circadian systems. V. The driving oscillation and the temporal sequence of development. *Proc. Nat. Acad. Sci. USA* 65:500–7
46. Poland, R. L., Odell, G. B. 1971. Physiological jaundice: the enterohepatic circulation of bilirubin. *New Engl. J. Med.* 284:1–6
47. Sjostrand, F. S. 1961. Electron microscopy of the retina. *The Structure of the Eye,* ed. G. K. Smelser, 1–28. New York: Academic
48. Smith, K. C., Hanawalt, P. C. 1969. *Molecular Photobiology.* New York: Academic
49. Szabo, G. 1969. *The Biology of the Pigment Cell.* New York: Academic
50. Taylor, A. N., Wilson, R. W. 1970. Electrophysiological evidence for the action of light on the pineal gland in the rat. *Experientia* 26:267–70
51. Thomson, A. P. D. 1954. The onset of oestrus in normal and blinded ferrets. *Proc. Roy. Soc. Bull.* 142:126–35
52. Thorington, L., Cunningham, L., Parascandola, J. 1971. The illuminant in the prevention and phototherapy of hyperbilirubinemia. *Illum. Eng.* 66: 240–50
53. Thorington, L., Parascandola, J., Cunningham, L. 1971. Visual and biological aspects of an artificial sunlight illuminant. *J. Illum. Eng. Soc.* 1:33–41
54. Urbach, F. 1969. Geographic pathology of skin cancer. *The Biologic Effects of Ultraviolet Irradiation,* ed. F. Urbach, 635–50. Oxford: Pergamon
55. Wald, G. 1964. The receptors of human color vision. *Science* 145:1007–16
56. Wilson, W. D., Abplanalp, H., Arrington, L. 1962. Sexual development of coturnix as affected by changes in photoperiods. *Poultry Sci.* 41:17–22
57. Wurtman, R. J. 1967. Effects of light and visual stimuli on endocrine function. *Neuroendocrinology,* ed. L. Martini, W. F. Ganong, 2:19–59. New York: Academic
58. Wurtman, R. J., Axelrod, J., Fischer, J. E. 1964. Melatonin synthesis in the pineal gland: effect of light mediated by the sympathetic nervous system. *Science* 143:1328–30
59. Wurtman, R. J., Axelrod, J., Kelly, D. E. 1968. *The Pineal.* New York: Academic
60. Wurtman, R. J., Shoemaker, W., Larin, F. 1968. Mechanism of the daily rhythm in hepatic tyrosine transami-

nase activity: role of dietary tryptophan. *Proc. Nat. Acad. Sci. USA* 59:800–7

61. Zacharias, L., Wurtman, R. J. 1969. Blindness and menarche. *Obstet. Gynecol.* 33:603–8
62. Zweig, M., Snyder, S. H., Axelrod, J. 1966. Evidence for a nonretinal pathway of light to the pineal gland of newborn rats. *Proc. Nat. Acad. Sci. USA* 56:515–20

Copyright 1975. All rights reserved

STRUCTURE-FUNCTION RELATIONSHIPS IN EXCITABLE MEMBRANES

◆1140

D. Landowne, L. T. Potter, and D. A. Terrar
Departments of Pharmacology and Physiology/Biophysics, University of Miami School of Medicine, P. O. Box 520875, Miami, Florida 33152

At least since the time of Bernstein (1902) (14) nerve impulses have been thought to be associated with transient changes in the structure of axonal membranes that allow an increased movement of ions across these membranes. Hodgkin & Huxley (51, 52) quantitatively described permeability changes that could account for action potentials in axons; however, they noted that their experiments were "unlikely to give any certain information about the nature of the molecular events underlying changes in permeability." In early works on synaptic potentials (20, 35, 128) a similar basis was laid for believing that structural changes in the postsynaptic membranes of skeletal muscles induced by the neurotransmitter acetylcholine (ACh), rather than by electrical depolarization, may also lead to sudden and transient increases in ion permeabilities. It is the recent attempts to delineate structures and changes in structures that could account for these permeability changes that are reviewed here.

Since more information has been accumulated concerning the molecules associated with permeability changes with regard to action potentials in axons and synaptic potentials at neuromuscular junctions and similar nerve-electroplaque junctions than at other locations, we limit our discussion to these sites. This limitation deserves comment. While action potentials in most cells are likely to have the same or a highly similar basis, it should be recognized that many neurotransmitters may induce permeability changes (either increases or decreases) in synaptic membranes by mechanisms other than the rapid and direct control of "channels" as discussed here. For example, slow synaptic potentials in sympathetic ganglia appear to have a metabolic basis (81, 107), and certain responses to neurotransmitters in these ganglia and in parts of the central nervous system have been suggested to be dependent upon cyclic nucleotide metabolism (55, 85).

The rate and direction of ion movements through axonal and postsynaptic membranes are dependent upon the electrochemical gradients present across the membranes; the ion movements occur in milliseconds, and the net ion flux per estimated permeability structure or unit is high (cf Table 2). Most investigators, therefore, have interpreted data concerning these processes in terms of diffusional ion movements through "channels" or pores rather than in terms of carrier mechanisms. While no unequivocal evidence for such ion channels has been obtained, we use the term "channel" for the structures involved in permeability changes.

This is a field of intense research at present and much of this review depends upon recent reports, including many given briefly at symposia, and some that are controversial. We expect that further publication, even of completed experiments, will provide many additional details and will alter the relative importance of the findings discussed here. This review was completed in May 1974.

THE ACTION POTENTIAL MECHANISM

Several different approaches to the study of the ion channels of the action potential mechanism are discussed. The first is an extension of Hodgkin & Huxley's work, in which the solutions bathing nerves are changed to those of different composition, and changes in transmembrane current during action potentials are examined by voltage clamp techniques. These experiments yield information about the ion selectivity of different channels, and thereby permit estimates of minimum channel size. The second is the approach where one looks for changes in the electrical or optical properties of axons associated with nerve impulses; in this section only newer voltage clamp studies that have revealed "gating currents" are examined in any detail. These currents may derive from the mechanism for the opening and closing of channels. The remaining approaches concern the effects of sulfhydryl group-reactive agents, which suggest that ion channels may be in part composed of protein, studies of the binding of radioactive tetrodotoxin (TTX) and saxitoxin (STX) to sodium channel components in situ and in solution, which describe their number and size, and application of the technique of electron microscopy.

Channel Size as Revealed by Ion Selectivities

Hodgkin & Huxley described the enhanced movement of ions during action potentials in terms of two permeability changes, an early one for sodium, and a delayed one for potassium (51). When axons were perfused with altered internal media, it became apparent that the specificity of each permeability change was not absolute. In voltage clamp studies with squid axons, Chandler & Meves (21) measured the effects of various media on the reversal potential for the early (sodium) current and then analyzed their results in terms of the constant field equation. The permeabilities relative to Na^+ were, Li^+, 1.1; K^+, 0.08; Rb^+, 0.025; and Cs^+, 0.016. These results were confirmed for the node of Ranvier in frogs and extended by Hille (47–49), whose results for both the early sodium current and the delayed potassium current are listed in Table 1.

When sodium is partially replaced by choline in the solution outside the axons, the maximum amplitude of the inward current during action potentials varies roughly as the external sodium concentration. This finding led to the "independence principle" of Hodgkin & Huxley (51), i.e. that the flux of an ion is proportional to its concentration and is not dependent upon the concentrations of other ions. Given this principle the relative permeabilities of various ions can be estimated from the magnitude of transmembrane currents. These estimates also are shown in Table 1, where it can be seen that they are not very well correlated with the permeabilities

Table 1 Relative permeabilities of the sodium and potassium channels of nerve membranes as estimated from the reversal potential using the constant field equation (column 1); from the peak current (column 2); or from measured influxes (column 3) or effluxes (column 4).

		SODIUM CHANNEL		
Na^+	1	1	1	1
NH_3OH^+	0.94[a]	0.21[a]	1.0[d]	
Li^+	0.93, 1.1[a,c]	0.72[a]		
NH_3NH^+	0.59[a]	0.44[a]		
Tl^+	0.33[a]	0.08[a]		<0.3[e]
NH_4^+	0.16[a]	0.10[a]		
guanidine$^+$	0.13[a]	0.03[a]		0.3[f]
HO-guanidine$^+$	0.12[a]	0.03[a]		
K^+	0.08[a,c]	0.08[a]		
NH_4-guanidine$^+$	0.06[a]	0.03[a]		
Rb^+	<0.012, 0.025[a,c]			
Cs^+	<0.013, 0.017[a,c]			0.01[f]
		POTASSIUM CHANNEL		
K^+	1	1	1	1
Tl^+	2.3[b]		1.0[e]	1.5[e]
Rb^+	0.9[b]	0.9[b]		
NH_4^+	0.13[b]	0.1[b]		
Cs^+	<0.08[b]			0.02[f]
NH_3OH^+	<0.03[b]			
guanidine$^+$	<0.013[b]			0.6[f]

[a] Frog node (47).
[b] Frog node (48).
[c] Squid axon (21).
[d] (23a) compared to (9a) frog node.
[e] Squid axon (Landowne, D. and Scruggs, V., unpublished).
[f] (128a) compared to (128b), squid axon.

calculated from reversal potentials. Other evidence suggests also that the independence principle is not always followed, e.g. tetraethylammonium (TEA) ions inside squid axons block outward but not inward potassium currents (7), internal perfusion with Li^+, Na^+, Rb^+, or Cs^+ apparently interferes with outward potassium current, and external Cs^+ but not external Na^+ interferes with inward potassium current (15, 21, 22). There does not seem to be evidence for ions (other than toxins) interfering with sodium currents, but the discrepancies between the results listed in columns 1 and 2 in Table 1 imply that the independence principle may not hold tightly here either. Thus permeabilities estimated from the constant field equation do not relate very well to the abilities of ions to carry current across axonal membranes.

Another, technically more difficult, way to measure permeabilities is with the use of radioactive ions (Table 1). In general the most reliable data have been obtained with relatively impermeable ions used in trace quantities, e.g. for Cs^+ there is good agreement between the permeabilities measured by flux, current, and reversal potential techniques. The time resolution of flux techniques does not permit discrimination between the permeabilities of sodium and potassium channels (e.g. thallium ions probably pass through both), and there are other problems, for example, the large amounts of hydroxylamine that enter nerves during nerve impulses are difficult to account for, and guanidinium ions appear considerably more permeable in squid than frog nerves (unpublished work by Chandler and Meves in ref. 47).

Based on permeability ratios estimated from the constant field equation, and on observations such as that methyl derivatives of several ions are more permeable than their simpler parent ions, Hille (47, 48) developed a rather specific geometric model for that portion of the sodium channel that is ion selective: he pictured a rectangular hole of about 3×5 Å surrounded by 8 oxygen atoms. Oxygen atoms are specifically suggested because hydrogen bonding could help to explain the permeability characteristics of methyl derivatives. Further discussion on relative selectivity is in terms of a high field strength site, as first suggested by Chandler & Meves (21), a concept that primarily concerns the accessibility of ions to channel ligands (29).

While it is apparent from studies of gramicidin (132) that channels with such a structure can exist, it must be recognized that other selectivity mechanisms than a pore are possible (82). Unfortunately, the dimensions involved are below the realized resolution of microscopic techniques, and unless it becomes possible to isolate channel structures from axons, crystallize them, and obtain useful X-ray data concerning their detailed structure (which seems, at best, far off), the types of measurements already discussed appear to be the only way to guess at the geometry of the cores of these sodium channels.

From similar steric arguments the potassium channel of action potentials has been postulated to have at least one selectivity portion approximately 3 Å in diameter capable of accepting dehydrated potassium ions. Considerable further information has been obtained by Armstrong (7) in a study of squid axons perfused internally with TEA derivatives having one bulky and highly hydrophobic sidechain. It was found that these quaternary ions acted only when K^+ permeability had been increased by membrane depolarization, and that they decreased potassium conductance to a low value even during continued depolarization. The partially occluded channels could be cleared, however, by hyperpolarization of the membrane or by raising the external concentration of K^+. The latter two findings strongly suggest that K^+ ions traverse the membrane through true channels that can be partially plugged at their inner end by TEA and its derivatives. Armstrong suggested that the inner end has a widened mouth (diameter ∼8–9 Å) that could serve as an initial selectivity filter for hydrated potassium ions.

Channel Control

GATING CURRENTS Hodgkin & Huxley (51) found that sodium conductance across axons changed e'-fold for each 4 mV change in membrane potential, and suggested that some charged structure in the membrane altered its conformation to allow the passage of these ions. The earliest model to account for permeability changes during action potentials was one having a charged carrier that could combine with sodium and then move across the membrane under the influence of the electrical field (53). This idea was soon rejected because it required a large and early outward current before the inward sodium current, and this was not observed. The idea that there must be a movement of charged groups (at least in the sense of dipoles) remained, however, and much effort has been directed towards trying to find an electrical change (gating current) of appropriate timing and magnitude.

Present attention is focused on tiny, outwardly directed currents that occur just before the usual sodium conductance change, and that are nearly obscured by the initial capacitative surge. On reexamination of early records (54, Figure 16; 21, Figure 4), it is clear that the currents during the capacity transients resulting from depolarizing pulses applied to squid axons were slightly larger than those from hyperpolarizing pulses. By averaging large and equal numbers of opposite pulses, and by special amplification techniques, Armstrong & Bezanilla (8, 9, 16) and Keynes & Rojas (74) have been able to quantify the magnitude of these small currents. The apparent charge movement contributes 0.25–0.5 $\mu F/cm^2$ to the low frequency capacitance of about 1 $\mu F/cm^2$ (9), which is in the appropriate range for the expected change in capacitance (126, 129). These gating currents are not dependent upon the presence of sodium or potassium on either side of the membrane and are not blocked by TTX.

The question remains as to whether these small currents are associated with the mechanism for controlling sodium conductance. In favor of this conclusion are observations that both these and sodium currents are reversibly blocked by intra-axonal Zn^{2+} ions and by brief or prolonged depolarization. Moreover, the small currents have the same opening time constants and half-maximal potential, as a function of both voltage and temperature, as the hypothetical "m" system described by Hodgkin & Huxley (52) to fit the kinetics of turning on the sodium current.

OTHER STUDIES Quite a number of potential-dependent changes in the optical properties of squid axons have been described (24), and it has been suggested that these could be due to changes in membrane thickness (electrostriction) or reorientation of dipoles. At the time these effects were described they were dissociated from sodium conductance changes because they were not affected by TTX, but since observed "gating currents" are also TTX-insensitive it seems reasonable to ask whether these currents and any of the optical changes are associated. Keynes & Rojas (74) have presented quantitative arguments against the electrostrictive effect producing these currents, but there is the unresolved possibility that some non-specific dipole rotation produces the observed currents. One of the voltage-dependent optical signals that does not appear to be associated with gating currents is the "rapid birefringence change," since the optical changes are faster and have too high a temperature coefficient (25).

Although not enough information is now available to predict the lifetime of open ion channels from knowledge of channel dipoles or other charged particles, some information about such lifetimes is available from other experiments. Analysis of membrane voltage "noise" in squid axons shows a TEA-sensitive component whose characteristics are similar to those of the voltage-dependent K^+ channel (37). If one assumes that the K^+ channel is either open or closed, then the channel lifetime is the same as that of the "n" reactive system controlling K^+ ion current (52), or about 1 msec at the resting potential and 22°C. Since there is reason to believe that the rate constant for the "m" reactive system controlling the Na^+ current is faster (by a factor of about 10) than that of the potassium system (52), the lifetime of the sodium channels may be shorter.

Channel Properties Revealed by the Use of Specific Ligands

SULFHYDRYL REAGENTS Heavy metal ions, including those of mercury, silver, copper, uranium, and cadmium, and the more selective SH-reactive agents, *N*-ethylmaleimide (NEM) and *p*-chloromercurobenzoate (PCMB), all reduce the electrical excitability of axons in proportion to their ability to form insoluble salts with sulfides; their effects can be prevented or reversed with cysteine or glutathione (19, 57, 125).

In the case of $HgCl_2$ and *p*-hydroxymercurobenzoate, blockade produced by internal or external perfusion can be reversed by the external application of β-mercaptoethanol (57, 123). Prolonged perfusion with high concentrations of cysteine or β-mercaptoethanol alone can also produce blockade of a type that is rapidly reversible after removal of the agent, unlike the action of NEM and PCMB. All of these results suggest the presence of essential SH-groups somewhere on or in sodium channels, and this in turn suggests that the channel is composed at least in part of protein. Observations that stimulation enhances the effectiveness of the blocking agents (95, 96) offer hope that sulfhydryl reagents may aid in the labelling and isolation of channel components. Unfortunately there have been few voltage clamp studies with these agents; it has been reported, however, that organic mercurials depressed both early and late (potassium) currents, and β-mercaptoethanol increased and prolonged the peak transient sodium current (94).

BINDING STUDIES WITH TTX AND STX Since TTX and STX block the sodium current of action potentials, many investigators now use these agents for the labelling, characterization, and isolation of sodium channel components. Studies with radioactive TTX and STX (28, 45) have extended earlier binding studies with nonradioactive TTX and demonstrated that the amounts and packing density of saturable TTX sites on nerves are very low. In the garfish olfactory nerve, used because of its lack of myelination and the high surface/volume ratio of its small axons, the number of sites is only about $2/\mu m^2$; larger axons in the crab, lobster, and rabbit have about 10 times this number. Although squid axons have not yet been studied in detail, relative estimates based on electrical measurements would suggest 200–500 sites/μm^2 (75). Preliminary data from direct measurements of STX binding suggest a number near $200/\mu m^2$ (Y. Sheline and G. Strichartz, personal communication).

TTX and STX each prevent binding of the other, and since their only common feature is a guanidinium group, it has been postulated that this group serves to plug the external end of sodium channels; it could fit in the 3×5 Å slot postulated by Hille (47, 48). Since both toxins are inactive inside squid axons (102), the inner end of sodium channels is presumably different from the outer end. Additional evidence for the latter point is that batrachotoxin, which causes sodium channels to remain partially open, appears to act only at the inner membrane surface (2).

Happily for prospective isolation studies, tritiated TTX and STX bind with the same affinities ($K_d \approx 3 \mu M$ and $9 \mu M$ respectively) and to the same degree to intact and homogenized nerves and to their detergent-dispersed membrane proteins (12, 13, 45, 46). The fact that TTX and STX displace each other on dissolved proteins further indicates that they react with the same molecule rather than with neighboring molecules. Specific toxin binding is reduced by calcium but not by sodium ions, and at low pH; the log acid dissociation constant (pK_a) of the binding site appears to be about 5.8, a value close to that (5.4) of a membrane component known to reduce sodium currents (134). In membrane fragments, toxin binding is reduced by phospholipase but not trypsin. But after treatment with phospholipase or after solubilization, binding is reduced by proteases (12), suggesting that the channel is composed of protein embedded in phospholipid. Dithiothreitol (DTT) reduces binding as well (12), but only to solubilized proteins, and it has, therefore, been suggested that at least one disulfide bond is necessary for binding and that it is normally protected from the action of DTT in the membrane. Toxin binding is also reduced by Tl^+ ions, in situ and in solution, with a K_d of about 20 mM (45), a value close to that predicted for thallium ion binding from ion effects on sodium currents (Hille, cf 45).

The size of the toxin-binding molecule has not been accurately determined. Based on the loss of TTX binding following progressive irradiation of nerves in a linear electron accelerator, a rough molecular weight of about 230,000 has been calculated (80), and this size is close to that of other membrane proteins believed to traverse unit membranes. The apparent sedimentation rate (9.2 *s*) and Stokes radius (roughly 8 nm) of detergent-coated TTX-binding molecules would suggest a larger or longer protein molecule if it were water soluble, but these values (Table 2) are not useful for size measurements because of the presence of detergent binding. In fact, the values obtained are close to those for the nicotinic acetylcholine receptor, another

Table 2 Characteristics of permeability structures in excitable membranes

	Action potential (Na^+ channel)[a]	*Synaptic potential* (Na^+ and K^+channel)
Packing density of toxin sites on membranes	TTX: 2–400/μ^2	α-Bungarotoxin: 10,000–30,000/μ^2
Conductance of channels	1–50 × 10^{-11}mho	3–10 × 10^{-11} mho
Ion flux $msec^{-1}$ $channel^{-1}$	10–40 × 10^4	Net: 2–5 × 10^4
Estimated molecular weight	230,000	240,000 ± 40,000
Sedimentation rate of toxin-binding complex with Triton X-100	9.2s	9.3s
Morphology at membrane surface	(not established)	Ring of 5 subunits, 6 nm overall diameter

[a]Not enough is known about the characteristics of K^+ channels to warrant inclusion in this table. Please see the text for references.

membrane protein whose molecular weight is believed to be about 240,000 (Table 2).

The amounts of TTX-binding protein in the nerves studied so far have been just sufficient for the above investigations, but they are grossly inadequate for attempts at protein characterization. The electric tissue of the eel *Electrophorus electricus,* which produces shocks because of summed action potentials in stacks of thin electroplaques, appears to be a richer source (13) and one available in the kilogram quantities required for obtaining milligram amounts of channel protein. Development of affinity columns will probably be necessary for purification, but experience to date with suitable TTX derivatives has not been encouraging. The instability of the TTX binding site in solution (12, 46) is also a major problem, and other means of channel labelling (e.g. with radioiodine, SH-reactive agents, anesthetics, batrachotoxin, or Tl^+ ions under appropriate site protection conditions) may prove necessary or at least helpful during purification.

Morphological Studies

A molecule the size of the TTX-binding protein that also spans the axonal membrane should be visible in membranes by thin sectioning and freeze-cleaving techniques, and, if it has an end projecting from one face of the membrane (like the postsynaptic acetylcholine receptor) it should also be revealed by negative staining. The latter technique requires pure or morphologically identifiable membrane fragments not now available, and so far, thin sectioning of fixed tissues has not revealed any specific structure(s) that might be sodium or potassium channels. The membranes of squid giant axons (and other cells) have osmophilic structures containing calcium phosphate whose function is not known (50, 109). Squid axonal membranes, like Schwann cell membranes, inner mitochondrial membranes, and endoplasmic reticulum, appear thicker after nerve stimulation, asphyxia, or treatment with reducing agents, perhaps because of the unmasking of SH groups (112).

A more interesting specialization of axonal membranes has been revealed by freeze cleaving of crayfish nerves. Peracchia (111) found longitudinally arranged depressions in the axonal surface lined with hundreds of particles, about 80 Å in diameter, closely packed in square arrays. (It may be noted that such arrays most likely represent proteins with 4, or some multiple of 4, subunits, and that the "m^3h" analysis of sodium gating by Hodgkin & Huxley suggests a four-component system.) The number of particles per μm^2 of total axonal surface, about 200–400, appears somewhat higher than the average calculated packing density of TTX sites on other crustacean nerves, but a direct comparison in one species is not available. Similar square arrays occur on many cells, and present attention is directed towards delineating whether or not they represent structures involved in excitatory or other processes.

THE SYNAPTIC POTENTIAL MECHANISM

At the frog neuromuscular junction, where synaptic potentials have been studied most fully, the arrival of an action potential in the motor nerve leads to the liberation of ACh, which acts on the outside of the postsynaptic (muscle cell) membrane to produce an increase in permeability to several types of cations at once (20, 35, 128). The change in permeability associated with the amount of ACh released by a single nerve impulse permits a net charge transfer across the postsynaptic membrane equivalent to approximately 10^{10} univalent ions in several milliseconds, and results in an action potential in the muscle fiber membrane (35).

Conceptually, the synaptic potential mechanism can be viewed as composed of an ACh "receptor" coupled to at least one channel for cations. Receptors are associated with a large integral membrane glycoprotein composed of a ring of 5–6 (probably 5) subunits, and having 2–3 binding sites for ACh (see below). (To accord with the pharmacological literature and with the symbols used for receptor models we use the term "receptor" or "receptor subunit" for protein subunits having specific recognition sites for ACh, and "receptor molecule" for the observed pentamer.)

Because the permeability increase resulting from the application of ACh begins in tens of microseconds after the application of ACh, it seems probable that receptor molecules are either very closely coupled to channel molecules or that one receptor-channel macromolecule subserves both functions. Present biochemical and morphological evidence favors the latter possibility. What is not clear is whether conformational changes in receptor subunits are sufficient to cause effective gating of channels or whether additional conformational changes in other subunits are required for normal channel control. The time course of the permeability change of these channels is clearly voltage-dependent (5, 91), perhaps because conformational changes in receptors are sensitive to the transmembrane potential, or because additional channel components are, or both. At present there is reasonable evidence for channel activation or blockade only by receptor activation or blockade. In the following discussion, however, it should be borne in mind that agents thought to combine with receptors may affect other channel structures as well.

As for the action potential mechanism, several approaches have yielded considerable information about the synaptic potential mechanism. These are considered in the same order, namely ion selectivity as a measure of minimum channel core size, normal channel control, receptor-channel properties revealed by the use of specific ligands, and morphological studies.

Channel Size as Revealed by Ion Selectivity

The permeability increase induced by ACh in the membranes of frog muscle cells is mostly to sodium and potassium ions (128), although it extends also to calcium ions (65, 127). Studies of the movement of radioactive tracers in denervated mammalian muscle also indicate that ACh increases membrane permeability to Na^+, K^+, and Ca^{2+} (59). Several small organic cations can apparently substitute for these inorganic ions, including ammonium, methylammonium, ethylammonium, and hydrazinium (40, 41, 77, 103), and, to a lesser extent, tetramethylammonium, trimethylethylammonium, choline, and dimethyldiethanolammonium (103). If dehydrated, most of these ions would pass through a channel about 3 Å in diameter.

Unlike the situation with action potentials, the increases in permeability to sodium and potassium at postsynaptic membranes occur simultaneously. That for sodium is somewhat greater than the change in permeability to potassium. Although several conditions have been found that appear to alter the ratio of these permeabilities, the bulk of the available evidence concerning factors that modify permeability suggests that both ions pass through one type of channel (42, 43).

Channel Control

NOISE MEASUREMENTS An interesting new method that has provided useful information about the kinetics of receptor activation has been described by Katz & Miledi (66–68). They found that the action of depolarizing agonists, applied to frog skeletal muscle either by iontophoresis or in the bathing solution, is accompanied by an increase in voltage "noise" across the postsynaptic membrane. There is no such noise when depolarization of similar magnitude is evoked by passing direct current from an intracellular microelectrode to the outside solution. They suggested that the noise could reflect "elementary" events, the combined effect of which was the depolarization produced by the drug. It seemed possible that each individual event could reflect the opening and closing of individual "channels" by means of which small cations could cross the membrane, and that this could be linked to the binding of agonist to single, or to small groups of, receptors.

An estimation of the mean lifetime of these events can be made from an analysis of the "power spectra" of the noise; the variance of the noise is expected to vary with its frequency in a way determined by the lifetime of individual events, and this provides the basis for the estimation (67, 68). However, such an analysis of intracellularly recorded voltage noise is limited by the passive electrical properties of muscle fibers, in particular the resistance and capacitance of their surface membranes. In an attempt to circumvent this problem, Katz & Miledi (68) recorded voltage noise with an extracellular electrode placed close to the postsynaptic membrane. By this method they were able to estimate that each elementary conductance change lasts for approximately 1 msec at 20°C.

The conductance changes underlying voltage noise can be examined more directly by voltage-clamping endplate membranes. Using this technique, Anderson & Stevens (4–6) analyzed the temporal characteristics of current noise produced by ACh. Their estimate for the mean lifetime of an elementary event was about 11 msec at 8°C at a membrane potential of –100 mV; the mean lifetime was less at higher temperature and more positive membrane potential. The magnitude of the elementary conductance change was found to be 0.3×10^{-10} mho, in good agreement with Katz & Miledi's (68) value of 10^{-10} mho, determined from intracellular voltage noise. A similar value (0.8×10^{-10} mho) has been found for the action of ACh on chick pectoral muscle grown in tissue culture (122). It may be calculated from these values that at the resting potential each elementary event is associated with a net charge transfer equivalent to approximately $2–5 \times 10^4$ univalent ions per msec (6, 68).

The precise time course of the elementary conductance change remains uncertain. Katz & Miledi assumed that the average current pulse associated with an elementary event conformed to an exponentially declining blip, but they pointed out that if individual events were of rectangular shape (in other words, the conductance is fixed while the channel is open) and if the duration of individual "on" states varies in a random fashion, the final result might be approximately the same.

The latter suggestion was made by Magleby & Stevens (91, 92) in their quantitative analysis of endplate currents. The time course of endplate currents, which became more prolonged at more negative membrane potentials, was accurately described by the model they proposed. They pointed out that it follows from their model, which includes the postulate that active drug-receptor complexes corresponding to open channels decay with a rate constant α, that the mean lifetime of channels opened by acetylcholine is α^{-1}. In keeping with this hypothesis, Anderson & Stevens (5, 6) found that α, whether determined from the decay of endplate currents, the decay of miniature endplate currents, or from a spectral analysis of current noise, has the same value and varies in the same way with membrane potential.

Katz & Miledi (67–69) found that channel lifetimes resulting from the action of carbachol, decamethonium, and acetylthiocholine are shorter than those produced by ACh, whereas suberyldicholine activates channels with a longer lifetime. These results indicate that the lifetimes of active receptor complexes and conductance channels are closely related, most likely because a channel lifetime reflects the time during which an agonist remains bound to a receptor. Another important finding is that blocking of receptors with curare or α-bungarotoxin leads to a reduction in the frequency of the elementary events evoked by ACh, while there is little or no change in their amplitude or time course (68, 72). These results suggest that blocking receptor subunits with curare or toxin leads to all-or-nothing inactivation of individual conductance channels. Similarly, it has been found that desensitizing doses of ACh cause a reduction in the frequency of the elementary events but do not modify their amplitude or time course (6). However, it should be mentioned that on skeletal muscle the blocking action of atropine at very high doses (about 140 μM) is accompanied by a marked shortening of elementary events, though this may reflect a nonspecific effect on the endplate membrane rather than a direct effect on receptors (71).

COOPERATIVE ACTIVATION OF RECEPTORS While it seems clear that the activation of individual channels is closely linked to receptor occupation, it may be questioned whether each channel is activated by an individual ACh molecule or by the cooperative action of several ACh molecules. Such a possibility is suggested by the finding that dose-response curves (plotted linearly) for the action of acetylcholine and other depolarizing agents at the neuromuscular junction begin with a region of increasing slope (58, 60, 73, 116).

Further evidence (93) for a cooperative action of ACh is provided by a less direct method that does not rely on dose-response curves, but takes advantage of the finding that endplate potentials are prolonged in the presence of neostigmine, apparently because ACh molecules bind repeatedly to receptors as they diffuse from the synaptic cleft (70). If an ACh molecule binds n times with receptors for t msec each as it escapes from the synaptic cleft, then the time required for a molecule to diffuse from the synaptic cleft is prolonged by nt msec. It follows that if the number of receptors free to combine with ACh is experimentally reduced, then ACh should bind less often and be delayed less as it escapes from the synaptic cleft; consequently, the decay of the endplate current should be less prolonged. In keeping with this hypothesis, it has been found that curare and snake toxins (which reduce the number of free receptors) decrease the time constant of decay both of externally recorded miniature endplate potentials (70) and of endplate currents (93) in the presence of neostigmine. It might be expected that increasing the number of agonist molecules should also reduce the number of free receptors and lead to a faster decay of endplate currents. But, in the presence of neostigmine, it has been found that when the number of ACh molecules in the synaptic cleft is increased (either by releasing more from the nerve terminal or by superimposing the evoked release on a background concentration of bath-applied ACh), the decay of endplate currents in neostigmine is prolonged, rather than shortened (93). To account for these findings, a cooperative action of ACh has been suggested in which the association of ACh with one binding site favors the binding or retention of ACh at other sites (93). In such a case, nt (and consequently the time constant of decay of endplate currents in neostigmine) would increase with an increasing concentration of ACh in the synaptic cleft, as observed.

It is not yet clear whether the cooperative binding or retention of acetylcholine (for which there is also biochemical evidence; see below) is sufficient to explain the increasing slope of dose-response curves at low agonist concentrations.

DESENSITIZATION OF RECEPTORS A change in receptors during their activation by agonists has been postulated to account for observations that activating drugs seem to lose their effectiveness during prolonged application. In particular, the depolarization of the endplate membrane of frog skeletal muscle caused by ACh and other agonists declines even while the drug concentration is maintained (34, 60,

73, 86, 89, 104, 118, 131), and it has been suggested that receptors become transformed to a "desensitized" or inactive form (73, 118).

In keeping with the idea that receptors can exist in more than one conformation, it has been found that desensitized receptors have an increased affinity for certain decamethonium analogs that alkylate receptors (119). The proportion of receptors alkylated increased linearly with the proportion of receptors desensitized (calculated using dose-ratio techniques); moreover, the same degree of potentiation of alkylation was found when a fixed proportion of receptors was desensitized. Evidence of a quite different kind suggests that desensitized receptors have a reduced affinity for certain snake toxins. Thus the binding of ^{131}I-labelled α-bungarotoxin to frog skeletal muscle is inhibited by desensitizing doses of ACh or carbachol (100); frog muscles that have been partially desensitized with carbachol are protected from the blocking action of cobratoxin (79). These studies suggest that receptors can be irreversibly stabilized in at least two states.

A striking feature of desensitization is that its kinetics change markedly with the method of applying the desensitizing drug. Thus desensitization develops within seconds when the agonist is applied iontophoretically to localized regions of the endplate (73), whereas when the agonist is applied in the solution bathing the muscle, the membrane potential response falls slowly over a period of minutes (118). Recovery from desensitization is also much slower, with a halftime of minutes rather than seconds, when the agonist is applied in the solution bathing the muscle rather than by iontophoresis.

Despite these as yet unexplained kinetic differences, desensitization during agonist application by either of these two methods can be markedly increased by SKF-525A and several structurally similar analogs of ACh (87–89, 130). However, although the decline in depolarization caused by ACh in the presence of SKF-525A congeners has been described as "desensitization," it is not certain that a change in receptors is concerned. It has been suggested instead that such agents may modify a process intervening between receptor occupation and the resultant conductance change (87, 88). The possible modification of receptors during desensitization enhanced by SKF-525A congeners may perhaps be experimentally tested by examining the interaction of such compounds with snake toxins that seem to bind to active (sensitive) but not to desensitized receptors (38, 79, 90, 100).

The finding that all agonists cause some desensitization has led to the suggestion that desensitization is a normal and possibly obligatory result of receptor-channel activation (73, 118, but see 117). However, although the same cyclic model seems to describe desensitization caused either by ionotophoretically or bath-applied agonists (73, 118), the relationships of the two processes to one another and to receptor activation remain uncertain. In this connection, it should be borne in mind that the duration of the conductance change caused by nerve-released acetylcholine is of the order of milliseconds, whereas the time constants for desensitization are of the order of seconds (iontophoretic application) or minutes (bath applied).

Receptor-Channel Properties Revealed by the Use of Specific Ligands

SULFHYDRYL REAGENTS Early observations indicated that heavy metal ions interfered with the action of ACh on skeletal muscles. Karlin and his colleagues and many other groups of workers (cf 61, 62) recently demonstrated that agents that react with disulfide bonds alter the effects of agonists on eel electroplaques and a variety of vertebrate skeletal muscles. In each case reduction of S-S bonds to SH groups with dithiothreitol (DTT) markedly reduced the effects of carbachol and other agonists. In electroplaques, the Hill coefficient for the carbachol response is also decreased (suggesting less "cooperativity"); however, decamethonium yields increased responses, and hexamethonium, normally an antagonist, becomes an agonist. These effects are fully reversible with the use of any of several oxidizing agents, notably 5,5'-dithiobis(2-nitrobenzoic acid) (DTNB). In the blocked (reduced) state, the response mechanism becomes sensitive to the alkylation of free SH groups by bromoacetylcholine (61) and bromoacetylcholamine (11), or by compounds like *N*-ethylmaleimide (NEM). The bromoacetyl compounds, which act reversibly before the use of DTT, become irreversibly bound agonists, apparently rotating about their bonds of covalent attachment to each receptor so that their quaternary ammonium groups repeatedly activate the receptors; nonetheless, their action can be competitively antagonized in the usual manner by *d*-tubocurarine. In eel electroplaques (61), but not certain muscles (83, 119), NEM derivatives [notably 4-(*N*-maleimido)benzyltrimethylammonium) (MBTA)] having a quaternary ammonium group about 1 nm from the reactive double bond react with reduced receptors at rates many orders of magnitude faster than NEM, and receptor agonists and antagonists protect receptors from the irreversible blocking actions of NEM and MBTA. Thus the actions of the bromoacetyl compounds after DTT, and the action of MBTA after DTT in electroplaques, are those expected of true affinity labelling agents for receptors. Karlin and his colleagues (cf 63) have taken advantage of such selective labelling and of the large amount of receptor material in the electric tissue of *Electrophorus* to assess the molecular weight (about 40,000) of the acetylcholine binding subunits of receptors, and, by techniques involving the same affinity ligands attached to resins, have obtained purified protein preparations containing protein subunits of about 53,000, 47,000, and 41,000 Daltons.

It may be concluded from these observations that nicotinic receptors of the type found in skeletal muscles and electric tissues have an S-S bond, essential for receptor-channel function, about 1 nm from the site that reacts with the quaternary ammonium group of agonists (in eels), that this region undergoes a conformational change when activated, and that the receptor subunit involved has a molecular weight of about 40,000.

AGONISTS AND ANTAGONISTS The binding of small ligands to membrane fragments from electric tissues and to crude and purified detergent-dispersed receptor protein preparations has been measured directly by equilibrium dialysis and indirectly by competition both with another small ligand like decamethonium and by measurement of the retardation of the rate of specific binding of snake α-neurotoxins.

In general, studies with the latter two methods have revealed binding sites similar to those of receptors in functioning cells. In *Electrophorus,* the dissociation constants for a variety of cholinergic agonists and antagonists are quite similar to the K_d values determined from ion flux measurements with whole cells (cf 133) and isolated vesicles (64). Both agonists and antagonists are usually capable of fully antagonizing the binding of toxins to soluble and insoluble preparations from *Electrophorus* and *Torpedo* (38, 101, 108, 133). The pattern of inhibition with *d*-tubocurarine, nicotine, tetramethylammonium, and alloferin is that of hyperbolic competitive inhibition (as defined for enzymes; the implication is that the small ligand and the toxin may bind to receptors or receptor molecules simultaneously), whereas with hexamethonium and decamethonium there is linear competition (39). The character of the reaction with *d*-tubocurarine (39) and with agonists (38, 97) appears to change with receptor solubilization and purification.

Direct measurements of the binding of agonists and antagonists to receptors have yielded less clear (or more controversial) results, an unfortunate fact since firm quantitative measurements of the number of ACh binding sites on each receptor molecule are needed for correlations with physiological evidence for the cooperative binding and cooperative effects of agonists (see above), and with evidence for the binding of several (2–3) toxin molecules to independent receptor molecules (see below). Most investigators have found 50–90% as much binding of ACh and similar ligands (30, 101, 108) as of toxins [about 1 μmol for soluble or membrane-bound material derived from a kg of fresh *Torpedo* tissue (99); about one thirteenth much in *Electrophorus* (cf 113); and about 1.3 μmol/kg for *Narcine* electric tissue (3)]. In interpreting the data in the literature, the following problems should be kept in mind:

(*a*) The binding of agonists may be largely due to the desensitized state of receptors, whereas the binding of toxins (79, 100) and some antagonists (cf 116) appears to be to a nondesensitized state; the numbers of total sites in the two states could differ.

(*b*) Some workers have described results suggesting positive or negative cooperativity or autoinhibition of binding of ACh (31, 32, 133).

(*c*) There appear to be several types of binding sites for small ligands (having different dissociation constants) in some preparations of membranes and solubilized receptor proteins (cf 30,108); the saturation of one class may alter the binding characteristics of another. Most groups have found a single class of binding sites for toxins (see below).

(*d*) The affinity of receptors for small ligands has been reported to change with solubilization and purification (e.g. 30, 38, 97), and varies depending on the tissue source. Values for dissociation constants as far apart as 2–3 orders of magnitude have been reported for tissues from various species of *Torpedo* [5–6 μM (101); 8 nM (133)]. In contrast, there is little or no change in the rate of toxin binding to receptors upon solubilization (38) and purification (39).

(*e*) In some membrane preparations (64, 101) there appear to be only half as many binding sites for agonists and antagonists as sites for toxins, in keeping with results of experiments on cellular preparations in which diquaternary antagonists appeared to readily protect only half the available toxin sites (1, 100).

(*f*) Different aggregation states of detergent-receptor-toxin complexes are apparent after dissolution of postsynaptic membranes, and these may have altered binding properties for small ligands (cf 113).

(*g*) Homogenization of postsynaptic membranes produces sheets of membranes and vesicles from which acetylcholinesterase is at least partially detached, and some of the vesicles have inverted such that their toxin sites are no longer accessible (cf 3, 113). These factors can clearly affect the binding of both small ligands and toxins.

(*h*) Agonists bind to acetylcholinesterase (e.g. 99), and the introduction of sufficient amounts of esterase inhibitors to prevent esteratic action may alter receptors or not block agonist binding to either the negative enzyme site that attracts quaternary ammonium groups or to allosteric sites.

Despite these many problems in obtaining definitive data from in vitro preparations, it seems probable that there are equal numbers of toxin sites and ACh binding sites on receptors, since many recent experiments indicate full protection of one site by the other agent (e.g. 133), and approximately equal amounts of protein in purified receptor preparations per toxin (76) and per ACh (30) binding site. The latter evidence, for 1 mol of ACh binding to 80,000–120,000 g of purified protein, coupled with evidence that the molecular weight of receptor molecules is 240,000 ± 40,000 (see below), provides a basis for believing that there are 2–3 ACh sites per molecule.

The question of whether or not there is cooperativity in the binding of ACh to purified preparations of membranes or proteins remains controversial. Some experiments indicate positive and/or negative cooperativity (30, 31, 133), whereas others show no evidence for cooperative binding (101, 133). Both may be right, since there is a change in the slope of Hill plots during the purification of receptors (30). On the basis of the evidence for cooperativity, which includes good physiological evidence (93), it may be concluded that cooperative binding or retention *can* occur, whether it always does or not; one may ask why else there should be more than one ACh binding site per receptor molecule. None of the experiments to date have distinguished cooperative binding (facilitation of the binding of ACh to one receptor after its interaction with another) from cooperative retention (delayed release of ACh following two or more independent or facilitated interactions, perhaps because of conformational changes in receptor molecules).

A variety of small nicotinic agonists and antagonists have been used as ligands attached to resins for the purification of nitoconic receptors. The properties of the protein so obtained are entirely similar to those of the protein obtained on affinity resins having toxins as the ligands, and are therefore discussed below in that connection.

ALPHA-NEUROTOXINS Most investigators now feel that the α-neurotoxins of elapid snakes, notably *Bungarus multicinctus* (a krait), *Naja naja siamensis,* and *Naja nigricolis* (cobras), represent the most specific, reliable, and generally useful ligands for nicotinic receptors in vertebrate skeletal muscles and electric tissues (10, 17, 23, 33, 39, 44, 61, 62, 78, 113–115). The specificity of these toxins is so high that they do not react with nicotinic receptors in rabbit sympathetic ganglia (D. McAfee, personal communication). The major problem with their use is that they do not assess the functional state of receptors (108), and also their binding is not sufficiently reversible for some experiments. The kinetics of binding of the toxins to cells (79, 100), membranes (38, 133), and soluble receptor proteins (38, 39) from different sources indicate that a single class of sites accounts for the observed binding. Purification of the toxin-binding material from electric tissues of three genera has yielded a single glycoprotein in each case, with similar if not identical properties in the different tissues, even to the point of immunological cross-reactivity (83, 98). The toxins have therefore been widely used to assess the identity, number, packing density, cellular and tissue distribution, fine-structural localization, and cellular control of nicotinic receptors, and to purify the receptor protein.

In most skeletal muscles there are tens of millions of toxin sites per endplate (10, 33, 44, 100); binding is localized to the tips of the postsynaptic folds of muscle membrane nearest motor nerve terminals, at a packing density of about $30,000/\mu m^2$ (36). Toxin sites occur in patches on muscles before innervation (cf 26, 33) and remain at endplates after denervation (33). [Curiously, there are equal numbers of bound toxin and di-isopropylfluoro phosphate (DFP) molecules at normal endplates, but the latter are localized throughout postjunctional muscle folds (10). Acetylcholinesterase can be removed from intact muscles without disrupting neuromuscular transmission (44), and the esterase level falls rather than increases following denervation (33).]

In growing cells the rate of formation of new toxin sites can be measured (33). After denervation there is a 10–20-fold increase in the total number of toxin sites and a change in their distribution to cover the whole surface of muscle cells, sometimes in broad peaks not corresponding to sites of innervation at any time (33, 100); the appearance of new sites depends partly upon muscle activity, whether or not ACh is present (27, 84). New receptors turn over more rapidly than those at endplates, and have slightly different physical and pharmacological properties (44). Blockade of receptors with toxins (124) or *d*-tubocurarine (26) does not prevent growth of nerves to prospective endplates. Agonists that cause desensitization of receptors apparently reduce toxin binding (79, 100). *d*-Tubocurarine readily protects only half of the total, specific toxin sites in frog sartorius and mouse diaphragm muscles, and these are essential for receptor-channel function (1, 100). In contrast, histrionicotoxin readily protects curare-resistant sites, and these can be irreversibly occluded with toxins without completely stopping neuromuscular transmission (1). The fact that *d*-tubocurarine readily protects all the toxin sites of dissolved rat diaphragm membranes (44) provides further evidence for a change in the state of receptors after tissue breakage.

As expected from the richness of their cholinergic innervation, the electric tissues of eels (*Electrophorus*) and rays (*Torpedo* and *Narcine*) contain over 10- and 100-fold more toxin binding sites than muscle, respectively. As noted previously, toxin sites in muscles and electric tissues are highly similar with respect to their pharmacological properties, packing density on postsynaptic membranes (23, 99; see also below under morphological studies), antigen specificity (98, 110), and the sedimentation and molecular sieving behavior of detergent-dispersed complexes (44, 113). Electric tissues have, therefore, been the logical choice for many morphological studies and for the purification of receptor protein.

Many groups have now purified the nicotinic receptor protein to near homogeneity, utilizing first the isolation of receptor-rich membrane fragments, followed primarily by affinity chromatography with sulfhydryl reagents, nicotinic agonists, or toxins as the ligands (10, 17, 23, 39, 44, 62, 113–115). Although many details remain to be settled, a single protein component has been found by polyacrylamide gel electrophoresis, by electrofocusing, and by ion exchange techniques; its size by the first technique is approximately 240,000 ± 40,000 Daltons. All groups have found subunits of about 43,000 Daltons; many note larger subunits of about 53,000 Daltons. Most find bands in polyacrylamide gels slightly more mobile than one or both of these, which may represent breakdown products or smaller subunits. All bands stain for sugars, implying that the subunits are glycoproteins. Present evidence suggests that there are more smaller than larger subunits, and that these bind sulfhydryl reagents, which are affinity ligands for ACh receptors (61, 62). Both cross-linking experiments (56) and morphological studies now indicate 5 subunits per receptor molecule; clearly 5 times the average subunit weight yields the estimated molecular weight. While estimates of the amount of receptor protein required to bind one mole of toxin range from 67,000 to 220,000, the more recent values are at the lower end of this range. Division of the estimated molecular weight for the receptor molecule by such values suggests 2–3 toxin sites per receptor molecule. As noted previously, there is good evidence against cooperative binding of toxins at any level of organization.

Preliminary amino acid analyses of the purified receptor protein indicate that it has somewhat more proline and hydrophobic residues than some other integral membrane proteins, and little (30) or no (76) tryptophan. Nonetheless, the composition shows more similarities than differences to the nonintegral membrane protein, acetylcholinesterase (30). It may be noted that a channel protein would be expected to have a composition balanced between the hydrophobic residues required for dissolving the molecule in the membrane and the hydrophilic residues lining the core through which ions pass.

Morphological Studies

Examination of thin sections of skeletal muscles and electric tissues by electron microscopy has shown that the tips of the postjunctional folds of muscle membrane nearest motor nerves (36) and all the corresponding folds of the postsynaptic membranes of *Torpedo* (105) and *Narcine* electroplaques (3) are thicker and more densely staining than other membranes. Many globules are apparent in the postsynaptic membranes of these electric tissues, with a diameter of about 7 nm and a packing density of roughly 5000/μm^2, much like the appearance of the putative cholinergic receptor molecules in earthworm body wall muscle (121). The latter intramembranous globules are attached by long stalks to head pieces in the synaptic cleft (121) that may represent acetylcholinesterase molecules.

Replicas of freeze cleavings of muscles (120) and electric tissues (3, 105) show particles about 9 nm in diameter at the same locations and packing density as noted above. Although patches and "herringbone" patterns of the particles can be seen, there is no organization of these particles in any kind of true lattice (cf 18 for a different result with some isolated membranes). When electric tissues are fixed before cleaving, almost all the particles are found to protrude from the fractured intramembranous face of the inner leaflet of the postsynaptic membrane. These particles show central pits. Without fixation of electric tissues, many particles remain attached to the outer leaflet and protrude from its intramembranous face (3, 105).

Some preparations of freeze-cleaved electric tissues, particularly those of unfixed tissue (3), show many small and regularly arrayed particles about 0.3–0.4 nm in diameter protruding from the fractured face of the outer membrane leaflet; the presence of these particles has been otherwise undetected. It remains to be established whether or not these small particles are protein in nature, and what, if any, relationship they bear to toxin-binding material.

The most interesting information about receptor morphology has been gained from the negative staining of highly purified preparations (vesicles) of postsynaptic membranes from *Torpedo* (18, 106) and, especially, *Narcine* (3). When such vesicles are dried on grids under conditions where they break, more than 95% are seen to be covered by ring-shaped structures about 6 nm in diameter, composed of 5–6 subunits each about 2 nm in diameter. The packing density of these rings varies with the degree of drying and stain used; with prefixed vesicles and uranyl acetate the packing is about $6000/\mu m^2$ (3), in close correspondence to the packing of particles seen by freeze cleaving in fixed tissue (3), and with the number of receptor molecules/μm^2 estimated from toxin binding (99) after allowance for 2–3 toxin sites per molecule. Frequently the vesicles do not break upon drying; then only about half show the rings described (3). It is possible to fully separate vesicles having inward- and outward-facing toxin binding sites by affinity chromatography: only those that have toxin sites facing inwards show the 6 nm rings of subunits. Receptor molecules purified by affinity chromatography on resins having *Naja naja siamensis* α-toxin as the ligand show, after negative staining, the same end ring structure. It may be concluded that receptor molecules, which bind toxin only at the outer surface of the postsynaptic membrane in situ, extend through the membrane and project from its cytoplasmic surface (3).

Literature Cited

1. Albuquerque, E. X. et al 1973. Acetylcholine receptor and ion conductance modulator sites at the murine neuromuscular junction. Evidence from specific toxin reactions. *Proc. Nat. Acad. Sci. USA* 70:949–53
2. Albuquerque, E. X., Seyama, I., Narahashi, T. 1973. Characterization of batrachotoxin-induced depolarization of the squid giant axons. *J. Pharmacol. Exp. Ther.* 184:308–14
3. Allen, T. et al 1974. Molecular organization of receptor-channel molecules in postsynaptic membranes. In *Biomembranes—Lipoproteins and Receptors,* ed. R. M. Burton, L. Packer. Webster Groves, Missouri: Bi-Science Publ.
4. Anderson, C. R., Stevens, C. F. 1972. Membrane conductance fluctuations associated with acetylcholine depolarization of frog neuromuscular junction. *Biophys. Soc. Ann. Meet. Abstr.* 12:77a
5. Anderson, C. R., Stevens, C. F. 1973. Conductance and voltage dependence of acetylcholine sensitive ionic channels in voltage clamped endplate. *Biophys. Soc. Ann. Meet. Abstr.* 13:71a
6. Anderson, C. R., Stevens, C. F. 1973. Voltage clamp analysis of acetylcholine produced endplate current fluctuations at frog neuromuscular junction. *J. Physiol.* 235:655–91
7. Armstrong, C. M. 1971. Interaction of tetraethylammonium ion derivatives

with the potassium channels of giant axons. *J. Gen. Physiol.* 58:413–37
8. Armstrong, C. M., Benzanilla, F. 1973. Currents related to movement of the gating particles of the sodium channels. *Nature* 242:459–61
9. Armstrong, C. M., Benzanilla, F. 1974. Charge movements associated with the opening and closing of the activation gates of the Na channels. *J. Gen. Physiol.* 63:533–52
9a. Asano, T., Hurlbut, W. P. 1958. Effects of potassium, sodium, and azide on the ionic movements that accompany activity in frog nerves. *J. Gen. Physiol.* 41:1187–1203
10. Barnard, E. A. 1974. The acetylcholine receptor and the ionic conductance modulation system. *Fed. Proc.* In press
11. Ben-Haim, D., Landau, E. M., Silman, I. 1973. The role of a reactive disulphide bond in the function of the acetylcholine receptor at the frog neuromuscular junction. *J. Physiol.* 234:305–25
12. Benzer, T., Raftery, M. A. 1972. Partial characterization of a tetrodotoxin-binding component from nerve membranes. *Proc. Nat. Acad. Sci. USA* 69:3634–37
13. Benzer, T. I., Raftery, M. A. 1973. Solubization and partial characterization of the tetrodotoxin binding component from nerve axons. *Biochem. Biophys. Res. Commun.* 51:939–44
14. Bernstein, J. 1902. Untersuchungen zur thermodynamik der bioelectrischen ströme. *Pfluegers Arch.* 92:521–62
15. Bezanilla, F., Armstrong, C. M. 1972. Negative conductance caused by entry of sodium and cesium ions into the potassium channels of squid axons. *J. Gen. Physiol.* 60:588–608
16. Bezanilla, F., Armstrong, C. M. 1974. Gating currents of the sodium channels: three ways to block them. *Science* 183:753–54
17. Biesecker, G. 1973. Molecular properties of the cholinergic receptor purified from *Electrophorus electricus. Biochemistry* 12:4403–9
18. Cartaud, J., Benedetti, E. L., Cohen, J. B., Meunier, J.-C., Changeux, J.-P. 1973. Presence of a lattice structure in membrane fragments rich in nicotinic receptor protein from the electric organ of *Torpedo marmorata. FEBS Lett.* 33:109–13
19. del Castillo-Nicolau, J., Hufschmidt, H. J. 1951. Reversible poisoning of nerve fibers by heavy-metal ions. *Nature* 167:146–47
20. del Castillo, J., Katz, B. 1954. The membrane change produced by the neuromuscular transmitter. *J. Physiol.* 125:546–65
21. Chandler, W. K., Meves, H. 1965. Voltage clamp experiments on internally perfused giant axons. *J. Physiol.* 180: 788–820
22. Chandler, W. K., Meves, H. 1970. Sodium and potassium currents in squid axons perfused with fluoride solutions. *J. Physiol.* 211:623–52
23. Changeux, J.-P. et al 1973. Studies on the mode of action of cholinergic agonists at the molecular basis. In *Drug Receptors,* ed. H. P. Rang, 273–93. London: Macmillan
23a. Cheng, S.-C. 1962. Functional uptake of hydrazine by frog nerve in sodium-deficient Ringer's solution. *Nature* 193:691–92
24. Cohen, L. B. 1973. Changes in neuron structure during action potential propagation and synaptic transmission. *Physiol. Rev.* 53:373–418
25. Cohen, L. B., Hille, B., Keynes, R. D., Landowne, D., Rojas, E. 1971. Analysis of the potential-dependent changes in optical retardation in the squid giant axon. *J. Physiol.* 218:205–37
26. Cohen, M. W. 1974. Acetylcholine receptors and synaptogenesis. *Fed. Proc.* In press
27. Cohen, S. A., Fischbach, G. D. 1973. Regulation of muscle acetylcholine sensitivity by muscle activity in cell culture. *Science* 181:76–78
28. Colquhoun, D., Henderson, R., Ritchie, J. M. 1972. The binding of labelled tetrodotoxin to non-myelinated nerve fibers. *J. Physiol.* 227:95–126
29. Eisenman, G. 1962. Cation selective glass electrodes and their mode of operation. *Biophys. J.* 2(2):259–323
30. Eldefrawi, M. E., Eldefrawi, A. T. 1973. Purification and molecular properties of the acetylcholine receptor from *Torpedo electroplax. Arch. Biochem. Biophys.* 159:362–73
31. Eldefrawi, M. E., Eldefrawi, A. T. 1973. Cooperativities in the binding of acetylcholine to its receptors. *Biochem. Pharmacol.* 22:3145–50
32. Eldefrawi, M. E., O'Brien, R. D. 1971. Autoinhibition of acetylcholine binding to *Torpedo electroplax;* a possible molecular mechanism for desensitization. *Proc. Nat. Acad. Sci. USA* 68: 2006–7
33. Fambrough, D. M. 1974. Cellular and developmental biology of acetylcholine

receptors in skeletal muscle. In *Neurochemistry of Cholinergic Receptors,* ed. E. de Robertis, J. Schacht, 85–113. New York: Raven
34. Fatt, P. 1950. The electromotive action of acetylcholine at the motor end-plate. *J. Physiol. London* 111:408–22
35. Fatt, P., Katz, B. 1951. An analysis of the end-plate potential recorded with an intracellular electrode. *J. Physiol.* 115: 320–70
36. Fertuck, H. C., Salpeter, M. M. 1974. Localization of acetylcholine receptor by ^{125}I-labelled α-bungarotoxin binding at mouse motor endplates. *Proc. Nat. Acad. Sci. USA* 71:1376–78
37. Fishman, H. 1973. Relaxation spectra of potassium channel noise from squid axon membranes. *Proc. Nat. Acad. Sci. USA* 70:876–79
38. Franklin, G. I., Potter, L. T. 1972. Studies of the binding of α-bungarotoxin to membrane-bound and detergent-dispersed acetylcholine receptors from *Torpedo* electric tissue. *FEBS Lett.* 28:101–6
39. Fulpius, B. W., Klett, R. P., Reich, E. 1974. Purification and properties of a nicotinic cholinergic receptor from the electric eel. See Ref. 33, 19–29
40. Furukawa, T., Furukawa, A. 1959. Effects of methyl- and ethyl-derivatives of NH_4^+ on the neuromuscular junction. *Jap. J. Physiol.* 9:130–42
41. Furukawa, T., Takagi, T., Sugihara, T. 1956. Depolarization of end-plates by acetylcholine externally applied. *Jap. J. Physiol.* 6:98–107
42. Ginsborg, B. L. 1967. Ion movements in junctional transmission. *Pharmacol. Rev.* 19:289–316
43. Ginsborg, B. L. 1973. Electrical changes in the membrane in junctional transmission. *Biochem. Biophys. Acta* 300:289–317
44. Hall, Z. W. 1974. Acetylcholine receptors in normal and denervated muscles. *Fed. Proc.* In press
45. Henderson, R., Ritchie, J. M., Strichartz, G. D. 1973. The binding of labelled saxitoxin to the sodium channels in nerve membranes. *J. Physiol.* 235:783–804
46. Henderson, R., Wang, J. H. 1972. Solubilization of a specific tetrodotoxin-binding component from garfish olfactory nerve membrane. *Biochemistry* 11:4565–69
47. Hille, B. 1971. The permeability of the sodium channel to organic cations in myelinated nerve. *J. Gen. Physiol.* 58:599–619
48. Hille, B. 1972. The permeability of the sodium channel to metal cations in myelinated nerve. *J. Gen. Physiol.* 59:637–58
49. Hille, B. 1973. Potassium channels in myelinated nerve. Selective permeability to small cations. *J. Gen. Physiol.* 61:669–86
50. Hillman, D. E., Llinás, R. 1974. Calcium-containing electron-dense structures in the axons of the squid giant synapse. *J. Cell Biol.* 61:146–55
51. Hodgkin, A. L., Huxley, A. F. 1952. Currents carried by sodium and potassium ions through the membrane of the giant axon of *Loligo. J. Physiol.* 116:449–72
52. Hodgkin, A. L., Huxley, A. F. 1952. A quantitative description of membrane current and its application to conduction and excitation in nerve. *J. Physiol.* 117:500–44
53. Hodgkin, A. L., Huxley, A. F., Katz, B. 1949. Ionic currents underlying activity in the giant axon of the squid. *Arch. Sci. Physiol.* 3:129–50
54. Hodgkin, A. L., Huxley, A. F., Katz, B. 1952. Measurement of current-voltage relations in the membrane of the giant axon of *Loligo. J. Physiol.* 116:424–48
55. Hoffer, B. J., Siggins, G. R., Oliver, A. P., Bloom, F. E. 1972. Cyclic AMP mediated adrenergic synapses to cerebellar Purkinje cells. *Advan. Cyclic Nucleotide Res.* 1:411–24
56. Hucho, F., Changeux, J.-P. 1973. Molecular weight and quaternary structure of the cholinergic receptor protein extracted by detergents from *Electrophorus electricus* electric tissue. *FEBS Lett.* 38:11–15
57. Huneeus-Cox, F., Fernandez, H. L., Smith, B. H. 1966. Effects of redox and sulfhydryl reagents on the bioelectric properties of the giant axon of the squid. *Biophys. J.* 6:675–89
58. Jenkinson, D. H. 1960. The antagonism between tubocurarine and substances which depolarize the motor end-plate. *J. Physiol. London* 152:309–24
59. Jenkinson, D. H., Nicholls, J. G. 1961. Contractures and permeability changes produced by acetylcholine in depolarized denervated muscle. *J. Physiol.* 159:111–27
60. Jenkinson, D. H., Terrar, D. A. 1973. Influence of chloride ions on changes in membrane potential during prolonged application of carbachol to frog skeletal

muscle. *Brit. J. Pharmacol.* 47:363–76
61. Karlin, A. 1973. Molecular interactions of the acetylcholine receptor. *Fed. Proc.* 32:1847–53
62. Karlin, A. 1974. The acetylcholine receptor: progress report. *Life Sci.* 14:1385–1415
63. Karlin, A., Cowburn, D. A. 1974. Molecular properties of membrane-bound and of solubilized and purified acetylcholine receptor identified by affinity labelling. See Ref. 33, 37–48
64. Kasai, M., Changeux, J.-P. 1971. In vitro excitation of purified membrane fragments by cholinergic agonists. I. Pharmacological properties of the excitable membrane fragments. *J. Membrane Biol.* 6:1–23
65. Katz, B., Miledi, R. 1969. Spontaneous and evoked activity of motor nerve endings in calcium ringer. *J. Physiol.* 203:689–706
66. Katz, B., Miledi, R. 1970. Membrane noise produced by acetylcholine. *Nature* 226:962–63
67. Katz, B., Miledi, R. 1971. Further observations on acetylcholine noise. *Nature New Biol.* 232:124–26
68. Katz, B., Miledi, R. 1972. The statistical nature of the acetylcholine potential and its molecular components. *J. Physiol.* 224:665–99
69. Katz, B., Miledi, R. 1973. The characteristics of "end-plate noise" produced by different depolarizing drugs. *J. Physiol.* 230:707–17
70. Katz, B., Miledi, R. 1973. The binding of acetylcholine to receptors and its removal from the synaptic cleft. *J. Physiol.* 231:549–74
71. Katz, B., Miledi, R. 1973. The effect of atropine on acetylcholine action of the neuromuscular junction. *Proc. Roy. Soc. London B* 184:221–26
72. Katz, B., Miledi, R. 1973. The effect of α-bungarotoxin on acetylcholine receptors. *Brit. J. Pharmacol.* 49:138–39
73. Katz, B., Thesleff, S. 1957. A study of the "desensitization" produced by acetylcholine at the motor end-plate. *J. Physiol. London* 138:63–80
74. Keynes, R. D., Rojas, E. 1974. Kinetics and steady-state properties of the charged system controlling sodium conductance in the squid giant axon. *J. Physiol.* 239:393–434
75. Keynes, R. D., Rojas, E., Taylor, R. E. 1973. Saxitoxin, tetrodotoxin barriers, and binding sites in squid giant axons. *J. Gen. Physiol.* 61:267
76. Klett, R. P. et al 1973. The acetylcholine receptor I. Purification and characterization of a macromolecule isolated from *Electrophorus electricus. J. Biol. Chem.* 248:6841–53
77. Koketsu, K., Nishi, S. 1959 Restoration of neuromuscular transmission in sodium-free hydrazinium solution. *J. Physiol. London* 147:239–52
78. Lee, C. Y. 1972. Chemistry and pharmacology of polypeptide toxins in snake venoms. *Ann. Rev. Pharmacol.* 12:265–81
79. Lester, H. A. 1972. Vulnerability of desensitized or curare-treated acetylcholine receptors to irreversible blockade by cobra toxin. *Mol. Pharmacol.* 8:632–44
80. Levinson, S. R., Ellory, J. C. 1973. Molecular size of the tetrodotoxin binding site estimated by irradiation inactivation. *Nature* 245:122–23
81. Libet, B. 1970. Generation of slow inhibitory and excitatory postsynaptic potentials. *Fed. Proc.* 29:1945–56
82. Lieb, W. R., Stein, W. D. 1969. Biological membranes behave as nonporous polymeric sheets with respect to diffusion of non-electrolytes. *Nature* 224:240–43
83. Lindstrom, J. M., Singer, S. J., Lennox, E. S. 1973. The effects of reducing and alkylating agents on the acetylcholine receptor activity of frog sartorius muscle. *J. Membrane Biol.* 11:217–26
84. Lomo, T., Rosenthal, J. 1972. Control of acetylcholine sensitivity by muscle activity in the rat. *J. Physiol.* 221:493–513
85. McAfee, D. A., Greengard, P. 1972. Adenosine 3',5'-monophosphate: electrophysiological evidence for a role in synaptic transmission. *Science* 178:310–12
86. Magazanik, L. G. 1968. On the mechanism of the desensitization of muscle postsynaptic membrane. *Biophysika* 13:199–203
87. Magazanik, L. G. 1970. Mechanism of the influence of the diethylaminoethyl ester of dephenylpropyl acetic acid (SKF-525A) on neuromuscular synapses. *Byull, Eksp. Biol. Med.* 69(3):10–14
88. Magazanik, L. G. 1971. On the mechanism of antiacetylcholine effects of some mononitrogen anticholinergics in the neuromuscular synapse. *Farmakol. Toksikol. Moscow* 34(3):292–97
89. Magazanik, L. G., Vyskocil, F. 1970. Dependence of acetylcholine desensiti-

zation on the membrane potential of frog muscle fibre and on ionic changes in the medium. *J. Physiol. London* 210:507–18
90. Magzanik, L. G., Vyskocil, F. 1972. The desensitization of postjuctional muscle membrane after intracellular application of membrane stabilizers and snake venom polypeptides. *Brain Res.* 48:417–19
91. Magleby, K. L., Stevens, C. F. 1972. The effect of voltage on the time course of end-plate currents. *J. Physiol.* 223:151–71
92. Magleby, K. L., Stevens, C. F. 1972. A quantitative description of end-plate currents. *J. Physiol.* 223:173–97
93. Magleby, K. L., Terrar, D. A. 1974. Factors affecting the time course of decay of end-plate currents: a possible cooperative action of acetylcholine on receptors at the frog neuromuscular junction. *J. Physiol.* In press
94. Marquis, J. K., Bushen, B., Mautner, H. G. 1973. On the nature of the "stimulation effect" observed with thiol reagents in axonal preparations. *Abstr. N. Engl. Pharmacol. Soc.* Hanover, N. H. In press
95. Marquis, J. K., Mautner, H. G. 1974. The binding of thiol reagents to axonal membranes: the effect of electrical stimulation. *Biochem. Biophys. Res. Commun.* 57:154–61
96. Marquis, J. K., Mautner, H. G. 1974. The effect of electrical stimulation on the action of sulfhydryl reagents in the giant axon of squid; suggested mechanisms for the role of thiol and disulfide groups in electrically-induced conformational changes. *J. Membrane Biol.* 15:249–60
97. Meunier, J.-C., Changeux, J.-P. 1973. Comparison between the affinities for reversible cholinergic ligands of a purified and membrane bound state of the acetylcholine-receptor protein from *Electrophorus electricus. FEBS Lett.* 32:143–48
98. Meunier, J.-C., Sugiyama, H., Cartaud, J., Sealock, R., Changeux, J.-P. 1973. Functional properties of the purified cholinergic receptor protein from *Electrophorus electricus. Brain Res.* 62: 307–15
99. Miledi, R., Molinoff, P., Potter, L. T. 1971. Isolation of the cholinergic receptor protein of Torpedo electric tissue. *Nature* 229:554–57
100. Miledi, R., Potter, L. T. 1971. Acetylcholine receptors in muscle fibres. *Nature* 233:599–603
101. Moody, T., Schmidt, J., Raftery, M. A. 1973. Binding of acetylcholine and related compounds to purified acetylcholine receptor from *Torpedo californica* electroplax. *Biochem. Biophys. Res. Commun.* 53:761–72
102. Narahashi, T., Anderson, N. C., Moore, J. W. 1966. Tetrodotoxin does not block excitation from inside the nerve membrane. *Science* 153:765–67
103. Nastuk, W. L. 1959. Some ionic factors that influence the action of acetylcholine at the muscle end-plate membrane. *Ann. NY Acad. Sci.* 81:317–27
104. Nastuk, W. L., Parsons, R. L. 1970. Factors in the inactivation of postjunctional membrane receptors of frog skeletal muscle. *J. Gen. Physiol.* 56:218–49
105. Nickel, E., Potter, L. T. 1970. Synaptic vesicles in freeze-etched electric tissue of *Torpedo. Brain Res.* 23:95–100
106. Nickel, E., Potter, L. T. 1973. Ultrastructure of isolated membranes of *Torpedo* electric tissue. *Brain Res.* 57: 508–17
107. Nishi, S., Koketsu, K. 1968. Analysis of slow inhibitory postsynaptic potential of bullfrog sympathetic ganglion. *J. Neurophysiol.* 31:717–28
108. O'Brien, R. D., Eldefrawi, M. E., Eldefrawi, A. T. 1972. Isolation of acetylcholine receptors. *Ann. Rev. Pharmacol.* 12:19–34
109. Oschman, J. L., Hall, T. A., Peters, P. D., Wall, B. J. 1974. Association of calcium with membranes of squid giant axon. Ultrastructure and microscope analysis. *J. Cell Biol.* 61:156–65
110. Patrick, J., Lindstrom, J. 1973. Autoimmune response to acetylcholine receptor. *Science* 180:871–72
111. Peracchia, C. 1974. Excitable membrane ultrastructure. I. Freeze fracture of crayfish axons. *J. Cell Biol.* 61: 107–22
112. Peracchia, C., Robertson, J. D. 1971. Increase in osmophilia of axonal membranes of crayfish as a result of electrical stimulation, asphyxia or treatment with reducing agents. *J. Cell Biol.* 51:223–39
113. Potter, L. T. 1973. Acetylcholine receptors in vertebrate skeletal muscles and electric tissues. See Ref. 23, 295–312
114. Potter, L. T. 1974. Alpha-bungarotoxin and nicotinic acetylcholine receptors. In *Methods in Enzymology,* ed. S. Fleischer, L. Packer, R. W. Estabrook. New York: Academic

115. Raftery, M. A., Schmidt, J., Vandlen, R., Moody, T. 1974. Large-scale isolation and characterization of an acetylcholine receptor. See Ref. 33, 5–18
116. Rang, H. P. 1971. Drug receptors and their function. *Nature* 231:91–96
117. Rang, H. P. 1973. Receptor mechanisms. *Brit. J. Pharmacol.* 48:475–95
118. Rang, H. P., Ritter, J. M. 1970. On the mechanism of desensitization of cholinergic receptors. *Mol. Pharmacol.* 6: 357–82
119. Rang, H. P., Ritter, J. M. 1970. The relationship between desensitization and the metaphilic effect at cholinergic receptors. *Mol. Pharmacol.* 6:383–90
120. Rash, J. E., Ellisman, M. H., Staehelin, L. A. 1973. Freeze-cleaved neuromuscular junctions: Macromolecular architecture of post-synaptic membranes of normal vs. denervated muscle. *J. Cell Biol.* 59:280a
121. Rosenbluth, J. 1972. Myoneural junctions of two ultrastructurally distinct types in earthworm body wall muscle. *J. Cell Biol.* 54:566–79
122. Sachs, F., Lecar, H. 1973. Acetylcholine noise in tissue culture muscle cells. *Nature New Biol.* 246:214–16
123. Smith, H. M. 1958. Effects of sulfhydryl blockade on axonal function. *J. Cell. Comp. Physiol.* 51:161–71
124. Steinbach, J. H., Harris, A. J., Patrick, J., Schubert, D., Heinemann, S. 1973. Nerve-muscle interaction *in vitro*. Role of acetylcholine. *J. Gen. Physiol.* 62: 255–70
125. Takahashi, H., Murai, T., Sasaki, T. 1958. Plateau formation and sulphydryl groups in the plasma membrane. *Nature* 182:1675–77
126. Takashima, S., Schwan, H. P. 1974. Passive electrical properties of squid axon membrane. *J. Membrane Biol.* 17:51–68
127. Takeuchi, N. 1963. Some properties of conductance changes at the end-plate membrane during the action of acetylcholine. *J. Physiol.* 167:128–40
128. Takeuchi, A., Takeuchi, N. 1960. On the permeability of end-plate membrane during the action of transmitter. *J. Physiol.* 154:52–67
128a. Tasaki, I., Spyropoulos, C. S. 1961. Permeability of the squid axon membrane to several organic molecules. *Am. J. Physiol.* 201:413–19
128b. Tasaki, I., Teorell, T., Spyropoulos, C. S. 1961. Movement of radioactive tracers across squid axon membrane. *Am. J. Physiol.* 200:11–22
129. Taylor, R. E. 1965. Impedance of the squid axon membrane. *J. Cell. Comp. Physiol.* 66:21–25
130. Terrar, D. A. 1974. Influence of SKF-525A congeners, strophanthidin and tissue-culture media on desensitization in frog skeletal muscle. *Brit. J. Pharmacol.* 51:259–68
131. Thesleff, S. 1955. Neuromuscular block caused by acetylcholine. *Nature* 175: 594–95
132. Urry, D. W., Goodall, M. C., Glickson, J. D., Mayers, D. F. 1971. The gramicidin A transmembrane channel. *Proc. Nat. Acad. Sci. USA* 68:1907–11
133. Weber, M., Changeux, J.-P. 1974. Binding of *Naja nigricollis* (^{3}H) α-toxin to membrane fragments from *Electrophorus* and *Torpedo* electric organs. *Mol. Pharmacol.* 10:15–34
134. Woodhull, A. M. 1973. Ionic blockage of sodium channels in nerve. *J. Gen. Physiol.* 61:687–708

RELATED ARTICLES APPEARING IN OTHER *ANNUAL REVIEWS*

From the *Annual Review of Biochemistry,* Volume 44 (1975)
Chemotaxis in Bacteria, J. Adler
Bioluminescence: Recent Advances, M. J. Cormier, J. Lee & J. E. Wampler
Basic Mechanisms in Blood Coagulation, E. W. Davie & K. Fujikawa
Cooperative Interaction of Hemoglobin, S. J. Edelstein
Amino Acid Metabolism in Man, P. Felig
Lipoproteins: Structure and Function, J. D. Morrisett, R. L. Jackson & A. M. Gotto Jr.
Energy Capture in Photosynthesis, R. Radmer & B. Kok
Inherited Disorders of Lysosomal Metabolism, E. F. Neufeld, T. Lim & L. J. Shapiro
Role of Cyclic Nucleotides in Growth Control, I. H. Pastan, G. Johnson & W. Anderson
Prostaglandins, B. Samuelsson, E. Granström, K. Green, M. Hamberg & S. Hammarström
The Energetics of Bacterial Active Transport, R. D. Simoni & P. W. Postma

From the *Annual Review of Biophysics and Bioengineering,* Volume 4 (1975)
Computer-Aided Instruction in Medicine, E. P. Hoffer, G. O. Barnett, B. B. Farquhar & P. A. Prather
Chemotaxis in Bacteria, H. C. Berg
Survival Distributions, V. Clark
Fluorescent Probes in Nerve Membranes, F. Conti
Electron Microspectroscopy, M. S. Isaacson & A. V. Crewe
Calcium Transport in Sarcoplasmic Reticulum, D. H. MacLennan & P. C. Holland
On the Evolution of the Physiological Model, W. Yamamoto

From the *Annual Review of Medicine,* Volume 26 (1975)
Neuroregulators and Sleep Mechanisms, R. B. Holman, G. R. Elliott & J. D. Barchas
Active Form of Thyroid Hormone, S. H. Ingbar & L. E. Braverman
The Role of Hormone Receptors in the Action of Adrenal Steroids, D. Feldman
Mechanisms of Supraventricular Tachycardias, B. N. Goldreyer
Pathophysiology of Heart Block, J. F. Moran & R. M. Gunnar
Low Renin Hypertension, J. C. Gunnells Jr. & W. L. McGuffin Jr.
Endocrine Therapy of Breast Cancer, W. P. McGuire
Left Ventricular Function in Acute and Chronic Coronary Artery Disease, C. E. Rackley & R. O. Russell Jr.
Relation Between Growth Hormone and Somatomedin, J. J. Van Wyk & L. E. Underwood

Oxygen Toxicity, W. G. Wolfe & W. C. DeVries
Gonadotropin Releasing Hormone, S. S. C. Yen
From the *Annual Review of Materials Science,* Volume 5 (1975)
Prosthetic Implant Materials, L. L. Hench
From the *Annual Review of Psychology,* Volume 26 (1975)
Hypnosis, E. R. Hilgard
Neurophysiology of Learning, I. Kupfermann
Biological Rhythms and Animal Behavior, B. Rusak & I. Zuker
From the *Annual Review of Plant Physiology,* Volume 26 (1975)
Genetics Analysis and Plant Improvement, T. B. Rice & P. S. Carlson
Membrane Biogenesis, D. J. Morré
Regulation of Carbohydrate Metabolism, J. F. Turner & D. H. Turner
From the *Annual Review of Anthropology,* Volume 4 (1975)
Concept of Adaptation, A. Alland Jr.
Biology and Language, J. N. Spuhler
From the *Annual Review of Genetics,* Volume 9 (1975)
Recent Developments in Screening for Human Genetic Traits and Diseases, B. Childs
Genetic Aspects of Human Intelligence, R. C. Lewontin
From the *Annual Review of Fluid Mechanics,* Volume 7 (1975)
Hemodynamics, H. L. Goldsmith & R. Skalak
From the *Annual Review of Pharmacology,* Volume 15 (1975)
The Cholinergic Receptor Protein in its Membrane Environment, J. B. Cohen & J.-P. Changeux
Pharmacology of the Esophageal Motor Function, J. Christensen
Mechanisms of Drug Action at the Voluntary Muscle Endplate, D. Colquhoun
Physiological and Pharmacological Roles of Prostaglandins, P. J. Kadowitz, P. D. Joiner & A. L. Hyman
The Effect of Carbon Monoxide on Humans, R. D. Stewart
From the *Annual Review of Physical Chemistry,* Volume 26 (1975)
The Genetic Code, G. W. Hoffman
From the *Annual Review of Ecology and Systematics,* Volume 6 (1975)
The Ecological Significance of Imprinting and Early Learning, K. Immelmann
Ecological Aspects of Animal Orientation, R. Jander
From the *Annual Review of Entomology,* Volume 20 (1975)
Brain Structure and Behavior in Insects, P. E. Howse
Neuromuscular Pharmacology of Insects, T. J. McDonald
Structure of Cuticular Mechanoreceptors of Arthropods, S. McIver
From the *History of Entomology* (a special publication)
The History of Insect Physiology, V. B. Wigglesworth
Genetics—The Long Story, S. W. Brown
A History of Biological Control, K. S. Hagen

AUTHOR INDEX

H

M

U

V

SUBJECT INDEX

D

R

CUMULATIVE INDEXES

CONTRIBUTING AUTHORS 33-37

CHAPTER TITLES VOLUMES 33-37

COMPARATIVE PHYSIOLOGY